Test Item File
to accompany

Electric Circuits Fundamentals
Fifth Edition

and

Electronics Fundamentals
Fifth Edition

Thomas L. Floyd

Prepared by
William P. Kist

Prentice
Hall

Upper Saddle River, New Jersey
Columbus, Ohio

10 9 8 7 6 5 4 3 2 1

ISBN 0-13-019388-7

This Test Item File is just one part of Prentice Hall's comprehensive testing support service, which also includes Prentice Hall Test Manager for Windows 95/98/NT, Prentice Hall Custom Test for the Macintosh and for DOS, and Prentice Hall Telephone Testing Service.

Prentice Hall Test Manager

To run the Prentice Hall Test Manager you must have a Pentium 133 or greater, with a minimum of 32 MB of RAM, and Windows 95, 98, or NT installed. This powerful program makes organization a snap by using five basic databases: User, Course, Question, Test, and Grade. "Screen Wizards" are incorporated into all five databases. Each one will walk you through the important tasks from start to finish.

The User database stores information about your students that allows you to issue on-line tests and assign grades. The Course database stores information about the classes you teach. The Question database stores the content for each question in your question bank. The test-generation process, contained in the Test database, is fast, simple, and error-free. Once you create a test, you can make it available to students on-line using the On-Line Testing Facility.* After each student completes an on-line test, the results appear in the Grade database.

Finally, Test Manager also produces full sets of various class and individual statistics. These allow you to analyze the performance of test questions, students, an individual class or section, a course with multiple sections, or assignment types such as homework and on-line tests.

Prentice Hall Custom Test

This powerful computerized testing package is available for DOS and Macintosh. It offers full mouse support, complete question editing capabilities, random test generation, graphics, and printing capabilities. It has a unique two-tier design—*Easytest* for the novice computer user, and *Fulltest* for those who wish to write their own questions or create their own graphics.

The built-in algorithmic module enables the instructor to create thousands of questions and answers from a single question template.

The Prentice Hall Test Manager and the Prentice Hall Custom Test are free. To order a specific Prentice Hall Custom Test title, you may contact your local rep or call our Faculty Support Services Department at 1-800-526-0485. Please identify the main text author and title.

Toll-free **technical support** is offered to users of Prentice Hall Test Manager and Custom Test at 1-800-550-1701, or via e-mail at support@esatest.com.

Prentice Hall Telephone Testing Service

This service is offered to those instructors without access to a computer. It's simple, fast, and efficient. Simply pick the questions you'd like on your test from this test item file, and call the Prentice Hall Testing Service at 1-800-550-1701; outside the US and Canada call 612-550-1705. Identify the main text and test questions you'd like, as well as any special instructions. We will create the test (or multiple versions if you wish) and send you a master copy for duplication within 48 hours. This service is free to adopters for the duration of text use.

*Prentice Hall Test Manager provides on-line testing via these networks: Windows 95, Windows NT server, Novell Netware Network, and Windows NT Workstation.

Chapter 1: Components, Quantities and Units

TRUE/FALSE

1. The unit of resistance is the ohm.
   a. True
   b. False

2. 0.0047 amps can be expressed in metric units as 47 μA.
   a. True
   b. False

3. An electronic device which stores electric charge is known as an inductor.
   a. True
   b. False

4. 0.00015 volts can be expressed in powers of ten as 1.5×10^{-4}.
   a. True
   b. False

5. The symbol μ is an abbreviation for 10^{-6} or *micro*.
   a. True
   b. False

MULTIPLE CHOICE

6. The electrical symbol for inductance is _____.
   a. C
   b. I
   c. V
   d. L

7. The symbol for electrical charge is _____.
   a. Q
   b. C
   c. V
   d. I

8. The _____ is a device that magnetically couples ac voltages from one point in a circuit to another.
   a. transistor
   b. capacitor
   c. transformer
   d. inductor

9. A resistor is a device that _____.
   a. stores a charge
   b. opposes the flow of electrons
   c. is a type of semiconductor
   d. stores energy in a magnetic field

10. The value 1.2×10^{-6} can be expressed as _____.
    a. 0.00012
    b. 1.2 m or milli
    c. 1.2 μ or micro
    d. 1.2 M or Meg

11. If your calculator displays **3.456 07**, the equivalent metric value is _____.
    a. 3.456 micro
    b. 3.456 Mega
    c. 34.56 Mega
    d. 3.456 kilo

12. The metric value 16 mA can be expressed as _____.
    a. 16×10^{-6} A
    b. 16×10^{3} A
    c. 16×10^{-3} A
    d. 16×10^{0} A

13. To enter 0.00000056 volts into your calculator, use the entry _____.
    a. 56 -06
    b. 5.6 -08
    c. 56 -08
    d. 00056 -05

14. Determine the correct calculation.
    a. $5600 \times (9.6 \times 10^{-7}) = 5.376$ milli
    b. $4.7m + 1.24 = .379m$
    c. $89.4k \times 1.2m = 1.072km$
    d. $5.6 + 17m = 32.9m$

15. The correct expression for 8.54×10^{-5} is _____.
    a. 854 pico
    b. 85.4 milli
    c. 85.4 micro
    d. 85.4 kilo

16. If you are trying to enter the number 16000 into your calculator, the correct entry is _____.
    a. 1.6 02
    b. 1.6 03
    c. 1.6 05
    d. 1.6 04

17. Express 7.5×10^{-4} in milli, basic units, and micro.
    a. 7.5 milli, 0.075, 75000 micro
    b. 75 milli, 0.075, 7500 micro
    c. 75 milli, 0.0075, 750 micro
    d. 0.75 milli, 0.00075, 750 micro

18. Express these two calculator displays in correct metric units: **5.6 -07**
    2.2 05
    a. 56 micro, 22 kilo
    b. 0.56 micro, 0.022 Meg
    c. 0.56 micro, 220 kilo
    d. 56 micro, 220 kilo

19. The electrical symbol for voltage is _____.
    a. I
    b. V
    c. C
    d. R

20. The _____ is a typical semiconductor device.
    a. transformer
    b. diode
    c. resistor
    d. capacitor

21. The _____ is used to resist the flow of dc current in a circuit.
    a. capacitor
    b. inductor
    c. resistor
    d. transformer

22. The _____ stores electric charge.
    a. transformer
    b. capacitor
    c. resistor
    d. inductor
    e. semiconductor

23. The _____ stores energy in an electromagnetic field.
    a. capacitor
    b. inductor
    c. transistor
    d. diode

24. If your calculator displays **3.5 -06**, the equivalent metric value is
    _____.
    a. 35 milli
    b. 35 micro
    c. 3.5 Meg
    d. 3.5 micro
    e. 3.5 pico

25. Express 5.6×10^{-2} in milli, basic units, and micro.
    a. 5.6 milli, 0.056, 56000 micro
    b. 56 milli, 0.056, 56000 micro
    c. 560 milli, 5.600, 5600 micro
    d. 5600 milli, 56, 560

26. An electronic instrument used for measuring voltage, current, and resistance is called a:
    a. measuring instrument.
    b. digital multimeter.
    c. oscilloscope.
    d. function generator.

27. The difference between scientific and engineering notation is:
    a. powers of ten representation.
    b. single vs multiple digits before decimal point.
    c. groupings of multiple of three digits.
    d. all of these.

28. Mega is what relation to kilo?
    a. 10 times.
    b. 100 times.
    c. 1000 times.
    d. 1,000,000 times.

29. Pico is what relation to micro?
    a. $1/10^{th}$.
    b. $1/100^{th}$.
    c. $1/1,000^{th}$.
    d. $1/1,000,000^{th}$.

30. Convert 0.00047 microfarads (μF) to the equivalent picofarads ($_p$F):
    a. 0.47 $_p$F.
    b. 4.7 $_p$F.
    c. 47 $_p$F.
    d. 470 $_p$F.

31. Add 21 mA and 8000 μA and express the result in milliamperes:
    a. 21.8 mA.
    b. 218 mA.
    c. 29 mA.
    d. 290 mA.

32. Multiply 3 mA by 1000 μA and express the result in microamperes:
    a. 3 μA.
    b. 30 μA.
    c. 300 μA.
    d. 3000 μA.

1. Answer: a

2. Answer: b

3. Answer: b

4. Answer: a

5. Answer: a

6. Answer: d

7. Answer: a

8. Answer: c

9. Answer: b

10. Answer: c

11. Answer: c

12. Answer: c

13. Answer: c

14. Answer: a

15. Answer: c

16. Answer: d

17. Answer: d

18. Answer: c

19. Answer: b

20. Answer: b

21. Answer: c

22. Answer: b

23. Answer: b

24. Answer: d

25. Answer: b

26. Answer: b

27. Answer: d

28. Answer: c

29. Answer: d

30. Answer: d

31. Answer: c

32. Answer: a

Chapter 2: Voltage, Current and Resistance in Electric Circuits

TRUE/FALSE

1. The movement of free electrons through a conductor is called *current*.
   a. True
   b. False

2. Electrons attract each other.
   a. True
   b. False

3. A resistor color coded with yellow, violet and orange bands has a value of 4.7 kΩ.
   a. True
   b. False

4. A *SPST* switch is used to control one circuit.
   a. True
   b. False

5. To measure the current through a resistor, place the ammeter so the current must pass through the meter.
   a. True
   b. False

6. The *ohm* is the basic unit of resistance.
   a. True
   b. False

7. A resistor color coded with brown, black and orange bands has a value of 10,000 Ω.
   a. True
   b. False

8. A *Normally Open Push Button* switch can carry current when not pushed.
   a. True
   b. False

9. Electrons have a positive charge.
   a. True
   b. False

10. *Resistance* is the opposition to the flow of current.
    a. True
    b. False

MULTIPLE CHOICE

11. The _____ is a material that has many free electrons.
    a. conductor
    b. insulator
    c. semiconductor
    d. poor conductor

12. An insulator is a material with _____.
    a. some free electrons
    b. very many free electrons
    c. very few free electrons
    d. all free electrons

13. A resistor with orange, orange, red and gold bands has a value and tolerance of _____.
    a. 3.3 kΩ, ± 10 %
    b. 3.3 kΩ, ± 5%
    c. 33 kΩ, ± 5 %
    d. 33 kΩ, ± 10 %

14. If a resistor is color coded with red, red, orange and silver bands, the resistance equals _____, the lower tolerance limit equals _____ and the upper tolerance limit equals _____.
    a. 22 kΩ, 17.6 kΩ, 26.4 kΩ
    b. 22 kΩ, 20.9 kΩ, 23.1 kΩ
    c. 22 kΩ, 19.8 kΩ, 24.2 kΩ
    d. 22 kΩ, 21.5 kΩ, 22.4 kΩ

15. The opposition to the flow of current is called _____.
    a. voltage
    b. current
    c. capacitance
    d. resistance

16. If the current in a circuit equals 0 A, it is likely that the _____.
    a. voltage is too high
    b. resistance is too low
    c. circuit has a short
    d. circuit is open

17. If the measured circuit current is zero, it is likely that the _____.
    a. circuit has a short
    b. power is turned off
    c. resistance is very low
    d. circuit voltage is very high

(a)   (b)   (c)

(d)   (e)

Figure 2-1

18. Identify the *Normally Open Push Button* switch in **Figure 2-1**.
    a. graph (a)
    b. graph (b)
    c. graph (c)
    d. graph (d)
    e. graph (e)

19. Identify the *Rotary* switch in **Figure 2-1**.
    a. graph (a)
    b. graph (b)
    c. graph (c)
    d. graph (d)
    e. graph (e)

20. Which switch in **Figure 2-1** could be used to simultaneously open and close two circuits?
    a. graph (a)
    b. graph (b)
    c. graph (c)
    d. graph (d)
    e. graph (e)

21. What do you call a diagram that shows the electrical connections of a circuit's components?
    a. A pictorial diagram
    b. A block diagram
    c. A schematic diagram
    d. An electrical diagram

22. To measure a circuit's source voltage, the voltmeter must _____.
    a. be placed in series in the circuit
    b. have the red lead towards the negative side of the source
    c. have the black lead towards the positive side of the source
    d. be placed across the source

23. A source, a path, and a load _____.
    a. make up a basic circuit
    b. can only be an open circuit
    c. will allow current to flow if the switch is open
    d. do not make up a complete circuit

24. Voltage is _____.
    a. the opposition to the flow of current
    b. the movement of free electrons
    c. the force that exists between charged particles
    d. the force that causes water to flow

25. Which unit of charge contains 6.25×10^{18} electrons?
    a. An ampere
    b. A joule
    c. A volt
    d. A coulomb

26. A conductor is a material that has _____.
    a. few free electrons
    b. a positive charge
    c. many free electrons
    d. a structure similar to semiconductors

27. If a resistor equals 1.2 Ω ±5 %, its color code is _____.
    a. Brown, black, red, gold
    b. Brown, red, silver, gold
    c. Brown, black, gold, silver
    d. Brown, red, gold, gold

28. Identify the *DPST* switch in **Figure 2-1**.
    a. graph (a)
    b. graph (b)
    c. graph (c)
    d. graph (d)
    e. graph (e)

29. Every electrical circuit must contain _____.
    a. a source, a load and a resistor
    b. a battery, a resistor and a capacitor
    c. a source, a load and a path
    d. a battery, a path and a switch

30. In order to measure the current in a circuit, an ammeter must _____.
    a. be placed across the load
    b. be placed so the current must pass through the meter
    c. be placed across the source
    d. all of these

31. A resistor with yellow, violet, orange and silver bands equals
    _____.
    a. 47 MΩ ±10 %
    b. 47 kΩ ±5 %
    c. 47 kΩ ±10 %
    d. 4.7 kΩ ±10 %

32. A resistor with yellow, violet, orange, and gold bands equals
    _____.
    a. 47 MΩ ±10 %
    b. 47 kΩ ±5 %
    c. 47 kΩ ±10 %
    d. 4.7 kΩ ±10 %

33. If a resistor is color coded with orange, orange, orange and silver
    bands, the resistance equals _____, the lower tolerance limit
    equals _____ and the upper tolerance limit equals _____.
    a. 33 kΩ, 32,670 Ω, 33,330 Ω
    b. 33 kΩ, 31,350 Ω, 34,650 Ω
    c. 33 kΩ, 29,700 Ω, 36,300 Ω
    d. 33 kΩ, 26,400 Ω, 39,600 Ω

34. A 100 kΩ ±10 % resistor is color coded _____.
    a. black, brown, yellow, silver
    b. brown, green, black, gold
    c. brown, black, yellow, gold
    d. brown, black, yellow, silver

Figure 2-2

35. In **Figure 2-2**, if you place a voltmeter's red lead on point E and its
    black lead on point H, you will be measuring _____.
    a. V_{R4}
    b. V_{R7}
    c. V_{R5}
    d. V_{R6}

36. To measure the current that flows through R_6 in **Figure 2-2**, the circuit must be opened and the ammeter placed at point _____.
    a. E
    b. F
    c. G
    d. H

37. In **Figure 2-2**, the voltage V_{GH} is the same as _____.
    a. V_{R5}
    b. V_{R6}
    c. V_{R7}
    d. V_{R8}

38. In **Figure 2-2**, the voltage V_{FG} is the same as _____.
    a. V_{R6}
    b. V_{R7}
    c. V_{R8}
    d. V_{R9}

39. In **Figure 2-2**, a voltmeter placed across points C and D will measure _____.
    a. V_{R1}
    b. V_{R2}
    c. V_{R3}
    d. V_{R4}

40. In **Figure 2-2**, the voltage V_{CE} is the same as _____.
    a. V_{R5}
    b. $V_{R3} + V_{R4}$
    c. $V_{R4} + V_{R5}$
    d. V_{R6}

41. An analog meter has _____.
    a. a digital readout
    b. a needle and a scale to indicate the value
    c. no moving parts
    d. is very accurate

42. An ohmmeter should _____.
    a. be connected across a circuit with the power on
    b. be inserted into the circuit so the current flows through it
    c. be placed across the resistor after the resistor has been disconnected from the circuit
    d. have the polarity carefully checked before its use

43. Most DMMs will measure _____, _____ and _____.
    a. frequency, voltage, current
    b. voltage, current, capacitance
    c. voltage, frequency, resistance
    d. voltage, current, resistance

Figure 2-1

44. Identify the *Normally Closed Push Button* switch in **Figure 2-1**.
    a. graph (a)
    b. graph (b)
    c. graph (c)
    d. graph (d)
    e. graph (e)

45. Which switch in **Figure 2-1** is usually used to control a doorbell?
    a. graph (a)
    b. graph (b)
    c. graph (c)
    d. graph (d)
    e. graph (e)

46. The *Rotary* switch in **Figure 2-1** is most likely to be used as
    _____.
    a. an old manual TV channel selector.
    b. a selector for different voltages in a power supply.
    c. a range selector switch in an analog voltmeter.
    d. all of the above

47. Identify the *DPDT* switch in **Figure 2-1**.
    a. graph (a)
    b. graph (b)
    c. graph (c)
    d. graph (d)
    e. graph (e)

48. Which switch in **Figure 2-1** could be used to control a light and a fan
    at the same time?
    a. graph (a)
    b. graph (b)
    c. graph (c)
    d. graph (d)
    e. graph (e)

49. Which switch in **Figure 2-1** could be used to switch two inputs to different output positions?
    a. graph (a)
    b. graph (b)
    c. graph (c)
    d. graph (d)
    e. graph (e)

50. Which switch in **Figure 2-1** could be used to open a circuit momentarily?
    a. graph (a)
    b. graph (b)
    c. graph (c)
    d. graph (d)
    e. graph (e)

51. On a resistor with five bands of color code, the fifth band may represent:
    a. the resistor is a precision resistor.
    b. the tolerance in percentage of value.
    c. the reliability in percentage of failure.
    d. all of these.

52. On a resistor with four bands of color code, the fourth band represents:
    a. the voltage rating.
    b. the wattage rating.
    c. the multiplier value.
    d. the tolerance percentage.

53. On a resistor with numbers and letters, the position of the letter in the sequence represents:
    a. the numerical total.
    b. the tolerance.
    c. the decimal point.
    d. the resistance value.

54. Interpret the following mixed numbers and letters 4R7 on a resistor to the correct resistance of:
    a. 4.7 ohms.
    b. 47 ohms.
    c. 4.7 Kilohms.
    d. 4.7 Megohms.

55. Interpret the following mixed numbers and letters 3M3 on a resistor to the correct resistance of:
    a. 3.3 Kilohms.
    b. 33 Kilohms.
    c. 330 Kilohms.
    d. 3300 Kilohms.

56. Potentiometers and rheastats differ in that:
    a. potentiometers are used to vary voltages, while rheostats vary currents.
    b. potentiometers utilize three terminals, while rheostats usually use only two terminals.
    c. potentiometers utilize linear and nonlinear tapers, while rheostats utilize usually only linear tapers.
    d. all of these.

57. The most popular type of resistors are
    a. carbon film.
    b. metal film.
    c. carbon-composition.
    d. wirewound.

58. In the American Wire Guage sizes, as the numerical AWa goes higher, the cross sectional area of the wire
    a. decreases.
    b. halves.
    c. increases.
    d. doubles.

59. The basic difference between a fuse and a circuit breaker is
    a. a fuse is faster.
    b. a fuse is reusable.
    c. a circuit breaker is reusable.
    d. a circuit breaker is more reliable.

1. Answer: a

2. Answer: b

3. Answer: b

4. Answer: a

5. Answer: a

6. Answer: a

7. Answer: a

8. Answer: b

9. Answer: b

10. Answer: a

11. Answer: a

12. Answer: c

13. Answer: b

14. Answer: c

15. Answer: d

16. Answer: d

17. Answer: b

18. Answer: c

19. Answer: e

20. Answer: a

21. Answer: c

22. Answer: d

23. Answer: a

24. Answer: c

25. Answer: d

26. Answer: c

27. Answer: d

28. Answer: a

29. Answer: c

30. Answer: b

31. Answer: c

32. Answer: b

33. Answer: c

34. Answer: d

35. Answer: b

36. Answer: b

37. Answer: d

38. Answer: a

39. Answer: c

40. Answer: b

41. Answer: b

42. Answer: c

43. Answer: d

44. Answer: d

45. Answer: c

46. Answer: d

47. Answer: b

48. Answer: a

49. Answer: b

50. Answer: d

51. Answer: d

52. Answer: d

53. Answer: c

54. Answer: a

55. Answer: d

56. Answer: d

57. Answer: c

58. Answer: c

59. Answer: c

Chapter 3: Ohm's Law, Energy and Power

TRUE/FALSE

1. If the current is constant, voltage and resistance are directly proportional.
   a. True
   b. False

2. If a circuit's supply voltage is 15 V and its resistance is 4700 Ω, its current is 3.19 mA.
   a. True
   b. False

3. If a 1 kΩ resistor has 32 mA flowing through it, it dissipates 1.024 W.
   a. True
   b. False

4. If a circuit's resistance increases, its current decreases.
   a. True
   b. False

5. If a 47 kΩ resistor carries 5 mA, it's safe to use a 1W resistor.
   a. True
   b. False

6. If a circuit's supply voltage is 20 V and its resistance is 3300 Ω, its current is 6.06 mA.
   a. True
   b. False

7. If a 2.5 kΩ resistor carries 45 mA, it is dissipating 5.0625 W.
   a. True
   b. False

8. If a circuit's resistance decreases, its current also decreases.
   a. True
   b. False

9. If a 56 kΩ resistor carries 10 mA, it is safe to use a 10 W resistor.
   a. True
   b. False

10. If a 12 kΩ resistor carries 12 mA, the resistor drops 1 V.
    a. True
    b. False

MULTIPLE CHOICE

11. Voltage and current are _____.
    a. directly proportional
    b. inversely proportional
    c. unrelated
    d. quantities that add

12. If the voltage across a circuit increases, _____.
    a. the current decreases
    b. the resistance increases
    c. the resistance decreases
    d. the current increases

Figure 3-1

13. If V = 25 V and R = 50 kΩ in **Figure 3-1**, the current equals _____.
    a. 50 mA
    b. 5 mA
    c. 0.5 mA
    d. 2 mA

14. If I = 64 mA and R = 470 Ω in **Figure 3-1**, the voltage equals _____.
    a. 30.08 V
    b. 3.008 V
    c. 73.43 V
    d. 7.343 V

15. If V = 72 V and I = 12 mA in **Figure 3-1**, the resistance equals _____.
    a. 0.166 Ω
    b. 6 kΩ
    c. 864 Ω
    d. 47 kΩ

16. If V = 12 V and a 12 kΩ resistor shorts in **Figure 3-1**, the current is _____.
    a. 1 mA
    b. 10 mA
    c. 0 A
    d. extremely large

17. If the voltage is suddenly switched off in **Figure 3-1**, _____.
    a. the current will suddenly drop to 0 A
    b. the current will gradually decrease to 0 A
    c. the current will first increase and then decrease to 0 A
    d. there is no way to predict the current

18. If V = 100 V and I = 1 mA in **Figure 3-1**, the power dissipated by the resistor equals _____.
    a. 10 W
    b. 1 W
    c. 100m W
    d. 10m W

19. If a resistor that is color coded yellow-violet-orange-gold is placed across a 15 V source, the resistance and wattage rating could be _____.
    a. 4.7 kΩ 1/8 W
    b. 47 kΩ 1/4 W
    c. 4700 Ω 1/4 W
    d. 0.47M Ω 1/4 W

20. A 220 Ω 1/2 W resistor has burned open so you look in your parts box to find a replacement. Which one of the following resistors could you use to repair the circuit?
    a. 2200 Ω 1/2 W
    b. 220 Ω 1/4 W
    c. 220 Ω 1/8 W
    d. 220 Ω 1 W

21. If the resistor opens in **Figure 3-1**, the _____.
    a. power dissipation decreases
    b. current increases
    c. resistance decreases
    d. voltage increases

22. What is the resistance of a 100 W bulb when it is operating in a circuit with a supply of 120 V?
    a. 56 Ω
    b. 2.14 Ω
    c. 144 Ω
    d. 560 Ω

23. If a resistor is rated at 1/2 W, it _____.
    a. can safely dissipate 1/2 W of power
    b. always dissipates 1/2 W
    c. always provides 1/2 W of power
    d. can only dissipate more than 1/2 W of power

24. Which is the correct formula for Ohm's Law?
    a. V = I + R
    b. R = V × I
    c. I = V ÷ R
    d. P = V × I

25. If a resistor that is color coded yellow-violet-brown-gold is connected to a 12 V source, then what is the maximum current that can flow?
    a. 24.3 mA
    b. 25.5 mA
    c. 26.9 mA
    d. 255 mA

26. Resistance and current are _____.
    a. directly proportional
    b. inversely proportional
    c. not related
    d. similar to voltage

27. If I = 32 mA and R = 469 Ω in **Figure 3-1**, the voltage equals
    _____.
    a. 12 V
    b. 15 V
    c. 19 V
    d. 22 V

28. Which of the following terms is **not** a resistor rating?
    a. resistor value in ohms
    b. resistor tolerance
    c. current
    d. power rating

29. If voltage is 12 V and the resistance is color coded brown-black-orange
    in **Figure 3-1**, what are the minimum and maximum possible currents?
    a. $I_{MINIMUM}$ = 1.2 mA, $I_{MAXIMUM}$ = 1.4 mA
    b. $I_{MINIMUM}$ = 1 mA, $I_{MAXIMUM}$ = 1.6 mA
    c. $I_{MINIMUM}$ = 0.8 mA, $I_{MAXIMUM}$ = 1.2 mA
    d. $I_{MINIMUM}$ = 1 mA, $I_{MAXIMUM}$ = 1.5 mA

30. If the resistor opens in **Figure 3-1**, the _____.
    a. power dissipation increases
    b. circuit current drops to 0 A
    c. source voltage decreases to 0 V
    d. resistance decreases

31. A 250 μA current flowing through a 4.7 kΩ resistor produces a _____
    voltage drop.
    a. 53.2 V
    b. 1.175 mV
    c. 18.8 V
    d. 1.175 V

32. If a resistance of 2.2 MΩ is connected across a 1 kV source, current
    equals about _____.
    a. 2.2 mA
    b. 0.455 mA
    c. 45.5μ A
    d. 0.455 A

33. If a 2.2 kΩ resistor dissipates 0.5 W, its current equals _____.
    a. 15.1 mA
    b. 0.227 mA
    c. 1.1 mA
    d. 4.4 mA

34. If a 330 Ω resistor dissipates 2 W, its voltage drop equals _____.
    a. 2.57 V
    b. 660 V
    c. 6.6 V
    d. 25.7 V

35. The power rating of a resistor that must dissipate up to 1.1 W should be _____.
    a. 0.25 W
    b. 1 W
    c. 2 W
    d. 5 W

36. If V = 50 V and R = 25 kΩ in **Figure 3-1**, the current equals _____.
    a. 50 mA
    b. 5 mA
    c. 0.5 mA
    d. 2 mA

37. If I = 64 mA and R = 47 Ω in **Figure 3-1**, the voltage equals _____.
    a. 30.08 V
    b. 3.008 V
    c. 73.43 V
    d. 7.343 V

38. If V = 85 V and I = 15 mA in **Figure 3-1**, the resistance equals _____.
    a. 1.275 Ω
    b. 52.3 Ω
    c. 5.667 kΩ
    d. 566 Ω

39. If V = 50 V and I = 37 mA in **Figure 3-1**, _____ is dissipated by the resistor.
    a. 1.85 W
    b. 1.35 W
    c. 0.185m W
    d. 135m W

40. What is the resistance of a 150 W bulb when it is operating in a circuit with a supply of 125 V?
    a. 75 Ω
    b. 104 Ω
    c. 9375 Ω
    d. 2.14 Ω

41. Which is the correct formula for finding power?
    a. $P = V \times I$
    b. $P = I^2 \times R$
    c. $P = V^2 \div R$
    d. all of these

42. If a resistor that is color coded red-red-brown-silver is connected to a 15 V source, what is the maximum current that can flow?
    a. 75.8 mA
    b. 62 mA
    c. 68.2 mA
    d. 71.9 mA

43. If I = 45 mA and R = 40 kΩ in **Figure 3-1**, the voltage equals
    _____.
    a. 1.125 V
    b. 1800 V
    c. 18 V
    d. 1.8 V

44. If a 10 kΩ resistor dissipates 0.5 W in **Figure 3-1**, then the supply voltage equals _____.
    a. 5000 V
    b. 70.7 V
    c. 7.07m V
    d. 50 V

45. If the voltage is 15 V and resistance is color coded red-red-brown-silver in **Figure 3-1**, what are the maximum and minimum possible current?
    a. $I_{MINIMUM}$ = 71.8 mA, $I_{MAXIMUM}$ = 64.9 mA
    b. $I_{MINIMUM}$ = 75.8 mA, $I_{MAXIMUM}$ = 62.0 mA
    c. $I_{MINIMUM}$ = 85.2 mA, $I_{MAXIMUM}$ = 56.8 mA
    d. none of these

46. If a resistor that is color coded yellow-violet-red is placed across a 25 V source voltage, what value resistor and wattage rating could be used?
    a. 47000 Ω, 1/4 W
    b. 4700 Ω, 1/8 W
    c. 470 Ω, 1/2 W
    d. 4700 Ω, 1/4 W

47. If V = 60 V and R = 47 kΩ in **Figure 3-1**, the current equals
    _____.
    a. 1.28 mA
    b. 12.8 mA
    c. 128 mA
    d. 0.128 mA

48. If a 1/2 W resistor is used in the circuit in **Figure 3-1**, the current value _____.
    a. is over 12 mA
    b. is less than 12 mA
    c. depends upon the voltage applied
    d. depends upon the circuit's voltage and resistance

49. If the voltage were suddenly switched on in **Figure 3-1**, _____.
    a. the current would gradually decrease
    b. the current would be zero
    c. the current would flow
    d. the current would gradually decrease and then increase

50. If I = 27 mA and R = 4.7 Ω in **Figure 3-1**, the voltage equals
    _____.
    a. 127m V
    b. 5.74 V
    c. 174m V
    d. 7.8 V

51. Using Watt's law and substituting power can be calculated as:
    a. $P = V^2/R$.
    b. $P = T^2R$.
    c. $P = VI$.
    d. All of these.

52. Power as it is used in electric circuits can be best defined as:
    a. the rate motion is exerted over time.
    b. the rate current flows over time.
    c. the rate voltage is applied over time.
    d. the rate energy is used over time.

53. The symbol for a certain amount of energy used over time is:
    a. P.
    b. W.
    c. I.
    d. V.

54. A kilowatt-hour is best defined as:
    a. a kilo divided by 1 watt-hour.
    b. 1,000 watts divided by 1 hour.
    c. a kilo multiplied by 1 watt-hour.
    d. 1,000 watts multiplied by 1 hour.

55. The average cost for a kilowatt-hour of electric power in the United
    States is:
    a. 0.1 cent.
    b. 1 cent.
    c. 10 cents.
    d. 50 cents.

56. The ampere-hour rating of a battery is defined as the:
    a. number of amperes supplied in 1 hour.
    b. number of amperes supplied over the number of hours at a given
       current.
    c. number of hours per amperes supplied.
    d. all of these.

1. Answer: a

2. Answer: b

3. Answer: a

4. Answer: a

5. Answer: b

6. Answer: a

7. Answer: a

8. Answer: b

9. Answer: a

10. Answer: b

11. Answer: a

12. Answer: d

13. Answer: c

14. Answer: a

15. Answer: b

16. Answer: d

17. Answer: a

18. Answer: c

19. Answer: b

20. Answer: d

21. Answer: a

22. Answer: c

23. Answer: a

24. Answer: c

25. Answer: b

26. Answer: b

27. Answer: b

28. Answer: c

29. Answer: d

30. Answer: b

31. Answer: d

32. Answer: b

33. Answer: a

34. Answer: d

35. Answer: c

36. Answer: d

37. Answer: b

38. Answer: c

39. Answer: a

40. Answer: b

41. Answer: d

42. Answer: a

43. Answer: b

44. Answer: b

45. Answer: b

46. Answer: d

47. Answer: a

48. Answer: d

49. Answer: c

50. Answer: a

51. Answer: d

52. Answer: d

53. Answer: b

54. Answer: d

55. Answer: c

56. Answer: b

Chapter 4:   Series Circuits

1. In a series circuit, the current is the same at every point in the circuit.
   a. True
   b. False

2. *Kirchhoff's Voltage Law* states that the algebraic sum of all the voltages around a closed path is zero.
   a. True
   b. False

3. The total power dissipated in a series circuit equals the sum of the individual powers.
   a. True
   b. False

4. If 6.8 kΩ, 1.2 kΩ and 5.6 kΩ resistors are wired in series, the total resistance is 13.6 kΩ.
   a. True
   b. False

5. If a resistor is dissipating 1/4 W, it can supply 1/4 W to the load
   a. True
   b. False

6. If 4.7 kΩ, 2.2 kΩ and 1.2 kΩ resistors are wired in series, the total resistance is 8.7 kΩ.
   a. True
   b. False

7. Total power dissipated in a series circuit equals source voltage multiplied by current.
   a. True
   b. False

8. If a resistor is rated at 1/2 W, it can safely dissipate 0.325 W.
   a. True
   b. False

9. According to *Kirchhoff's Voltage Law*, the sum of the individual voltage drops in a series circuit equals the source voltage.
   a. True
   b. False

10. If a 1/4 W resistor and a 1/2 W resistor are wired in series, they can safely dissipate 3/4 W.
    a. True
    b. False

MULTIPLE CHOICE

Figure 4-1

11. What is the total resistance in **Figure 4-1** if $R_1 = 10$ kΩ, $R_2 = 10$ kΩ and $R_3 = 15$ kΩ.
    a. 25 kΩ
    b. 35 kΩ
    c. 0 kΩ
    d. infinite Ω

12. Calculate the current in **Figure 4-1** if $V_{R1} = 16$ V, $R_1 = 10$ kΩ, $R_2 = 10$ kΩ and $R_3 = 15$ kΩ.
    a. 3.2 mA
    b. 1.6 mA
    c. 0 A
    d. 12 mA

13. Calculate V_{R2} and V_{R3} in **Figure 4-1** if $V_{R1} = 16$ V, $R_1 = 10$ kΩ, $R_2 = 10$ kΩ and $R_3 = 15$ kΩ.
    a. $V_{R2} = 16$ V, $V_{R3} = 12$ V
    b. $V_{R2} = 16$ V, $V_{R3} = 24$ V
    c. $V_{R2} = 16$ V, $V_{R3} = 16$ V
    d. $V_{R2} = 24$ V, $V_{R3} = 12$ V

14. Calculate P_{R2} in **Figure 4-1** if $V_{R1} = 16$ V, $R_1 = 10$ kΩ, $R_2 = 10$ kΩ and $R_3 = 15$ kΩ.
    a. 25.6m W
    b. 2.56m W
    c. 0.256m W
    d. 0.0256m W

15. Calculate V_T in **Figure 4-1** if $V_{R1} = 16$ V, $R_1 = 10$ kΩ, $R_2 = 10$ kΩ and $R_3 = 15$ kΩ.
    a. 16 V
    b. 24 V
    c. 56 V
    d. 112 V

16. V_{R1} = 16 V, R_1 = 10 kΩ, R_2 = 10 kΩ and R_3 = 15 kΩ in **Figure 4-1**. If R_2 opens, then R_T is _____.
    a. 25 kΩ
    b. 10 kΩ
    c. 0 Ω
    d. infinite Ω

17. If R_2 opens in **Figure 4-1**, the total power dissipated _____.
    a. increases to maximum
    b. decreases to zero
    c. remains the same
    d. will depend upon the source voltage

18. What is the total supply voltage if 16 V and 12 V sources are wired in series opposing?
    a. 28 V
    b. 16 V
    c. 12 V
    d. 4 V

19. If 12 V and -19 V sources are connected so their total voltage is -7 V, they are _____.
    a. series aiding
    b. series opposing
    c. in parallel
    d. connected dangerously

20. Calculate P_T in **Figure 4-1** if V_T = 100 V and all three resistors are each 47 kΩ.
    a. 70.9m W
    b. 23.6m W
    c. 22 W
    d. 709m W

21. Calculate V_{R3} in **Figure 4-1** if V_T = 50 V, V_{R1} = 19.7 V and V_{R2} = 2.7 V.
    a. 30.3 V
    b. 47.3 V
    c. 22.4 V
    d. 27.6 V

22. The polarity on the side of the resistor where current enters is _____. The polarity on the side of the resistor where current exits is _____.
    a. positive, positive
    b. negative, negative
    c. negative, positive
    d. positive, negative

23. When 50 V is applied to four series resistors, 100μ A flows. If R_1 = 12 kΩ, R_2 = 47 kΩ and R_3 = 56 kΩ, what is the value of R_4?
    a. 38.5 kΩ
    b. 3.85 kΩ
    c. 385 kΩ
    d. 3.85M Ω

31

24. If R_1 = 12 kΩ and R_2 = 5 kΩ and they are wired in series across a 20 V source, what is V_{R1} and V_{R2}?
    a. V_{R1} = 5.88 V, V_{R2} = 14.12 V
    b. V_{R1} = 14.12 V, V_{R2} = 5.88 V
    c. V_{R1} = 10 V, V_{R2} = 10 V
    d. V_{R1} = 0 V, V_{R2} = 20 V

25. Four resistors are connected in series across an 18 V source. Three resistors drop 0 V and one resistor drops 18 V. What's the trouble?
    a. Two of the resistors are shorted
    b. The three resistors are open
    c. One resistor is open
    d. There is no trouble; these voltages are normal.

26. If 12 V and 17 V sources are wired in series aiding, what is the total supply voltage?
    a. 5 V
    b. 12 V
    c. 29 V
    d. 17 V

27. Two 100 kΩ resistors are wired in series across a 20 V source. How much voltage does each resistor drop?
    a. 20 V
    b. 10 V
    c. 100 mA
    d. 100 kΩ

28. A 22 kΩ and 12 kΩ resistor are connected across a 68 V source. How is the voltage divided?
    a. 44 V and 24 V
    b. 34 V and 34 V
    c. 22 V and 12 V
    d. 68 V and 68 V

29. A 500 kΩ potentiometer is connected across a 5 V source. If the voltage from the wiper to the lower end of the potentiometer is 1.2 V, what is the resistance of that lower part?
    a. 380 kΩ
    b. 120 kΩ
    c. 500 kΩ
    d. 0 Ω

30. -1.2 V, +5 V and +6 V batteries are connected in series. The total voltage is _____.
    a. 12.2 V
    b. 9.8 V
    c. 1.2 V
    d. 1.3 V

31. If a 100 Ω, 220 Ω, and 330 Ω resistor are connected in series, total resistance equals _____.
    a. less than 100 Ω
    b. the average of the three values
    c. 650 Ω
    d. 1650 Ω

32. If a 68 Ω, 33 Ω, 100 Ω and 47 Ω resistor are connected in series across a 9 V battery, the current equals _____.
    a. 36.29 mA
    b. 27.56 A
    c. 22.32 mA
    d. 326.6 mA

33. If each of the six resistors in a series circuit drops 5 V, the source voltage _____.
    a. equals 5 V
    b. equals 30 V
    c. depends on the resistor values
    d. depends on the current

34. If a 4.7 kΩ, 5.6 kΩ and 10 kΩ resistor are in series, which resistor drops the most voltage?
    a. the 4.7 kΩ resistor
    b. the 5.6 kΩ resistor
    c. the 10 kΩ resistor
    d. That can't be determined from the given information

35. If five equal resistors dissipate a total of 10 W in a series circuit, how much power does each resistor dissipate?
    a. 10 W
    b. 50 W
    c. 5 W
    d. 2 W

36. How much voltage is dropped across R_2 and R_3 in **Figure 4-1** if $R_1 = 4.7$ kΩ, $V_{R1} = 10$ V, $R_2 = 4.7$ kΩ and $R_3 = 4.7$ kΩ?
    a. $V_{R2} = 10$ V, $V_{R3} = 10$ V
    b. $V_{R2} = 4.7$ V, $V_{R3} = 10$ V
    c. $V_{R2} = 10$ V, $V_{R3} = 4.7$ V
    d. $V_{R2} = 14.7$ V, $V_{R3} = 14.7$ V

37. Calculate I_T in **Figure 4-1** if $R_1 = 4.7$ kΩ, $V_{R1} = 10$ V, $R_2 = 4.7$ kΩ and $R_3 = 4.7$ kΩ.
    a. 1 mA
    b. 2.13 mA
    c. 4.26 mA
    d. 6 mA

38. Calculate V_T in **Figure 4-1** if R_1 = 4.7 kΩ, V_{R1} = 10 V, R_2 = 4.7 kΩ and R_3 = 4.7 kΩ.
    a. 4.7 V
    b. 10 V
    c. 14.7 V
    d. 30 V

39. If R_2 shorts in **Figure 4-1**, the total circuit power _____.
    a. increases
    b. decreases
    c. remains the same
    d. depends upon the source voltage

40. R_1 = 4.7 kΩ, R_2 = 4.7 kΩ and R_3 = 4.7 kΩ in **Figure 4-1**. What is R_T if R_2 shorts?
    a. 0 Ω
    b. 4.7 kΩ
    c. 9.4 kΩ
    d. infinite Ω

41. If 18 V and 6 V sources are connected in series opposing, what is the total voltage?
    a. 2 V
    b. 6 V
    c. 18 V
    d. 12 V

42. If -12 V and -6 V are connected so they equal -18 V, these sources are _____.
    a. series aiding
    b. series opposing
    c. in parallel
    d. connected dangerously

43. If three 2.2 kΩ resistors are connected in series across a 50 V source, P_T equals _____.
    a. 52.08m W
    b. 104.2m W
    c. 379m W
    d. 402m W

44. Three resistors are connected in series across a 60 V source. If V_{R1} = 19 V and V_{R2} = 14.3 V, then what is the voltage drop across R_3?
    a. 26.7 V
    b. 19 V
    c. 14.3 V
    d. 45.7 V

45. If 5 V and 16 V power supplies are connected in series aiding, what is the total voltage?
    a. 21 V
    b. 16 V
    c. 24 V
    d. 80 V

46. Two resistors are in series across a 12 V source. If each resistor equals 470 kΩ, what is the voltage across each resistor?
    a. 3 V
    b. 6 V
    c. 9 V
    d. 12 V

47. If a 10 kΩ and 5 kΩ resistor are connected in series across a 12 V source, the voltage across the 10 kΩ resistor is _____ and the voltage across the 5 kΩ resistor is _____.
    a. 8 V, 4 V
    b. 4 V, 8 V
    c. 8 V, 8 V
    d. 4 V, 4 V

48. Four series resistors are connected across a 30 V source and carry 0.125 mA. If R_1 = 10 kΩ, R_2 = 33 kΩ and R_3 = 47 kΩ, what is the value of R_4?
    a. 150 Ω
    b. 1.5 kΩ
    c. 15 kΩ
    d. 150 kΩ

49. The voltage drop across any resistor or combination of resistors in a series circuit equals
    a. the applied voltaage across the resistor (A).
    b. the ratio of the resistance values times the source voltage.
    c. the product of the circuit current times the resistance value.
    d. all of these.

50. A 50 kΩ potentiometer is connected across a 15 V source. If the voltage from the wiper to the lower end of the potentiometer is 3.2 V, what is the resistance of that lower part?
    a. 10.67 kΩ
    b. 39.3 kΩ
    c. 50 kΩ
    d. 0 Ω

51. One of the most popular applications of a potentiometer is as an adjustable voltage divider also known as a:
    a. voltage control.
    b. current control.
    c. volume control.
    d. divider control.

52. In a series circuit, total power P_T is calculated as:
    a. $P_1 + P_2 + P_3 +$ etc.
    b. $1/P_1 + 1/P_2 + 1/P_3 +$ etc.
    c. $P_1 \div P_2 \div P_3 \div$ etc.
    d. $P_1 \times P_2 \times P_3 \times$ etc.

53. In a series circuit, the largest amount of power is dissipated by:
    a. the first resistor.
    b. the smallest resistor.
    c. the largest resistor.
    d. any resistor since the current is the same throughout the circuit.

54. Circuit ground or chassis ground can be thought of as a:
    a. common point.
    b. reference point.
    c. neutral connection point.
    d. all of these.

55. An open in a series circuit results in
    a. no current flow.
    b. no power dissipation.
    c. source voltage appearing at the open.
    d. all of these.

56. A short in a series circuit results in
    a. decreased or reduced current flow.
    b. increased or maximum current flow.
    c. decreased power consumption.
    d. increased circuit resistance.

1. Answer: a

2. Answer: a

3. Answer: a

4. Answer: a

5. Answer: b

6. Answer: b

7. Answer: a

8. Answer: a

9. Answer: a

10. Answer: b

11. Answer: b

12. Answer: b

13. Answer: b

14. Answer: a

15. Answer: c

16. Answer: d

17. Answer: b

18. Answer: d

19. Answer: b

20. Answer: a

21. Answer: d

22. Answer: c

23. Answer: c

24. Answer: b

25. Answer: c

26. Answer: c

27. Answer: b

28. Answer: a

29. Answer: b

30. Answer: b

31. Answer: c

32. Answer: a

33. Answer: b

34. Answer: c

35. Answer: d

36. Answer: a

37. Answer: b

38. Answer: d

39. Answer: a

40. Answer: c

41. Answer: d

42. Answer: a

43. Answer: c

44. Answer: a

45. Answer: a

46. Answer: b

47. Answer: a

48. Answer: d

49. Answer: d

50. Answer: a

51. Answer: c

52. Answer: a

53. Answer: c

54. Answer: d

55. Answer: d

56. Answer: b

Chapter 5: Parallel Circuits

TRUE/FALSE

1. If three equal resistors are connected in parallel across 12 V, each resistor drops 4 V.
   a. True
   b. False

2. The total resistance of four resistors in parallel is always less than the smallest resistance.
   a. True
   b. False

3. If $I_{R1} = 0.065$ mA and $I_{R2} = 0.098$ mA in a two branch parallel circuit, $I_T = 0.163$ mA.
   a. True
   b. False

4. If one branch of a parallel circuit opens, the total resistance decreases.
   a. True
   b. False

5. The total power dissipated by a parallel circuit can be found by adding the individual powers.
   a. True
   b. False

6. Kirchoff's Current Law states that the sum of the currents into a junction must equal the sum of the currents out of that junction.
   a. True
   b. False

7. The total resistance of three parallel resistors equals the sum of the individual resistor values.
   a. True
   b. False

8. If $I_{R1} = 75$ mA and $I_{R2} = 12.7$ mA in a two branch parallel circuit, $I_T = 85.7$ mA.
   a. True
   b. False

9. If one branch of a parallel circuit shorts, the total resistance decreases.
   a. True
   b. False

10. $P_{R1} = 0.25$ W and $P_{R2} = 1.2$ W in a parallel circuit. The total power dissipated is 1.25 W.
    a. True
    b. False

MULTIPLE CHOICE

11. If a 5.5 kΩ, 22 kΩ and 500 Ω resistor are connected in parallel, what is R_T?
    a. 28.1 kΩ
    b. 27.6 kΩ
    c. 449 Ω
    d. 330 Ω

12. If a 500 Ω, 1200 Ω and 10 kΩ resistor are connected in parallel across a 25 V source, how much current flows through the 1200 Ω resistor?
    a. 20.83 mA
    b. 50 mA
    c. 2.5 mA
    d. 2.4 mA

13. If a 2.2 kΩ resistor and a 3.3 kΩ resistor are connected in parallel, R_T equals _____ .
    a. 2.2 kΩ
    b. 3.3 kΩ
    c. greater than 2.2 kΩ
    d. less than 2.2 kΩ

14. In a three-resistor parallel circuit, R_1 = 0.22 MΩ and R_2 = 1 MΩ. If R_T = 0.1166 MΩ, then what is the value of R_3?
    a. 1.34M Ω
    b. 0.33M Ω
    c. 0.134M Ω
    d. 13,400 Ω

15. If a 1 MΩ resistor, 0.47 MΩ resistor and 0.5 MΩ resistor are connected in parallel across an 18 V source, what is the total current if the 1 MΩ resistor opens?
    a. 74.3μ A
    b. 74.3 mA
    c. 92.3μ A
    d. 92.3 mA

16. If twelve 1.5 MΩ resistors are connected in parallel across 50 V, R_T equals _____ .
    a. 1.5M Ω
    b. 1.25M Ω
    c. 1M Ω
    d. 0.125M Ω

17. I_T equals 0.1 mA in a 3-branch parallel circuit. If I_1 = 0.022 mA and I_2 = 0.007 mA, I_3 = ?
    a. 0.029 mA
    b. 0.071 mA
    c. 0.142 mA
    d. 0.213 mA

18. If one resistor opens in a parallel circuit, the total circuit resistance _____ and the total circuit current _____.
    a. decreases, increases
    b. increases, increases
    c. decreases, decreases
    d. increases, decreases

19. If three 22 kΩ resistors are connected in parallel across a 10 V source, P_T equals _____.
    a. 4.5m W
    b. 13.6m W
    c. 18.1m W
    d. 22.6m W

20. If one resistor shorts in a parallel circuit, the total current _____.
    a. equals 0A
    b. increases
    c. decreases
    d. decreases momentarily then returns to the original value

21. If four 100 W lamps are connected in parallel across a 120 V source, what is the total current?
    a. 3.33 A
    b. 833 mA
    c. 33.3 A
    d. 8.33 A

22. If you measure a lower than normal total current in a parallel circuit, _____
    a. a resistor shorted.
    b. the power supply is off.
    c. all of the resistors are opened.
    d. a resistor opened

23. A formula that applies to a two-branch parallel circuit is _____.
    a. $R_T = R_1 + R_2$
    b. $V_T = V_{R1} + V_{R2}$
    c. $I_T = I_{R1} + I_{R2}$
    d. $R_T = V_1 + R_2$

24. The current through any branch of a parallel circuit _____.
    a. depends on the power rating of the resistor
    b. only depends on the circuit voltage
    c. is directly proportional to the branch resistance
    d. is inversely proportional to the branch resistance

25. If you want to measure a load voltage with a DVM, connect the meter _____.
    a. in series with the load
    b. across the source
    c. in parallel with the load
    d. in series with the source

26. The total resistance of a three-branch parallel circuit is 76.92 Ω. If
    $R_1 = 100$ Ω and $R_2 = 500$ Ω, what is the value of R_3?
    a. 140 Ω
    b. 1000 Ω
    c. 1850 Ω
    d. More information is needed to calculate R_3

27. A two-branch parallel circuit contains these values: $R_1 = 1200$ Ω, $I_T = 0.005$ mA, $I_2 = 0.003$ mA. What is the value of V_{R1}?
    a. 6 m V
    b. 18 m V
    c. 3.6 m V
    d. 2.4 m V

28. As additional branch resistors are connected in a parallel circuit,
    _____.
    a. I_T decreases and R_T increases
    b. I_T decreases and R_T decreases
    c. I_T increases and R_T decreases
    d. I_T increases and R_T increases

29. If a 4.7 kΩ resistor, a 3.3 kΩ resistor and a 5.43 kΩ resistor are
    connected in parallel across a 50 V source, what is the current through
    the 5.43 kΩ resistor?
    a. 10.64 mA
    b. 15.15 mA
    c. 9.21 mA
    d. 4.72 mA

30. $R_T = 330$ Ω and $R_1 = 470$ Ω in a two-branch parallel circuit. What is the
    value of R_2?
    a. 770 Ω
    b. 1108 Ω
    c. 194 Ω
    d. 110 Ω

31. If a 330 Ω resistor, 270 Ω resistor and 68 Ω resistor are connected in
    parallel, what is the approximate value for R_T?
    a. 668 Ω
    b. 47 Ω
    c. 68 Ω
    d. 22 Ω

32. If 5 A and 3 A enter a junction from two separate paths, how much
    current flows out of the junction?
    a. 2 A
    b. 3 A
    c. 8 A
    d. the larger of the two

33. Each branch in a four-branch parallel circuit carries 10 mA. If one of the branches opens, then the current in each of the other three branches equals _____.
    a. 13.33 mA
    b. 10 mA
    c. 0 A
    d. 30 mA

34. If there is 100 mA of current flowing into a three-branch parallel circuit and two of the branch currents are 40 mA and 20 mA, the third branch current is _____.
    a. 60 mA
    b. 20 mA
    c. 160 mA
    d. 40 mA

35. If the power dissipation in each of four parallel branches is 1 W, P_T equals _____.
    a. 1 W
    b. 4 W
    c. 0.25 W
    d. 0 W

36. If a 2.2 kΩ resistor, 10 kΩ resistor and 1.2 kΩ resistor are connected in parallel, the total resistance equals _____.
    a. 721 Ω
    b. 13.4 kΩ
    c. 2.27 kΩ
    d. 1.2 kΩ

37. If a 470 Ω resistor, 680 Ω resistor and 830 Ω resistor are connected in parallel, the total resistance equals _____.
    a. 1980 Ω
    b. 1510 Ω
    c. 1150 Ω
    d. 208 Ω

38. If a 4.7 kΩ resistor and 2.2 kΩ resistor are connected in parallel, the total resistance is _____.
    a. 2200 Ω
    b. 4700 Ω
    c. greater than 2200 Ω
    d. less than 2200 Ω

39. In a three-branch parallel circuit, R_1 = 1.2 MΩ, R_2 = 1 MΩ and R_T = 0.5 MΩ. Calculate R_3.
    a. 6 MΩ
    b. 1.7 MΩ
    c. 2 MΩ
    d. 7.7 MΩ

40. A 5.2 MΩ resistor, 1.2 MΩ resistor and 1 MΩ resistor are connected in parallel across a 15 V source. What is the total current if the 1.2 MΩ resistor opens?
    a. 2.88 μA
    b. 17.88 μA
    c. 12.5 μA
    d. 2.41 μA

41. If eight 47 kΩ resistors are connected in parallel across a 25 V source, R_T equals _____.
    a. 376 kΩ
    b. 6.71 kΩ
    c. 5.875 kΩ
    d. 4.7 kΩ

42. A three-branch parallel circuit carries a total current of 1.2 mA. If I_1 = 0.2 mA and I_2 = 0.7 mA, then what is the value of I_3?
    a. 2.4 mA
    b. 0.3 mA
    c. 7.2 mA
    d. 8.7 mA

43. If three 4.7 kΩ resistors are connected in parallel across a 12V source, what is the value of P_T?
    a. 91.9 mW
    b. 14.1 mW
    c. 1.41 W
    d. 141 mW

44. If one resistor opens in a parallel circuit, the total current
    _____.
    a. increases
    b. decreases
    c. remains unchanged
    d. varies wildly

45. If three 75 W lamps are connected in parallel across a 125 V source, I_T equals _____.
    a. 18 mA
    b. 180 mA
    c. 1.8 A
    d. 18 A

46. If the total current equals 0 A in a four-branch parallel circuit, the trouble is _____.
    a. one of the resistors has shorted
    b. the power supply is off
    c. three of the resistors have opened
    d. one resistor has opened

47. The power dissipated by any branch of a parallel circuit _____.
    a. depends on the power rating of the resistor
    b. only depends on the circuit voltage
    c. only depends on the total current
    d. depends on the voltage and value of the resistor

48. To measure the current through one branch of a parallel circuit, the meter is connected _____.
    a. in series with the branch resistor
    b. across the source
    c. in parallel with the branch resistor
    d. in series with the source

49. If the R_T = 6.8 kΩ and R_1 = 10 kΩ in a two-branch parallel circuit, what is the value of R_2?
    a. 16.8 kΩ
    b. 3.2 kΩ
    c. 21.25 kΩ
    d. 12 kΩ

50. As resistors are disconnected from a parallel circuit, _____.
    a. I_T decreases and R_T increases
    b. I_T decreases and R_T decreases
    c. I_T increases and R_T decreases
    d. I_T increases and R_T increases

51. The most popular application for a parallel circuit in electronics is as a:
    a. voltage divider.
    b. current divider.
    c. resistance divider.
    d. power divider.

52. In a parallel circuit, total power P_T is calculated as:
    a. $P_1 + P_2 + P_3$ + etc.
    b. $1/P_1 + 1/P_2 + 1/P_3$ + etc.
    c. $P_1 + P_2 + P_3$ + etc.
    d. $P_1 \times P_2 \times P_3 \times$ etc.

53. In a parallel circuit, the largest amount of power is dissipated by:
    a. the first resistor.
    b. the smallest resistor.
    c. the largest resistor.
    d. any resistor since the voltage is the same across each of the branch circuits.

54. An open in one branch of a parallel circuit results in:
    a. increased circuit resistance.
    b. decreased or reduced current flow.
    c. decreased power consumption.
    d. all of these

55. A short in one branch of a parallel circuit results in:
    a. increased circuit resistance.
    b. increased current flow.
    c. decreased power consumption.
    d. increased voltage drops in the remaining branches.

1. Answer: b

2. Answer: a

3. Answer: a

4. Answer: b

5. Answer: a

6. Answer: a

7. Answer: b

8. Answer: b

9. Answer: a

10. Answer: b

11. Answer: c

12. Answer: a

13. Answer: d

14. Answer: b

15. Answer: a

16. Answer: d

17. Answer: b

18. Answer: d

19. Answer: b

20. Answer: b

21. Answer: a

22. Answer: d

23. Answer: c

24. Answer: d

25. Answer: c

26. Answer: b

27. Answer: d

28. Answer: c

29. Answer: c

30. Answer: b

31. Answer: b

32. Answer: c

33. Answer: b

34. Answer: d

35. Answer: b

36. Answer: a

37. Answer: d

38. Answer: d

39. Answer: a

40. Answer: b

41. Answer: c

42. Answer: b

43. Answer: a

44. Answer: b

45. Answer: c

46. Answer: b

47. Answer: d

48. Answer: a

49. Answer: c

50. Answer: a

51. Answer: b

52. Answer: a

53. Answer: b

54. Answer: d

55. Answer: b

Chapter 6:   Series-Parallel Circuits

TRUE/FALSE

Figure 6-1

1. R_2 is in parallel with R_3 in **Figure 6-1**.
   a. True
   b. False

2. R_1 is in series with R_3 in **Figure 6-1**.
   a. True
   b. False

3. R_1 is in series with the parallel combination R_2 and R_3 in **Figure 6-1**.
   a. True
   b. False

4. If two resistors are in parallel, they drop the same voltage.
   a. True
   b. False

5. A *combination* circuit consists of resistors in both series and parallel.
   a. True
   b. False

6. R_1 is in series with the series combination R_2 and R_3 in **Figure 6-1**.
   a. True
   b. False

7. No problems could occur if a 10 V source and a 20 V source were connected in parallel.
   a. True
   b. False

8. A loaded voltage divider is a *combination* circuit.
   a. True
   b. False

9. Two or more resistors connected in series form a circuit known as a *voltage divider*.
   a. True
   b. False

10. If two resistors are in parallel, they carry the same current.
    a. True
    b. False

MULTIPLE CHOICE

11. In **Figure 6-1**, R_2 is connected in _____.
    a. series with R_1
    b. series with R_3
    c. parallel with R_1
    d. parallel with R_3

Figure 6-2

12. In **Figure 6-2**, R_3 and R_4 are connected in _____.
    a. series with each other and R_5
    b. series with each other and R_1 and R_2
    c. series with each other
    d. parallel with R_1 and R_2

13. If all of the resistors in **Figure 6-2** are 4.7 kΩ, what is the value of R_T?
    a. 12.53 kΩ
    b. 18.8 kΩ
    c. 9.4 kΩ
    d. 4.7 kΩ

14. If R_1 = 50 kΩ, R_2 = 10 kΩ, R_3 = 10 kΩ, R_4 = 50 kΩ and R_5 = 10 kΩ in **Figure 6-2**, what is the value of R_T?
    a. 8.57 kΩ
    b. 130 kΩ
    c. 68.57 kΩ
    d. 85.7 kΩ

15. If all resistors equal 4.7 kΩ and V_s equals 20 V in **Figure 6-2**, what is the value of I_{R3}?
    a. 12.53 mA
    b. 0.53 mA
    c. 11.99 mA
    d. 1.06 mA

Figure 6-1

16. If R_3 opens in **Figure 6-1**, V_{R1} _____.
    a. increases
    b. decreases
    c. remains the same
    d. decreases to zero

Figure 6-2

17. If R_2 opens in **Figure 6-2**, V_{R3} _____.
    a. increases
    b. decreases
    c. remains the same
    d. causes the fuse to blow

18. If R_4 shorts in **Figure 6-2**, V_{R5} _____.
    a. increases
    b. decreases
    c. remains the same
    d. decreases to zero

Figure 6-3

19. What is the resistance between points B and E in **Figure 6-3**?
    a. 10 kΩ
    b. 20 kΩ
    c. 30 kΩ
    d. 40 kΩ

20. If V_{R4} = 10 V in **Figure 6-3**, what is the value of V_{AD}?
    a. 10 V
    b. 20 V
    c. 30 V
    d. 40 V

21. If V_s = 22 V in **Figure 6-3**, what is the voltage between points D and B?
    a. 5.5 V
    b. -22 V
    c. 11 V
    d. -11 V

22. If V_s = 12 V in **Figure 6-3**, what is the value of V_{EB} if R_3 shorts?
    a. -3 V
    b. -8 V
    c. 6 V
    d. 8 V

23. If a 10 kΩ resistor is placed in parallel with R_4 in **Figure 6-3**, how will V_{R4} change?
    a. V_{R4} will increase
    b. V_{R4} will decrease
    c. V_{R4} will remain the same
    d. V_{R4} will change to 4 volts

Figure 6-1

24. If V_s = 20 V, R_1 = 10 kΩ, R_2 = 50 kΩ and R_3 = 15 kΩ in **Figure 6-1**, P_{R2}
    equals _____.
    a. 2.29 mW
    b. 7.64 mW
    c. 8.63 mW
    d. 18.6 mW

Figure 6-2

25. If R_1 shorts in **Figure 6-2**, V_{R4} _____.
    a. increases
    b. decreases
    c. remains the same
    d. equals V_{R2}

Figure 6-1

26. In **Figure 6-1**, R_1 is connected in _____.
    a. series with R_2
    b. series with R_3
    c. parallel with R_2
    d. parallel with R_3
    e. none of the above

Figure 6-2

27. In **Figure 6-2**, R_3 and R_4 are connected in _____.
    a. series with each other and in parallel with R_5
    b. parallel with each other
    c. series with R_2
    d. series with R_5

Figure 6-1

28. If $R_1 = 4.7$ kΩ, $R_2 = 3.3$ kΩ and $R_3 = 1$ kΩ in **Figure 6-1**, the total resistance equals _____.
    a. 5700 Ω
    b. 5467 Ω
    c. 4125 Ω
    d. 660 Ω

29. If $R_1 = 4.7$ kΩ, $R_2 = 3.3$ kΩ, $R_3 = 1$ kΩ and $V_s = 50$ V in **Figure 6-1**, I_T equals _____.
    a. 8.8 mA
    b. 9.15 mA
    c. 12.1 mA
    d. 75.7 mA

30. If four parallel 10 kΩ resistors are connected in series with a single 20 kΩ resistor and one of the parallel resistors opens, how does the voltage across the other parallel resistors change?
    a. It increases
    b. It decreases
    c. It remains the same

31. Two series 1 kΩ resistors are connected in parallel with a 2.2 kΩ resistor. If the voltage across one of the 1 kΩ resistors is 6 V, what is the voltage across the 2.2 kΩ resistor?
    a. 6 V
    b. 3 V
    c. 12 V
    d. 13.2 V

32. The parallel combination of a 330 Ω resistor and a 470 Ω resistor is connected in series with the parallel combination of four 1 kΩ resistors. If a 100 V source is connected across the circuit, then which resistor carries the most current?
    a. 1 kΩ
    b. 330 Ω
    c. 470 Ω

33. The parallel combination of a 330 Ω resistor and a 470 Ω resistor is connected in series with the parallel combination of four 1 kΩ resistors. If a 100 V source is connected across the circuit, then which resistor drops the most voltage?
    a. 1 kΩ
    b. 330 Ω
    c. 470 Ω

34. If a voltage divider consists of two 10 kΩ resistors, which one of these load resistors will change the output voltage the most?
    a. 1M Ω
    b. 20 kΩ
    c. 100 kΩ
    d. 10 kΩ

35. In a two-source circuit, one source alone produces 10 mA through a branch. If the other source alone produces 8 mA in the opposite direction through the same branch, what is the total current through the branch?
    a. 10 mA
    b. 8 mA
    c. 18 mA
    d. 2 mA

Figure 6-2

36. If every resistor in **Figure 6-2** equals 2.2 kΩ, what is the value of R_T?
    a. 5.87 kΩ
    b. 5.5 kΩ
    c. 4.4 kΩ
    d. 2.2 kΩ

37. If V_s = 15 V and every resistor equals 2.2 kΩ in **Figure 6-2**, what is the value of I_{R4}?
    a. 2.55 mA
    b. 5.11 mA
    c. 0.85 mA
    d. 0.42 mA

38. If R_1 = 10 kΩ, R_2 = 4.7 kΩ, R_3 = 4.7 kΩ, R_4 = 10 kΩ and R_5 = 4.7 kΩ in **Figure 6-2**, R_T = ?
    a. 6.1 kΩ
    b. 18.3 kΩ
    c. 24.7 kΩ
    d. 0 Ω

All resistors = 10 kΩ

Figure 6-3

39. What is the resistance between points A and D in **Figure 6-3**?
    a. 10 kΩ
    b. 20 kΩ
    c. 30 kΩ
    d. 40 kΩ

40. If V_{R1} = 15 V in **Figure 6-3**, what is the value of V_{BD}?
    a. 60 V
    b. –30 V
    c. 30 V
    d. –60 V

41. If V_s = 50 V in **Figure 6-3**, what is the value of V_{CA}?
    a. 5 V
    b. 25 V
    c. –5 V
    d. –25 V

42. If V_s = 40 V and R_3 opens in **Figure 6-3**, what is the value of V_{R3}?
    a. 0 V
    b. 10 V
    c. 20 V
    d. 30 V
    e. 40 V

43. If a fifth 10 kΩ resistor is connected in series in **Figure 6-3**, how does V_{R4} change?
    a. V_{R4} increases
    b. V_{R4} decreases
    c. V_{R4} remains the same
    d. V_{R4} increases to 10 V

44. If the current is 12 mA in **Figure 6-3**, what is the value of V_{EB}?
    a. 360 V
    b. -360 V
    c. -240 V
    d. 240 V

45. If the current is 1.2 mA in **Figure 6-3**, what is the value of P_T?
    a. 0.576 mW
    b. 5.76 mW
    c. 57.6 mW
    d. 576 mW

46. If V_{R3} = 17 V in **Figure 6-3**, what is the value of P_1?
    a. 1.7 mW
    b. 28.9 mW
    c. 2.89 W
    d. 17 mW

Figure 6-2

47. If R_3 shorts in **Figure 6-2**, V_{R5} _____.
    a. increases
    b. decreases
    c. remains the same

Figure 6-1

48. If R_1 = 10 kΩ, R_2 = 15 kΩ and R_3 = 50 kΩ in **Figure 6-1**, R_T equals
    _____.
    a. 21.5 kΩ
    b. 11.5 kΩ
    c. 10 kΩ
    d. 9.5 kΩ

49. If V_s = 25 V, R_1 = 10 kΩ, R_2 = 15 kΩ and R_3 = 50 kΩ in **Figure 6-1**, I_T
    equals _____.
    a. 2.17 mA
    b. 2.5 mA
    c. 1.58 mA
    d. 1.16 mA

50. If four parallel 10 kΩ resistors are in series with a single 20 kΩ
    resistor and one of the parallel resistors shorts, the voltage across
    the other parallel resistors _____.
    a. increases
    b. decreases
    c. remains the same

51. Power in a series-parallel resistor circuit is dissipated as:
    a. voltage loss.
    b. current flow.
    c. resistance change.
    d. heat.

52. In solving series-parallel circuits using Ohm's law, first solve for:
    a. IT.
    b. RT.
    c. ET.
    d. any of these, it doesn't matter.

53. In solving series-parallel circuits using Ohm's law, first solve for
    a. the series resistance.
    b. the parallel resistance.
    c. the series current.
    d. the parallel current.

54. In solving series-parallel circuits, the last and easiest to solve for is:
    a. ET.
    h. IT.
    c. RT.
    d. PT.

55. One Ohm's law formula $P_T = P_1 + P_2$ ι ctc. can be used to solve for total power in:
    a. series circuits.
    b. parallel circuits.
    c. serics-parallel circuits.
    d. all of these.

56. In the series portion of series-parallel circuits, the total resistance is:
    a. less than any one resistance.
    b. greater than the largest resistance.
    c. less than the largest resistance.
    d. equal to the largest resistance.

57. In the parallel portion of series-parallel circuits, the total resistance is:
    a. less than any one resistance.
    b. greater than the largest resistance.
    c. less than the smallest resistance.
    d. equal to the smallest resistance.

58. The Wheatstone bridge circuit is widely used to measure:
    a. exact voltages.
    b. accurate currents.
    c. precise reistances.
    d. all of these.

59. The difference between a balanced and an unbalanced Wheatstone bridge is measured by:
    a. an ohmmeter.
    b. an ammeter.
    c. a voltmeter.
    d. a galvanometer.

60. Thevenin's theorem provides a method for
    a. building complex series-parallel circuits.
    b. simplifying complex series-parallel circuits.
    c. designing complex series-parallel circuits.
    d. all of these.

61. According to the maximum power transfer theorem, maximum power is delivered to any load when the load resistance is:
    a. less than one-half of the source resistance.
    b. larger than source resistance.
    c. at least twice or more than the source resistance.
    d. exactly equal to the source resistance.

62. The super position theorem provides a method for:
    a. building complex series-parallel circuits.
    b. analyzing complex series-parallel circuits.
    c. designing complex series-parallel circuits.
    d. all of these.

1. Answer: a

2. Answer: b

3. Answer: a

4. Answer: a

5. Answer: a

6. Answer: b

7. Answer: b

8. Answer: a

9. Answer: a

10. Answer: b

11. Answer: d

12. Answer: c

13. Answer: a

14. Answer: c

15. Answer: b

16. Answer: b

17. Answer: b

18. Answer: b

19. Answer: c

20. Answer: c

21. Answer: d

22. Answer: b

23. Answer: b

24. Answer: a

25. Answer: a

26. Answer: e

27. Answer: a

28. Answer: b

29. Answer: b

30. Answer: a

31. Answer: c

32. Answer: b

33. Answer: a

34. Answer: d

35. Answer: d

36. Answer: a

37. Answer: c

38. Answer: b

39. Answer: c

40. Answer: c

41. Answer: d

42. Answer: e

43. Answer: b

44. Answer: b

45. Answer: c

46. Answer: b

47. Answer: b

48. Answer: a

49. Answer: d

50. Answer: b

51. Answer: d

52. Answer: b

53. Answer: b

54. Answer: d

55. Answer: d

56. Answer: b

57. Answer: c

58. Answer: c

59. Answer: d

60. Answer: b

61. Answer: d

62. Answer: b

Chapter 7:   Magnetism and Electromagnetism

TRUE/FALSE

1. A permanent magnet will retain its magnetism for a long period of time.
   a. True
   b. False

2. Unlike magnetic poles repulse one another.
   a. True
   b. False

3. *Magnetic flux* is another name for a *magnetic field*.
   a. True
   b. False

4. A conductor with no current through it will still have a magnetic field around it.
   a. True
   b. False

5. Aluminum, brass, and iron make good magnets.
   a. True
   b. False

6. Two north magnetic poles attract one another.
   a. True
   b. False

7. A magnetic field around a conductor is a good indication that current is flowing.
   a. True
   b. False

8. A *strong* magnetic field around a conductor indicates a *small* current flowing through the conductor.
   a. True
   b. False

9. The opposition to being magnetized is called *permeability*.
   a. True
   b. False

10. Soft iron, copper, and silver make good magnets.
    a. True
    b. False

MULTIPLE CHOICE

11. A solenoid consists of _____.
    a. two plates separated by an insulator
    b. a burglar alarm relay
    c. a coil of wire wound around a core
    d. a permanent magnet

12. A coil of wire with current flowing through it is called a(n)
_____.
   a. capacitor
   b. north pole
   c. south pole
   d. electromagnet

13. If two north magnetic poles are brought close to each other, _____.
   a. a force of attraction pulls them together
   b. an electromagnet is created
   c. a force of repulsion pushes them apart
   d. a current is induced

14. How does the magnetic field change around a conducting wire if the
current increases?
   a. The field grows stronger
   b. The field grows weaker
   c. There is no magnetic field around a conducting wire
   d. It is impossible to predict

15. Permeability is _____.
   a. the shielding effect of a material
   b. the ease of a material to be magnetized
   c. the opposition to being magnetized
   d. the ability of a magnetic material to conduct a current

16. Which one of the statements below does NOT apply to the voltage induced
into a wire when it is moved through a magnetic field?
   a. It depends on the strength of the magnetic field
   b. It depends on the current flowing in the wire
   c. It depends on the speed of wire motion
   d. It depends on the length of moving wire in the field

17. Unlike magnetic poles _____ and like poles _____.
   a. repel, repel
   b. repel, attract
   c. attract, attract
   d. attract, repel

18. According to the *left-hand rule* for the magnetic field around a
conductor, what points in the direction of current flow?
   a. fingers
   b. meter
   c. thumb
   d. index finger

19. In which one of the following applications is electromagnetism used?
   a. tape recorders
   b. loudspeakers
   c. relays
   d. all of these

20. If the cross-sectional area of a magnetic field decreases, the flux density _____.
    a. increases
    b. decreases
    c. remains the same

21. If a basic one-loop, dc generator rotates at 60 revolutions each second, how many times each second does its dc output voltage reach a peak value?
    a. 0
    b. 60
    c. 120
    d. 240

22. A _____ is a type of electromagnetic device that has a movable iron core called a *plunger*.
    a. relay
    b. speaker
    c. solenoid
    d. analog meter

23. If a relay picks up and makes a contact but does not stay picked up, what's the trouble?
    a. The magnetic field is too strong
    b. The magnetic field is too weak
    c. The relay coil is open
    d. There is no trouble. The relay is operating normally

24. If a tape recorder's output voltage increases and decreases when you shake the recorder, a possible problem might be _____.
    a. an open circuit in the speaker
    b. loose circular magnet around the speaker's voice coil
    c. too high a source voltage
    d. an open capacitor

25. If the contacts fail to open when a relay is de-energized, what is the trouble?
    a. There is too little current in the relay coil
    b. Dirt is causing the relay armature to stick
    c. The return spring tension is too large
    d. There is no trouble. The relay is operating normally

26. How will two permanent bar magnets react if they are brought close to each other?
    a. They will attract if their north poles are together
    b. They will attract if their south poles are together
    c. They will repel if the north and south poles are together
    d. They will attract if the north and south poles are together

27. The quantity of lines of force per unit of area is known as _____.
    a. magnetic flux
    b. flux density
    c. ampere-turns
    d. permeability

28. The voltage produced by a magnetic field cutting through a conductor depends on the _____.
    a. direction of motion
    b. speed of motion
    c. length of the conductor
    d. all of the above

29. The polarity of an induced voltage depends on the _____.
    a. time that the conductor remains stationary in a magnetic field
    b. length of a conductor in a magnetic field
    c. direction of motion of a conductor in a magnetic field
    d. amount of current flowing

30. The magnetic term that is equivalent to *voltage* is _____.
    a. reluctance
    b. flux density
    c. magnetomotive force
    d. current

31. The permeability of air is _____.
    a. 1
    b. 7
    c. 19.2
    d. 22

32. The magnetic field around an electromagnet is produced by _____.
    a. the conductor's permeability
    b. a permanent magnet
    c. the laminated iron core
    d. a current flowing through the winding

33. A *weber* is a unit of _____.
    a. magnetic flux
    b. magnetomotive force
    c. reluctance
    d. permeability

34. A *tesla* is a unit of _____.
    a. magnetic flux density
    b. magnetomotive force
    c. reluctance
    d. permeability

35. The term *reluctance* in magnetic circuits is like the term _____ in electrical circuits.
    a. current
    b. voltage
    c. resistance
    d. capacitance

36. Soft iron has a high _____.
    a. mmf
    b. permeability
    c. resistance
    d. reactance

37. Magnetic lines that are close to each other are said to have a high _____.
    a. reluctance
    b. inductance
    c. flux density
    d. current

38. Reversing the current through an electromagnet _____ the magnetic field.
    a. increases
    b. decreases
    c. collapses
    d. reverses

39. An *ampere-turn* is a unit of _____.
    a. magnetomotive force (mmf)
    b. permeability
    c. resistance
    d. reactance

40. If the number of turns of wire on an electromagnet increases, the magnetomotive force *mmf* _____.
    a. increases
    b. decreases
    c. remains the same

41. The amount of voltage that is induced in a conductor depends on the _____.
    a. the length of time a conductor remains stationary in the magnetic field
    b. length of the conductor in the magnetic field
    c. direction of motion of the conductor in the magnetic field
    d. direction of the current flowing

42. Increasing the speed at which a magnet moves through a coil of wire causes the induced voltage to _____.
    a. increase
    b. decrease
    c. remain the same

43. If more turns of wire are added to a coil and then that coil is moved through a magnetic field, the voltage produced will _____.
    a. be more than the original coil
    b. be less than the original coil
    c. be the same as the original coil

44. The _____ electromagnet cannot be further magnetized.
    a. capacitive
    b. saturated
    c. open
    d. shorted

45. An iron core electromagnet has a higher _____ than an air core electromagnet.
    a. permeability
    b. resistance
    c. reactance
    d. current

46. Applying an ac voltage to an electromagnet's coil will produce a _____.
    a. steady magnet field
    b. north magnetic field
    c. south magnetic field
    d. changing magnetic field

47. If some turns of wire are removed from an electromagnet, the magnetic field will _____.
    a. be more than the original electromagnet
    b. be less than the original electromagnet
    c. be the same as the original electromagnet

48. Like magnetic poles _____.
    a. attract each other
    b. repel each other
    c. have no effect on each other
    d. have the same current through them

49. A simple electric door bell probably uses _____ to ring the bell.
    a. transistor
    b. a *DPDT* switch
    c. an electromagnet
    d. a permanent magnet

50. A relay is a device that _____.
    a. uses an electromagnet to open and close contacts.
    b. isolates the actuating signal from the control signal.
    c. has a coil to actuate some contacts that control other circuits.
    d. all of these.

51. The principal difference between a solenoid and a relay is:
    a. solenoids do mechanical work, relays do electrical work.
    b. solenoids do electrical work, relays do mechanical work.
    c. relays relay electricity, solenoids do not.
    d. relays use magnets, solenoids do not.

52. The movable part of the solenoid is the:
    a. magnetic field.
    b. electromagnetic coil.
    c. the plunger.
    d. all of these.

53. The movable part of the relay is the:
    a. magnetic field.
    b. electromagnetic coil.
    c. the armature.
    d. all of these.

54. Hysteresis is a characteristic of magnetic materials wherein a change in magnetization:
    a. occurs before the application of a magnetizing force.
    b. occurs after the application of a magnetic force.
    c. occurs exactly with the application of a magnetic force.
    d. varies according to the current flow.

55. Electromagnetic induction is best defined as the process by which a voltage is produced in a conductor when there is:
    a. motion between the magnetic poles.
    b. motion between the conductor and the magnetic field.
    c. motion around the magnetic fields.
    d. energy produced by the rotating coils.

56. Induced voltage resulting from electromagnetic induction is proportional to
    a. the rate at which the conductor and magnetic fields move relative to each other.
    b. the number of turns of wire in the coil.
    c. the angle at which the conductor cuts the magnetic field.
    d. all of these.

57. Faraday's law states that the voltage induced across a coul of wire is proportional to two factors:
    a. the size of the coil and the rate of change of the magnetic flux.
    b. the number of turns in the coil and the rate of change of the magnetic flux.
    c. the size of the magnets and the rate of change of the magnetic flux.
    d. the diameter of the conductor and the rate of change of the magnetic flux.

58. Faraday's law and Lenz's law are related in that they deal with
    a. varying magnetic field.
    b. an induced voltage.
    c. a resulting current flow.
    d. all of these.

1. Answer: a

2. Answer: b

3. Answer: a

4. Answer: b

5. Answer: b

6. Answer: b

7. Answer: a

8. Answer: b

9. Answer: b

10. Answer: b

11. Answer: c

12. Answer: d

13. Answer: c

14. Answer: a

15. Answer: b

16. Answer: b

17. Answer: d

18. Answer: c

19. Answer: d

20. Answer: a

21. Answer: c

22. Answer: c

23. Answer: b

24. Answer: b

25. Answer: b

26. Answer: d

27. Answer: b

28. Answer: d

29. Answer: c

30. Answer: c

31. Answer: a

32. Answer: d

33. Answer: a

34. Answer: a

35. Answer: c

36. Answer: b

37. Answer: c

38. Answer: d

39. Answer: a

40. Answer: a

41. Answer: b

42. Answer: a

43. Answer: a

44. Answer: b

45. Answer: a

46. Answer: d

47. Answer: b

48. Answer: b

49. Answer: c

50. Answer: d

51. Answer: a

52. Answer: c

53. Answer: c

54. Answer: b

55. Answer: b

56. Answer: d

57. Answer: b

58. Answer: d

Chapter 8: Introduction to Alternating Current and Voltage

TRUE/FALSE

1. A sine wave's frequency equals the reciprocal of its period.
   - a. True
   - b. False

2. The higher a sine wave's frequency, the shorter its period.
   - a. True
   - b. False

3. A sine wave's peak value is smaller than its RMS value.
   - a. True
   - b. False

4. An ac current is inversely proportional to an ac voltage.
   - a. True
   - b. False

5. One complete sine wave contains 360°.
   - a. True
   - b. False

6. *RMS* is another name for *peak*.
   - a. True
   - b. False

7. 7.07 V_{PP} is approximately equal to 2.5 V_{RMS}.
   - a. True
   - b. False

8. The term *RMS* stands for "root-mean-square."
   - a. True
   - b. False

9. The period of a 5 Hz wave form is 200 ms.
   - a. True
   - b. False

10. Commercial line voltages are usually square waves at a frequency of 60 Hz.
    - a. True
    - b. False

MULTIPLE CHOICE

11. A formula for V_{PP} is _____.
    - a. $0.707 \times V_{RMS}$
    - b. $0.707 \times V_P$
    - c. $2 \times V_P$
    - d. $2.8 \times V_P$

12. The *RMS* value of a sine wave means _____.
    a. the same as $I_{PP} \times R$
    b. the *root mean square* value
    c. the heating effect of an ac generator of the same voltage
    d. the same as $I_P \times R$

13. What is the instantaneous voltage at 42° on a 230 V_P sine wave?
    a. 76.09 V
    b. 115 V
    c. 149 V
    d. 153.9 V

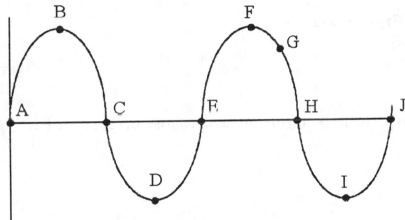

Figure 8-1

14. Which one of these represents the value at point G in **Figure 8-1**?
    a. The period
    b. The RMS voltage
    c. The peak voltage
    d. The frequency

15. What is the time from points B to F in **Figure 8-1**?
    a. The frequency
    b. The angle
    c. The period
    d. The peak-to-peak voltage

16. V_{PP} is measured between points _____ in **Figure 8-1**.
    a. A and B
    b. G and I
    c. C and H
    d. D and F

17. Which point in **Figure 8-1** is 180° away from point E?
    a. A
    b. B
    c. C
    d. D

Figure 8-2

18. Calculate V_{R2} in **Figure 8-2**.
    a. 6.84 V_{PP}
    b. 13.15 V_P
    c. 6.84 V_P
    d. 4.83 V_P

19. What is the approximate peak input voltage to the circuit in **Figure 8-2**?
    a. 28.28 V_P
    b. 14.14 V_P
    c. 20 V_P
    d. 10 V_P

20. Calculate V_{R1} in **Figure 8-2**.
    a. 21.44 V_P
    b. 6.84 V_P
    c. 13.15 V_P
    d. 13.68 V_P

21. What is the instantaneous voltage at 284° on a 22 V_{PP} sine wave?
    a. 10.67 V
    b. 0.33 V
    c. -10.67 V
    d. -2.66 V

22. V_{R2} _____ if R_1 opens in **Figure 8-2**.
    a. increases
    b. decreases
    c. remains the same

23. In **Figure 8-2**, what is the instantaneous voltage across R_1 at an angle of 22° ?
    a. 8.03 V
    b. 11.96 V
    c. 2.56 V
    d. 20.25 V

24. If a rectangular wave's pulse width is 50μ S and its frequency is 4 kHz, its duty cycle is _____.
    a. 80 %
    b. 20 %
    c. 1.25 %
    d. 98.75 %

25. The time required by a 10 V square wave to change from 1 V to 9 V is known as the _____.
    a. fall time
    b. period
    c. pulse width
    d. rise time

26. What is the approximate instantaneous voltage at 37° on a 169 V_P sine wave?
    a. 135 V
    b. 119 V
    c. 239 V
    d. 102 V

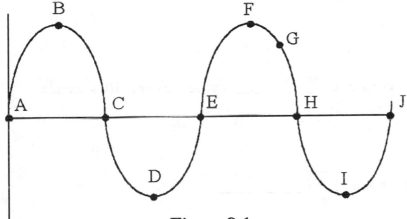

Figure 8-1

27. In **Figure 8-1**, the time from point C to E is called _____.
    a. an alternation
    b. the period
    c. a cycle
    d. peak voltage

28. In **Figure 8-1**, the voltage from point E to point F represents _____.
    a. the RMS voltage
    b. the peak voltage
    c. the peak to peak voltage
    d. one cycle of voltage

29. If the time from point A to H is 60 µs in **Figure 8-1**, the frequency is
_____.
   a. 25 kHz
   b. 16.67 kHz
   c. 50 kHz
   d. More information is required to calculate the frequency.

Figure 8-2

30. Calculate I_T in **Figure 8-2**.
   a. 4.55m A_{PP}
   b. 3.22m A_{PP}
   c. 9.12m A_{PP}
   d. 6.44m A_{PP}

31. A 60 Hz sine wave completes _____ cycles every 10 seconds.
   a. 6
   b. 10
   c. 1/16
   d. 600

32. A 10 V_P sine wave is equal to _____.
   a. 20 V_{PP}
   b. 5 V_{PP}
   c. 100 V_{PP}
   d. None of the above

33. A sine wave's instantaneous voltage is 0 V at _____ degrees.
   a. 0
   b. 180
   c. 360
   d. all of these

34. If a 10 kΩ resistor carries 5 mA_{RMS} of current, its voltage drop equals
_____.
   a. 70.7 V_{RMS}
   b. 7.07 V_{RMS}
   c. 5 V_{RMS}
   d. 50 V_{RMS}

35. In a two-resistor series circuit $V_{R1} = 6.5$ V_{RMS} and $V_{R2} = 3.2$ V_{RMS}. The source voltage is _____.
    a. 9.7 V_P
    b. 9.19 V_P
    c. 13.72 V_P
    d. 4.53 V_P

36. A formula for V_{RMS} is _____.
    a. $0.707 \times V_{PP}$
    b. $0.707 \times V_P$
    c. $2 \times V_P$
    d. $2.8 \times V_P$

37. What is the instantaneous voltage at 17° on a 169 V_P sine wave?
    a. 49.4 V
    b. 98.8 V
    c. 161 V
    d. 80.5 V

38. A 12 V_P sine wave equals _____.
    a. 24 V_{PP}
    b. 8.48 V_{RMS}
    c. 7.64 V_{AVG}
    d. all of these

39. Find R_T in **Figure 8-2**.
    a. 1.13 kΩ
    b. 4.7 kΩ
    c. 4.77 kΩ
    d. 6.2 kΩ

40. Find P_{R1} in **Figure 8-2**.
    a. 97.84 mW
    b. 195.69 mW
    c. 48.91 mW
    d. 0 W

41. If R_2 shorts in **Figure 8-2**, V_{R2} _____.
    a. increases
    b. decreases
    c. remains the same

42. In **Figure 8-2**, what is the instantaneous voltage across R_1 at 122°?
    a. 18.19 V
    b. 5.8 V
    c. 11.15 V
    d. 11.6 V

43. An oscilloscope's volts/division switch is set on 50 mV/cm. If the vertical deflection of the oscilloscope's trace is 1.6 cm, what voltage is being measured?
    a. 80 mV
    b. 50 mV
    c. 1.6 mV
    d. 0.008 V

44. An oscilloscope's seconds/division switch is set on 20 ms/cm. If a sine wave measures 4 cm horizontally, what frequency is being measured?
    a. 50 Hz
    b. 25 Hz
    c. 12.5 Hz
    d. More information is needed

45. An oscilloscope's seconds/division switch is set on 20 μs/cm. If the trace is 7.5 cm long, what is the period?
    a. 1.5 μs
    b. 5 μs
    c. 150 μs
    d. 0.0015 s

46. When an accurate oscilloscope measurement is needed, _____.
    a. the trace can be any size
    b. the trace should be large and you should look straight at the trace
    c. no particular care is required
    d. the trace need only be large

47. In **Figure 8-2**, if you look at V_{R1} with an oscilloscope and you find no trace, a possible trouble might be _____.
    a. R_1 is open
    b. R_2 is shorted
    c. R_2 is open
    d. the resistance of R_2 has changed

48. If the period of a square wave is 22 ms, what is its frequency?
    a. 45.45 kHz
    b. 45.45 Hz
    c. 22 Hz
    d. 22 kHz

49. If you measure about 56 V_{PP} across the source in **Figure 8-2**, what is the trouble?
    a. R_1 is open
    b. R_2 is open
    c. Both R_1 and R_2 are open
    d. There is no trouble. 56 V_{PP} is a normal measurement for the source voltage.
    e. Any of these

50. Calculate the total power dissipation in the circuit in **Figure 8-2**.
    a. 64.5 mW
    b. 45.6 mW
    c. 9.12 mW
    d. 182 mW

51. The symbol for the period of a wave form is:
    a. P.
    b. T.
    c. W.
    d. F.

52. The period of most AC waveforms is measured in units of:
    a. cycles.
    b. revolutions.
    c. seconds.
    d. alternations.

53. The time (T) and the frequency (f) of an AC waveform are related as:
    a. complimentary proportional.
    b. directly proportional.
    c. inversely proportional.
    d. universally proportional.

54. Superimposed DC and AC voltages mean the two voltages are combined:
    a. in series aiding or opposing.
    b. in parallel aiding or opposing.
    c. in sereis-parallel aiding or opposing.
    d. all of these.

55. The AC sine wave varies from zero to its maximum value in accordance with:
    a. a geometric progression.
    b. an algebraic function.
    c. a trigonometric relationship.
    d. a mathematical formula.

56. A square wave is a unique form of the rectangular pulse wave in that:
    a. the positive and negative halves are equal.
    b. the wave is symmetrical.
    c. the duty cycle is 50%.
    d. all of these.

57. The average value of a rectangular pulse wave is calculated as:
    a. Vaug = 0.637Vp.
    b. Vaug = V baseline + Vp.
    c. Vaug = V baseline + (duty cycle) × Vp.
    d. Vaug = 1.57 Vp.

58. The formula to convert degrees to radians is:

   a. $\text{degrees} = \left[\dfrac{180°}{\pi \text{ rad}}\right] \times \text{radians}$.

   b. $\text{radians} = \left[\dfrac{\pi \text{ rad}}{180°}\right] \times \text{degrees}$.

   c. $180° = \pi$ radians.
   d. all of these.

59. The value of a AC sine wave at any instant can be represented by:
   a. a graph of the voltage or current vs. the angular measurement.
   b. a phasor whose angle and magnitude are representative of the AC signal.
   c. the formula $V_i = V_p \times \sin \theta$.
   d. all of these.

60. The square wave is made up of:
   a. just the fundamental frequency.
   b. the fundamental frequency and all the odd harmonics.
   c. the fundamental frequency and all the even harmonics.
   d. the fundamental frequency and both the odd and even harmonics.

1. Answer: a

2. Answer: a

3. Answer: b

4. Answer: b

5. Answer: a

6. Answer: b

7. Answer: a

8. Answer: a

9. Answer: a

10. Answer: b

11. Answer: c

12. Answer: b

13. Answer: d

14. Answer: b

15. Answer: c

16. Answer: d

17. Answer: c

18. Answer: c

19. Answer: a

20. Answer: a

21. Answer: c

22. Answer: b

23. Answer: a

24. Answer: b

25. Answer: d

26. Answer: d

27. Answer: a

28. Answer: b

29. Answer: a

30. Answer: c

31. Answer: d

32. Answer: a

33. Answer: d

34. Answer: d

35. Answer: c

36. Answer: b

37. Answer: a

38. Answer: c

39. Answer: d

40. Answer: c

41. Answer: b

42. Answer: a

43. Answer: a

44. Answer: c

45. Answer: c

46. Answer: b

47. Answer: c

48. Answer: b

49. Answer: e

50. Answer: a

51. Answer: b

52. Answer: c

53. Answer: c

54. Answer: a

55. Answer: c

56. Answer: d

57. Answer: c

58. Answer: b

59. Answer: d

60. Answer: b

Chapter 9: Capacitors

1. *Capacitance* is the ability to store voltage.
   a. True
   b. False

2. A capacitor blocks dc and passes ac.
   a. True
   b. False

3. When two capacitors are connected in parallel across a dc source, the smaller capacitor drops the larger voltage.
   a. True
   b. False

4. If the distance between the plates of a capacitor increases, the capacitance decreases.
   a. True
   b. False

5. A capacitor can fully charge in one *time constant*.
   a. True
   b. False

6. *Capacitance* is a capacitor's ability to store resistance.
   a. True
   b. False

7. When two capacitors are connected in series across a dc source, the smallest capacitor drops the largest voltage.
   a. True
   b. False

8. A capacitor will fully charge in about five time constants.
   a. True
   b. False

9. To find the total capacitance of two capacitors in parallel, you must combine them using a similar procedure as resistors in parallel.
   a. True
   b. False

10. If the plate area of a capacitor decreases, the capacitance decreases.
    a. True
    b. False

MULTIPLE CHOICE

11. What is the capacitance of a capacitor that drops 50 V and stores 0.500 μ C of charge?
    a. 0.1 μF
    b. 1 μF
    c. 0.001 μF
    d. 0.01 μF

12. How much charge is stored in a 0.022 μF capacitor that drops 22 V?
    a. 0.0484 μC
    b. 4.84 μC
    c. 0.484 μC
    d. 48.4 μC

13. If the dc working voltage of a capacitor is 100 V, the dielectric must withstand _____.
    a. 100 V_{DC}.
    b. 75 V_{RMS}
    c. 220 V_{PP}
    d. 85 V_{RMS}

14. If a 0.05 μF and 0.1 μF capacitor are connected in parallel across a 20 V source, the total capacitance equals _____ and each capacitor drops _____.
    a. 0.15 μF, 10 V
    b. 0.05 μF, 15 V
    c. 0.10 μF, 20 V
    d. 0.15 μF, 20 V

15. If a 0.022 μF, 0.022 μF and 0.05 μF capacitor are connected in series across a 25 V source, the voltage drop across the largest capacitor equals _____.
    a. 10.24 V
    b. 11.76 V
    c. 4.5 V
    d. 17.5 V

16. What is the time constant of a 4.7 μF capacitor in series with a 22 kΩ resistor?
    a. 0.103 ms
    b. 1.03 ms
    c. 10.3 ms
    d. 103 ms

17. How long will it take a 0.047 μF capacitor to fully charge through a 100 kΩ resistor?
    a. 2.35 s
    b. 0.235 ms
    c. 23.5 ms
    d. 235 ms

18. How long will it take a 1 µF capacitor to completely discharge through a
    47 kΩ resistor?
    a. 47 s
    b. 235 s
    c. 47 ms
    d. 235 ms

19. If a 1 µF capacitor and a 10 kΩ resistor are connected in series across
    20 V_{DC}, approximately how much voltage will the capacitor drop after
    charging for just one time constant?
    a. 17 V
    b. 12.06 V
    c. 10.99 V
    d. 12.6 V

20. If a 4.7 µF capacitor and a 10 kΩ resistor are connected in series
    across 25 V_{DC}, approximately how much voltage will the resistor drop
    after charging for just one time constant?
    a. 9.2 V
    b. 23.75 V
    c. 21.63 V
    d. 15.8 V

21. If a 4.7 µF capacitor operates at 10 kHz, X_C equals _____.
    a. 338.8 Ω
    b. 294 µΩ
    c. 3.38 Ω
    d. infinite Ω

22. At what frequency is a 2000 *p*F capacitor operating if its reactance is
    745 Ω?
    a. 106.8 kHz
    b. 10.14 kHz
    c. 1.014 kHz
    d. 1014 Hz

23. If an ohmmeter measurement of a large electrolytic capacitor is always
    infinite, the capacitor is probably _____.
    a. shorted
    b. leaking
    c. open
    d. completely charged

24. If a 22 µF capacitor is connected to a 15 V 400 Hz source, its current
    equals _____.
    a. 55 mA
    b. 18.1 mA
    c. 829 mA
    d. 1.81 A

25. When measuring a large electrolytic capacitor with an ohmmeter, the resistance reading starts at a low value and keeps increasing. The capacitor is _____.
    a. open
    b. leaky
    c. shorted
    d. OK; this is a normal reading for large electrolytic capacitors

26. If a 0.1 µF, 0.1 µF and 0.05 µF capacitor are connected in series across a 75 V source, the voltage drop across the smallest capacitor equals _____.
    a. 18.75 V
    b. 50 V
    c. 37.5 V
    d. 100 V

27. How long will it take to completely charge a 0.047 µF capacitor through a 1 MΩ resistor?
    a. 0.047 s
    b. 0.029 s
    c. 0.235 s
    d. 0.47 s

28. If a 0.1 µF capacitor and a 2.2 kΩ resistor are connected in series across 30 V_{DC}, how much voltage will the capacitor drop after charging for just one time constant?
    a. 29.4 V
    b. 28.5 V
    c. 25.9 V
    d. 18.9 V

29. If the frequency applied to a capacitor increases, the capacitive reactance _____.
    a. increases
    b. decreases
    c. remains the same
    d. varies up and down

30. A capacitor that transfers an ac signal from one stage to another is called a _____ capacitor.
    a. bypass
    b. filter
    c. coupling
    d. transfer

31. If a 1 µF, 2.2 µF and 0.05 µF capacitor are connected in series, C_T is less than _____.
    a. 1 µF
    b. 2.2 µF
    c. 0.05 µF
    d. 0.001 µF

32. If four 0.022 μF capacitors are connected in parallel, C_T equals _____.
    a. 0.022 μF
    b. 0.088 μF
    c. 0.044 μF
    d. 0.049 μF

33. If an uncharged capacitor, a resistor, a switch and a 12 V battery are connected in series, what is the voltage across the capacitor at the instant the switch is closed?
    a. 12 V
    b. 6 V
    c. 24 V
    d. 0 V

34. If an uncharged capacitor, a resistor, a switch and a 12 V battery are connected in series, what is the voltage across the capacitor after it is fully charged?
    a. 12 V
    b. 6 V
    c. 24 V
    d. -6 V

35. If an uncharged capacitor, a resistor, a switch and a 12 V battery are connected in series, at approximately what time will the capacitor reach full charge?
    a. R×C
    b. 5×R×C
    c. 12×R×C
    d. The time cannot be predicted

36. What is the capacitance that stores 1.175 μC of charge and drops 25 V?
    a. 0.047 μF
    b. 0.47 μF
    c. 4.7 μF
    d. 47 μF

37. How much charge is stored in a 0.47 μF capacitor that drops 18 V?
    a. 846 μC
    b. 84.6 μC
    c. 8.46 μC
    d. 0.846 μC

38. What is the minimum dc working voltage rating for a capacitor that must drop 120 V_{RMS}?
    a. 120 V
    b. 169.7 V
    c. 84.8 V
    d. 339 V

39. If a 0.047 µF, 0.047 µF and 0.47 µF capacitor are connected in series across a 25 V source, the total capacitance equals _____ and each 0.047 µF capacitor drops _____.
    a. 0.022 µF, 11.9 V
    b. 0.022 µF, 25 V
    c. 0.564 µF, 1.2 V
    d. 0.564 µF, 11.9 V

40. If a 22 µF and 100 µF capacitor are connected in parallel across a 15 V source, the total capacitance equals _____ and the 22 µF capacitor drops _____.
    a. 18 µF, 15 V
    b. 18 µF, 5.2 V
    c. 122 µF, 15 V
    d. 1220 µF, 30 V

41. What is the time constant of a 47 µF capacitor in series with a 120 kΩ resistor?
    a. 0.564 ms
    b. 564 ms
    c. 5.64 s
    d. 54.6 s

42. How long will it take for a 22 µF capacitor to completely charge through a 47 kΩ resistor?
    a. 1.034 s
    b. 2.068 s
    c. 8.272 s
    d. 5.17 s

43. How long will it take for a 22 µF capacitor to completely discharge through a 4.7 kΩ resistor?
    a. 0.827 s
    b. 0.517 s
    c. 0.207 s
    d. 0.103 s

44. How much voltage is dropped across a 150 µF capacitor after 3.33 seconds if it is charged by a 50 V source through a 22K Ω resistor?
    a. 31.7 V
    b. 43.25 V
    c. 47.5 V
    d. 49 V

45. If a 0.047 µF capacitor operates at 220 kHz, X_C equals _____.
    a. 15.4 kΩ
    b. 1.54 kΩ
    c. 154 Ω
    d. 15.4 Ω

46. At what frequency is a 0.001 µF capacitor operating if its reactance is 45 kΩ?
    a. 3.54 kHz
    b. 35.4 kHz
    c. 354 kHz
    d. 3.54 MHz

47. If a 47 µF capacitor is connected to a 20 V, 400 Hz source, the current is _____.
    a. 425 A
    b. 23.6 A
    c. 8.51 A
    d. 0.851 A

48. If an ohmmeter measurement of a capacitor is 0 Ω in both directions, the capacitor is probably _____.
    a. shorted
    b. leaking
    c. open
    d. completely charged

49. When connecting a large electrolytic capacitor to a circuit with a 100 V_{DC} source, place the negative end of the capacitor _____.
    a. towards the positive side of the source
    b. towards the negative side of the source
    c. in either position; the polarity is not important

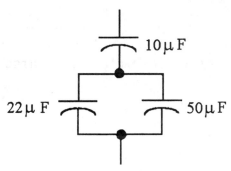

Figure 9-1

50. What is C_T in **Figure 9-1**?
    a. 82 µF
    b. 8.78 µF
    c. 25.2 µF
    d. 70.1 µF

51. Electrolytic capacitors differ from all other capacitors in construction in that they are:
    a. smaller.
    b. larger.
    c. polarized.
    d. sensitized.

52. Electrolytic capacitors must be connected into a circuit such that:
    a. positive lead to positive voltage; negative lead to negative voltage.
    b. voltage rating marked is not exceeded.
    c. reversal of polarity does not happen.
    d. all of these.

53. When capacitors are connected in series, their total capacitance act like:
    a. resistance connected in series.
    b. resistance connected in parallel.
    c. resistance connected in series-parallel.
    d. all of these.

54. When capacitors are connected in parallel, their total capacitance act like:
    a. resistance connected in series.
    b. resistance connected in parallel.
    c. resistance connected in series-parallel.
    d. all of these.

55. The time constant of a capacitor is:
    a. the time required to charge to 63% or discharge to 37%.
    b. directly proportional to the capacitance in the circuit.
    c. directly proportional to the resistance in the circuit.
    d. all of these.

56. The time constant for a capacitor for each time period is:
    a. 63% of the increase in value.
    b. 37% of the decrease in value.
    c. a constant factor.
    d. all of these.

57. Reactive power (P_r) in a capacitor is defined as the rate at which a capacitor stores or returns energy and is measured in:
    a. volts per time constant.
    b. current per time constant.
    c. volt-ampere reactive.
    d. watts reactive.

58. In a capacitive AC circuit, the phase relationship between the voltage and the current is such that the:
    a. current is leading the voltage.
    b. voltage is leading the current.
    c. current is 180 degrees out of phase with voltage.
    d. voltage is 360 degrees out of phase with current.

59. The most common place use for capacitors in electronics is:
    a. pass AC voltages.
    b. pass DC voltages.
    c. block AC voltages.
    d. block DC voltages.

1. Answer: b

2. Answer: a

3. Answer: b

4. Answer: a

5. Answer: b

6. Answer: b

7. Answer: a

8. Answer: a

9. Answer: b

10. Answer: a

11. Answer: d

12. Answer: c

13. Answer: a

14. Answer: d

15. Answer: c

16. Answer: d

17. Answer: c

18. Answer: d

19. Answer: d

20. Answer: a

21. Answer: c

22. Answer: a

23. Answer: c

24. Answer: c

25. Answer: d

26. Answer: c

27. Answer: c

28. Answer: d

29. Answer: b

30. Answer: c

31. Answer: c

32. Answer: b

33. Answer: d

34. Answer: a

35. Answer: b

36. Answer: a

37. Answer: c

38. Answer: b

39. Answer: a

40. Answer: c

41. Answer: c

42. Answer: d

43. Answer: b

44. Answer: a

45. Answer: d

46. Answer: a

47. Answer: b

48. Answer: a

49. Answer: b

50. Answer: b

51. Answer: c

52. Answer: d

53. Answer: b

54. Answer: a

55. Answer: d

56. Answer: d

57. Answer: c

58. Answer: a

59. Answer: d

Chapter 10: RC Circuits

TRUE/FALSE

1. The total current in an RC circuit always leads the source voltage.
   a. True
   b. False

2. The phasor combination of V_R and V_C in an RC series circuit equals the source voltage.
   a. True
   b. False

3. An RC circuit can be used as a filter to eliminate certain frequencies.
   a. True
   b. False

4. As the frequency applied to an RC circuit is decreased, the phase angle decreases.
   a. True
   b. False

5. As the frequency applied to an RC circuit varies, both X_C and resistance vary.
   a. True
   b. False

6. The total current in an RC circuit always lags the source voltage.
   a. True
   b. False

7. The phasor combination of X_C and R is called Z.
   a. True
   b. False

8. As the frequency applied to an RC circuit increases, the impedance decreases.
   a. True
   b. False

9. The phase angle of an RC circuit varies inversely with frequency.
   a. True
   b. False

10. When the frequency applied to an RC circuit varies, the value of X_C varies.
    a. True
    b. False

MULTIPLE CHOICE

Figure 10-1

11. If the frequency equals 60 Hz in **Figure 10-1**, what is the value of capacitance?
    a. 22 μF
    b. 44 μF
    c. 66 μF
    d. 88 μF

12. What is the circuit's impedance in **Figure 10-1**?
    a. 120 Ω
    b. 280 Ω
    c. 418 Ω
    d. 520 Ω

13. What is the true power in **Figure 10-1**?
    a. 916 mW
    b. 5.72 mW
    c. 5.72 W
    d. 275 mW

14. If the operating frequency increases in **Figure 10-1**, how does the current change?
    a. It increases
    b. It remains the same
    c. It decreases
    d. It decreases to zero

15. If the operating frequency increases in **Figure 10-1**, how does the phase angle change?
    a. It increases
    b. It remains the name
    c. It decreases
    d. It changes to another quadrant

16. If the operating frequency increases in **Figure 10-1**, how does the resistor value change?
    a. It increases
    b. It remains the same
    c. It decreases
    d. It opens

Figure 10-2

17. If the resistor value increases in **Figure 10-2**, then how does the total current change?
    a. It increases
    b. It remains the same
    c. It decreases
    d. It decreases to zero

18. How much voltage does the resistor drop in **Figure 10-2**?
    a. 10 V
    b. 20 V
    c. 59 mV
    d. 19.94 V

19. What change would increase the power factor in **Figure 10-2**?
    a. Increasing the value of the source voltage
    b. Increasing the value of the resistor
    c. Increasing the value of the capacitor
    d. Decreasing the value of the capacitor

20. Which statement describes the relationship of I_C and I_R in **Figure 10-2**?
    a. They are in phase
    b. I_C leads I_R
    c. I_C lags I_R
    d. They are 180° out of phase

21. How much voltage does the capacitor drop in **Figure 10-2**?
    a. 10 V
    b. 20 V
    c. 59 mV
    d. 19.94 V

22. What change would decrease the power factor in **Figure 10-2**?
    a. Increasing the value of Vs
    b. Increasing the value of the resistor
    c. Increasing the value of the capacitor
    d. Decreasing the value of the capacitor

Figure 10-3

23. The circuit in **Figure 10-3** is known as a _____.
    a. high-pass filter
    b. band-pass filter
    c. low-pass filter
    d. parallel RC circuit

24. What is the cutoff frequency in **Figure 10-3**?
    a. 85 Hz
    b. 118 Hz
    c. 995 Hz
    d. 1012 Hz

25. What is the output voltage at the cutoff frequency in **Figure 10-3**?
    a. 6.446 V
    b. 31.12 V
    c. 15.554 V
    d. 22 V

26. If the output were taken across the resistor in **Figure 10-3**, the circuit would be known as a _____.
    a. low-pass filter
    b. high-pass filter
    c. band-pass filter
    d. band-notch filter

27. If the circuit in **Figure 10-3** has an output voltage that's too high at the cutoff frequency, _____.
    a. the resistor has opened
    b. the capacitor has shorted
    c. the resistor has shorted
    d. the capacitor has become leaky

28. If the resistor is changed to 100 kΩ in **Figure 10-3**, what is the new cutoff frequency?
    a. 38.8 Hz
    b. 79.6 Hz
    c. 159.2 Hz
    d. 318 Hz

Figure 10-1

29. Calculate the voltage drop across the capacitor in **Figure 10-1**.
    a. 11.53 V
    b. 4.82 V
    c. 3.69 V
    d. 2.10 V

30. Calculate the apparent power in **Figure 10-1**.
    a. 1.70 VA
    b. 5.66 VA
    c. 5.91 VA
    d. 6.67 VA

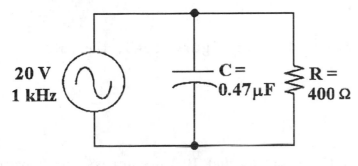

Figure 10-2

31. Calculate the total impedance in **Figure 10-2**.
    a. 1000 Ω
    b. 880 Ω
    c. 321 Ω
    d. 62 Ω

Figure 10-1

32. If the frequency increases in **Figure 10-1**, the phase angle _____ and the impedance _____.
   a. decreases, increases
   b. decreases, decreases
   c. increases, decreases
   d. increases, increases

Figure 10-3

33. If the resistance is reduced to 4 kΩ in **Figure 10-3**, the cutoff frequency equals _____.
   a. 6250 Hz
   b. 99 Hz
   c. 480 Hz
   d. 995 Hz

34. If there is 10 V_{RMS} across the resistor and 10 V_{RMS} across the capacitor in a series RC circuit, then the source voltage equals _____.
   a. 20 V_{RMS}
   b. 14.14 V_{RMS}
   c. 28.28 V_{RMS}
   d. 10 V_{RMS}

35. If there is 1 A$_{RMS}$ through the resistor and 1 A$_{RMS}$ through the capacitor in a parallel RC circuit, then the total current equals _____.
   a. 1 A$_{RMS}$
   b. 2 A$_{RMS}$
   c. 2.28 A$_{RMS}$
   d. 1.414 A$_{RMS}$

36. A power factor of 1 indicates that the circuit phase angle is _____.
   a. 90°
   b. 45°
   c. 180°
   d. 0°

37. If the true power is 100 W and the reactive power is 100 VAR, the apparent power is _____.
   a. 200 VA
   b. 100 VA
   c. 141.4 VA
   d. 141.4 W

38. If the bandwidth of a low-pass filter is 0 to 1 kHz, the cutoff frequency is _____.
   a. 0 Hz T
   b. 500 Hz
   c. 2 kHz
   d. 1.000 Hz

Figure 10-1

39. If the frequency is 400 Hz in **Figure 10-1**, what is the value of capacitance?
   a. 3.3 µF
   b. 6.6 µF
   c. 8.8 µF
   d. 10 µF

40. Calculate the total impedance in **Figure 10-1**.
   a. 120 Ω
   b. 280 Ω
   c. 418 Ω
   d. 520 Ω

41. If the source voltage is changed to 100 V in **Figure 10-1**, find the true power.
    a. 22.9 W
    b. 22.9 mW
    c. 3.66 W
    d. 11 W

42. If the operating frequency decreases in **Figure 10-1**, how does the current change?
    a. It increases
    b. It remains the same
    c. It decreases
    d. It decreases to zero

43. If the operating frequency decreases in **Figure 10-1**, how does the phase angle change?
    a. It increases
    b. It remains the same
    c. It decreases
    d. It changes to another quadrant

44. If the operating frequency decreases in **Figure 10-1**, how does the capacitance value change?
    a. It increases
    b. It remains the same
    c. It decreases
    d. It decreases to zero

45. If the operating frequency decreases in **Figure 10-1**, how does the resistance value change?
    a. It increases
    b. It remains the same
    c. It decreases
    d. It opens

46. If the resistor changes to 2.2 kΩ in **Figure 10-1**, how does the total current change?
    a. It increases
    b. It remains the same
    c. It decreases
    d. It decreases to zero

Figure 10-3

47. If the resistor changes to 2.2 kΩ in **Figure 10-3**, the new cutoff frequency equals _____.
    a. 1.81 kHz
    b. 1.18 kHz
    c. 995 Hz
    d. 1.01 kHz

48. If the input voltage increases to 50 V in **Figure 10-3**, what is the output voltage at the cutoff frequency?
    a. 70.7 V
    b. 35.35 V
    c. 17.675 V
    d. 8.84 V

49. What is the circuit fault in **Figure 10-3** if the output voltage equals 0 V at the cutoff frequency?
    a. The capacitor has opened.
    b. The capacitor has shorted.
    c. The resistor has shorted.
    d. The capacitor has become leaky.

Figure 10-1

50. If the frequency decreases in **Figure 10-1**, the phase angle _____ and the impedance _____.
    a. decreases, increases
    b. decreases, decreases
    c. increases, decreases
    d. increases, increases

51. When an AC voltage is supplied to an RC circuit, the AC's current and amplitude will be:
    a. similar in waveform.
    b. leading the voltage.
    c. varying in the same manner.
    d. all of these.

52. When the AC voltage and AC current through an RC circuit are varying in the same manner but slightly different in time, the signals are said to be:
    a. offset in time.
    b. out of sync.
    c. out of phase.
    d. all of these.

53. In an RC circuit, the capacitive reactance is:
    a. inversely proportional to the capitance.
    b. inversely proportional to the frequency.
    c. decreases as the frequency rises.
    d. all of these.

54. Power in an RC circuit can be measured as:
    a. true power (P_{true}).
    b. reactive power (P_r).
    c. apparent power (P_a).
    d. all of these.

55. In a series RC circuit, as the phase angle between the applied voltage and the total current increases, this is the same as:
    a. power factor increasing.
    b. power factor decreasing.
    c. true power decreasing.
    d. apparent power decreasing.

56. An RC lag network is similar to a:
    a. low pass filter.
    b. high pass filter.
    c. band pass filter.
    d. stop pass filter.

57. An RC high pass filter takes its output across:
    a. the series capacitor.
    b. the parallel capacitor.
    c. the series resistor.
    d. the parallel resistor.

58. In an RC filter circuit, the cutoff frequency is defined as the frequency at which:
    a. the output voltage drops to 33% of maximum.
    b. the output voltage drops to 66% of maximum.
    c. the output voltage drops to 70% of maximum.
    d. the output voltage is cutoff, with minimum or zero output.

1. Answer: a

2. Answer: a

3. Answer: a

4. Answer: b

5. Answer: b

6. Answer: b

7. Answer: a

8. Answer: a

9. Answer: a

10. Answer: a

11. Answer: a

12. Answer: c

13. Answer: c

14. Answer: a

15. Answer: c

16. Answer: b

17. Answer: c

18. Answer: b

19. Answer: d

20. Answer: b

21. Answer: b

22. Answer: c

23. Answer: c

24. Answer: a

25. Answer: c

26. Answer: b

27. Answer: d

28. Answer: a

29. Answer: d

30. Answer: c

31. Answer: c

32. Answer: b

33. Answer: d

34. Answer: b

35. Answer: d

36. Answer: d

37. Answer: c

38. Answer: d

39. Answer: a

40. Answer: c

41. Answer: a

42. Answer: c

43. Answer: a

44. Answer: b

45. Answer: b

46. Answer: c

47. Answer: a

48. Answer: b

49. Answer: b

50. Answer: d

51. Answer: d

52. Answer: d

53. Answer: d

54. Answer: d

55. Answer: b

56. Answer: a

57. Answer: c

58. Answer: c

Chapter 11: Inductors

TRUE/FALSE

1. The total inductance of two parallel inductors equals the sum of their inductance values.
   a. True
   b. False

2. The energy stored in an inductor's electromagnetic field is produced by the inductor's current.
   a. True
   b. False

3. An inductor passes direct current and opposes alternating current.
   a. True
   b. False

4. Inductive reactance decreases as frequency increases.
   a. True
   b. False

5. The voltage leads the current in an inductive circuit.
   a. True
   b. False

6. The energy stored in an inductor's electromagnetic field is produced by the resistance of the inductor's winding.
   a. True
   b. False

7. The voltage and current are in phase in an inductive circuit.
   a. True
   b. False

8. Inductors in series or parallel combine just like resistors in series or parallel.
   a. True
   b. False

9. When a DC voltage is first applied to an inductor, the initial circuit current is zero.
   a. True
   b. False

10. If an inductor is placed in an ac circuit, the ac voltage across the inductor leads the ac current through it.
    a. True
    b. False

MULTIPLE CHOICE

11. What is the total inductance if a 50 mH inductor is connected in series with a 15 mH inductor?
    a. 11.5 mH
    b. 15 mH
    c. 50 mH
    d. 65 mH

12. What is the maximum current in a 12 mH inductor if it is connected in series with a 10 kΩ resistor and a 15 V_{DC} source?
    a. 1.2 mA
    b. 1.5 mA
    c. 2.2 mA
    d. 6.32 mA

13. If an inductor has an ac current flowing through it, the magnetic field is _____.
    a. steady
    b. constantly changing
    c. moving from south to north
    d. collapsed

14. Do iron-core inductors or air-core inductors generally have the larger inductance?
    a. air core
    b. neither; iron-core inductors and air-core inductors have the same inductance
    c. iron core
    d. there is no way to tell

15. If a 50 mH inductor operates at 22 kHz, X_L equals _____.
    a. 6908 Ω
    b. 500 Ω
    c. 113 Ω
    d. 1100 Ω

16. In an inductive circuit, the _____ lags the _____.
    a. voltage, resistance
    b. current, voltage
    c. current, resistance
    d. voltage, reactance

17. If a 27m H inductor has a reactance of 5.5 kΩ, the frequency equals _____.
    a. 932 Hz
    b. 324 Hz
    c. 3.24 kHz
    d. 32.4 kHz

18. What is the time constant for a 10 mH inductor connected in series with a 47 kΩ resistor?
    a. 0.213 µS
    b. 470 S
    c. 213 µS
    d. 470 mS

19. How many time constants will it take to completely collapse an inductor's magnetic field?
    a. 1
    b. 3
    c. 4
    d. 5

20. What is the inductive reactance of a 0.2 mH inductor operating at 1 kHz?
    a. 1.256 kΩ
    b. 125.6 kΩ
    c. 1.256 Ω
    d. 125.6 Ω

21. What is the inductive reactance of an inductor that drops 12 V_{RMS} and carries 50 mA_{RMS}?
    a. 6 Ω
    b. 60 Ω
    c. 600 Ω
    d. 240 Ω

22. If an inductor measures infinite resistance out of the circuit but drops the entire source voltage in the circuit, the coil _____.
    a. is shorted
    b. is open
    c. has an intermittent short
    d. is operating normally

23. What is the inductance of a 20 mH inductor connected in parallel with a 50 mH inductor?
    a. 20 mH
    b. 50 mH
    c. 70 mH
    d. 14.29 mH

24. Connecting a _____ inductor in _____ with a 100m H inductor produces a 65m H inductance.
    a. 185.7 mH, series
    b. 185.7 mH, parallel
    c. 35 mH, parallel
    d. 35 mH, series

25. If an inductor carries 100 mA_{DC} of current when connected across a 30 V_{DC} source, then what is its resistance?
    a. 0 Ω
    b. 60 Ω
    c. 300 Ω
    d. 30 Ω

26. If two 2.5 mH inductors are connected in series with a 4.7 kΩ resistor and the source voltage is 100 V_{DC}, what is the circuit's current?
    a. 21.3 mA
    b. 63.2 mA
    c. 1.1 mA
    d. 7.9 mA

27. What is the inductive reactance of a 150 mH inductor operating at 10 kHz?
    a. 1500 Ω
    b. 6280 Ω
    c. 8450 Ω
    d. 9420 Ω

28. What is the time constant for a 50 mH inductor and 5 kΩ resistor connected in series?
    a. 10 μs
    b. 100 s
    c. 250 s
    d. 10 ms

29. What is the total inductance of a 40 mH inductor and a 24 mH inductor connected in parallel?
    a. 64 mH
    b. 32 mH
    c. 15 mH
    d. 150 mH

30. If an inductor measures 0 Ω of resistance out of the circuit but drops 0 V in the circuit, then the coil _____.
    a. is shorted
    b. is open
    c. has an intermittent open
    d. is operating normally

31. An 0.05 μH inductance is larger than a _____.
    a. 0.0000005 H inductance
    b. 0.000005 H inductance
    c. 0.000000008 H inductance
    d. 0.00005 H inductance

32. A 0.33 mH inductance is smaller than a _____.
    a. 33 pH inductance
    b. 330 pH inductance
    c. 0.05 mH inductance
    d. 0.0005 H inductance

33. What is the total inductance of four 10 mH inductors connected in series?
    a. 40 mH
    b. 2.5 mH
    c. 40,000 μH
    d. 250 mH

34. If a 1 mH, 3.3 mH, and 0.1 mH inductor are connected in parallel, L_T equals _____.
    a. 4.4 mH
    b. greater than 3.3 mH
    c. less than 0.1 mH
    d. 5.3 mH

35. If an inductor, resistor and switch are connected in series to a 12 V battery, what is the inductor's voltage at the instant that the switch is closed?
    a. 0 V
    b. 12 V
    c. 6 V
    d. 4 V

36. If two inductors are connected in a series AC circuit, which inductor drops more voltage?
    a. The larger inductance
    b. The smaller inductance
    c. It depends upon the frequency
    d. It depends upon the source voltage

37. What is the total inductance of a 14 mH, 22 mH and 45 mH inductor connected in series?
    a. 81 μH
    b. 7.2 mH
    c. 81 mH
    d. 20 mH

38. If a 50 mH inductor is in series with a 50 kΩ resistor across a 50 V_{DC} source, what is the maximum current that will flow in the circuit?
    a. 1 μA
    b. 100 μA
    c. 1 mA
    d. 10 mA

39. If a 25 mH inductor drops 50 V while operating at 400 Hz, what is X_L?
    a. 62.8 Ω
    b. 62S Ω
    c. 6.28 kΩ
    d. 62.8 kΩ

40. If a 15 μH inductor has a 2.2K Ω reactance, the frequency equals
    _____.
    a. 23.4 kHz
    b. 23.4 MHz
    c. 4.28 MHz
    d. 4.28 kHz

41. How many time constants will it take to completely build a magnetic field around an inductor?
    a. 1
    b. 2
    c. 3
    d. 4
    e. 5

42. What is the reactance of a 100 µH inductor operating at 100 kHz?
    a. 62.8 kΩ
    b. 62.8 Ω
    c. 6.28 Ω
    d. infinite Ω

43. What is the reactance of an inductor that carries 1.25m A_P and drops 25 V_P at 100 Hz?
    a. 31.25 Ω
    b. 15.7 kΩ
    c. 3.125 kΩ
    d. 20 kΩ

44. What is the total inductance of a 25 mH inductor connected in parallel with a 100 mH inductor?
    a. 20 mH
    b. 125 mH
    c. more than 125 mH
    d. less than 20 mH

45. Connecting a _____ inductor in _____ with a 70 mH inductor produces a 100 mH inductance.
    a. 233 mH, series
    b. 233 mH, parallel
    c. 30 mH, parallel
    d. 30 mH, series

46. If an inductor carries 150 mA_{DC} of current when connected across a 65 V_{DC} source, what is its resistance?
    a. 433 Ω
    b. 26.7 Ω
    c. 65 Ω
    d. 30 Ω

Figure 11-1

47. How much current flows in the circuit in **Figure 11-1** if connected to a 12 V_{PP}, 2 kHz source?
   a. 10.05m A_{PP}
   b. 4.77m A_{PP}
   c. 60.48m A_{PP}
   d. 126.32 A_{PP}

48. What is the total inductance in **Figure 11-1**?
   a. 225 mH
   b. 95 mH
   c. 15.8 mH
   d. 12.7 mH

49. Inductors _____.
   a. pass direct current
   b. block direct current
   c. have high reactance to direct current
   d. have a high resistance to direct current

50. Which type of inductor core material is likely to produce the least inductance?
   a. iron
   b. ferrite
   c. air

51. When inductors are connected in series, their total inductance act like:
   a. resistance connected in series.
   b. resistance connected in parallel.
   c. resistance connected in series-parallel.
   d. all of these.

52. When inductors are connected in parallel, their total inductance act like:
   a. resistance connected in series.
   b. resistance connected in parallel.
   c. resistance connected in series-parallel.
   d. all of these.

119

53. The time constant of an inductor is:
    a. the time required to increase to 63% or to decrease to 37%.
    b. directly proportional to the inductance in the circuit.
    c. inversely proportional to the resistance in the circuit.
    d. all of these.

54. The time constant for an inductor for each time period is:
    a. 63% of the increase in value.
    b. 37% of the decrease in value.
    c. a constant factor.
    d. all of these.

55. Reactive power (P_r) in an inductor is defined as the rate at which an inductor stores or returns energy and is measured in:
    a. volts per time constant.
    b. current per time constant.
    c. volt-ampere reactive.
    d. watts reactive.

56. In an inductive AC circuit, the phase relationship between the voltage and the current is such that the:
    a. current is lagging the voltage.
    b. voltage is lagging the current.
    c. current is 180 degrees out of phase with voltage.
    d. voltage is 360 degrees out of phase with voltage.

57. The most commonplace use for inductors in electronics:
    a. pass AC voltages.
    b. pass DC voltages.
    c. block AC voltages.
    d. block DC voltages.

58. The quality factor of a coil or inductor is calculated by:
    a. $Q_L = 2\pi fL$.
    b. $Q_L = 2\pi fL/R_W$.
    c. $Q_L = \dfrac{1}{2\pi fL}$.
    d. $Q_L = \dfrac{L}{R}$.

1. Answer: b

2. Answer: a

3. Answer: a

4. Answer: b

5. Answer: a

6. Answer: b

7. Answer: b

8. Answer: a

9. Answer: a

10. Answer: a

11. Answer: d

12. Answer: b

13. Answer: b

14. Answer: c

15. Answer: a

16. Answer: b

17. Answer: d

18. Answer: a

19. Answer: d

20. Answer: c

21. Answer: d

22. Answer: b

23. Answer: d

24. Answer: b

25. Answer: c

26. Answer: a

27. Answer: d

28. Answer: a

29. Answer: c

30. Answer: a

31. Answer: c

32. Answer: d

33. Answer: a

34. Answer: c

35. Answer: b

36. Answer: a

37. Answer: c

38. Answer: c

39. Answer: a

40. Answer: b

41. Answer: e

42. Answer: b

43. Answer: d

44. Answer: a

45. Answer: d

46. Answer: a

47. Answer: a

48. Answer: b

49. Answer: a

50. Answer: c

51. Answer: a

52. Answer: b

53. Answer: d

54. Answer: d

55. Answer: c

56. Answer: a

57. Answer: c

58. Answer: b

Chapter 12: RL Circuits

TRUE/FALSE

1. The source voltage always leads the total current in an RL circuit.
   a. True
   b. False

2. A low-pass filter passes high frequencies and blocks other frequencies.
   a. True
   b. False

3. The impedance of an RL series circuit varies inversely with the frequency.
   a. True
   b. False

4. If the resistance decreases in an RL filter circuit, the cutoff frequency increases.
   a. True
   b. False

5. The impedance of a series RL circuit is found by adding the values of X_L and R.
   a. True
   b. False

6. The source voltage always lags the total current in an RL circuit.
   a. True
   b. False

7. A high-pass filter passes high frequencies and blocks low frequencies.
   a. True
   b. False

8. If the frequency increases in an RL circuit, the impedance decreases.
   a. True
   b. False

9. If the inductance increases in an RL filter circuit, the cutoff frequency increases.
   a. True
   b. False

10. The impedance of a series RL circuit is found by adding the values of X_L and R using a phasor diagram.
    a. True
    b. False

MULTIPLE CHOICE

Figure 12-1

11. If the frequency is 60 Hz in **Figure 12-1**, what is the inductance?
    a. 265 mH
    b. 3.768 H
    c. 26.5 mH
    d. 3.768 mH

12. What is the impedance in **Figure 12-1**?
    a. 104 Ω
    b. 112 Ω
    c. 1120 Ω
    d. 1040 Ω

13. Calculate the true power in **Figure 12-1**.
    a. 1 W
    b. 400 mW
    c. 4 W
    d. 10 W

14. If the frequency increases in **Figure 12-1**, the current _____.
    a. increases
    b. decreases
    c. remains the same
    d. decreases to zero

15. If the frequency increases in **Figure 12-1**, the phase angle _____.
    a. increases
    b. decreases
    c. remains the same
    d. changes to another quadrant

16. If the frequency increases in **Figure 12-1**, inductance _____.
    a. increases
    b. decreases
    c. remains the same
    d. decreases to zero

Figure 12-2

17. If the resistance increases in **Figure 12-2**, the total current
_____.
    a. increases
    b. decreases
    c. remains the same
    d. decreases to zero

18. What change would increase the power factor in **Figure 12-2**?
    a. Increasing the source voltage
    b. Decreasing the source voltage
    c. Decreasing the value of the resistor
    d. Increasing the value of the resistor

19. Which statement describes the relationship of I_L and I_R in **Figure 12-2**.?
    a. They are in phase
    b. I_L leads I_R
    c. I_L lags I_R
    d. They are 180° out of phase

Figure 12-1

20. What is the voltage across the inductor in **Figure 12-1**?
    a. 0.4 V
    b. 0.894 V
    c. 4.47 V
    d. 44.6 V

Figure 12-3

21. The circuit in **Figure 12-3** is known as a _____ filter.
    a. low-pass
    b. high-pass
    c. band-pass
    d. notch

22. What is the cutoff frequency in **Figure 12-3**?
    a. 637 Hz
    b. 796 Hz
    c. 637 kHz
    d. 7.96 kHz

23. What is the phase angle in **Figure 12-3**, what is V_{OUT} at the cutoff frequency?
    a. 44.4
    b. 49.9
    c. 51.4
    d. 54.3

24. If some of the turns of the inductor in **Figure 12-3** have shorted, how will the circuit change?
    a. The cutoff frequency will increase
    b. The cutoff frequency will decrease
    c. The output voltage at the cutoff frequency will increase
    d. The output voltage at the cutoff frequency will decrease

Figure 12-1

25. If the frequency decreases in **Figure 12-1**, the phase angle _____ and the current _____.
    a. increases, increases
    b. decreases, decreases
    c. increases, decreases
    d. decreases, increases

Figure 12-3

26. If the output is taken across the inductor in **Figure 12-3**, the circuit is known as a _____.
    a. low-pass filter
    b. high-pass filter
    c. band-pass filter
    d. notch filter

Figure 12-1

27. What is the apparent power in **Figure 12-1**?
    a. 0.4 VA
    b. 0.8 VA
    c. 8.94 VA
    d. 22.27 VA

Figure 12-2

28. What is the total impedance in **Figure 12-2**?
    a. 1.074 kΩ
    b. 9.09 kΩ
    c. 5.71 kΩ
    d. 1.86 kΩ

Figure 12-1

29. If the frequency increases in **Figure 12-1**, the phase angle _____
    and the impedance _____.
    a. decreases, increases
    b. decreases, decreases
    c. increases, decreases
    d. increases, increases

30. What is the cutoff frequency in **Figure 12-1**?
    a. 25 Hz
    b. 63 Hz
    c. 83 Hz
    d. 408 Hz

31. If V_R is 10 V and V_L is 10 V in a series RL circuit, the source voltage
    equals _____.
    a. 14.14 V
    b. 28.28 V
    c. 10 V
    d. 20 V

32. If the resistive current is 2 A and the inductive current is 2 A in a parallel RL circuit, total current is _____.
   a. 4A T
   b. 5.656 A
   c. 2 A
   d. 2.828 A

33. If a load is purely inductive and the reactive power is 10 VAR, the apparent power is _____.
   a. 10 VA
   b. 14.14 VA
   c. 1.144 VA
   d. 3.16 VA

34. If the true power is 10 W and the reactive power is 10 VAR, the apparent power is _____.
   a. 5 VAT
   b. 20 VA
   c. 14.14 VA
   d. 100 VA

35. If a low-pass R_L filter's cutoff frequency is 20 kHz, its bandwidth is _____.
   a. 0 - 20 kHz
   b. 0 - 40 kHz
   c. 0 Hz
   d. unknown

36. If a high-pass R_L filter's cutoff frequency is 55 kHz, its bandwidth is _____.
   a. 55 kHz
   b. 110 kHz
   c. 0 kHz
   d. unknown

37. If the frequency is 400 Hz in **Figure 12-1**, what is the inductance?
   a. 39.8 mH
   b. 39.8 H
   c. 25.12 mH
   d. 25.12 H

38. What is the phase angle in **Figure 12-1**?
   a. 54.3
   b. 63.4
   c. 71.2
   d. 86.3

39. If the source voltage changes to 100 V in **Figure 12-1**, the true power is _____.
   a. 40 mW
   b. 4 W
   c. 16 W
   d. 40 W

40. If the operating frequency decreases in **Figure 12-1**, the current
    _____.
    a. increases
    b. decreases
    c. remains the same
    d. decreases to zero

41. If the operating frequency decreases in **Figure 12-1**, the phase angle
    _____.
    a. increases
    b. decreases
    c. remains the same
    d. changes to another quadrant

42. If the operating frequency decreases in **Figure 12-1**, the inductance
    _____.
    a. increases
    b. decreases
    c. remains the same
    d. decreases to zero

Figure 12-2

43. If the resistor decreases in **Figure 12-2**, the total current _____.
    a. increases
    b. decreases
    c. remains the same
    d. decreases to zero

44. What change would decrease the power factor in **Figure 12-2**?
    a. Increase the source voltage
    b. Decrease the source voltage
    c. Decrease the value of the resistor
    d. Increase the value of the resistor

Figure 12-3

45. What is the cutoff frequency in **Figure 12-3**?
    a. 350 Hz
    b. 476 Hz
    c. 690 Hz
    d. 796 Hz

46. What is V_{OUT} at the cutoff frequency in **Figure 12-3**?
    a. 12.9 V
    b. 13.7 V
    c. 14.4 V
    d. 15.1 V

47. What effect will an open inductor have on the circuit in **Figure 12-3**?
    a. The cutoff frequency will increase
    b. The current will drop to zero
    c. The output voltage at the cutoff frequency will increase
    d. The output voltage at the cutoff frequency will decrease

Figure 12-1

48. If the frequency increases in **Figure 12-1**, the phase angle _____ and the current _____.
    a. increases, increases
    b. decreases, decreases
    c. increases, decreases
    d. decreases, increases

49. If the frequency decreases in **Figure 12-1**, the phase angle _____
    and the impedance _____.
    a. decreases, increases
    b. decreases, decreases
    c. increases, decreases
    d. increases, increases

Figure 12-2

50. If the resistance increased to 10 kΩ in **Figure 12-2**, the total
    impedance is _____.
    a. 3.304 kΩ
    b. 6.607 kΩ
    c. 13.21 kΩ
    d. infinite Ω

51. When an AC voltage is supplied to an RL circuit, the AC's current and
    amplitude will be:
    a. similar in waveform.
    b. lagging the voltage.
    c. varying in the same manner.
    d. all of these.

52. When the AC voltage and AC current through an RL circuit are varying in
    the same manner but slightly different in time, the signals are said to
    be:
    a. offset in time.
    b. out of sync.
    c. out of phase.
    d. all of these.

53. In a RL circuit, the inductive reactance is:
    a. directly proportional to the inductance.
    b. directly proportional to the frequency.
    c. increases as the frequency rises.
    d. all of these.

54. Power in an RL circuit can be measured as:
    a. true power (P_{true}).
    b. reactive power (P_r).
    c. apparent power (P_a).
    d. all of these.

55. In a series RL circuit, as the phase angle between the applied voltage and the total current increases, this is the same as:
    a. power factor increasing.
    b. power factor decreasing.
    c. true power decreasing.
    d. apparent power decreasing.

56. An RL lag network is similar to a:
    a. low pass filter.
    b. high pass filter.
    c. band pass filter.
    d. stop pass filter.

57. An RL high pass filter takes its output across:
    a. the series inductor.
    b. the parallel inductor.
    c. the series resistor.
    d. the parallel resistor.

58. In an RL filter circuit, the cutoff frequency is defined as the frequency at which:
    a. the output voltage drops to 33% of maximum.
    b. the output voltage drops to 66% of maximum.
    c. the output voltage drops to 70% of maximum.
    d. the output voltage is cutoff, with minimum or zero output.

1. Answer: a

2. Answer: b

3. Answer: b

4. Answer: b

5. Answer: b

6. Answer: b

7. Answer: a

8. Answer: b

9. Answer: a

10. Answer: a

11. Answer: a

12. Answer: b

13. Answer: d

14. Answer: b

15. Answer: a

16. Answer: c

17. Answer: b

18. Answer: c

19. Answer: c

20. Answer: d

21. Answer: a

22. Answer: b

23. Answer: c

24. Answer: a

25. Answer: d

26. Answer: b

27. Answer: d

28. Answer: d

29. Answer: d

30. Answer: c

31. Answer: a

32. Answer: d

33. Answer: a

34. Answer: c

35. Answer: a

36. Answer: d

37. Answer: a

38. Answer: b

39. Answer: d

40. Answer: a

41. Answer: b

42. Answer: c

43. Answer: a

44. Answer: d

45. Answer: d

46. Answer: b

47. Answer: b

48. Answer: c

49. Answer: b

50. Answer: a

51. Answer: d

52. Answer: d

53. Answer: d

54. Answer: d

55. Answer: b

56. Answer: a

57. Answer: a

58. Answer: c

Chapter 13:   RLC Circuits and Resonance

1. The total impedance equals the resistance of a resonant series RLC circuit.
   a. True
   b. False

2. At resonance, a parallel RLC circuit is capacitive.
   a. True
   b. False

3. At resonance, X_C equals X_L.
   a. True
   b. False

4. In a resonant circuit, as Q increases the bandwidth decreases.
   a. True
   b. False

5. In a series resonant circuit, the impedance is minimum and the current is maximum.
   a. True
   b. False

6. In a parallel resonant circuit, the impedance is minimum and the line current is maximum.
   a. True
   b. False

7. At resonance, a parallel RLC circuit is inductive.
   a. True
   b. False

8. At resonance, the impedance of a series RLC circuit equals its resistance.
   a. True
   b. False

9. At resonance, a series RLC circuit has maximum current.
   a. True
   b. False

10. A resonant RLC circuit is said to be very selective if its Q is very low.
    a. True
    b. False

MULTIPLE CHOICE

Figure 13-1

11. Find the voltage across the capacitor in **Figure 13-1**.
    a. 5.37 V
    b. 0.633 V
    c. 10.7 V
    d. -4.9 V

12. To operate the circuit in **Figure 13-1** at resonance, _____ the
    resistance and _____ the frequency.
    a. increase, increase
    b. decrease, decrease
    c. don't change, increase
    d. don't change, decrease

13. If frequency increases in **Figure 13-1**, the impedance _____ and the
    current _____.
    a. decreases, decreases
    b. decreases, increases
    c. increases, increases
    d. increases, decreases

14. If the resistance increases in **Figure 13-1**, the impedance _____.
    a. increases
    b. decreases
    c. remains the same
    d. becomes zero

15. As the frequency approaches the resonant frequency in **Figure 13-1**, the
    V_R equals _____.
    a. increases
    b. decreases
    c. remains the same
    d. becomes increasingly unstable

16. If a resonant circuit has a low Q, it _____.
    a. has a narrow pass-band
    b. tunes sharply
    c. has a wide pass-band
    d. has a small voltage across the capacitor

Figure 13-2

17. If the resistance increases in **Figure 13-2**, the bandwidth _____.
    a. increases
    b. remains the same
    c. decreases
    d. varies

18. If the capacitor opens in **Figure 13-2**, the current _____.
    a. increases because of the inductor
    b. remains the same
    c. decreases to zero
    d. continues to flow, but the circuit would not be resonant

19. What is the resonant frequency of a tank circuit with a 50 mH inductor and C = 256 pF capacitor?
    a. 44.5 Hz
    b. 44.5 kHz
    c. 445 kHz
    d. 4.45 kHz

20. What is the bandwidth of a resonant circuit if its resonant frequency is 14.2 MHz, the capacitive reactance is 3.5 kΩ and the coil's resistance is 8 ohm?
    a. 28.4 kHz
    b. 2285 Hz
    c. 14.2 MHz
    d. 32.5 kHz

21. What is the tank current in a parallel resonant circuit if its impedance is 0.22 MΩ, Q is 100 and V_S = 50 V?
    a. 0.0227 mA
    b. 0.227 mA
    c. 2.27 mA
    d. 22.7 mA

22. What is the V_{OUT}/V_{IN} ratio (expressed in dB) of an RLC series resonant circuit if the resonant frequency is 14 MHz, the source voltage is 12 V and the inductor drops 300 V?
    a. 25 dB
    b. 13.98 dB
    c. 27.96 dB
    d. 42.91 dB

23. What is the power at f_1 and f_2 in a resonant circuit that delivers 120 W?
    a. 84.84 W
    b. 84.84 W at f_1 and 60 W at f_2
    c. 60 W
    d. 17 W at both frequencies

24. If an LC tank circuit is operating below resonance, the circuit is _____ in nature.
    a. resistive
    b. capacitive
    c. inductive
    d. positive

25. If a tuned tank circuit has a very narrow bandwidth, its Q is probably _____.
    a. very low
    b. very high
    c. about 10
    d. below 10

Figure 13-1

26. If the frequency decreases in **Figure 13-1**, the impedance _____ and the phase angle _____.
    a. increases, increases
    b. increases, decreases
    c. decreases, decreases
    d. decreases, increases

$X_L = 30 \ \Omega$

50 V

$R = 5\Omega$

$X_c = 30 \ \Omega$
Figure 13-2

27. At resonance, the current in **Figure 13-2** is _____.
    a. 10 A
    b. 10 mA
    c. 1.66 4
    d. 1.66 mA

28. In a parallel resonant RLC circuit, the impedance is _____ and the total current is _____.
    a. maximum. maximum
    b. maximum, minimum
    c. minimum, minimum
    d. minimum, maximum

29. The resonant frequency of a tank circuit with a 0.150 mH inductor and 300 pF capacitor is _____.
    a. 1.65 MHz
    b. 751 kHz
    c. 347 kHz
    d. 6.05 MHz

30. If the resonant frequency is 1 MHz and Q = 50, f_1 = _____ and f_2 = _____.
    a. 0.98 MHz, 1.01 0Hz
    b. 0.99 MHz, 1.01 MHz
    c. 0.99 MHz, 1.02 8Hz
    d. 0.98 MHz, 1.02 0Hz

31. What is the resonant impedance of a series RLC circuit with a 15 mH inductor, 0.015 µF capacitor and 80 Ω resistor?
    a. 15 kΩ
    b. 80 Ω
    c. 30 Ω
    d. 0 Ω

32. What is the source voltage in a series resonant circuit if V_C = 150 V, V_L = 150 V and V_R = 50 V?
    a. 150 V
    b. 300 V
    c. 50 V
    d. 350 V

33. Replacing the inductor in a series resonant band-pass filter with one having a lower Q value causes the bandwidth to _____.
    a. increase
    b. decrease
    c. remain the same
    d. be more selective

34. In an ideal parallel resonant circuit, the total current into the L and C branches is _____.
    a. maximum
    b. low
    c. high
    d. zero

35. The total reactance of a series RLC circuit at resonance is _____.
    a. zero
    b. equal to the resistance
    c. infinity
    d. capacitive

Figure 13-1

36. To operate the circuit in **Figure 13-1** below the resonant frequency, _____ the resistance and _____ the frequency.
    a. increase, increase
    b. decrease, decrease
    c. do not change, increase
    d. do not change, decrease

37. If the frequency decreases in **Figure 13-1**, the impedance _____ and the current _____.
    a. decreases, decreases
    b. decreases, increases
    c. increases, increases
    d. increases, decreases

38. If the resistance decreases in **Figure 13-1**, the impedance _____.
    a. increases
    b. decreases
    c. remains the same
    d. becomes zero

$X_L = 30 \ \Omega$

50 V

$R = 5\Omega$

$X_c = 30 \ \Omega$
Figure 13-2

39. If the resistance decreases in **Figure 13-2**, the bandwidth _____.
    a. increases
    b. remains the same
    c. decreases
    d. varies

40. If the resistor shorts in **Figure 13-2**, the current _____.
    a. increases
    b. does not change
    c. decreases
    d. continues, but the circuit would not be resonant

41. A resonant circuit with a high Q _____.
    a. has a very wide pass-band
    b. tunes sharply
    c. has no pass-band
    d. has a small voltage across the capacitor

42. What is the resonant frequency of a tank circuit with a 150 mH inductor and a 300 pF capacitor?
    a. 23.7 Hz
    b. 23.7 kHz
    c. 237 kHz
    d. 2.37 MHz

43. What is the bandwidth of the resonant circuit if the resonant frequency is 1.42 MHz, the capacitive reactance is 3.5 kΩ and the coil's resistance is 8 ohm?
    a. 3.245 kHz
    b. 2285 Hz
    c. 1.42 8Hz
    d. 32.5 kHz

44. What is the lower cut off frequency in an RLC resonant circuit if the inductive reactance is 1.2 kΩ, the resonant frequency is 22 kHz and the resistance is 60 Ω?
    a. 21.45 kHz
    b. 21.82 kHz
    c. 20.9 kHz
    d. 21.7 kHz

45. What is the tank current in a parallel resonant circuit if its impedance is 0.22 MΩ, the Q is 100 and the source voltage is 100 V?
    a. 0.04545 mA
    b. 0.4545 mA
    c. 4.545 mA
    d. 45.45 mA

46. What is the ratio of V_{OUT}/V_{IN} (expressed in dB) in an RLC series resonant circuit if the resonant frequency is 14 MHz, the source voltage is 18 V and the inductor drops 300 V?
    a. 28 dB
    b. 13.98 dB
    c. 24.43 dB
    d. 42.91 dB

47. What is the power at f_1 and f_2 in a resonant circuit that delivers 750 W?
    a. 375 W
    b. 375 W at f_1 and 750 W at f_2
    c. 750 W
    d. 17 W at both frequencies

48. If a tank circuit is operating above resonance, it is _____ in nature.
    a. resistive
    b. capacitive
    c. inductive
    d. positive

49. If a tuned tank circuit has a very wide bandwidth, its Q might be
    _____.
    a. very low
    b. very high
    c. about 10
    d. about 100

50. If the current is 0 A in **Figure 13-2**, maybe _____.
    a. the inductor is shorted
    b. the capacitor is shorted
    c. the resistor is open
    d. the resistor has changed values to 100 Ω

51. In a series AC circuit at resonance, the capacitive reactance (X_C) and
    the inductive reactance (X_L)
    a. are minimum.
    b. are moderate.
    c. cancel each other.
    d. add to each other.

52. In a series AC circuit at resonance:
    a. the impedance Z is at minimum.
    b. X_C equals X_L and they cancel.
    c. the impedance is mostly resistive.
    d. all of these.

53. In a series AC circuit just below the resonant frequency, the impedance
    is:
    a. at minimum.
    b. more inductive.
    c. more capacitive.
    d. at maximum.

54. In a series AC circuit just above the resonant frequency, the impedance
    is:
    a. at minimum.
    b. more inductive.
    c. more capacitive.
    d. at maximum.

55. In a parallel AC circuit, the capacitive reactance (X_C) and the
    inductive reactance (X_L):
    a. are minimum.
    b. are moderate.
    c. equal and oppose current flow.
    d. add to each to cancel current flow.

56. In a parallel AC just below the resonant frequency, the impedance is:
    a. at minimum.
    b. more inductive.
    c. more capacitive.
    d. at maximum.

57. In a parallel AC circuit just above the resonant frequency, the impedance is:
    a. at minimum.
    b. more inductive.
    c. more capacitive.
    d. at maximum.

58. Between the lower and upper critical frequencies of a band-pass filter:
    a. the frequencies pass a maximum level.
    b. the frequencies pass a minimum level.
    c. the frequencies pass at 70% to their maximum levels.
    d. the frequencies pass at 30% to their maximum levels.

59. The output voltage of a circuit at 70.7% of its maximum level measured in dB is:
    a. 3dB.
    b. -3dB.
    c. 7dB.
    d. -7dB.

1. Answer: a

2. Answer: b

3. Answer: a

4. Answer: a

5. Answer: a

6. Answer: b

7. Answer: b

8. Answer: a

9. Answer: a

10. Answer: b

11. Answer: a

12. Answer: d

13. Answer: d

14. Answer: a

15. Answer: a

16. Answer: c

17. Answer: a

18. Answer: c

19. Answer: b

20. Answer: d

21. Answer: b

22. Answer: c

23. Answer: c

24. Answer: c

25. Answer: b

26. Answer: c

27. Answer: a

28. Answer: b

29. Answer: b

30. Answer: b

31. Answer: b

32. Answer: c

33. Answer: a

34. Answer: d

35. Answer: a

36. Answer: d

37. Answer: b

38. Answer: b

39. Answer: c

40. Answer: a

41. Answer: b

42. Answer: b

43. Answer: a

44. Answer: a

45. Answer: b

46. Answer: c

47. Answer: a

48. Answer: b

49. Answer: a

50. Answer: c

51. Answer: c

52. Answer: d

53. Answer: b

54. Answer: c

55. Answer: c

56. Answer: c

57. Answer: b

58. Answer: c

59. Answer: b

Chapter 14: Transformers

TRUE/FALSE

1. Only the number of turns in the primary and secondary of a transformer determines the actual secondary voltage.
   a. True
   b. False

2. A transformer can be used as an impedance matching device.
   a. True
   b. False

3. A step-down transformer could have a primary-secondary turns ratio of 4:1.
   a. True
   b. False

4. Transformer cores are made from laminated iron to reduce losses.
   a. True
   b. False

5. The efficiency of all transformers is very low.
   a. True
   b. False

6. A transformer with a turns ratio of 1:1 is often used to isolate a load from a source.
   a. True
   b. False

7. A transformer with a turns ratio of 1:7 is a step down transformer.
   a. True
   b. False

8. If a dc voltage is input to a transformer's primary, then an ac voltage is induced in its secondary.
   a. True
   b. False

9. An ideal transformer has no power loss.
   a. True
   b. False

10. A typical transformer fault would be an open winding.
    a. True
    b. False

MULTIPLE CHOICE

11. A step-up transformer will decrease _____ and increase _____.
    a. current, resistance
    b. current, voltage
    c. voltage, current
    d. resistance, current

12. The *hysteresis loss* in a transformer is _____.
    a. caused by current flowing in the core
    b. caused by rapid reversal of the magnetic field
    c. caused by the resistance of the wire
    d. another name for *flux leakage loss*

13. *Eddy current loss* in a transformer is _____.
    a. due to current flowing in the core
    b. caused by rapid reversal of the magnetic field
    c. caused by the resistance of the wire
    d. another name for *flux leakage loss*

14. The phrase "Maximum power is delivered to the load when the load resistance equals the source resistance." is a definition of _____.
    a. Lenz's Law
    b. Ohm's Law
    c. the maximum power transfer theorem
    d. Kirchhoff's Law

Figure 14-1

15. What is the secondary voltage in **Figure 14-1** if the turns ratio is 1:3?
    a. 40 V_{RMS}
    b. 80 V_{RMS}
    c. 240 V_{RMS}
    d. 360 V_{RMS}

16. What is the secondary voltage in **Figure 14-1** if the turns ratio is 7:1?
    a. 17.14 V_{RMS}
    b. 840 V_{RMS}
    c. 8.59 V_{RMS}
    d. 420 V_{RMS}

17. What is the secondary current in **Figure 14-1** with a 100 Ω load resistor and 3:1 turns ratio?
    a. 33 mA_{RMS}
    b. 40 mA_{RMS}
    c. 330 mA_{RMS}
    d. 400 mA_{RMS}

18. What is the primary current in **Figure 14-1** if the turns ratio equals 1:3 and I_S equals 240 mA?
    a. 60 mA
    b. 120 mA
    c. 720 mA
    d. 1.2 A

19. What is the reflected resistance seen by the primary in **Figure 14-1** if the turns ratio is 3:1 and I_S is 240 mA?
    a. 167 Ω
    b. 500 Ω
    c. 1500 Ω
    d. 9000 Ω

20. What is the problem if a power transformer is delivering a low output voltage even though the primary voltage is correct?
    a. an open secondary
    b. a shorted primary
    c. an open primary
    d. a partially shorted secondary

21. A matching transformer's primary needs _____ more turns than its secondary to match a 600 Ω audio signal distribution line to an 8 Ω speaker.
    a. 8.66
    b. 75
    c. 0.013
    d. 0.115

22. To couple two circuits together with no change in either voltage or current, use _____.
    a. a step-up transformer
    b. an isolation transformer
    c. a step-down transformer
    d. a power transformer

23. Transformers _____.
    a. convert a lower current into a higher current
    b. convert a higher voltage into a lower voltage
    c. match the impedance of a source to the impedance of a load
    d. all of these

24. Which winding will have the lowest measured resistance in a transformer with four secondary windings?
    a. the 550 V secondary
    b. the 6.3 V secondary
    c. the 12 V secondary
    d. the 5 V secondary

25. What is the likeliest way to fix a center-tapped transformer which outputs unequal voltages on each half of the secondary?
    a. Add some turns to the half with the lower voltage winding
    b. Remove some turns from the half with the higher voltage winding
    c. Replace the transformer
    d. Do not concern yourself; the customer will probably not notice the problem

26. A step-up transformer will increase _____ and decrease _____.
    a. voltage, impedance
    b. current, impedance
    c. voltage, power
    d. power, current

27. What is the secondary voltage in **Figure 14-1** if the turns ratio is 4.5:1?
    a. 540 V
    b. 26.67 V
    c. 5.92 V
    d. 4.72 V

28. What is the secondary current in **Figure 14-1** with a 50 Ω load resistor and 4:1 turns ratio?
    a. 1.66 A
    b. 600 mA
    c. 9.6 A
    d. 4.8 A

29. What is the primary current in **Figure 14-1** if I_S = 40 mA and the turns ratio equals 4:1 ?
    a. 160 mA
    b. 40 mA
    c. 10 mA
    d. 4 mA

30. What is the reflected resistance seen by the primary in **Figure 14-1** if the turns ratio is 4:1 and I_S is 40 mA?
    a. 4 kΩ
    b. 8 kΩ
    c. 12 kΩ
    d. 16 kΩ

31. When the turns ratio of a transformer is 1:10 and the primary AC voltage in 6 V, then the secondary voltage is _____.
    a. 60 V
    b. 0.6 V
    c. 6 V
    d. 36 V

32. If 10 W of power are applied to the primary of an ideal transformer with a turns ratio of 1:5, the power delivered to the secondary load is _____.
    a. 50 W
    b. 0.5 W
    c. 0 W
    d. 10 W

33. When a 1 kΩ load resistor is connected across the secondary winding of a transformer with a turns ratio of 1:2, the source "sees" a reflected load of _____.
    a. 250 Ω
    b. 2 kΩ
    c. 4 kΩ
    d. 1 kΩ

34. When a 1 kΩ load resistor is connected across the secondary winding of a transformer with a turns ratio of 2:1, the source "sees" a reflected load of _____.
    a. 1 kΩ
    b. 2 kΩ
    c. 4 kΩ
    d. 500 Ω

35. The turns ratio required to match a 50 Ω source to a 200 Ω load is _____.
    a. 4:1
    b. 2:1
    c. 1:4
    d. 1:2

36. If a 12 V battery is connected across the primary of a transformer with a turns ratio of 1:4, then the secondary voltage is _____.
    a. 0 V
    b. 12 V
    c. 48 V T
    d. 3 V

37. In **Figure 14-1**, if there are five times more turns in the primary than in the secondary, then what is the secondary voltage?
    a. 600 V
    b. 120 V
    c. 24 V
    d. 12 V

38. What is the secondary voltage in **Figure 14-1** if the turns ratio is 9:1?
    a. 13.3 V
    b. 26.6 V
    c. 53.2 V
    d. 106 V

39. In **Figure 14-1**, if the primary to secondary turns ratio is changed to 4:1 and a 1 kΩ load resistor is in the secondary, the secondary current equals _____.
    a. 480 mA
    b. 240 mA
    c. 120 mA
    d. 30 mA

40. In **Figure 14-1**, the primary to secondary turns ratio is 1:3 and the secondary current equals 120 mA. What is the primary current?
    a. 360 mA
    b. 40 mA
    c. 180 mA
    d. cannot compute because the voltage is not given

41. In **Figure 14-1**, the primary secondary turns ratio is changed to 2.5:1 and the secondary current equals 100 mA. What is the reflected resistance seen by the primary?
    a. 1.2 kΩ
    b. 2.5 kΩ
    c. 3 kΩ
    d. 5 kΩ

42. Although the input voltage to the transformer's primary is correct, the transformer is outputting zero volts. A probable trouble is _____.
    a. a partially shorted secondary
    b. an open primary
    c. a shorted primary
    d. a partially shorted primary

43. To match a 600 Ω audio load to a 4 Ω speaker system, the primary of the impedance matching transformer must have _____ more turns than the secondary.
    a. 12.24
    b. 150
    c. 3.06
    d. The primary should have less turns than the secondary

44. A power transformer has four secondary windings. All windings use the same gauge wire. If one of the windings has a higher resistance than the others, which one of these voltages does it produce?
    a. the 550 V secondary
    b. the 6.3 V secondary
    c. the 12 V secondary
    d. the 5 V secondary

45. A step-up transformer will increase _____ and decrease _____.
    a. current, impedance
    b. voltage, impedance
    c. impedance, current
    d. current, voltage

46. In **Figure 14-1**, if the primary to secondary turns ratio is 7.5:1, the output voltage equals _____.
    a. 16 V_{RMS}
    b. 16 V_{RMS}
    c. 9 V_{RMS}
    d. 900 V_{RMS}

47. In **Figure 14-1**, if a load resistor of 75 Ω is placed in the secondary circuit, what is the secondary current?
    a. 533 mA
    b. 5.33 A
    c. 4.8 A
    d. 16 A

48. In **Figure 14-1**, if the secondary current is 50 mA, the primary current is _____.
    a. 50 mA
    b. 150 mA
    c. 48.7 mA
    d. 300 mA

49. In **Figure 14-1**, if the secondary current is 50 mA, the reflected resistance seen by the primary equals _____.
    a. 800 Ω
    b. 2.4 kΩ
    c. 7.2 kΩ
    d. 14.4 kΩ

50. In **Figure 14-1**, if the primary to secondary turns ratio is 9:1 and a 1 kΩ load resistor is placed in the secondary, the reflected resistance seen by the primary equals _____.
    a. 111 Ω
    b. 1 kΩ
    c. 81 kΩ
    d. 162 kΩ

51. The small dot placed on schematics of transformers indicates:
    a. the polarity of the voltages.
    b. the phase of the voltages.
    c. the direction of the winding.
    d. all of these.

52. For a transformer to operate properly, it must be:
    a. connected to a load.
    b. supplied with the proper AC signal.
    c. work within its voltage, current and power ratings.
    d. all of these.

53. The turns ratio of a transformer (n) is defined as:
    a. the number of turns in the primary multiplied by the number of turns in the secondary.
    b. the number of turns in the primary divided by the number of turns in the secondary.
    c. the number of turns in the secondary multiplied by the number of turns in the primary.
    d. the number of turns in the secondary divided by the number of turns in the primary.

54. The relationship for the voltage ratio (V_{sec}/V_{pri}) in a transformer is:
    a. less than the turns ratio (N_{sec}/N_{pri}).
    b. more than the turns ratio (N_{sec}/N_{pri}).
    c. same as the turns ratio (N_{sec}/N_{pri}).
    d. opposite to the turns ratio (N_{sec}/N_{pri}).

55. The relationship for the current ration (I_{sec}/I_{pri}) in a transformer is:
    a. less than the turns ration (N_{sec}/N_{pri}).
    b. more than the turns ration (N_{sec}/N_{pri}).
    c. same as the turns ration (N_{sec}/N_{pri}).
    d. opposite to the turns ratio (N_{sec}/N_{pri}).

56. The relationship for the impedance matching ratio (R_L/R_{pri}) in a transformer is:
    a. equal to the turns ratio (N_{sec}/N_{pri}).
    b. opposite to the turns ratio (N_{sec}/N_{pri}).
    c. equal to the turns ratio (N_{sec}/N_{pri}) squared.
    d. opposite to the turns ratio (N_{sec}/N_{pri}) squared.

57. The reflected load in a transformer is defined as actual load as it appears to the source and results from:
    a. the voltage ratio.
    b. the current ratio.
    c. the power ratio.
    d. the turns ratio.

58. An autotransformer differs from most transformers in that:
    a. primary and secondary windings are the same.
    b. source voltage flows through on the windings.
    c. does not isolate the primary voltage from the secondary voltage.
    d. all of these.

59. A center tap transformer has a connection at the midpoint of the secondary winding resulting in:
    a. two equal magnitude secondary voltages.
    b. two 180 degree out of phase secondary voltages.
    c. secondary voltages half that of a non-center tapped transformer with the same turns ratio.
    d. all of these.

1. Answer: b

2. Answer: a

3. Answer: a

4. Answer: a

5. Answer: b

6. Answer: a

7. Answer: b

8. Answer: b

9. Answer: a

10. Answer: a

11. Answer: b

12. Answer: b

13. Answer: a

14. Answer: c

15. Answer: d

16. Answer: a

17. Answer: d

18. Answer: c

19. Answer: c

20. Answer: d

21. Answer: a

22. Answer: b

23. Answer: d

24. Answer: d

25. Answer: c

26. Answer: a

27. Answer: b

28. Answer: b

29. Answer: c

30. Answer: c

31. Answer: a

32. Answer: d

33. Answer: a

34. Answer: c

35. Answer: d

36. Answer: a

37. Answer: c

38. Answer: a

39. Answer: d

40. Answer: a

41. Answer: c

42. Answer: b

43. Answer: a

44. Answer: a

45. Answer: c

46. Answer: b

47. Answer: c

48. Answer: b

49. Answer: a

50. Answer: c

51. Answer: d

52. Answer: d

53. Answer: d

54. Answer: c

55. Answer: d

56. Answer: c

57. Answer: d

58. Answer: d

59. Answer: d

Chapter 15: Pulse Response of Reactive Circuits

1. In an RC integrating circuit, the output is taken across the capacitor.
   a. True
   b. False

2. When the input pulse width to an RC integrator is much less than 5τ, the output approaches the shape of the input.
   a. True
   b. False

3. In an RL integrating circuit, the output is taken across the inductor.
   a. True
   b. False

4. It takes a capacitor 5 time constants to nearly reach full charge.
   a. True
   b. False

5. The output of an RC differentiating circuit is taken across the resistor.
   a. True
   b. False

6. An RC integrating circuit is a basic high-pass filter with a pulse applied to it.
   a. True
   b. False

7. The output of an RC integrator is the capacitor's voltage drop.
   a. True
   b. False

8. An RL integrator is a basic RL low-pass filter with a pulse applied to it.
   a. True
   b. False

9. In an RC integrator, as the time constant gets longer, the maximum capacitor voltage gets smaller.
   a. True
   b. False

10. The output from an RL integrator can look exactly the same as the output from an RC integrator.
    a. True
    b. False

MULTIPLE CHOICE

11. What is the time constant in an integrating circuit if a 47 kΩ resistor is in series with a 0.01 µF capacitor?
    a. 0.047 ms
    b. 0.047 µs
    c. 0.47 ms
    d. 0.47 s

12. What is the time constant in an integrating circuit if a 10 kΩ resistor is in series with a 470 µF capacitor?
    a. 0.047 µs
    b. 0.47 µs
    c. 0.47 ms
    d. 4.7 s

13. How long will it take a 22 µF capacitor to completely charge through a 1.2 MΩ resistor?
    a. 13.2 s
    b. 132 s
    c. 0.264 s
    d. 2.64 s

14. How long will it take a 0.047 µF capacitor to completely discharge through a 10 kΩ resistor?
    a. 5 s
    b. 0.47 ms
    c. 2.35 ms
    d. 0.18 ms

15. What is V_C at the end of the input pulse to an RC integrator if the input pulse is 15 V and the pulse width equals one time constant?
    a. 14.7 V
    b. 14.25 V
    c. 12.975 V
    d. 9.48 V

16. What is V_C at the end of the input pulse to an RC integrator if the resistance is 5 kΩ, the capacitance is 0.47 µF and the input is a 15 V, 4.7 ms pulse?
    a. 9.48 V
    b. 12.975 V
    c. 14.25 V
    d. 14.7 V

17. If the input pulse to an RC differentiator is very short compared to the circuit's time constant, the differentiator's output is _____.
    a. zero volts
    b. a square wave very similar to the input voltage
    c. a dc value of about half the peak input voltage
    d. a dc voltage equal to the peak input voltage

18. The output from an RL differentiator is taken across the _____.
    a. resistor
    b. resistor and inductor
    c. inductor
    d. source

19. To charge a 100 µF capacitor in 15 seconds, use a _____ resistor.
    a. 15 kΩ
    b. 30 kΩ
    c. 25 kΩ
    d. 35 kΩ

20. What is output voltage at the end of the input pulse to an RL integrator if the resistance is 22 kΩ, the inductor is 2 H and the input is a 12 V, 0.0909 ms pulse?
    a. 7.58 V
    b. 10.38 V
    c. 11.4 V
    d. 11.76 V

21. What is the output voltage at the end of the input pulse to an RL integrator if the resistance is 1.2 kΩ, the inductor is 200 mH and the input is a 5 V, 1.2 ms pulse?
    a. 3.16 V
    b. 4.532 V
    c. 4.75 V
    d. 5 V

22. What is output voltage at the end of the input pulse to an RC integrator if the resistance is 10 kΩ, the capacitance is 100 µF and the input is a 50 V, 10 s pulse?
    a. 31.6 V
    b. 43.25 V
    c. 47.5 V
    d. 50 V

23. How does the RC differentiator output look when 5τ is much less than the pulse width?
    a. positive spikes
    b. positive and negative spikes
    c. negative spikes
    d. square waves

24. What is the output voltage at the end of the input pulse to an RL integrator if the resistance is 1 kΩ, the inductor is 1 H and the input is a 22 V, 2 ms pulse?
    a. 13.9 V
    b. 19.03 V
    c. 20.9 V
    d. 21.56 V

25. RC and RL integrators provide the same output when the inputs are
    _____.
    a. different
    b. the same
    c. the outputs are never the same

26. What is the time constant in an integrating circuit if a 4.7 kΩ resistor
    is in series with a 0.005 µF capacitor?
    a. 0.0235 ms
    b. 2.35 ms
    c. 235 ms
    d. 0.00235 ms

27. What is V_C at the end of the input pulse to an RC integrator if the
    input pulse is 12 V and the pulse width equals one time constant?
    a. 4.41 V
    b. 12 V
    c. 7.58 V
    d. 0 V

28. What is V_C at the end of the input pulse to an RC integrator if the
    resistance is 22 kΩ, the capacitance is 0.05 µF and the input is a 12 V,
    2.2 ms pulse?
    a. 10.38 V
    b. 12 V
    c. 7.58 V
    d. 4.42 V

29. If an RC integrator uses a 47 µF capacitor, a 12 kΩ resistor and a
    square wave input with a frequency of 200 kHz, its approximate output is
    _____.
    a. a square wave with a frequency of 100 kHz
    b. 0 V
    c. a square wave with a frequency of 200 kHz
    d. a near dc voltage of about half the peak square wave voltage

30. What is the output voltage from an RL integrator that uses a 10 mH
    inductor, a 10 Ω resistor and a 16 V, 1 ms input pulse?
    a. 10.11 V
    b. 13.84 V
    c. 15.2 V
    d. 16.32 V

31. The capacitor of an RC integrator charges to _____ if the input is
    a 10 V pulse with a pulse width equal to one time constant.
    a. 10 V
    b. 5 V
    c. 6.3 V
    d. 3.7 VC

32. The capacitor of an RC integrator charges to _____ if the input is
    a 10 V pulse with a pulse width equal to six time constants.
    a. 10 V
    b. 5 V
    c. 6.3 V
    d. 3.7 V

33. The output from an RC integrator resembles the input if _____.
    a. τ is much larger that the pulse width
    b. τ is equal to the pulse width
    c. τ is less than the pulse width
    d. τ is much less than the pulse width

34. The output from an RC differentiator resembles the input if _____.
    a. τ is much larger that the pulse width
    b. τ is equal to the pulse width
    c. τ is less than the pulse width
    d. τ is much less than the pulse width

35. If RC and RL differentiators with equal time constants receive the same
    pulse, _____.
    a. the RC has the widest output pulse
    b. the RL has the most narrow spikes on the output
    c. one outputs an increasing exponential while the other outputs a
       decreasing exponential
    d. you can't tell the difference by observing the output wave forms

36. What is the time constant in an RC integrating circuit if a 22 kΩ
    resistor is in series with a 0.02 μF capacitor?
    a. 0.044 ms
    b. 0.044 μs
    c. 0.44 ms
    d. 0.44 s

37. What is the time constant in an RC integrating circuit if a 10 kΩ
    resistor is in series with a 220 μF capacitor?
    a. 2.2 ms
    b. 22 ms
    c. 0.22 ms
    d. 2.2 s

38. How long will it take to completely charge a 0.22 μF capacitor through a
    5.2 MΩ resistor?
    a. 5.72 s
    b. 1.144 s
    c. 2.288 s
    d. 4.576 s

39. How long will it take to completely discharge a 0.47 μF capacitor
    through a 10 kΩ resistor?
    a. 2.35 s
    b. 0.47 ms
    c. 23.5 ms
    d. 0.18 ms

40. The capacitor of an RC integrator charges to _____ if the input is a 30 V pulse with a pulse width equal to one time constant.
   a. 18.96 V
   b. 25.95 V
   c. 28.5 V
   d. 29.4 V

41. What is V_C at the end of the input pulse to an RC integrator if the resistance is 5 kΩ, the capacitance is 47 μF and the input is a 15 V, 470 ms pulse?
   a. 9.48 V
   b. 12.975 V
   c. 14.25 V
   d. 14.7 V

42. If the input pulse to an RC differentiator is very short compared to the circuit's time constant, then the differentiator's output is _____.
   a. zero volts
   b. a square wave very similar to the input voltage
   c. a dc value of about half the peak input voltage
   d. a dc voltage equal to the peak input voltage

43. The output of an RL integrator is taken across the _____.
   a. resistor
   b. resistor and inductor
   c. inductor
   d. source

44. To completely charge a 500 μF capacitor in 15 seconds, use a _____ resistor.
   a. 6 kΩ
   b. 12 kΩ
   c. 18 kΩ
   d. 24 kΩ

45. What is the output voltage from an RL integrator that uses a 200 mH inductor, a 22 kΩ resistor and a 12 V, 9.09 μs input pulse?
   a. 7.58 V
   b. 10.38 V
   c. 11.4 V
   d. 11.76 V

46. What is the output voltage from an RL integrator that uses a 400 mH inductor, a 5 kΩ resistor and a 5 V, 1.2 ms input pulse?
   a. 3.16 V
   b. 4.532 V
   c. 4.75 V
   d. 5 V

47. What is the output voltage at the end of the input pulse to an RC integrator if the resistance is 12 kΩ, the capacitance is 10 µF and the input is a 50 V, 1 s pulse?
    a. 31.6 V
    b. 43.25 V
    c. 47.5 V
    d. 50 V

48. How does the RC differentiator output look when 5τ is much longer than the pulse width?
    a. positive spikes
    b. positive and negative spikes
    c. negative spikes
    d. square waves

49. What is the output voltage from an RL integrator that uses a 2 H inductor, a 10 kΩ resistor and a 32 V, 0.4 ms input pulse?
    a. 13.9 V
    b. 19.03 V
    c. 27.67 V
    d. 21.56 V

50. If a square wave input produces 0 V output from an RC integrator, _____.
    a. the capacitor is open
    b. the resistor is shorted
    c. the capacitor is leaky
    d. the resistor is open

51. RC integrators can be used in timing circuits to set a specified time delay if the output is coupled to:
    a. a voltage generating circuit.
    b. a current sensitive circuit.
    c. a voltage threshold sensitive circuit.
    d. a power threshold sensitive circuit.

52. RC integrators can be used to convert a repetitive pulse waveform to a constant dc voltage equal to the average voltage of the waveform if:
    a. τ is very small compared to t_W.
    b. τ is equal to t_W.
    c. τ is five times t_W.
    d. τ is very large compared to t_W.

53. Pulse width (t_W) is defined as:
    a. the time interval between identical points on the pulse.
    b. the time interval between opposite points on the pulse.
    c. the time interval between changes in the pulse.
    d. all of these.

54. In RC and RL integrators and differentiators; transient time is equal to the:
    a. pulse width.
    b. pulse width times five.
    c. time constant.
    d. time constant times five.

55. RC and RL integrators produce an output voltage that equals the:
    a. mathematical sum.
    b. mathematical difference.
    c. mathematical product.
    d. mathematical average.

56. RC and RL differentiators produce an output voltage that closely approximates the:
    a. mathematical sum.
    b. mathematical average.
    c. mathematical difference.
    d. mathematical rate of change process.

1. Answer: a

2. Answer: b

3. Answer: b

4. Answer: a

5. Answer: a

6. Answer: b

7. Answer: a

8. Answer: a

9. Answer: a

10. Answer: a

11. Answer: c

12. Answer: d

13. Answer: b

14. Answer: c

15. Answer: d

16. Answer: b

17. Answer: b

18. Answer: c

19. Answer: b

20. Answer: a

21. Answer: d

22. Answer: d

23. Answer: b

24. Answer: b

25. Answer: b

26. Answer: a

27. Answer: c

28. Answer: a

29. Answer: d

30. Answer: a

31. Answer: c

32. Answer: a

33. Answer: d

34. Answer: a

35. Answer: d

36. Answer: c

37. Answer: d

38. Answer: a

39. Answer: c

40. Answer: a

41. Answer: b

42. Answer: b

43. Answer: a

44. Answer: a

45. Answer: a

46. Answer: d

47. Answer: d

48. Answer: d

49. Answer: c

50. Answer: d

51. Answer: c

52. Answer: d

53. Answer: b

54. Answer: d

55. Answer: d

56. Answer: d

Chapter 16: Introduction to Semiconductor Devices

TRUE/FALSE

1. Most diodes are made from a semiconductor material called silicon.
   a. True
   b. False

2. Adding impurities to semiconductor materials is called *doping*.
   a. True
   b. False

3. A forward-biased silicon diode normally drops about 16 V.
   a. True
   b. False

4. Reverse breakdown usually occurs when a diode is forward biased by about 0.7 V.
   a. True
   b. False

5. A forward-biased germanium diode normally drops about 0.3 V.
   a. True
   b. False

6. Most diodes are made from a semiconductor material called germanium.
   a. True
   b. False

7. A forward-biased silicon diode normally drops about 0.7 V.
   a. True
   b. False

8. For every free electron there in a hole.
   a. True
   b. False

9. The movement of free electrons is called *electron current*.
   a. True
   b. False

10. A common name for a PN junction is the *transistor*.
    a. True
    b. False

MULTIPLE CHOICE

11. The smallest particle of an element is _____.
    a. an ion
    b. an electron
    c. an atom
    d. a molecule

12. A free electron is known also as _____.
    a. a positive ion
    b. a conduction band electron
    c. a negative ion
    d. an atom

13. Current flow through a diode is normally caused by _____.
    a. forward voltage across the diode
    b. a reverse voltage across the diode
    c. depletion layer breakdown
    d. thermally produced electron-hole pairs

14. If you measure the voltage across a diode and it measures 0.3 V, the diode is probably made of _____ and is _____ biased.
    a. silicon, forward
    b. germanium, forward
    c. silicon, reverse
    d. germanium, reverse

15. You test a diode with an ohmmeter. The two readings indicate a very low value of resistance. The diode is probably _____.
    a. open
    b. shorted
    c. normal
    d. conducting heavily

16. A forward biased silicon diode is in series with a 12 kΩ resistor. The source voltage is 5 V. The voltage across the diode is _____ and the voltage across the resistor is _____.
    a. 0.3 V, 4.7 V
    b. 4.3 V, 0.7 V
    c. 4.7 V, 0.3 V
    d. 0.7 V, 4.3 V

17. If the cathode voltage of a forward biased silicon diode is 4.5 V, what is the anode voltage?
    a. 0.7 V
    b. -0.7 V
    c. 5.2 V
    d. -5.2 V

18. To forward bias a silicon diode with -1.6 V on the anode, you must apply a voltage of _____ on the cathode.
    a. -0.9 V
    b. 0.9 V
    c. -2.3 V
    d. 2.3 V

Figure 16-1

19. If the diode is silicon, what is the voltage across the resistor in **Figure 16-1(a)**?
    a. 20 V
    b. 19.3 V
    c. 0 V
    d. 0.7 V

20. What is the voltage across the silicon diode in **Figure 16-1(b)**?
    a. -0.7 V
    b. 0.7 V
    c. 0.3 V
    d. 1.0 V

21. If the polarity of the silicon diode is reversed in **Figure 16-1(c)**, V_{R2} is _____.
    a. 0.7 V
    b. 49.3 V
    c. 0 V
    d. 25 V

22. What is the current through R_1 in **Figure 16-1(c)** if the diode is germanium?
    a. 49.7 mA
    b. 49.3 mA
    c. 0 A
    d. 25 mA

23. If the diode is made of silicon in **Figure 16-1(b)**, what is the current?
    a. 10 mA
    b. 8.6 mA
    c. 9.4 mA
    d. 0 A

24. If an ohmmeter check of a diode indicates a high resistance in one direction and low resistance in the other, the diode is probably _____.
    a. open
    b. shorted
    c. good
    d. bad

25. Diodes are commonly used as _____.
    a. switches
    b. resistors
    c. capacitors
    d. filters

26. If you measure 17 V across a diode, it is probably _____.
    a. forward biased
    b. in heavy conduction
    c. reverse biased
    d. shorted

27. If the "+" lead on an ohmmeter is connected to a diode's anode and the "-" lead on the ohmmeter is connected to the diode's cathode, the measured resistance is normally _____.
    a. very high
    b. very low
    c. 0 Ω
    d. 140 kΩ

28. What is the current through R_2 in **Figure 16-1(c)** if the diode is silicon?
    a. 50 mA
    b. 25 mA
    c. 0 A
    d. 0.3 mA

29. What is the voltage across R_1 in **Figure 16-1(c)** if the diode is silicon?
    a. 50 V
    b. 25 V
    c. 49.3 V
    d. 49.7 V

30. If the measured resistance of a diode is high in both directions, the diode is probably _____.
    a. shorted
    b. forward biased
    c. open
    d. reverse biased

31. The PN junction is found in _____.
    a. semiconductor diodes
    b. transistors
    c. all semiconductor materials
    d. both a and b

32. A DC voltage that sets the operating conditions of a semiconductor device is called the _____.
   a. bias
   b. depletion voltage
   c. battery
   d. barrier potential

33. In a semiconductor diode, the two bias conditions are _____.
   a. positive and negative
   b. blocking and non-blocking
   c. open and closed
   d. forward and reverse

34. When a diode is forward biased it is _____.
   a. blocking current
   b. conducting current
   c. similar to an open switch
   d. similar to a closed switch
   e. both b and d

35. When the positive lead of an ohmmeter is connected to the cathode of a diode and the negative lead is connected to the anode, the meter reads _____.
   a. a very low resistance
   b. an infinitely high resistance
   c. a high resistance initially, decreasing to about 100 Ω
   d. a gradually increasing resistance

36. The largest part of a compound is called _____.
   a. an ion
   b. an electron
   c. an atom
   d. a molecule

37. In silicon, electrons can be excited to become free by _____.
   a. light energy only
   b. heat energy only
   c. applied voltage
   d. all of these

38. Current through a diode is blocked by _____.
   a. forward voltage across the diode
   b. reverse voltage across the diode
   c. depletion layer breakdown
   d. thermally produced electron-hole pairs

39. If you measure 0.7 V across a diode, the diode is probably made of _____ and is _____ biased.
   a. silicon, forward
   b. germanium, forward
   c. silicon, reverse
   d. germanium, reverse

177

40. If the measured resistance of a diode is very high in both directions, the diode is probably _____.
    a. open
    b. shorted
    c. normal
    d. conducting heavily

41. If a forward biased silicon diode is in series with a 22 kΩ resistor and a 10 V source, the voltage across the diode is _____ and the voltage across the resistor is _____.
    a. 0.3 V, 9.7 V
    b. 9.3 V, 0.7 V
    c. 9.7 V, 0.3 V
    d. 0.7 V, 9.3 V

42. If the cathode voltage of a forward-biased silicon diode equals 6.5 V, the anode voltage equals _____.
    a. 0.7 V
    b. -0.7 V
    c. 7.2 V
    d. -7.2 V

43. To forward bias a silicon diode with a -71.6 V anode voltage, apply a _____ cathode voltage.
    a. +72.3 V
    b. -72.3 V
    c. +70.9 V
    d. -70.9 V

44. What is the voltage across the resistor in **Figure 16-1(a)** if the diode is germanium?
    a. 20 V
    b. 19.7 V
    c. 0 V
    d. 0.7 V

45. If the diode opens in **Figure 16-1(b)**, the voltage across the diode is _____.
    a. 0 V
    b. 0.7 V
    c. 1 V
    d. 4.3 V

46. If the polarity of the source voltage is reversed in **Figure 16-1(c)**, V_{R2} is _____.
    a. 0.7 V
    b. 49.3 V
    c. 0 V
    d. 25 V

47. What is the current through R_1 in **Figure 16-1(c)** if the diode is silicon?
    a. 49.7 mA
    b. 49.3 mA
    c. 0 A
    d. 25 mA

48. What is the current in **Figure 16-1(b)** if the diode is made of silicon and the polarity of the source voltage is reversed?
    a. 10 mA
    b. 5 mA
    c. 2 mA
    d. 0 A

49. The bon in the schematic symbol for a diode represents
    a. the anode.
    b. the catholde.
    c. the semiconductor lead.
    d. all of these.

50. Applying the reverse breakdown voltage to a diode will _____.
    a. cause it to act like a switch
    b. usually damage the diode
    c. cause it to act like a capacitor
    d. never do any harm

51. Materials whose molecules arrange themselves into a crystal structure are bound together by:
    a. sharing valence electrons.
    b. full valence shells.
    c. covalent bonding.
    d. all of these.

52. Doping a semiconductor material with trivalent impurities results in:
    a. P-type material.
    b. N-type material.
    c. P-N type material.
    d. P-N type material.

53. Doping a semiconductor material with pentavalent impurities results in:
    a. P-type material.
    b. N-type material.
    c. P-N type material.
    d. N-P type material.

54. In a P-N diode, the region near the P-N junction is called:
    a. the neutral region.
    b. the recombination region.
    c. the depletion region.
    d. the diffusion region.

55. The forward bias on a P-N diode to make the diode conduct must be greater than the:
    a. reverse bias.
    b. barrier potential.
    c. volence bond.
    d. conduction bond.

56. Reverse breakdown current is carried by:
    a. trualent impurity atoms.
    b. pentavalent impurity atoms.
    c. majority carrier.
    d. minority carriers.

1. Answer: a

2. Answer: a

3. Answer: b

4. Answer: b

5. Answer: a

6. Answer: b

7. Answer: a

8. Answer: a

9. Answer: a

10. Answer: b

11. Answer: b

12. Answer: b

13. Answer: a

14. Answer: b

15. Answer: b

16. Answer: d

17. Answer: c

18. Answer: c

19. Answer: b

20. Answer: d

21. Answer: d

22. Answer: a

23. Answer: d

24. Answer: c

25. Answer: a

26. Answer: c

27. Answer: b

28. Answer: a

29. Answer: c

30. Answer: c

31. Answer: d

32. Answer: a

33. Answer: d

34. Answer: e

35. Answer: b

36. Answer: d

37. Answer: d

38. Answer: b

39. Answer: a

40. Answer: a

41. Answer: d

42. Answer: c

43. Answer: a

44. Answer: b

45. Answer: c

46. Answer: d

47. Answer: b

48. Answer: c

49. Answer: b

50. Answer: b

51. Answer: d

52. Answer: a

53. Answer: b

54. Answer: c

55. Answer: b

56. Answer: d

Chapter 17:   Diodes and Applications

1. The ripple frequency of a half-wave rectifier equals the supply frequency.
   a. True
   b. False

2. A half-wave rectifier uses four diodes as rectifiers.
   a. True
   b. False

3. Diode clampers cut off voltage above or below specified levels.
   a. True
   b. False

4. A zener diode is used as a constant voltage regulator.
   a. True
   b. False

5. Ripple voltage is caused by the charging and discharging of the diodes.
   a. True
   b. False

6. To *rectify* is to convert dc to pulsating ac.
   a. True
   b. False

7. Zener diodes can be used for very large currents.
   a. True
   b. False

8. Varactor diodes are used as voltage-variable capacitors.
   a. True
   b. False

9. LEDs will emit light if a reverse voltage is applied to them.
   a. True
   b. False

10. Photodiodes will conduct more as the light intensity upon them increases.
    a. True
    b. False

MULTIPLE CHOICE

11. A half-wave rectifier uses _____ diode(s) and its output frequency is _____ the input frequency.
    a. two, one-half
    b. two, equal to
    c. one, twice
    d. one, equal to

12. If a half-wave rectifier outputs 58 V$_P$, the diode's PIV should be more than _____.
 a. 116 V
 b. 58 V
 c. 29 V
 d. 15 V

13. If a full-wave rectifier outputs 38 V$_P$, its average output equals _____.
 a. 24.19 V
 b. 19.26 V
 c. 76.67 V
 d. 38 V

14. A full-wave rectifier requires _____.
 a. four diodes and a center-tapped transformer
 b. two diodes and a transformer with a single secondary
 c. two diodes and a center-tapped transformer
 d. a high voltage to operate it

15. The ripple voltage from a power supply _____.
 a. is very high
 b. is zero
 c. is about 1 V
 d. varies with load

16. If the diode in a half-wave rectifier shorts, the _____.
 a. output ripple would be very small
 b. output voltage would not change
 c. output voltage would equal the transformer secondary voltage
 d. output voltage would be zero

17. A circuit that will cut off a signal at some voltage is called a _____.
 a. clamper
 b. clipper
 c. filter
 d. rectifier

18. A *clamper* circuit _____.
 a. clips a signal
 b. is used to filter ac
 c. adds a dc level to a signal
 d. acts as a noise limiter

Transformer	Rectifier	Filter	Regulator	Load
1	2	3	4	5

Figure 17-1

19. Which block in **Figure 17-1** changes ac to pulsating dc?
    a. 1
    b. 2
    c. 3
    d. 4

20. Which block in **Figure 17-1** will change the amplitude of the ac voltage?
    a. 1
    b. 2
    c. 3
    d. 4

21. Which block conditions in **Figure 17-1** will keep the output voltage nearly constant under varying load?
    a. 1
    b. 2
    c. 3
    d. 4

22. Which block will smooth out the pulsating dc in **Figure 17-1**?
    a. 1
    b. 2
    c. 3
    d. 4

23. If the filter capacitor opens in **Figure 17-1**, _____.
    a. the output dc will be very low
    b. the ripple voltage increases
    c. the diodes would open
    d. a loud hum will be heard

24. If the load current decreases in a simple zener regulator, the _____.
    a. current through the series resistor decreases
    b. voltage across the series resistor decreases
    c. zener current decreases
    d. zener current increases

25. A *dc restorer* is another name for a _____.
    a. filter
    b. clamper
    c. clipper
    d. bridge rectifier

26. A full-wave bridge rectifier requires _____.
    a. a center-tapped transformer
    b. four diodes and a transformer with a single secondary
    c. two diodes and a transformer with a single secondary
    d. a high voltage to operate it

27. If a diode in a full-wave rectifier opens, _____.
    a. the dc output voltage will decrease and the ripple voltage will decrease
    b. the dc output voltage will increase and the ripple frequency will decrease
    c. the dc output voltage will increase and the ripple voltage will decrease
    d. the dc output voltage will decrease and the ripple frequency will decrease

28. The purpose of Block 4 in **Figure 17-1** is to _____.
    a. adjust the output voltage to the correct ac value
    b. keep the dc output voltage constant as the load changes
    c. make sure that the fuse will not blow
    d. maintain a constant output current when the load current changes

29. If the load current increases in a simple zener regulator, the _____.
    a. total current increases
    b. current through the series resistor increases
    c. voltage across the series resistor decreases
    d. zener current decreases

30. If the source voltage increases in a simple zener regulator, _____.
    a. the load current increases
    b. the voltage across the zener increases
    c. the voltage across the series resistor decreases
    d. the zener current increases

31. If a 60 Hz sine wave is input to a half-wave rectifier, its output frequency is _____.
    a. 30 Hz
    b. 60 Hz
    c. 120 Hz
    d. 0 Hz

32. If a 75 V_p sine wave is applied to a half-wave rectifier, the diode's peak inverse voltage is _____.
    a. 75 V
    b. 150 V
    c. 37.5 V
    d. 0 V

33. If a 60 Hz sine wave is input to a full-wave rectifier, its output frequency is _____.
    a. 30 Hz
    b. 60 Hz
    c. 120 Hz
    d. 0 Hz

34. Zener diodes are widely used as _____.
    a. current limiters
    b. power distributors
    c. voltage regulators
    d. variable resistors

35. The small variation in the output voltage of a dc power supply is called _____.
    a. average voltage
    b. ac to dc conversion
    c. residual voltage
    d. ripple voltage

36. A full-wave rectifier uses _____ diode(s) and its output frequency is _____ the input frequency.
    a. two, twice
    b. two, equal to
    c. one, twice
    d. one, equal to

37. If a half-wave rectifier outputs 36 V_P, the PIV of the diode should be more than _____.
    a. 116 V
    b. 36 V
    c. 29 V
    d. 15 V

38. If a full-wave rectifier outputs 36 V_P, the average output is _____.
    a. 22.9 V
    b. 19 V
    c. 76 V
    d. 38 V

39. A full-wave rectifier uses _____ diodes and a transformer with a _____.
    a. four, center tap
    b. two, single secondary
    c. two, center tap
    d. one, single secondary

40. The ripple voltage from a power supply is _____.
    a. zero
    b. very high
    c. about 1 V
    d. dependent upon the load

41. If the diode in a half-wave rectifier opens, _____.
    a. the output ripple would be very small
    b. the output voltage would not change
    c. the output voltage would equal the transformer secondary voltage
    d. the output voltage would be zero

42. If the filter capacitor becomes leaky in **Figure 17-1**, _____.
    a. the output dc will be very low
    b. the ripple voltage will increase
    c. the diodes would open
    d. a loud hum will be heard

43. If the load current increases in a simple zener regulator, the
    _____.
    a. total current decreases
    b. current through the series resistor decreases
    c. zener current decreases
    d. zener current increases

44. A circuit that will cut off a signal at some voltage is called a
    _____.
    a. clamper
    b. filter
    c. swamper
    d. none of these

45. A clipping circuit _____.
    a. clips a signal
    b. is used to filter ac
    c. adds a dc level to a signal
    d. acts like a noise limiter

46. A *limiter* is another name for a _____.
    a. filter
    b. clamper
    c. clipper circuit
    d. bridge rectifier

47. The output of Block 2 in **Figure 17-1** is:
    a. a pulsating AC voltage
    b. a pulsating DC voltage
    c. a steady DC voltage
    d. a steady DC current

48. If a diode in a half-wave rectifier opens in **Figure 17-1**, _____.
    a. the output dc voltage decreases and the ripple voltage increases
    b. the output dc voltage increases and the ripple frequency decreases
    c. the output dc voltage increases and the ripple voltage decreases
    d. the output dc voltage decreases and the ripple voltage decreases

49. If a diode shorts in a full-wave rectifier, _____.
    a. the output dc voltage will increase
    b. the output dc voltage will decrease and possibly damage the power
       supply
    c. no change would occur in the output
    d. the output current would increase

50. If an aircraft full-wave, dc power supply operates from a 400 Hz sine wave, the ripple frequency is _____.
    a. 60 Hz
    b. 120 Hz
    c. 400 Hz
    d. 800 Hz

51. The formula for line regulation is:
    a. $\dfrac{\Delta V_{IN}}{\Delta V_{OUT}} \times 100\%$.

    b. $\dfrac{\Delta V_{OUT}}{\Delta V_{IN}} \times 100\%$.

    c. $\dfrac{\Delta V_{NL}}{\Delta V_{FL}} \times 100\%$.

    d. $\dfrac{\Delta V_{FL}}{\Delta V_{NL}} \times 100\%$.

52. The formula for load regulation is:
    a. $\left[\dfrac{V_{NL} - V_{FL}}{V_{FL}}\right] \times 100\%$.

    b. $\left[\dfrac{V_{FL} - V_{NL}}{V_{FL}}\right] \times 100\%$.

    c. $\left[\dfrac{V_{FL} - V_{NL}}{V_{NL}}\right] \times 100\%$.

    d. $\left[\dfrac{V_{NL} - V_{FL}}{V_{NL}}\right] \times 100\%$.

53. In the simplest sense, a zener diode is really a:
    a. voltage regulator.
    b. current regulator.
    c. reference voltage.
    d. reference current.

54. To operate as a voltage regulator, a zener diode requires a:
    a. transformer.
    b. silicon diode.
    c. series resistor.
    d. series capacitor.

55. To generate light, an LED requires:
    a. avalanche breakdown.
    b. zener breakdown.
    c. forward DC bias.
    d. reverse DC bias.

56. To detect light, a photodiode requires:
    a. avalanche breakdown.
    b. zener breakdown.
    c. forward bias.
    d. reverse bias.

1. Answer: a

2. Answer: b

3. Answer: b

4. Answer: a

5. Answer: b

6. Answer: b

7. Answer: b

8. Answer: a

9. Answer: b

10. Answer: a

11. Answer: d

12. Answer: b

13. Answer: a

14. Answer: c

15. Answer: d

16. Answer: c

17. Answer: b

18. Answer: c

19. Answer: b

20. Answer: a

21. Answer: d

22. Answer: c

23. Answer: b

24. Answer: d

25. Answer: b

26. Answer: b

27. Answer: d

28. Answer: b

29. Answer: d

30. Answer: d

31. Answer: b

32. Answer: a

33. Answer: c

34. Answer: c

35. Answer: d

36. Answer: a

37. Answer: b

38. Answer: a

39. Answer: c

40. Answer: d

41. Answer: d

42. Answer: b

43. Answer: c

44. Answer: d

45. Answer: a

46. Answer: c

47. Answer: b

48. Answer: d

49. Answer: b

50. Answer: d

51. Answer: b

52. Answer: a

53. Answer: c

54. Answer: c

55. Answer: c

56. Answer: d

Chapter 18: Transistors and Thyristors

TRUE/FALSE

1. The two types of BJTs are the NPN and PNP.
   a. True
   b. False

2. A BJT has three elements: emitter, gate, and collector.
   a. True
   b. False

3. The gate current in a JFET is normally zero.
   a. True
   b. False

4. A depletion-tape MOSFET can operate with a positive or negative value of V_{GS}.
   a. True
   b. False

5. A transistor can be used as an electronic switch.
   a. True
   b. False

6. The two types of BJTs are the PNP and the P-channel.
   a. True
   b. False

7. An N-channel JFET has three elements: source, gate, and drain.
   a. True
   b. False

8. An enhancement-type MOSFET can operate with a positive value of V_{GS}.
   a. True
   b. False

9. To correctly bias a BJT, reverse-bias the base-emitter junction and forward-bias the base-collector junction.
   a. True
   b. False

10. Two types of FETs are the JFET and the MOSFET.
    a. True
    b. False

MULTIPLE CHOICE

Figure 18-1

11. Find V_{BE} in **Figure 18-1**.
    a. 5.71 V
    b. 0.7 V
    c. 5 V
    d. 15 V

12. If V_C = 20 V in **Figure 18-1**, which statement describes a possible trouble?
    a. The power is off
    b. The amplifier is cut off
    c. The amplifier is saturated
    d. This is normal

Figure 18-2

13. The amplifier in **Figure 18-2** uses a _____ and the gate current is
    _____.
    a. BJT, 0 A
    b. TRIAC, 10 mA
    c. JFET, 0 A
    d. JFET, 5 mA

14. Find V_G in **Figure 18-2**.
    a. 5 V
    b. 10 V
    c. 15 V
    d. 0 V

15. The device used in the amplifier in **Figure 18-2** is the _____.
    a. P-channel MOSFET
    b. NPN type BJT
    c. N-channel JFET
    d. depletion type MOSFET

16. In all FETs, the drain current equals the _____ current.
    a. collector
    b. emitter
    c. gate
    d. source

(a)   (b)   (c)   (d)

Figure 18-3

17. The symbol in **Figure 18-3(c)** represents a(n) _____.
    a. TRIAC
    b. UJT
    c. SCR
    d. DIAC

18. The symbol in **Figure 18-3(b)** represents a(n) _____.
    a. UJT
    b. TRIAC
    c. DIAC
    d. SCR

19. The symbol in **Figure 18-3(d)** represents a(n) _____.
    a. UJT
    b. TRIAC
    c. DIAC
    d. SCR

(a)   (b)

Figure 18-4

20. The symbol in **Figure 18-4(b)** represents the _____.
    a. N-channel depletion-type JFET
    b. P-channel enhancement-type MOSFET
    c. N-channel enhancement-type MOSFET
    d. N-channel enhancement-type JFET

Figure 18-1

21. If the base-emitter junction opened in **Figure 18-1**, V_E equals _____.

    a. 5 V
    b. 20 V
    c. 0 V
    d. 10 V

22. If the BJT's collector opened internally in **Figure 18-1**, V_{RC} equals _____.

    a. 20 V
    b. 0 V
    c. 10 V
    d. V_{BE}

23. When a BJT amplifier is saturated, V_{CE} is about _____ and I_C is _____.
    a. zero, maximum
    b. zero, minimum
    c. V_{CC}, minimum
    d. 25 V, 10 mA

24. If a BJT amplifier is operated as a switch that is off, this operating condition is known as _____.
    a. saturation
    b. V_P
    c. cutoff
    d. thermal runaway

25. Generally, thyristors are devices that _____.
    a. are turned on by a gate current
    b. can control the power delivered to a load
    c. are four-layer semiconductor devices
    d. all of these

26. Find V_{CE} in **Figure 18-1**.
    a. 11.4 V
    b. 5 V
    c. 6.4 V
    d. 16.4 V

27. Which voltage might indicate that the amplifier in **Figure 18-1** is cut off?
    a. $V_C = 20$ V
    b. $V_E = 20$ V
    c. $V_{CE} = 0$ V
    d. $V_{BE} = 0.7$ V

+20 V

$R_D = 1\text{ k}\Omega$

$I_D = 10\text{ mA}$

R_G

$R_S = 500\ \Omega$

Figure 18-2

28. Find V_{GS} in **Figure 18-2**.
   a. 5 V
   b. -5 V
   c. -10 V
   d. 10 V

    (a)   (b)   (c)   (d)

Figure 18-3

29. The symbol in **Figure 18-3(a)** represents the _____.
   a. DIAC
   b. MOSFET
   c. N-channel JFET
   d. UJT

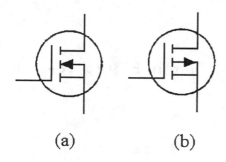

    (a)   (b)

Figure 18-4

30. The symbol in **Figure 18-4(a)** represents the _____.
   a. N-channel depletion-type JFET
   b. P-channel enhancement-type MOSFET
   c. N-channel enhancement-type MOSFET
   d. N-channel enhancement-type JFET

31. For normal operation of a NPN transistor, the base must be _____.
   a. disconnected
   b. negative with respect to the emitter
   c. positive with respect to the emitter
   d. positive with respect to the collector

32. Beta (β) is the ratio of _____.
   a. collector current to emitter current
   b. collector current to base current
   c. emitter current to base current
   d. output voltage to input voltage

33. If a transistor's beta equals 30 and I_B equals 1 mA, I_C equals
    _____.
    a. 0.33 mA
    b. 1 mA
    c. 30 mA
    d. unknown

34. If the base current increases, _____.
    a. the collector current increases and the emitter current decreases
    b. the collector current decreases and the emitter current decreases
    c. the collector current increases and the emitter current does not change
    d. the collector current increases and the emitter current increases

35. When a negative gate-to-source voltage is applied to an N-channel MOSFET, it operates _____.
    a. in the cutoff state
    b. in the saturated state
    c. in the enhancement mode
    d. in the depletion mode

Figure 18-1

36. If V_{CC} equals 15 V in **Figure 18-1**, V_{BE} equals _____.
    a. 4.71 V
    b. 0.7 V
    c. 5 V
    d. 15 V

37. If the collector-to-emitter voltage is about 0 V in **Figure 18-1**, the possible trouble is _____.
    a. the transistor is open
    b. the amplifier is cutoff
    c. the amplifier is saturated
    d. this is a normal condition

Figure 18-2

38. If I_D = 20 mA in **Figure 18-2**, V_G equals _____.
   a. 5 V
   b. 10 V
   c. 15 V
   d. 0 V

39. If I_D = 15 mA in **Figure 18-2**, V_{GS} equals _____.
   a. 0 V
   b. -7.5 V
   c. 15 V
   d. 25 V

40. In all N-channel FET's, the current into the source equals the current leaving the _____.
   a. collector
   b. emitter
   c. drain
   d. source

Figure 18-1

41. If the emitter resistor opened in **Figure 18-1**, V_B equals _____.
    a. 5.71 V
    b. 0 V
    c. 0.7 V
    d. 20 V

42. If R_1 opens in **Figure 18-1**, V_C equals _____.
    a. 0 V
    b. 0.7 V
    c. 10 V
    d. 20 V

43. If R_2 opens in **Figure 18-1**, I_C _____.
    a. increases
    b. decreases
    c. remains the same
    d. decreases to zero

44. If V_C equals V_E in **Figure 18-1**, the _____.
    a. power is off
    b. emitter has opened
    c. emitter is shorted to the collector
    d. transistor is cutoff

+20 V

$R_D = 1\ k\Omega$

$I_D = 10\ mA$

R_G

$R_S = 500\ \Omega$

Figure 18-2

45. The amplifier in **Figure 18-2** uses a _____ and V_D equals _____.
   a. BJT, 10 V
   b. JFET, 0 V
   c. JFET, 10 V
   d. TRIAC, 5 V

46. A device which has an emitter and two bases is called the _____.
   a. TRIAC
   b. BJT
   c. MOSFET
   d. UJT

47. An SCR is controlling a light. If the light remains on after the gate pulse has been removed, then
   a. the SCR is faulty.
   b. the light is faulty.
   c. the power is off.
   d. this is normal operation.

48. An SCR will conduct only on _____.
   a. positive alternations
   b. only on negative alternations
   c. on both positive and negative alternations
   d. DC operation

49. A UJT is often used to _____.
   a. amplify an ac signal
   b. amplify a dc signal
   c. trigger an SCR
   d. trigger a BJT

50. A device which will conduct in both directions and is triggered by a gate voltage is called the _____.
    a. DIAC
    b. TRIAC
    c. UJT
    d. BJT

51. To analyze the operation of a BJT in an amplifier circuit, use characteristic curves of:
    a. emitter current versus emitter to collector voltage.
    b. base current versus collector to emitter voltage.
    c. collector current versus emitter to collector voltage.
    d. collector current versus collector to emitter voltage.

52. In using BJT characteristic curves, the intersection of the load line with a specific base current curve is called:
    a. intersection point.
    b. nudpoint.
    c. Q point.
    d. base point.

53. In using BJT characteristic curves, the straight line drawn between the cutoff and the saturation points is called:
    a. cutoff line.
    b. saturation line.
    c. load line.
    d. operating line.

54. On transistor spec sheets, the current gain β_{DC} is also known as:
    a. h_{BE}.
    b. h_{CE}.
    c. h_{FE}.
    d. h_{GE}.

55. On transistor spec sheet, the key difference between β_{DC} and α_{DC} is:
    a. β_{DC} represents I_E/I_C; α_{DC} represents I_C/I_E.
    b. β_{DC} represents I_C/I_B; α_{DC} represents I_B/I_C.
    c. β_{DC} represents I_C/I_E; α_{DC} represents I_C/I_B.
    d. β_{DC} represents I_E/I_C; α_{DC} represents I_B/I_C.

56. Although BJT transistors are current operated devices, a key characteristic is the signal voltage gain as an amplifier specified as:
    a. $A_v \cong R_C/R_B$.
    b. $A_v \cong R_C/R_E$.
    c. $A_v \cong R_E/R_C$.
    d. $A_v \cong R_B/R_E$.

57. To recognize transistor packages and identify the terminals, look for:
    a. the protruding tab.
    b. the flat side.
    c. the imprinted dot.
    d. all of these.

1. Answer: a

2. Answer: b

3. Answer: a

4. Answer: a

5. Answer: a

6. Answer: b

7. Answer: a

8. Answer: a

9. Answer: b

10. Answer: a

11. Answer: b

12. Answer: b

13. Answer: c

14. Answer: d

15. Answer: c

16. Answer: d

17. Answer: a

18. Answer: d

19. Answer: c

20. Answer: b

21. Answer: c

22. Answer: b

23. Answer: a

24. Answer: c

25. Answer: d

26. Answer: b

27. Answer: a

28. Answer: b

29. Answer: d

30. Answer: c

31. Answer: c

32. Answer: b

33. Answer: c

34. Answer: d

35. Answer: d

36. Answer: b

37. Answer: c

38. Answer: d

39. Answer: b

40. Answer: c

41. Answer: a

42. Answer: d

43. Answer: a

44. Answer: c

45. Answer: c

46. Answer: d

47. Answer: d

48. Answer: a

49. Answer: c

50. Answer: b

51. Answer: d

52. Answer: c

53. Answer: c

54. Answer: c

55. Answer: c

56. Answer: b

57. Answer: d

Chapter 19:   Amplifiers and Oscillators

TRUE/FALSE

1. The general characteristics of a common-emitter amplifier are low voltage gain, low current gain and very high power gain.
   a. True
   b. False

2. The overall voltage gain of a multistage amplifier is the product of the individual stage gains.
   a. True
   b. False

3. A current gain of almost one is a characteristic of a common-base amplifier.
   a. True
   b. False

4. Voltage gain can be found by $A_V = V_{IN} + V_{OUT}$
   a. True
   b. False

5. An amplifier that provides its own input is called an oscillator.
   a. True
   b. False

6. The general characteristics of a common-emitter amplifier are high voltage gain, high current gain and no phase reversal between the input and output voltages.
   a. True
   b. False

7. The voltage gain of several amplifiers in series is found by adding the individual stage voltage gains.
   a. True
   b. False

8. A common-collector amplifier has a high input impedance compared to a common-emitter amplifier.
   a. True
   b. False

9. If a common-emitter amplifier measures the same voltage on the collector as V_{CC}, the amplifier is operating in saturation.
   a. True
   b. False

10. Class C amplifiers are used primarily at radio frequencies.
    a. True
    b. False

MULTIPLE CHOICE

11. The Class B amplifier conducts for _____ of the input cycle.
    a. a small portion
    b. 180°
    c. 360°
    d. only 10°

12. Which one of these amplifiers has very low input resistance and very high output resistance?
    a. common-emitter
    b. common-collector
    c. common-base
    d. common-gate

13. Which one of these characteristics is found in a common-collector amplifier?
    a. A low input resistance
    b. A very high power gain
    c. A current gain of one
    d. A high input resistance

14. What is the total voltage gain of a three-stage amplifier that has stage gains of 22, 112, and 8?
    a. 142
    b. 1,420
    c. 19,712
    d. 197,120

15. What type of amplifier normally has a voltage gain of one?
    a. common-drain
    b. common-emitter
    c. common-source
    d. common-base

16. Which one of these amplifiers does NOT have the output in phase with the input?
    a. common-drain
    b. common-source
    c. common-collector
    d. common-base

17. Crossover distortion occurs in a _____ amplifier when the amplifier is biased at _____.
    a. common-emitter, saturation
    b. push-pull, saturation
    c. push-pull, cutoff
    d. common-source, cutoff

18. Which one of these amplifiers has high input resistance and low output resistance?
    a. common-emitter
    b. common-collector
    c. common-base
    d. common-gate

$V_{cc} = +18$ V

Input

Output

C_1

R_1

R_C

C_2

R_2

R_E

C_3

Figure 19-1

19. Which voltage might allow the circuit in **Figure 19-1** to operate with minimum distortion?
    a. $V_{BC} = 0$ V
    b. $V_{CE} = 0.15$ V
    c. $V_C = 18$ V
    d. $V_{BE} = 0.7$ V

20. Which voltage would indicate that the amplifier in **Figure 19-1** is operating in saturation?
    a. $V_{BE} = 9$ V
    b. $V_{CE} = 0.15$ V
    c. $V_C = 18$ V
    d. $V_{BE} = 0.7$ V

21. If C_3 opens in **Figure 19-1**, _____.
    a. the dc emitter voltage decreases
    b. the voltage gain increases
    c. the dc emitter voltage increases
    d. the voltage gain decreases

22. If R_1 opens in **Figure 19-1**, V_C equals _____.
    a. 9 V
    b. 0 V
    c. 18 V
    d. V_E

23. If the collector opens in **Figure 19-1**, the output voltage _____.
    a. increases
    b. decreases to zero
    c. remains the same
    d. varies with temperature

Figure 19-2

24. The circuit in **Figure 19-2** is a _____ oscillator and uses _____ feedback.
    a. Colpitts, positive
    b. Hartley, positive
    c. Clapp, negative
    d. Colpitts, negative

25. A Clapp oscillator is similar to a Colpitts oscillator EXCEPT that _____.
    a. the feedback is negative
    b. there is an additional series capacitor in the tank
    c. the feedback network is an RC circuit
    d. no coupling capacitor is used

26. A Class _____ amplifier is very efficient. It is useful mainly at _____ frequencies.
    a. B, audio
    b. C, audio
    c. A, radio
    d. C, radio

Figure 19-1

27. Which voltage would enable the circuit in **Figure 19-1** to operate with little distortion?
    a. $V_{BC} = 0$ V
    b. $V_{CE} = 9$ V
    c. $V_C = 18$ V
    d. $V_{BE} = 7$ V

28. Which voltage would indicate that the amplifier in **Figure 19-1** is operating in cutoff?
    a. $V_{BC} = 9$ V
    b. $V_{CE} = 9$ V
    c. $V_C = 18$ V
    d. $V_{BE} = 7$ V

Figure 19-2

29. The circuit in **Figure 19-2** is known as a _____ oscillator because it has a _____ coil.
    a. Colpitts, dual
    b. Clapp, dual
    c. Hartley, dual
    d. crystal, dual

30. In **Figure 19-2**, L_1, L_2 and C_1 form a _____ that provides _____ feedback to the amplifier.
    a. tank circuit, positive
    b. tank circuit, negative
    c. feedback network, negative
    d. tank circuit, out-of-phase

31. The output signal of a CE amplifier is always _____.
    a. in-phase with the input signal
    b. out-of-phase with the input signal
    c. larger than the input signal
    d. equal to the input signal

32. The largest theoretical voltage gain obtainable with a CC amplifier is _____.
    a. 100
    b. 10
    c. 1
    d. dependent on β

33. One advantage of the darlington pair is _____.
    a. increased overall voltage gain
    b. less cost
    c. decreasing the input impedance
    d. increased overall beta

34. In a class A amplifier, the output signal is _____.
    a. distorted
    b. clipped
    c. the same shape as the input
    d. smaller in amplitude than the input

35. Oscillators operate on the principle of _____.
    a. signal feed-through
    b. positive feedback
    c. negative feedback
    d. attenuation

36. A class C amplifier conducts during _____ of the input cycle.
    a. a small portion
    b. 180°
    c. 360°
    d. only 50%

37. Which one of these amplifiers has a very high power gain?
   a. common-emitter
   b. common-collector
   c. common-base
   d. common-gate

38. Which one of these characteristics is found in a common-base amplifier?
   a. A very low output resistance
   b. A very high power gain
   c. A current gain of one
   d. A high input resistance

39. What is the total voltage gain of a three stage amplifier that has stage gains of 17, 142, and 4?
   a. 163
   b. 2414
   c. 9656
   d. 28,968

40. What type of amplifier normally has a current gain of one?
   a. common drain
   b. common-emitter
   c. common-source
   d. common-base

41. Which of the following amplifiers has phase inversion?
   a. common-drain
   b. common-emitter
   c. common-collector
   d. common-base

Figure 19-1

42. If the base-emitter junction opens in **Figure 19-1**, V_C _____.
    a. increases to V_{CC}
    b. decreases to 0 volts
    c. decreases to V_E
    d. does not change

43. If R_1 shorts in **Figure 19-1**, V_C _____.
    a. increases to V_{CC}
    b. decreases to 0 V
    c. decreases to V_E
    d. does not change

44. If the BJT's collector opens internally in **Figure 19-1**, V_B _____.
    a. increases
    b. decreases
    c. remains the same
    d. drops almost to zero

45. If R_2 opens in **Figure 19-1**, V_E _____.
    a. increases
    b. decreases
    c. remains the same
    d. drops almost to zero

46. If the BJT's emitter internally shorted to its collector in **Figure 19-1**, V_{CE} _____.
    a. increases
    b. decreases
    c. remains the same
    d. drops almost to zero

Figure 19-2

47. If C_1 opens in **Figure 19-2**, the circuit will probably _____.
    a. continue to operate normally
    b. decrease its oscillating frequency
    c. increase its oscillating frequency
    d. stop oscillating entirely

48. If the value of C_1 increases in **Figure 19-2**, the circuit _____.
    a. operates at a higher frequency
    b. operates at a lower frequency
    c. operates at dc
    d. does not change at all

49. A crystal oscillator uses a crystal to determine the _____.
    a. dc output
    b. amount of positive feedback
    c. output frequency
    d. amount of negative feedback

50. A crystal oscillator usually has a very high _____.
    a. V
    b. I
    c. Q
    d. BW

51. Amplifiers are electronic circuits that accept an AC input signal and produce an output signal that represents a:
    a. voltage gain.
    b. current gain.
    c. power gain.
    d. all of these.

52. The terms common-base, common-emitter and common-collector mean that:
    a. one of the leads is a common reference to the other two leads.
    b. one of the leads is a common input signal point.
    c. one of the leads is a common DC bias point.
    d. all of these.

53. The most popular and widely used transistor amplifier configuration is the:
    a. common-base.
    b. common-emitter.
    c. common-collector.
    d. common-drain.

54. The classification of transistor amplifiers by classes: A, B, C, is based on:
    a. voltage flow.
    b. current flow.
    c. signal voltages.
    d. bias voltages.

55. The most accurate signal reproduction in transistor amplifiers is provided by:
    a. class A.
    b. class B.
    c. class C.
    d. class AB.

56. Oscillators are amplifiers that produce a repetitive waveform and that utilize:
    a. negative feedback.
    b. degenerative feedback.
    c. positive feedback.
    d. both negative and positive feedback.

57. Positive feedback is defined as feeding back a portion of the output to the input such that:
    a. the two are in phase.
    b. there is no net phase shift.
    c. it reinforces the signal at the input.
    d. all of these.

1. Answer: b

2. Answer: a

3. Answer: a

4. Answer: b

5. Answer: a

6. Answer: b

7. Answer: b

8. Answer: a

9. Answer: b

10. Answer: a

11. Answer: b

12. Answer: c

13. Answer: d

14. Answer: c

15. Answer: a

16. Answer: b

17. Answer: c

18. Answer: b

19. Answer: d

20. Answer: b

21. Answer: d

22. Answer: c

23. Answer: b

24. Answer: b

25. Answer: b

26. Answer: d

27. Answer: b

28. Answer: c

29. Answer: c

30. Answer: a

31. Answer: b

32. Answer: c

33. Answer: d

34. Answer: c

35. Answer: c

36. Answer: a

37. Answer: a

38. Answer: c

39. Answer: c

40. Answer: d

41. Answer: b

42. Answer: a

43. Answer: b

44. Answer: c

45. Answer: a

46. Answer: d

47. Answer: d

48. Answer: b

49. Answer: c

50. Answer: c

51. Answer: d

52. Answer: d

53. Answer: b

54. Answer: b

55. Answer: a

56. Answer: c

57. Answer: d

Chapter 20:   Operational Amplifiers

1. The ideal amplifier has infinite gain, infinite input impedance, and zero output impedance.
   a. True
   b. False

2. The slew rate of an op-amp is determined by the frequency response of the internal amplifiers.
   a. True
   b. False

3. An op-amp with a low CMRR easily rejects noise signals that appear at both inputs.
   a. True
   b. False

4. A voltage-follower op-amp has a voltage gain greater than one.
   a. True
   b. False

5. The open-loop voltage gain of an op-amp is very large.
   a. True
   b. False

6. Practical op-amps come reasonably close to the requirements for an ideal amplifier.
   a. True
   b. False

7. Differential amplifiers provide high voltage gain and low common-mode rejection.
   a. True
   b. False

8. An op-amp's CMRR is usually expressed in dB.
   a. True
   b. False

9. An op-amp's input offset voltage, V_{OS}, is the differential input voltage required to make the differential output voltage zero.
   a. True
   b. False

10. A typical value of input bias current for an op-amp is around 80 nA.
    a. True
    b. False

MULTIPLE CHOICE

11. Which one of these op-amp terminals provides an output that is in phase
    with the input?
    a. V_{CC}
    b. non-inverting
    c. inverting
    d. offset null

12. Which of these amplifiers provide a variable input resistance and a
    variable gain?
    a. a voltage-follower amp
    b. an open-loop amp
    c. a non-inverting amp
    d. an inverting amp with potentiometer

(c)   **Figure 20-1**

13. What is the voltage gain of the amplifier in **Figure 20-1(a)**?
    a. 100000
    b. 1000
    c. 10
    d. 1

14. Identify the open-loop amplifier in **Figure 20-1**.
    a. Figure 20-1(a)
    b. Figure 20-1(b)
    c. Figure 20-1(c)
    d. none of these

15. Identify the non-inverting amplifier in **Figure 20-1**.
    a. Figure 20-1(a)
    b. Figure 20-1(b)
    c. Figure 20-1(c)
    d. none of these

16. If R_i = 4.7 kΩ and R_f = 0.18 MΩ in **Figure 20-1(c)**, the voltage gain equals _____ .
    a. 38.3
    b. 39.3
    c. 1
    d. infinite

17. Which of the amplifiers in **Figure 20-1** would be used as a buffer amplifier?
    a. Figure 20-1(a)
    b. Figure 20-1(b)
    c. Figure 20-1(c)
    d. none of these

18. If R_f = 0.5 MΩ and R_i = 10 kΩ in **Figure 20-1(b)**, the voltage gain equals _____ .
    a. 50
    b. 51
    c. 5
    d. 6

19. A CMRR of 35,000 equals a decibel CMRR of _____ .
    a. 88 dB
    b. 35000 dB
    c. 91 dB
    d. -91 dB

20. If R_f = 1.2 MΩ and A_V = 120 in **Figure 20-1(c)**, R_i equals _____ .
    a. 120 Ω
    b. 10 kΩ
    c. 1 kΩ
    d. 100 kΩ

21. To build an amplifier with a 5K Ω input impedance and a voltage gain of 40, use the _____ amplifier, R_i = _____ , R_f = _____ .
    a. non-inverting, 5 kΩ, 40 kΩ
    b. inverting, 5 kΩ, 2 kΩ
    c. non-inverting, 40 kΩ, 200 kΩ
    d. inverting, 5 kΩ, 200 kΩ

22. One characteristic of a noninverting amplifier is a _____ .
    a. voltage gain of one
    b. very low input impedance
    c. high output impedance
    d. voltage gain slightly more than an inverting amplifier with the same values

23. What trouble in the amplifier in **Figure 20-1(c)** could cause the voltage gain to drop to 1?
    a. R_i is open
    b. the power is off
    c. R_f is open
    d. V_{OUT} is grounded

24. V_{RF} equals _____ in **Figure 20-1(c)**.
    a. V_{CC}
    b. V_{RI}
    c. V_{OUT}
    d. V_{IN}

25. Which one of these devices produces amplifiers with characteristics close to those of an ideal amplifier?
    a. JFET
    b. MOSFET
    c. Op-amp
    d. BJT

26. A typical op-amp has _____ input impedance and _____ output impedance.
    a. high, high
    b. low, high
    c. low, low
    d. high, low

27. The circuit in **Figure 20-1(c)** is known as the _____.
    a. non-inverting amplifier
    b. open-loop amplifier
    c. inverting amplifier
    d. voltage follower amplifier

28. If R_f = 470 kΩ and R_i = 5 kΩ in **Figure 20-1(b)**, the voltage gain equals _____.
    a. 1.01
    b. 470
    c. 95
    d. 94

29. If R_f = 150 kΩ and R_i = 10 kΩ in **Figure 20-1(c)**, the voltage gain equals _____.
    a. 0.066
    b. 1
    c. 15
    d. 16

30. The circuit in **Figure 20-1(a)** is used as a(n) _____.
    a. high gain amplifier
    b. inverting amplifier
    c. buffer amplifier
    d. oscillator

31. If an op-amp's output increases 8 V every 12 µs in response to a step input voltage, the slew rate equals _____.
    a. 0.667 V/µs
    b. 1.5 V/µs
    c. 96 V/µs
    d. 0.75 V/µs

32. If R_i = 1 kΩ, R_f = 100 kΩ and V_{OUT} = 5 V in a noninverting op-amp, V_{RI} equals _____.
    a. 50 mV
    b. 49.5 mV
    c. 495 mV
    d. 500 mV

33. If R_i = 1 kΩ, R_f = 100 kΩ and V_{OUT} = 5 V in a noninverting op-amp, A_{CL} equals _____.
    a. 0.0099
    b. 1
    c. 99
    d. 101

34. One characteristic of a voltage follower is its _____.
    a. large voltage gain
    b. phase inversion
    c. high output impedance
    d. non-inversion

35. If R_i = 2.2 kΩ, R_f = 220 kΩ and A_{OL} = 25,000 in an inverting op-amp, A_{CL} equals _____.
    a. -100
    b. -0.01
    c. 100
    d. -250

36. Which of these amplifiers provides a high input resistance and a variable gain?
    a. voltage-follower amp
    b. open-loop amp
    c. inverting amp
    d. non-inverting amp with a potentiometer as R_f.

37. If R_f = 100 kΩ and R_i = 6.8 kΩ in **Figure 20-1(c)**, the voltage gain equals _____.
    a. 15.7
    b. 14.7
    c. 1
    d. infinite

38. If R_f = 150 kΩ and R_i = 2.2 kΩ in **Figure 20-1(c)**, the voltage gain equals _____.
    a. 68.2
    b. 69.2
    c. 1
    d. infinite

39. If R_f = 333 kΩ and R_i = 22 kΩ in **Figure 20-1(b)**, the voltage gain equals _____.
    a. 15
    b. 16
    c. 15.1
    d. 16.1

40. If R_f = 1.2 MΩ and R_i = 47 kΩ in **Figure 20-1(b)**, the voltage gain
    equals _____.
    a. 25.5
    b. 26.5
    c. 25
    d. 26

41. A CMRR of 90,000 equals a decibel CMRR of _____.
    a. 99 dB
    b. 90000 dB
    c. 91 dB
    d. -99 dB

42. If R_f= 100 kΩ and A_V = 833 in **Figure 20-1(c)**, R_i equals _____.
    a. 120 Ω
    b. 10 kΩ
    c. 1 kΩ
    d. 100 kΩ

43. To build an amplifier with a 10K Ω input impedance and a voltage gain of
    41, use the _____ amplifier, R_i = _____, R_f = _____.
    a. non-inverting, 10 kΩ, 410 kΩ
    b. inverting, 10 kΩ, 410 kΩ
    c. non-inverting, 40 kΩ, 200 kΩ
    d. inverting, 10 kΩ, 200 kΩ

44. What trouble in the amplifier in **Figure 20-1(c)** could cause the output
    voltage to clip severely?
    a. the power is off
    b. the input signal is too large
    c. the amplifier's gain is too low
    d. the input signal is too small for the amplifier to respond

45. What trouble in the amplifier in **Figure 20-1(b)** could cause the
    voltage between the inverting and non-inverting inputs to nearly equal 0
    V?
    a. R_f is open
    b. R_i is open
    c. The power is off
    d. There is no problem; 0 V is normal

46. The input impedance of the amplifier in **Figure 20-1(b)** is _____.
    a. very low
    b. very high.
    c. about 10 kΩ

47. To use an op-amp as a buffer, use the _____.
    a. inverting amplifier
    b. non-inverting amplifier
    c. voltage follower amplifier
    d. differential amplifier

48. Which one of these characteristics do an op-amp and a MOSFET have in common?
    a. high current gain
    b. high voltage gain
    c. high CMRR
    d. high input impedance

49. If an op-amp's output increases 6 V every 18 μs in response to a step input voltage, the slew rate equals _____.
    a. 3 V/μs
    b. 0.33 V/μs
    c. 33 V/μs
    d. 0.99 V/μs

50. If R_f = 5 kΩ and R_i = 10 kΩ in **Figure 20-1(c)**, the voltage gain equals _____.
    a. -5
    b. 0
    c. -0.5
    d. -2

51. A diff-amp with 1 input grounded and the signal voltage applied only to the other input is called:
    a. grounded input.
    b. single input.
    c. single ended.
    d. single output.

52. A diff-amp with two out-of-phase signal voltages applied to the two inputs is called:
    a. phase inverter input.
    b. phase inverter output.
    c. differential input.
    d. differential output.

53. A diff-amp with two identical signal voltage applied to the two inputs is called:
    a. same phase input.
    b. same signal input.
    c. common mode input.
    d. common mode output.

54. A practical differential amplifier provides:
    a. very small common mode gain < 1.
    b. very high differential voltage gain > 1000.
    c. very high input impedance.
    d. all of these.

55. A CMRR of 10,000 means that the op-amp provides that:
    a. the differential input is amplified highly.
    b. the common mode input is greatly reduced.
    c. $A_{v(d)}/A_c m$ = 10,000.
    d. all of these.

56. The principal operating characteristic of the voltage follower configuration is:
   a. non-inverting output.
   b. voltage gain of unity.
   c. very high input impedance.
   d. very low output impedance.

57. If you know an op-amp's open-loop gain only, you can determine the closed-loop gain of:
   a. an inverting op-amp.
   b. an non-inverting op-amp.
   c. a voltage follower op-amp.
   d. all of these.

58. The feedback attenuation of a voltage follower op-amp is:
   a. < 1.
   b. > 1.
   c. = 1.
   d. R_f/R_i.

59. The op-amp configuration with the highest possible input impedance is:
   a. inverting op-amp.
   b. non-inverting op-amp.
   c. differential op-amp.
   d. voltage-follower op-amp.

1. Answer: a

2. Answer: a

3. Answer: b

4. Answer: b

5. Answer: a

6. Answer: a

7. Answer: b

8. Answer: a

9. Answer: a

10. Answer: a

11. Answer: b

12. Answer: d

13. Answer: d

14. Answer: d

15. Answer: b

16. Answer: a

17. Answer: a

18. Answer: b

19. Answer: c

20. Answer: b

21. Answer: d

22. Answer: d

23. Answer: b

24. Answer: c

25. Answer: c

26. Answer: d

27. Answer: c

28. Answer: c

29. Answer: c

30. Answer: c

31. Answer: a

32. Answer: b

33. Answer: d

34. Answer: d

35. Answer: a

36. Answer: d

37. Answer: b

38. Answer: a

39. Answer: d

40. Answer: b

41. Answer: a

42. Answer: a

43. Answer: b

44. Answer: b

45. Answer: d

46. Answer: b

47. Answer: c

48. Answer: d

49. Answer: b

50. Answer: c

51. Answer: c

52. Answer: c

53. Answer: c

54. Answer: d

55. Answer: d

56. Answer: b

57. Answer: c

58. Answer: c

59. Answer: d

Chapter 21: Basic Applications of Op-Amps

TRUE/FALSE

1. The terminals on a three-terminal regulator are input voltage, output voltage and ground.
   a. True
   b. False

2. A series-pass transistor is used in a voltage regulator.
   a. True
   b. False

3. A Wien-bridge oscillator produces an excellent quality square wave.
   a. True
   b. False

4. Butterworth filters are characterized by a linear response in the pass band.
   a. True
   b. False

5. Op-amp comparators are often used as zero-level detectors.
   a. True
   b. False

6. An op-amp comparator can be used to determine when an input voltage crosses a certain reference voltage.
   a. True
   b. False

7. An op-amp summing amplifier has no limitations on the number of inputs it can handle.
   a. True
   b. False

8. An op-amp integrator will produce a linear increasing output voltage for a constant negative input voltage until cutoff is reached.
   a. True
   b. False

9. Hartley, Colpitts, and Clapp oscillators can use op-amps.
   a. True
   b. False

10. A second-order Butterworth filter rolls-off at 40 dB/decade.
    a. True
    b. False

MULTIPLE CHOICE

Figure 21-1

11. If V_{IN} equals 4 V in **Figure 21-1**, V_{OUT} equals _____.
   a. 1 V
   b. -1 V
   c. 13 V
   d. -13 V

12. If V_{IN} equals 8 V in **Figure 21-1**, V_{OUT} equals _____.
   a. 1 V
   b. -1 V
   c. 13 V
   d. -13 V

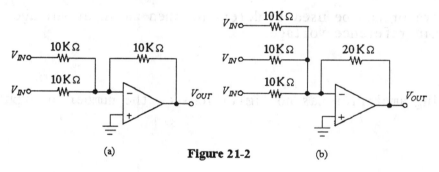

(a)   **Figure 21-2**   (b)

13. If the inputs are 8.4 V and 1.2 V in **Figure 21-2(a)**, the output voltage equals _____.
   a. 9.6 V
   b. 10.08 V
   c. -9.6 V
   d. 7.2 V

14. If the inputs are 4.1 V, -0.7 V and 3.1 V in **Figure 21-2(b)**, the output voltage equals _____.
   a. -13 V
   b. 13 V
   c. 6.5 V
   d. -6.5 V

15. What change causes the circuit in **Figure 21-2(b)** to output the average of the three input voltages?
    a. Change the feedback resistor to 10 kΩ
    b. Change the input resistors to 3.3 kΩ
    c. Change to a different type of op-amp
    d. Change the feedback resistor to 3.3 kΩ

R

V_{IN}

V_{OUT}

C

Figure 21-3

16. If R = 47 kΩ and C = 0.02 µF in **Figure 21-3**, f_{CO} equals _____.
    a. 169 Hz
    b. 16.9 Hz
    c. 51.9 Hz
    d. 5.19 Hz

17. If V_{IN} equals 22 V in **Figure 21-3**, V_{OUT} at the f_{CO} equals _____.
    a. 31.1 V
    b. 15.55 V
    c. 7.79 V
    d. 0

18. In **Figure 21-3**, what will change the circuit into a high-pass filter?
    a. Increasing the value of the resistor
    b. Decreasing the value of the capacitor
    c. Placing the capacitor in the feedback loop
    d. Switching the positions of the resistor and capacitor

19. If R = 1.5 kΩ and C = 256 pF in **Figure 21-3**, the F_{CO} equals _____.
    a. 41.5 kHz
    b. 415 kHz
    c. 257 Hz
    d. 25.7 Hz

Figure 21-4

20. The prime characteristic of the filter in **Figure 21-4** is _____.
    a. it has the largest response of any filter type
    b. it has a flat response curve in the pass band
    c. it only works in a high-pass configuration
    d. nothing special

21. If 22 V in the pass-band is input to the circuit in **Figure 21-4**, what is the output voltage at f_{CO} ?
    a. 15.5 V
    b. 31.1 V
    c. 7.75 V
    d. 8.92 V

22. If 22 V in the pass-band is input to the circuit in **Figure 21-4**, what is the output voltage at a frequency that is 1 decade higher?
    a. 15.5 V
    b. 31.1 V
    c. 7.75 V
    d. 22 V

23. In **Figure 21-4**, if the frequency is decreased from the pass band to 1 decade below f_{CO}, the output voltage drops _____.
    a. 3 dB
    b. 6 dB
    c. 20 dB
    d. 43 dB

24. The circuit in **Figure 21-4** is known as the _____ and it rolls off at a rate of _____.
    a. Butterworth high-pass filter, -40 dB/decade
    b. Butterworth low-pass filter, -40 dB/decade
    c. Butterworth high-pass filter, -20 dB/decade
    d. Butterworth low-pass filter, -20 dB/decade

A_V (dB)

0

-3

450 822 1500 f(Hz)

Figure 21-5

25. The frequency response curve in **Figure 21-5** represents the output from the _____ and the bandwidth is _____.
   a. band-reject filter, 1050 kHz
   b. band-pass filter, 678 Hz
   c. band-pass filter, 1050 Hz
   d. two-pole high-pass filter, 1050 Hz

26. If V_{OUT} equals 12 V at 822 Hz in **Figure 21-5**, the output voltage equals _____ at 450 Hz.
   a. 8.484 V
   b. 4.242 V
   c. 2.121 V
   d. 1.061 V

27. The curve in **Figure 21-5** is from a _____ and its lower cutoff frequency equals _____.
   a. band-reject filter, 450 kHz
   b. band-pass filter, 822 Hz
   c. band-pass filter, 450 Hz
   d. two-pole high-pass filter, 1500 Hz

28. If the output voltage is 6 V at 1500 Hz in **Figure 21-5**, what is the output voltage at 822 Hz?
   a. 8.48 V
   b. 4.24 V
   c. 2.12 V
   d. 1.06 V

29. If the output voltage is 27.4 V at 822 Hz in **Figure 21-5**, what is the output voltage at 1.5 kHz?
   a. 27.4 V
   b. 19.37 V
   c. 13.7 V
   d. 6.85 V

30. A three-terminal voltage regulator _____.
    a. comes in a variety of voltage and current ratings
    b. is very durable
    c. is available in both positive and negative voltage ratings
    d. all of the above

31. A series-pass voltage regulator has _____.
    a. an error amplifier
    b. a load
    c. a shunt regulator
    d. all of these

32. Short-circuit or overload protection is an integral part of _____.
    a. most three-terminal regulators
    b. most TRIACs
    c. most op-amps
    d. most JFETs

33. If an inverting amplifier has a capacitor in the feedback loop, the circuit is known as the _____. When a square wave input is applied, the output is a _____ wave.
    a. differentiator, triangle
    b. integrator, square
    c. integrator, triangle
    d. open loop, triangle

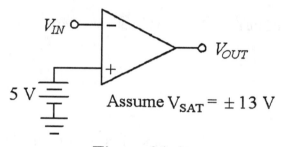

Figure 21-1

34. If V_{IN} = -3 V in **Figure 21-1**, V_{OUT} equals _____.
    a. 1 V
    b. -1 V
    c. 13 V
    d. -13 V

(a)   **Figure 21-2**   (b)

35. If the inputs are -7.1 V and 12 V in **Figure 21-2(a)**, what is the output voltage?
    a. -4.9 V
    b. 4.9 V
    c. 19.1 V
    d. -19.1 V

R

V_{IN}

V_{OUT}

C

Figure 21-3

36. If R = 22 kΩ and C = 0.05 μF in **Figure 21-3**, f_{CO} equals _____.
    a. 1.45 kHz
    b. 145 Hz
    c. 4.8 Hz
    d. 48 Hz

37. The purpose of a comparator is to _____.
    a. amplify an input voltage
    b. detect the occurrence of a changing input voltage
    c. produce a change in output when an input voltage equals a reference voltage
    d. maintain a constant output when the dc input voltage changes

38. If all four input resistors to a summing amplifier are 2.2 kΩ, the feedback resistor is 2.2 kΩ and all four input voltages are -2 V, the output voltage equals _____.
    a. 2 V
    b. 10 V
    c. 2.2 V
    d. 8 V

39. If all four input resistors to a summing amplifier are 2.2 kΩ and the feedback resistor is 2.2 kΩ, then the gain equals _____.
    a. 1
    b. 2.2
    c. 4
    d. unknown

40. In a scaling adder, the _____.
    a. input resistors are all the same value
    b. input resistors are all different values
    c. input resistors have values depending on the assigned weight of each input
    d. ratio R_F/R_{IN} must be the same for each input

41. The input frequency of a single-pole, low-pass active filter increases from 1.5 kHz to 150 kHz. If the critical frequency is 1.5 kHz, the gain decreases by _____.
    a. 3 dB
    b. 20 dB
    c. 40 dB
    d. 60 dB

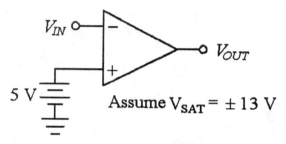

Figure 21-1

42. If V_{IN} = 4.2 V in **Figure 21-1**, V_{OUT} equals _____.
    a. 0.8 V
    b. -0.8 V
    c. 13 V
    d. -13 V

43. If V_{IN}= 8.3 V in **Figure 21-1**, V_{OUT} equals _____.
    a. 3.3 V
    b. -3.3 V
    c. 13 V
    d. -13 V

Figure 21-2

44. If the two input voltages are 9.2 V and 0.7 V in **Figure 21-2(a)**, what is the output voltage?
    a. 9.9 V
    b. -9.9 V
    c. 8.5 V
    d. -8.5 V

45. If the inputs are 1.2 V, -0.5 V and 2.4 V in **Figure 21-2(b)**, what is the output voltage?
    a. -6.2 V
    b. 13 V
    c. 6.2 V
    d. -4.1 V

Figure 21-3

46. If R = 56 kΩ and C = 0.05 μF in **Figure 21-3**, f_{CO} equals _____.
    a. 57 Hz
    b. 570 Mz
    c. 3.0 Hz
    d. 300 Hz

47. If V_{IN}= 70 V_P in **Figure 21-3**, the output voltage at f_{CO} equals _____.
    a. 44.2 V_P
    b. 49.5 V_P
    c. 13 V_P
    d. 0 V_P

48. If R = 1.2 kΩ and C = 0.005 μF in **Figure 21-3**, the f_{CO} equals _____.
    a. 2.65 kHz
    b. 26.5 kHz
    c. 65 Hz
    d. 650 Hz

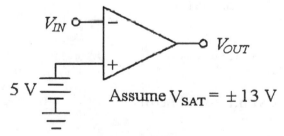

Figure 21-1

241

49. If $V_{IN} = -2$ V in **Figure 21-1**, V_{OUT} equals _____.
   a. 3 V
   b. -3 V
   c. 13 V
   d. -13 V

50. The output of an op-amp differentiator depends on the values of _____ and _____ .
   a. R_{IN}, C_F
   b. R_{IN}, R_F
   c. C_{IN}, C_F
   d. C_{IN}, R_F

51. In an inverting input op-amp integrator supplied with a square wave pulse or a step, the output is a:
   a. sine wave.
   b. opposite phase square wave.
   c. same phase ramp.
   d. opposite phase ramp.

52. In an inverting input op-amp, differentiator supplied with a ramp or triangular wave, the output is a:
   a. sine wave.
   b. same phase square wave.
   c. opposite phase square wave.
   d. opposite phase ramp.

53. In a Wein-bridge op-amp oscillator, the output is a repetitive:
   a. sine wave.
   b. square wave.
   c. triangular wave.
   d. all of these.

54. Using op-amps in a triangular wave, oscillator results in a:
   a. square wave output.
   b. triangular wave output.
   c. function generator output.
   d. all of these.

55. In a voltage-controlled oscillator (VCO), the output signal frequency is dependent on:
   a. the value of a resistor.
   b. the value of a capacitor.
   c. the value of a resistor-capacitor combination.
   d. the value of an applied voltage.

56. The basic op-amp square oscillator is actually a:
   a. Wein-bridge oscillator.
   b. sine wave oscillator.
   c. resistor-capacitor (RC) time constant oscillator.
   d. all of these.

57. In a filter circuit, the terminology single pole means:
    a. one fixed contact.
    b. one movable contact.
    c. one single RC circuit.
    d. two cascaded RC circuits.

58. Each pole in a filter circuit causes the output voltage to roll off or drop at a rate of:
    a. 3dB per decade or octave.
    b. 6dB per decade or octave.
    c. 10 dB per decade or octave.
    d. 20 dB per decade or octave.

59. At the cutoff frequency of a filter circuit, the output voltage is:
    a. - 3 dB.
    b. - 10 dB.
    c. = 20 dB.
    d. - 40 dB.

60. In a series voltage regulator, the four circuit blocks are:
    a. control element, reference voltage, error detector, current limiter.
    b. control element, reference voltage, error detector, sampling circuit.
    c. reference voltage, series load, reference voltage, current limiter.
    d. error detector, reference voltage, series regulator, sampling circuit.

61. A series and a shunt regulator are differentiated by the circuit placement of a:
    a. series resistor versus parallel resistor.
    b. series transistor versus parallel transistor.
    c. series reference voltage versus parallel reference voltage.
    d. none of these.

1. Answer: a

2. Answer: a

3. Answer: b

4. Answer: a

5. Answer: a

6. Answer: a

7. Answer: a

8. Answer: b

9. Answer: a

10. Answer: a

11. Answer: c

12. Answer: d

13. Answer: c

14. Answer: a

15. Answer: d

16. Answer: d

17. Answer: b

18. Answer: d

19. Answer: c

20. Answer: b

21. Answer: a

22. Answer: d

23. Answer: d

24. Answer: a

25. Answer: c

26. Answer: a

27. Answer: c

28. Answer: a

29. Answer: b

30. Answer: d

31. Answer: a

32. Answer: a

33. Answer: c

34. Answer: c

35. Answer: a

36. Answer: c

37. Answer: c

38. Answer: d

39. Answer: a

40. Answer: c

41. Answer: c

42. Answer: c

43. Answer: d

44. Answer: b

45. Answer: a

46. Answer: c

47. Answer: b

48. Answer: c

49. Answer: c

50. Answer: d

51. Answer: d

52. Answer: c

53. Answer: a

54. Answer: d

55. Answer: d

56. Answer: c

57. Answer: c

58. Answer: c

59. Answer: a

60. Answer: b

61. Answer: c

Nursing Now!

A Guide to
Nursing Now!
Today's Issues, Tomorrow's Trends, Fifth Edition

Learning Objectives

After completing this chapter, the reader will be able to:

- Apply the principles of delegation to nursing practice.
- Analyze and identify situations where delegation is used improperly.
- Discuss the legal implications of delegation in the current health-care setting.
- Distinguish between delegation and supervision.

Learning Objectives clearly define the knowledge you'll acquire from each chapter.

Key terms appear in bold type and highlighted in yellow. (Find a complete Glossary of Terms at the end of the book.)

Team Nursing

Team nursing has a more unified approach to client care, with team members functioning together to achieve client goals. The team leader functions as the person ultimately responsible for the clients' well-being. More cohesiveness is present among the members of the team than is found in the functional model. Rather than having a narrow task to accomplish, team members focus on team goals under the coordination of the team leader. The team conference provides for effective communication and follow-up among team members and is the key to successful team nursing.

Guidelines for Critiquing the Ethical Features of Research

1. Was the study approved by an institutional review board (IRB)?
2. Was informed consent obtained from every subject?
3. Is there information regarding anonymity or confidentiality?
4. Were vulnerable subjects used?
5. Does it appear that any coercion may have been used?
6. Is it evident that potential benefits of participation outweigh the possible risks?
7. Were participants invited to ask questions about the study and told how to contact the researcher, should the need arise?
8. Were participants informed how to obtain results of the study?

Evidence-based practice is emphasized throughout the book.

"ARE YOU SURE THIS NEW BATH TECHNIQUE WAS ON THE EVIDENCE-BASED PRACTICE LIST?"

Insightful quotes and colorful cartoons make concepts easy to grasp.

When nurses delegate nursing tasks to non-nurses, the RNs are always legally responsible for supervising those people to ensure that the care given meets the standards of care.

Be prepared for the rapidly evolving

Issues Now, case studies at the end of every chapter, present real-world challenges followed by **Questions for Thought.**

Issues Now

Leadership/Management Case Study

Resolving Staffing Issues

On a busy medical/surgical unit, a group of staff nurses were concerned about the process of making assignments. They believed that the usual practice of assigning nurses to a different group of clients each day eliminated any continuity of care, ~~among the staff. They agreed to~~ ~~ays of resolving the issues.~~ ~~The staff nurses expressed a~~ ~~h of assignments. The nurse~~ ~~eing uncooperative and didn't~~ ~~ssignments. She stated that her~~ ~~est nursing care possible for~~

QUESTIONS FOR THOUGHT:

1. How would a nurse manager who used an authoritarian system of management resolve this issue?
2. How would a nurse manager who used a laissez-faire system resolve this issue?
3. How would a nurse manager who used a participative system resolve this issue?
4. What initial mistake did the nurse manager make in dealing with this problem?

(Answers are found at the end of the chapter.)

Critical Thinking Questions

Critical Thinking Questions ask you to apply what you're learning and to think like a nurse.

- What was the style of leadership and management that Jill used when attempting to initiate the dressing procedure change?
- Other than the stated reason, why do you think the LPNs did not want to use the new procedures?
- How can Jill increase the level of compliance by the LPNs on the unit?
- What is the role of the unit manager in initiating the new dressing change procedures?

FREE Online Resources at DavisPlus

http://davisplus.fadavis.com

- **Annual Updates by the Author**—Stay up to date on the issues and trends affecting nursing practice now…and in the future.
- **Resume Builder**—Reference a sample and use a template to help you to create a better resume.
- **Competencies**—Understand what is expected of new graduates.
- **Web Links**—Visit a variety of online resources that you can use to research evidence-based practice.
- **Self-Assessment Tools**—Complete these activities to develop your leadership, followership, and delegation skills.
- **Test Prep**—Prepare for the issues and trends content on the exam with over 75 NCLEX-style questions.
- **Interactive Excercises**—Practice with "Crossword Puzzle," "Guess the Term," and "Paragraph Match" excercises for each chapter.

Nursing Now!
Today's Issues, Tomorrow's Trends

fifth edition

Joseph T. Catalano, PhD, RN
Department Chair
Professor of Nursing
East Central University
Ada, Oklahoma

F.A. DAVIS COMPANY • Philadelphia

F. A. Davis Company
1915 Arch Street
Philadelphia, PA 19103
www.fadavis.com

Copyright © 2009 by F. A. Davis Company

Printed in the United States of America

Last digit indicates print number: 10 9 8 7 6 5 4 3 2

Acquisitions Editor: Jonathan D. Joyce
Director of Content Development: Darlene D. Pedersen
Project Editor: Padraic J. Maroney
Art and Illustrations Manager: Carolyn O' Brien

As new scientific information becomes available through basic and clinical research, recommended treatments and drug therapies undergo changes. The author(s) and publisher have done everything possible to make this book accurate, up to date, and in accord with accepted standards at the time of publication. The author(s), editors, and publisher are not responsible for errors or omissions or for consequences from application of the book, and make no warranty, expressed or implied, in regard to the contents of the book. Any practice described in this book should be applied by the reader in accordance with professional standards of care used in regard to the unique circumstances that may apply in each situation. The reader is advised always to check product information (package inserts) for changes and new information regarding dose and contraindications before administering any drug. Caution is especially urged when using new or infrequently ordered drugs.

Library of Congress Cataloging-in-Publication Data

Catalano, Joseph T.
  Nursing now! : today's issues, tomorrow's trends / Joseph T.
Catalano.—5th ed.
     p. ; cm.
  Includes bibliographical references and index.
  ISBN-13: 978-0-8036-1856-5
  ISBN-10: 0-8036-1856-5
  1. Nursing—Vocational guidance—United States.   2. Nursing—Social
aspects—United States.   3. Nursing—Philosophy.   I. Title.
  [DNLM: 1. Nursing—trends.   WY 16 C357n 2009]
  RT82.C33 2009
  610.7306'9—dc22
                                        2008012454

Dedication

To all those hardworking students with high stress levels who are the future leaders of the nursing profession.

Unless you've been living in a cave for the past 5 years, it's been impossible to miss the impact of politics on all aspects of life in this country and throughout the world. From a disastrous war that there seems to be no way out of to an economy that is beginning to sputter and slow, our personal lives have all been touched to some degree. The health-care industry and the nursing profession have been affected as well. As nurses struggle to master some of the most advanced health-care technology on earth, they also struggle to justify and deal with an ever increasing number of citizens who do not have health insurance and an increasing immigrant population. Although medical errors have begun to decline, new drug-resistant infective organisms are increasing. Nursing education continues to struggle to increase class sizes and numbers of graduates but in a political atmosphere of "cut taxes at all costs" they continually struggle with reduced funding and inability to attract qualified faculty due to low salaries.

You might be asking yourself about now, "I'm just a lowly nursing student, what can I do about all these problems?" The answer is "a lot!" Because of the nursing shortage, society, politicians, and the medical community, are being forced to recognize the vital role nurses play in the health-care system. This recognition gives nurses today more political power than they have ever had in the past. Particularly at the state level, but also to some degree at the national level, nurses are being sought for membership on committees that deal with all aspects of health care. Nurses today finally are able to strongly influence the policies that control their lives and their practice.

Graduates from today's nursing programs have opportunities for professional practice and advancement that could only be dreamed about a few years ago. Yes, the demands are many, but the rewards are great. Today's nursing students must learn more, do more, and be more. Students entering nursing schools today come from diverse cultural, personal, and educational backgrounds. They must master a tremendous amount of information, and learn a wide variety of skills so that they can successfully pass the licensure exam and become highly skilled registered nurses.

The fifth edition of *Nursing Now! Today's Issues, Tomorrow's Trends* offers students a starting point to influence the future of health care in the United States. As with past editions, we listened to our readers and have incorporated many of their suggestions. We are very excited about the revised text and believe its quality and content meet the high standards demanded by our readers.

Based on our readers' suggestions, we have added Chapter 23, "Client Education, A Moral Imperative." Educating clients is one of the most important responsibilities that nurses have and probably one of the areas where they receive the least instruction. This chapter will initiate students into the basics of teaching/learning theory and provide a foundation for future client teaching. The chapter on the NCLEX exam was updated to reflect the recent changes by the NCSBN. All other chapters were revised with the addition of current content and resources.

As with past editions, we have retained the interactive format of the text. In addition to the journal layout, current issues boxes, and integrated questions throughout, we have added a number of new illustrations to increase the visual appeal of the book. The interactive Web site available for students with a number of interactive learning activities has been updated and expanded.

The book's primary purpose remains the same as past editions. It presents an overview and synthesis of the important issues and trends that are basic to the development of professional nursing, and affect nursing both today and into the future. Our readers tell us that the book can be used both at the beginning of the student's educational process as an "Introduction to Nursing" course, and also toward the end of the process as an "Issues and Trends" course. Some instructors even use it throughout their programs, incorporating chapters as the content is reflected in their course presentations. Nursing students remain the primary intended audience for *Nursing Now!* However, practicing nurses have reported that there is a sufficiently wide range of current issues and topics covered in enough depth as to be useful for their practice.

Another dichotomy that nurses face on a daily basis is the ability to hold onto key unchanging principles while working in a constantly changing environment. Simply stated, a nurse's ability to adapt to changes in the health-care system while remaining focused on providing high-quality care is the basis for successful professional practice. The only way that nurses will be able to effectively practice their profession in a demanding health-care system is to remain firmly rooted in those values and beliefs that have always served as their source of strength. Even more so than in the past, nurses need to look to each other for the inspiration and the strength that allow them to succeed. Professional organizations still serve as the single most powerful force for nurses, and membership in professional organizations is becoming increasingly important.

It is our belief that this book will help future nurses become familiar with the important issues and trends that affect the profession and health care. The nursing profession needs highly skilled nurses who can teach, do research, solve complicated client problems, provided highly skilled care, obtain advanced degrees, and have an effect on the political realm that so affects all aspects of life. The leaders of the profession will come from those students who have a clear understanding of what it means to be a professional nurse, and are willing to invest the effort in attaining their goals.

Joseph T. Catalano, PhD, RN

Acknowledgments

I would like to express my thanks to all of my students and colleagues who have over the years, shaped my thoughts and ideas about the nursing profession. I would also like to thank all the nurses who have contributed chapters to the book.

Mary Abadie, RN, PhD
Director, Family Health Care Center
Southern University
School of Nursing
Baton Rouge, Louisiana

Tonia Aiken, RN, BSN, JD
President and CEO,
Aiken Development Group
New Orleans, Louisiana

Sharon M. Bator, RN, MSN
Assistant Professor
Southern University
School of Nursing
Baton Rouge, Louisiana

Barbara Bellfield, MS, RNP-C, RN
Family Nurse Practitioner
Ventura County Public Health
Loma Vista Road
Ventura, California

Cynthia Bienemy, RN, PhD
Associate Professor
Southern University
School of Nursing
Baton Rouge, Louisiana

Sandra Brown, RN, DNS
Professor
Southern University
School of Nursing
Baton Rouge, Louisiana

Joseph T. Catalano, PhD, RN
Department Chair
Professor of Nursing
East Central University
Ada, Oklahoma

Lydia DeSantis, RN, PhD, FAAN
University of Miami
School of Nursing
Miami, Florida

Joan Anny Ellis, RN, PhD
Southern University
School of Nursing
Baton Rouge, Louisiana

Mary Evans, JD, RN
316 N. Tejon
Colorado Springs, Colorado

Betty L. Fomby-White, RN, PhD
Southern University
School of Nursing
Baton Rouge, Louisiana

Donna Gentile O'Donnell, RN, MSN
Deputy Health Commissioner (Retired)
Philadelphia, Pennsylvania

Anita H. Hansberry, RN, MS
Assistant Professor
Southern University
School of Nursing
Baton Rouge, Louisiana

Nicole Harder, RN, BN, MPA
Coordinator, Learning Laboratories
Helen Glass Centre for Nursing
Faculty of Nursing
University of Manitoba
Winnipeg, Manitoba, Canada

Jacqueline J. Hill, RN, PhD
Southern University
School of Nursing
Baton Rouge, Louisiana

Sharon W. Hutchinson, RN, PhD
Associate Professor
Southern University
School of Nursing
Baton Rouge, Louisiana

Roberta Mowdy, MS, RN
Instructor
Department of Nursing
East Central University
Ada, Oklahoma

Anyadie Onu, RN, MS
Assistant Professor
Southern University
School of Nursing
Baton Rouge, Louisiana

Janet S. Rami, RN, PhD
Southern University
School of Nursing
Baton Rouge, Louisiana

Mary Ann Remshardt, EdD, RN
Assistant Professor
Department of Nursing
East Central University
Ada, Oklahoma

Nancy C. Sharts-Hopko,
  RN, PhD, FAAN
Professor
Villanova University
Villanova, Pennsylvania

Enrika K. Singleton, RN, PhD
Professor
Southern University
School of Nursing
Baton Rouge, Louisiana

Kathleen Mary Young, RN,C, MA
Instructor
Western Michigan University
Kalamazoo, Michigan

Michelle Bunning, RN, MSN

Associate Professor
Good Samaritan College of Nursing
  and Health Science
Cincinnati, Ohio

Susan Golden, RN, MSN

Nursing Faculty
Eastern New Mexico University-Roswell
Roswell, New Mexico

Nancy Harms, RN, BS, BSN, MSN, PhD

Chair, Nursing Department
Midland Lutheran College
Fremont, Nebraska

Pamela D. Korte, RN, MSN, BSN

Associate Professor
Monroe Community College
Rochester, New York

Nancy E. Smith, MS, RN

Professor and Chair, Health Science Division
  and Nursing Department
Southern Maine Community College
South Portland, Maine

Arthur West, RN, BSN, MS

Lead Faculty, Nursing Department
Southeastern Community College
Whiteville, North Carolina

Michelle Willihnganz, RN, BSN, MS

Nursing Instructor
Rochester Community and Technical College
Rochester, New York

Contents

1

The Growth of Nursing

1

The Development of a Profession

Joseph T. Catalano

Learning Objectives

After completing this chapter, the reader will be able to:

- Define the terms *position, job, occupation,* and *profession.*
- Compare the three approaches to defining a profession.
- Analyze those traits defining a profession that nursing has attained.
- Evaluate why nursing has failed to attain some of the traits that define a profession.
- Correlate the concept of power with its important characteristics.

WHAT IS A PROFESSION?

Since the time of Florence Nightingale, each generation of nurses, in their own way, has fostered the movement to professionalize the image of nurses and nursing. The struggle to change the status of nurses from that of female domestic servants to one of high-level health-care providers who base their protocols on scientific principles has been a primary goal of nursing's leaders for many years. Yet some people, both inside and outside of the profession of nursing, question whether the search for and attainment of professional status is worth the effort and price that must ultimately be paid.

At some levels in nursing, the question of **professionalism** takes on immense significance. However, to the busy **staff nurse**—who is trying to allocate client assignments for a shift; distribute the medications at 9 a.m. to 24 clients; and supervise two aides, a licensed practical nurse (LPN) or licensed vocational nurse (LVN), and a nursing student—the issue may not seem very significant at all.

Indeed, when nurses were first developing their identity separately from that of physicians, there was no thought about their being part of a **profession.** Over the years, as the scope of practice has expanded and the responsibilities have increased, nurses have increasingly begun to consider what they do as professional activities.

This chapter presents some of the current thoughts concerning professions and where nursing stands in relationship to these viewpoints.

APPROACHES TO DEFINING A PROFESSION

In common usage, terms such as *position, job, occupation, profession, professional,* and *professionalism* often are used interchangeably and incorrectly. The following definitions will clarify what is meant by these terms within this text.

Position: A group of tasks assigned to one individual.

Job: A group of positions that are similar in nature and level of skill that can be carried out by one or more individuals.

Occupation: A group of jobs that are similar in type of work and that are usually found throughout an industry or work environment.

Profession: A type of occupation that meets certain criteria (discussed later in this chapter) that raise it to a level above that of an occupation.

Professional: A person who belongs to and practices a profession. (The term *professional* is probably the most misused of all these terms when describing people who are clearly involved in jobs or occupations, such as a "professional truck driver," "professional football player," or even "professional thief.")

Professionalism: The demonstration of high-level personal, ethical, and skill characteristics of a member of a profession.[1]

Experts in social science have been attempting to develop a "foolproof" approach to determine what constitutes a profession for almost 100 years, but with only minimal success. Three common models are the process approach, the power approach, and, most widely accepted, the trait approach.

Process Approach

The process approach views all occupations as points of development into a profession along a continuum ranging from position to profession.
Continuum of Professional Development:
        Position ↔ Profession
Using this approach, the question becomes not whether nursing and truck driving are professions, but where they are located along the continuum.

What Do You Think?

Do you really care if nursing is a profession? How will it affect the way you practice nursing?

> *Over the years, as the scope of practice has expanded and the responsibilities have increased, nurses have increasingly begun to consider what they do to be professional activities.*

Occupations such as medicine, law, and the ministry are widely accepted by the public as being closest to the professional end of the continuum.[2] Other occupations may be less clearly defined.

The major difficulty with this approach is that it lacks criteria on which to base judgments. Final determination of the status of an occupation or profession depends almost completely on public perception of the activities of that occupation. Nursing has always had a rather poor public image when it comes to being viewed as a profession.

Power Approach

The power approach uses two criteria to define a profession:

1. How much independence of practice does this occupation have?
2. How much power does this occupation control?

The concept of power is discussed later in this chapter, but in this context it refers to political power and the amount of money that the person in that occupation earns.[3]

Using this determinant, occupations such as medicine, law, and **politics** clearly would be considered professions. The members of these occupations earn high incomes, practice their skills with a great deal of independence, and exercise significant power over individuals, the public, and the political community, both individually and in organized groups. The ministry is generally perceived as having power and influence. However, most persons in this group, except for a few individuals, such as television evangelists, have relatively low-income levels. Nursing, of course, with its relatively lower salaries, low membership in professional organizations, and perceived lack of political power, would clearly not meet the power criteria for a profession.

The question that comes to mind is whether power, independence of practice, and high income are the only elements that determine professional status. Although those three factors confer status in our culture, other elements can be considered significant in how a profession is viewed. For example, to many people, members of the clergy have a great deal of power when they act as counselors, speakers of the truth, and community leaders.

Trait Approach

Of the many researchers and theorists who have attempted to identify the traits that define a profession, Abraham Flexner, Elizabeth Bixler, and Eliza Pavalko are most widely accepted as the leaders in the field. These three social scientists have determined that the following common characteristics are important:

- High intellectual level
- High level of individual responsibility and **accountability**
- Specialized body of knowledge
- Knowledge that can be learned in institutions of higher education
- Public service and altruistic activities
- Public service valued over financial gain
- Relatively high degree of **autonomy** and independence of practice
- Need for a well-organized and strong organization representing the members of the profession and controlling the quality of practice
- A **code of ethics** that guides the members of the profession in their practice

- Strong professional identity and commitment to the development of the profession
- Demonstration of professional competency and possession of a legally recognized license[4]

NURSING AS A PROFESSION

How does nursing compare with other professions when measured against these widely accepted professional traits? The profession of nursing meets most of the criteria but falls short in a few areas.

High Intellectual Level of Functioning

In the early stages of the development of nursing practice, this criterion did not apply. Florence Nightingale raised the bar for education, and graduates of her school were considered to be highly educated in comparison with other women of that time. However, most of the tasks performed by these early nurses are generally considered by today's standards to be menial and routine.

On the other hand, as health care has advanced and made great strides in technology, pharmacology, and all branches of the physical sciences, a high level of intellectual functioning is required for even relatively simple nursing tasks, such as taking a client's temperature or blood pressure using automated equipment. Nurses use assessment skills and knowledge, have the ability to reason, and make routine judgments based on clients' conditions daily. Without a doubt, professional nurses must and do function at a high intellectual level.

High Level of Individual Responsibility and Accountability

Not too long ago, a nurse was rarely, if ever, named as a defendant in a malpractice suit. The public, in general, did not view nurses as having enough knowledge to be held accountable for errors that were made in client care. This is not the case in the health-care system today. Nurses are often the primary, and frequently the only, defendants named when errors are made that result in injury to the client. Nurses must be accountable and demonstrate a high level of individual responsibility for the care and services they provide.[5]

The concept of accountability has legal, ethical, and professional implications that include accepting responsibility for actions taken to provide client care, as well as accepting responsibility for the consequences of actions that are not performed. Nurses can no longer state that "the physician told me to do it" as a method of avoiding responsibility for their actions.

Specialized Body of Knowledge

Most early nursing skills were based either on traditional ways of doing things or on the intuitive knowledge of the individual nurse. As nursing developed into an identifiable, separate discipline, a specialized body of knowledge called "nursing science" was compiled through the research efforts of nurses with advanced educational degrees.[6] As the body of specialized nursing knowledge continues to grow, it forms a theoretical basis for the practice of nursing today. As more nurses obtain advanced degrees, conduct research, and develop philosophies and theories about nursing, this body of knowledge will increase in scope and quantity.

Evidence-Based Practice

In professional nursing today, there is an increasing emphasis on evidence-based practice. Almost all the currently used nursing theories address this issue in

some way. Simply stated, evidence-based practice is the practice of nursing in which interventions are based on data from research that demonstrates that they are appropriate and successful. It involves a systematic process of uncovering, evaluating, and using information from research as the basis for deciding about and providing client care.[7] Many nursing practices and interventions of the past were performed merely because they had always been done that way (accustomed practice) or because of deductions from physiological or pathophysiological information. Clients are now more sophisticated and knowledgeable about health-care issues and demand a higher level of knowledge and skill from their health-care providers.

The development of information technology has made evidence-based practice in nursing a reality. In the past, nurses relied primarily on units within their own facilities for information about the success of treatments, decisions about health care, and outcomes for clients. Nursing education now requires nursing students to perform Web-based research for papers and projects, so that by the time of graduation, they feel comfortable accessing a wide range of the best and most current information through electronic sources. Of course, one of the key limiting factors of evidence-based practice is the quality of the information on which the practice is based. Evaluating the quality of information on the Web can be difficult at times.

The first step in developing an evidence-based practice is to identify exactly what the intervention is supposed to accomplish. Once the goal or client outcome is identified, the nurse needs to evaluate current practices to determine whether or not they are achieving the desired client outcomes. If they are unsuccessful, or if the nurse feels they can be more efficient with fewer complications, then research sources need to be collected. These can be from published journal articles (either electronic or hard copy) and from presentations at research or practice conferences, which often present the most current information. Then a plan should be developed to implement the new findings. This process can be applied to changing policy and procedures or developing training programs for facility staff. Research data should always be used when initiating new practices or modifying old ones (see Chapter 24).

Issues Now

Web Sites: Friend or Foe?

Have a paper or report to do for class? Need information on pheochromocytoma, Smith-Strang disease, Kawasaki's disease? No problem, look it up on the Web, right? Well, yes and no. Without any question, there is a tremendous amount of information about almost any subject available just a few mouse clicks away. But the bigger question is: how good is that information? The truth of the matter is that anyone can post almost anything on-line these days, and there are no organizations or agencies that oversee or review the information for quality, accuracy, or objectivity. So how are you supposed to know what is good and what is not? Although there is no foolproof method for determining the quality of any given Web site, some telltale markers can point you in the right direction when you are rating the quality of the information you seek.

Marker 1: Peer Review

All major professional journals have a peer review process that requires any manuscripts submitted to be reviewed by two or three professionals who are considered experts, or at least knowledgeable in the subject matter. Peer review is one of the key elements in ensuring the accuracy of the information in the manuscript. When considering a Web source, look for a clear statement of the source of the information and how that information is reviewed. If the information is from an established source, such as a recognized professional journal, then it has been peer reviewed and has a higher degree of accuracy. Examine the format and writing style of the document. If it seems to be very choppy, or if the style, tone, or person the article is written in changes throughout the article, it is an indication that it was not well edited and probably not peer reviewed. Use the information with caution.

Marker 2: Author Credentials

The name of the author and his or her titles and credentials should be listed. Be cautious if no author or publisher is listed. Of course, anyone can use another person's name as the author, but it is relatively easy to cross-check authors' names through other databases, such as those found in libraries. Before accepting the information as gospel, it is probably worth looking up the author and seeing what other articles or books he or she has written. Another key to establishing author credentials is to establish to whom the Web site belongs. In general, personal Web pages are less likely to contain authoritative information. You can also look at the last three letters in the Web site address. The ones that end in ".gov," ".org," or ".edu" will tend to have higher-quality information. Also, see whether the information has a copyright. If the information is copyrighted, then the person felt strongly enough about what he or she was posting to go to the effort of making sure no one else could use it as their original information.

Marker 3: Prejudice and Bias

Although there is almost always a small degree of prejudice and bias in all written material, most legitimate authors will strive to be as objective as possible. Many

(continued)

Issues Now (continued)

times, if you read a document with a critical eye, you can discern obvious prejudicial viewpoints. See if the author has a vested interest in the content of the document. You can be pretty sure that an article about the effects of tobacco use on the respiratory system written by a scientist who was hired by the R. J. Reynolds Company would have a decidedly different viewpoint than an article written by a scientist who was employed by the National Health Information Center. See if contact information is provided by the author and who the sponsor or publisher of the document is. If these are not provided, be suspicious about the information.

Marker 4: Timeliness

Of course, all of us want the most recent information we can find and sometimes mistakenly make the assumption that because it is on the Web, it is new. In reality, professional journals that post their partial-text or full-text articles on their Web sites usually take anywhere from 6 to 9 months to do so. If you want absolutely the most current information, the hard-copy journal texts found in the library still are your best bet. Some forms of the Web have been around for as long as 10 years now, so some of the material can be very outdated. See if you can determine when the site was last updated and how extensively the information was revised. It is also a good practice to look to other sources (Web, journals, books, etc.) to compare the material for currency. Many Web sites have links where you can access other related information. If those links have messages such as "Page discontinued" or "Link no longer available," be extremely cautious with the information. Good links should connect you to other reliable sites.

Marker 5: Presentation

Although the old saying is that "you can't tell a book by its cover," experienced Web surfers can often tell a lot about a Web site by its presentation. Some look well developed and professional and others look very amateurish. There is no guarantee that the slick-looking Web sites are better, but it is one factor to consider in the overall evaluation of the information you are seeking. Take a look at the graphics. They should be balanced with the text and help explain or demonstrate information in the text. If the graphics seem to be just decorative, it should raise a red flag about the content of the site. Some sites use a compressed format that requires special programs such as Adobe Acrobat to view them. If you do not have access to these programs, then the information in the site is unusable. Move on to the next site.

In summary, the Internet can be a valuable source of information about a wide variety of subjects. However, each source needs to be evaluated carefully. Following the five markers discussed here will place you on the path to deciding the quality of the information presented in any Web site.

Sources: DeBourgh, GA: Using Web technology in a clinical nursing course. Nurse Educator 26(5):227–233, 2001.

Take a byte: Evaluating Web sites. American Nursing Student 5(1):1, 2001.

Thurmond, VA: Considering theory in assessing quality of Web-based courses. Nurse Educator 27(1):20–24, 2002.

Timmons, S: Use of the Internet by patients: Not a threat to nursing, but an opportunity? Nurse Education Today 21(2):104–109, 2001.

www.mlanet.org/resources/medspeak/topten.html

Public Service and Altruistic Activities

Almost all major nursing theorists, when defining nursing, include a statement that refers to a goal of helping clients adapt to illness and achieve their highest level of functioning. The public (variously referred to as consumers, patients, clients, individuals, or humans) is the focal point of all nursing models and nursing practice. The public service function of nursing has always been recognized and acknowledged by society's willingness to continue to educate nurses in public, tax-supported institutions as well as in private schools. In addition, nursing has been viewed universally as an altruistic profession composed of selfless individuals who place the lives and well-being of their clients above their personal safety. In the earliest days, dedicated nurses provided care for victims of deadly plagues with little regard for their own welfare. Today, nurses are found in remote and often hostile areas, providing care for the sick and dying, working 12-hour shifts, being "on call," and working rotating shifts.

Few individuals enter nursing in order to become rich and famous. It is likely that those who do so for these reasons quickly become disappointed. Although the pay scale has increased tremendously since the 1990s, nursing is, at best, a middle-income occupation. Surveys among students entering nursing programs continue to indicate that the primary reason for wishing to become a nurse is to "help others" or "make a difference" in someone's life and to have "job security." Rarely do these beginning students include "to make a lot of money" as their motivation.[7]

Well-Organized and Strong Representation

Professional organizations represent the members of the profession and control the quality of professional practice. The National League for Nursing (NLN) and the American Nurses Association (ANA) are the two major national organizations that represent nursing in today's health-care system. The NLN is primarily responsible for regulating the quality of the educational programs that prepare nurses for the practice of nursing, whereas the ANA is more concerned with the quality of nursing practice in the daily health-care setting. These and other organizations are discussed in more detail in Chapter 3.

Both these groups are well organized, but neither can be considered powerful when compared with other professional organizations, such as the American Hospital Association, the American Medical Association (AMA), or the American Bar Association (ABA). One reason for their lack of strength is that fewer than 10 percent of all nurses in the United States are members of any professional organization at the national level.[3] Many nurses do belong to specialty organizations that represent a specific area of practice, but these lack sufficient political power to produce changes in health-care laws and policies at the national level.

> " Evidence-based practice is the practice of nursing in which interventions are based on data from research that demonstrates that they are appropriate and successful. "

Nurses' Code of Ethics

Nursing has several codes of ethics that are used to guide nursing practice. The ANA Code of Ethics for Nurses, the most widely used in the United States, was first published in 1971, updated in 1985, and last updated in 2001. The current ANA Code of Ethics, while maintaining the integrity found in earlier versions, is now more relevant to current health-care and nursing practices. This code of ethics is recognized by other professions as a standard with which others are compared. The nurses' code of ethics and its implications are discussed in greater detail in Chapter 7.

Competency and Professional License

Nurses must pass a national licensure examination to demonstrate that they are qualified to practice nursing. Only after passing this examination are nurses allowed to practice. The granting of a nursing **license** is a legal activity conducted by the individual state under the **regulations** contained in that state's nurse practice act.

WHEN NURSING FALLS SHORT OF THE CRITERIA

Before Florence Nightingale practiced nursing, people considered it to be unnecessary, if not outright dangerous, to educate nurses through independent nursing programs in publicly supported educational institutions. As nursing has developed, particularly in the United States, the recognition of the intellectual nature of the practice, as well as the vast amount of knowledge required for the job, has led to a belief by some nursing leaders that college education for nurses is now a necessity.

Nursing is the only major discipline that does not require its members to hold at least a baccalaureate degree in order to obtain licensure. Although the number of diploma programs in nursing has decreased tremendously since 1990, associate degree programs continue to maintain high enrollment and graduate large numbers of individuals. Whether a baccalaureate degree nursing program should be the minimum requirement for entry-level nurses remains a hotly debated issue.[1,6,7,10]

Autonomy and Independence of Practice

Historically, the handmaiden or servant relationship of the nurse to the physician was widely accepted. It was based on several factors, including social norms. For example, women became nurses, whereas men became physicians; women were subservient to men, the nature of the work being such that nurses cleaned and physicians cured. In terms of the relative levels of education of the two groups, the average nursing program lasted for 1 year, whereas physician education lasted for 6 to 8 years.

Unfortunately, despite efforts to expand nursing practice into more independent areas through updated nurse practice legislation, nursing retains much of its subservient image. In reality, nursing is both an independent and interdependent discipline. Nurses in all health-care settings must work closely with physicians, hospital administrators, pharmacists, and other groups in the provision of care. In some cases, nurses in **advanced practice** roles, such as **nurse practitioners,** can and do establish their own independent practices. Most state **nurse practice acts** allow nurses more independence in their practice than they realize. To be considered a true profession, nursing will need to be recognized by other disciplines as having practitioners who practice nursing independently.

Professional Identity and Development

The issue of job versus career is in question here. A job is a group of positions, similar in nature and level of skill, that can be carried out by one or more individuals. There is relatively little commitment to a job, and many individuals move from one job to another with little regard to the long-term outcomes. A career, in contrast, is usually viewed as a person's major lifework, which progresses and develops as the person grows older. Careers and professions have many of the same characteristics, including a formal education, full-time employment, requirement for lifelong learning, and a dedication to what is being achieved. Although an increasing number of nurses view nursing as their life's work, many still treat nursing more as a job.

The problem becomes circular. The reason nurses lack a strong professional identity and do not consider nursing a lifelong career is because nursing does not have full status as a profession. Until nurses are fully committed to the profession of nursing, identify with it as a profession, and are dedicated to its future development, nursing will probably not achieve professional status.

MEMBERS OF THE HEALTH-CARE TEAM

The health-care delivery system employs large numbers of diagnosticians, technicians, direct care providers, administrators, and support staff (Table 1.1). It is estimated that there are more than 300 job titles used to describe health-care workers. Among these are nurses, physicians, physician assistants, social workers, physical therapists, occupational therapists, respiratory therapists, clinical psychologists, and pharmacists. All these individuals provide services that are essential to daily operation of the health-care delivery system in this country.

Of particular importance among this array of health-care workers are various types of nurses: registered nurses, licensed practical (vocational) nurses, nurse practitioners, case managers, and clinical nurse specialists. Each of these requires a different type of educational background, clinical expertise, and, sometimes, professional credentialing. In general, all nurses make valuable contributions within the health-care delivery system. There has been an increased demand for nurses who are educated to deliver care in the community setting and in long-term health-care settings rather than in the hospital. There has also been a need for nurse case managers who are prepared to coordinate care for

Table 1.1 Other Key Health-Care Team Members

Title	Credential	Practice
Physician (MD)	License—Medical	Medical—limited only by specialization Some serve as primary care providers
Physician (DO)	License—Osteopath	Medical, with focus on body movement and holistic health—similar to MD Can serve as primary care providers
Physician (DC)	License—Chiropractor	Limited—focus on spinal column and nervous system Unable to prescribe medications
Physician (DPM)	License—Podiatry	Limited—foot problems Can prescribe medications, perform foot surgery
Physician Assistant	Certification—no individual license	Practices on physician's license Practice limited by medical practice act and wishes of supervising physician
Social Worker	License	Increasingly important as health care becomes more complex Resolves financial, housing, psychosocial, and employment problems, does discharge planning and assists clients in transfer between facilities May serve in case management roles to coordinate services
Physical Therapist	License	Focuses on helping clients maintain or regain the highest level of function possible after strokes, spinal cord injury, arthritis, or residual effects of traumatic accidents. Helps prevent physical decline and regain the ability to groom, eat, and walk through individualized range of motion and exercise programs. Therapy occurs in hospitals, clinics, or the community.
Respiratory Therapist	License	Strives to restore normal or as near normal pulmonary functioning as possible by conducting diagnostic tests and administering treatments that have been prescribed by a physician
Clinical Psychologist	License	Helps clients to manage mental health problems Private practice, clinics
Pharmacist	License	Distributes prescribed and over-the-counter medications, educates clients, monitors appropriate medication selections, detects interactions and untoward responses in community pharmacies and institutional settings Valuable resource for nurses

vulnerable populations requiring costly services over extended periods. Nursing education programs are attempting to meet these needs by preparing individuals who can practice independently and autonomously, network, collaborate, and coordinate services. These programs also offer more clinical experiences in rehabilitation, nursing home, and community settings.

Registered Nurses, Licensed Practical Nurses, and Unlicensed Assistive Personnel

Registered nurses (RNs) who have been educated at the associate, diploma, or baccalaureate level have traditionally been considered the cornerstone of the current health-care delivery system. In the past, most RNs worked within hospital settings and provided direct client care and nursing administration functions within these facilities. Owing to past trends in health-care funding, there were fewer hospital admissions, which temporarily decreased the demand for RNs in acute care facilities and increased the need for well-prepared nurses who could function autonomously within the community. However, current trends in population and health care have demonstrated a need for RNs in both acute care and community settings. The need still remains within institutional settings for licensed practical nurses (LPN) and unlicensed assistive personnel (UAP) who work under the supervision of an RN. This pattern of care is particularly evident in nursing homes and other long-term care facilities.[2]

Advanced Practice Nurses

For individuals who are unfamiliar with the health-care delivery system, it is sometimes difficult to understand the similarities and differences between nursing titles and roles. This confusion is particularly evident in the case of clinical nurse specialists (CNSs) and nurse practitioners (NPs), who are sometimes collectively referred to as advanced practice registered nurses (APRNs).[4]

The Nurse Practitioner. In general, NPs are prepared to provide direct client care in primary care settings, focusing on health promotion, illness prevention, early diagnosis, and treatment of common health problems. Their educational preparation varies, but in most cases individuals successfully complete a graduate nurse practitioner program and are certified by the American Nurses Credentialing Center (ANCC) or an appropriate professional nursing organization. Depending on the individual state nurse practice act, NPs have a range of responsibilities for diagnosing diseases and prescribing both treatments and medications. A growing number of states now grant NPs direct third-party reimbursement for their services without a physician.

The Clinical Nurse Specialist. Clinical nurse specialists usually practice in secondary or tertiary care settings and focus on care of individuals whom are experiencing an acute illness or an exacerbation of a chronic condition. In general, they are prepared at the graduate level and are ANCC certified. These highly skilled practitioners are comfortable working in high-tech environments with seriously ill individuals and their families. Because of the nature of their work, they are excellent health-care educators and physician collaborators.

Attempts have been made to combine the roles of the CNS and NP so that the best qualities of both roles are preserved. The goal of this combination is to provide high-quality care to individuals in a wide array of health-care settings who have a wide range of health problems. Advocates of this movement include the NLN, the American Association of Colleges of Nursing (AACN), and the ANA. Titling for this new blended role is unconfirmed, and state legislatures may make the final decisions through their licensing laws. As such, titling, educational preparation, and practice privileges will probably vary from one state to another.

Case Managers

One argument for the blended NP–CNS role is the need for case managers who possess the expertise of both levels of preparation. Case managers coordinate services for clients with high-risk or long-term health problems who have access to the full continuum of health-care services. Case managers provide services in various settings, such as acute care facilities, rehabilitation centers, and community agencies. They also work for managed-care companies, insurance companies, and private case management agencies. Their roles vary according to the circumstances of their employment; however, their overall goal is to coordinate the use of health-care services in the most efficient and cost-effective manner possible.

Case management is the glue that holds health-care services together across practitioners, agencies, funding sources, locations, and time. Titling, educational preparation, and certification of nurse case managers are now available. The ANCC has developed certification eligibility criteria for nurse case managers, and an examination is available. At this time, case managers can be physicians, social workers, registered nurses, and even well-intentioned laypersons with little health-care education.

EMPOWERMENT IN NURSING

One concern that has plagued nursing, almost from its development as a separate health-care specialty, is the relatively large amount of personal responsibility shouldered by nurses combined with a relatively small amount of control over their practice. Even in the more enlightened atmosphere of today's society, with its concerns about equal opportunity, equal pay, and collegial relationships, many nurses still seem uncomfortable with the concepts of power and control in their practice. Their discomfort may arise from the belief that nursing is a helping and caring profession whose goals are separate from issues of power.

Historically, nurses have never had much power, and previous attempts at gaining power and control over their practice have been met with much resistance from groups who benefit from keeping nurses powerless. Nevertheless, all nurses use power in their daily practice, even if they do not realize it. Until nurses understand the sources of their power, how to increase it, and how to use it in providing client care, they will be relegated to a subservient position in the health-care system.

The Nature of Power
The term *power* has many meanings. From the standpoint of nursing, power is probably best defined as the ability or capacity to exert influence over another person or group of persons. In other words, power is the ability to get other people to do things even when they do not want to do them. Although power in itself is neither good nor bad, it can be used to produce either good or bad results.

Power is always a two-way street. By its very definition, when power is exerted by one person, another person is affected; that is, the use of power by one person requires that another person give up some of his or her power. Individuals are always in a state of change, either increasing their power or losing some; the balance of power rarely remains static. **Empowerment** refers to the increased amount of power that an individual or group is either given or gains.

Origins of Power
If power is such an important part of nursing and the practice of nurses, where does it come from? Although there are many sources, some of them would be inappropriate or unacceptable for those in a helping and caring profession. The following list includes some of the more accessible and acceptable sources of power that nurses should consider using in their practice.[3,8,9] These sources are:

- Referent
- Expert
- Reward
- Coercive
- Legitimate
- Collective

Referent Power
The referent source of power depends on establishing and maintaining a close personal relationship with someone. In any close personal relationship, one individual often will do something he or she would really rather not do because of the relationship. This ability to change the actions of another is an exercise of power.

Nurses often obtain power from this source when they establish and maintain good therapeutic relationships with their clients. Clients take medications, tolerate uncomfortable treatments, and participate in demanding activities that they would clearly prefer to avoid because the nurse has good relationships with them. Likewise, nurses who have good collegial relationships with other nurses, departments, and physicians are often able to obtain what they want from these individuals or groups in providing care to clients.

Expert Power

The expert source of power derives from the amount of knowledge, skill, or expertise that an individual or group has. This power source is exercised by the individual or group when knowledge, skills, or expertise is either used or withheld in order to influence the behavior of others. Nurses should have at least a minimal amount of this type of power because of their education and experience. It follows logically that increasing the level of nurses' education will, or should, increase this expert power. As nurses attain and remain in positions of power longer, the increased experience will also aid the use of expert power. Nurses in advanced practice roles are good examples of those who have expert power. Their additional education and experience provide these nurses with the ability to practice skills at a higher level than nurses prepared at the basic education level.

> *By demonstrating their knowledge of the client's condition, recent laboratory tests, and other elements that are vital in the client's recovery, nurses demonstrate their expert power. This knowledge may increase the amount of respect that they are given by physicians.*

By demonstrating their knowledge of the client's condition, recent laboratory tests, and other elements that are vital in the client's recovery, nurses demonstrate their expert power. This knowledge may increase the amount of respect they are given by physicians. Nurses access this expert source of power when they use their knowledge to teach, counsel, or motivate clients to follow a plan of care. Nurses can also use expert power when dealing with physicians.

Power of Rewards

The reward source of power depends on the ability of one person to grant another some type of reward for specific behaviors or changes in behavior. The rewards can take on many different forms, including personal favors, promotions, money, expanded privileges, and eradication of punishments. Nurses, in their daily provision of care, can use this source of power to influence client behavior. For example, a nurse can give a client extra praise for completing the prescribed range-of-motion exercises. There are many aspects of the daily care of clients over which nurses have a substantial amount of reward power. This reward source of power is also the underlying principle in the process of behavior modification.

Coercive Power

The coercive source of power is the flip side of the reward source. The ability to punish, withhold rewards, and threaten punishment is the key element underlying the coercive source of power. Although nurses do have access to this source of power, it is probably one that they use minimally, if at all. Not only does the use of the coercive source of power destroy therapeutic and personal relationships, but it can also be considered unethical and even illegal in certain situations. Threatening clients with an injection if they do not take their oral medications may motivate them to take those medications, but it is generally not considered to be a good example of a therapeutic communication technique.

Issues in Practice

Kasey is a RN who has worked on the busy surgical unit of a large city hospital for the past 6 years. As one of three RNs on the unit's day shift, she often serves as the charge nurse when the assigned charge nurse has a day off. She is hard working, caring, and well organized and provides high-quality care for the often very unstable postoperative clients they receive on a daily basis.

Approximately 2 weeks ago, Kasey's mother was admitted for a high-risk surgical removal of a brain tumor that was not responding to chemotherapy or radiation therapy. The surgery did not go well, and Kasey's mother was admitted to the surgical unit after the procedure. During the past 2 weeks, she has shown a gradual but steady decline in condition and is no longer able to recognize her family, speak, or do any self care. It is believed she will probably not live more than a week longer.

Per hospital policy, Kasey is not assigned to care for her mother; however, during her shifts, Kasey is spending more and more time with her mother, sometimes to the detriment of her assigned clients. She is also beginning to make more demands on the unit nursing staff, often overseeing their care and requesting that only certain nurses care for her mother. One of the other nurses on the unit suggested that Kasey's mother be moved to a less specialized unit. When Kasey heard about the suggestion, she became livid and loudly scolded the nurse for her insensitivity in the middle of the nurses' station.

QUESTIONS FOR THOUGHT

1. Is the practice of not allowing nurses to provide care for their relatives evidence-based or accustomed practice?
2. Identify the steps in making this policy evidence based.
3. Do you think nurses should be allowed to care for relatives? Why? Why not?

Legitimate Power

The legitimate source of power depends on a legislative or legal act that gives the individual or organization a right to make decisions that they might not otherwise have the authority to make. Most obviously, political figures and **legislators** have this source of power. This power can also be disseminated and delegated to others through legislative acts. In nursing, the state board of nursing has access to the legitimate source of power because of its establishment under the nurse practice act of that state. Similarly, nurses have access to the legitimate source of power when they are licensed by the state under the provisions in the nurse practice act or when they are appointed to positions within a health-care agency. Nursing decisions made about client care can come only from individuals who have a legitimate source of power to make those decisions—that is, licensed nurses.

Collective Power

The collective source of power is often used in a broader context than individual client care and is the underlying source for many other sources of power. When a large group of individuals who have similar beliefs, desires, or needs become organized, a collective source of power exists.[6] For individuals who belong to professions, the professional organization is the focal point for this source of power. The main goal of any organization is to influence policies that affect the members of the organization. This influence is usually in the form of political activities carried out by politicians and **lobbyists.**

Professional organizations that can deliver large numbers of votes have a powerful means of influencing politicians. The use of the collective source of power contains elements of reward, coercive, expert, and even referent sources. Each source may come into play at one time or another.

How to Increase Power in Nursing

Despite some feelings of powerlessness, nurses really do have access to some important, and rather substantial, sources of power. What can nurses, either as individuals or as a group, do to increase their power?

Professional Unity

Probably the first, and certainly the most important, way in which nurses can gain power in all areas is through professional unity. The most powerful groups are those that are best organized and most united. The power that a professional organization has is directly related to the size of its membership. According to the ANA, there are approximately 2.7 million nurses in the United States. It is not difficult to imagine the power that the ANA could have to influence legislators and legislation if all of those nurses were members of the organization rather than the 250,000 who actually do belong. This point—that nurses need to belong to their national nursing organization—cannot be emphasized too much.

Political Activity

A second way in which nurses can gain power is by becoming involved in **political action.** Although this produces discomfort in many, nurses must realize that they are affected by politics and political decisions in every phase of their daily nursing activities.

The simple truth is that, if nurses do not become involved in politics and participate in important legislation that influences their practice, someone other than nurses will be making those decisions for them. Nurses need to become involved in political activities from local to national levels. The average legislator knows little about issues such as clients' rights, national health insurance, quality of nursing care, third-party reimbursement for nurses, and expanded practice roles for nurses, yet they make decisions about these issues almost daily. It would seem logical that more informed and better decisions could be made if nurses took an active part in the legislative process.

> *Probably the first, and certainly the most important, way in which nurses can gain power in all areas is through professional unity. The most powerful groups are those that are best organized and most united.*

Accountability and Professionalism

A third method of increasing power is by demonstrating the characteristics of accountability and professionalism. Nursing has made great strides in these two areas in recent years. Nurses, through professional organizations, have been working hard to establish standards for high-quality client care. More important, nurses are now concerned with demonstrating competence and delivering high-quality client care through processes such as peer review and evaluation. By accepting responsibility for the care that they provide and by setting the standards to guide that care, nurses are taking the power to govern nursing away from non-nursing groups.

Networking

Finally, nurses can gain power through establishing a nurse support network. It is common knowledge that the "old boy" system remains alive and well in many segments of our seemingly enlightened 21st century society. The old boy system, which is found in most large organizations ranging from universities to businesses and governmental agencies, provides individuals, usually men, with the encouragement, support, and nurturing that allow them to move up quickly through the ranks in the organization to achieve high administrative positions. An important element in making this system work involves never criticizing another "old boy" in public, even though there may be major differences of opinion in private. Presentation of a united front is extremely important in maintaining power within this system. Nursing and nursing organizations have never had this type of system for the advancement of nurses.

Part of the difficulty in establishing a nurse support network arises from the fact that nurses have not been in high-level positions for very long. The framework for a support system for nurses is now in place; with some commitment to the concept and some activity, it can grow into a well-developed network to allow the brightest, best, and most ambitious people in the profession to achieve high-level positions.

Future Trends in the Nursing Profession

Clearly, it would be difficult to make an airtight case for nursing as a profession. Yet nursing does meet many of the criteria proposed for a profession. Although it would probably be most accurate to call nursing a developing or aspiring profession, for the purposes of this book, nursing will be referred to as a profession. Only when nurses begin to think of nursing as a profession, work toward raising the educational standards for entry level, and begin practicing independently as professionals, will the status of profession become a reality for nursing. The movement of any discipline from the status of occupation to one of profession is a dynamic and ongoing process with many considerations.

All the experts now predict a severe shortage of professional nurses, ranging from 200,000 to 800,000, by the year 2020. In the past, the way that nursing shortages were handled was to use a quick-fix method of producing more nurses in a shorter period of time by reducing the educational requirements. The current nursing education system is producing approximately 40,000 graduates from diploma and associate degree programs every year.[10] Although this number may help alleviate the nursing shortage, the more critical question to ask is whether this level of education is going to prepare nurses to meet the challenges of a rapidly changing and demanding health-care system into the 21st century.

As the national employment picture continues to evolve for registered nurses from bedside caregivers to coordinators of care, and as financial resources become stressed, perhaps more nurses will begin to look on what they do as a lifelong commitment. Professional commitment is a complicated issue, but little doubt exists that nurses will not have increased independence of practice until they begin to demonstrate that they are professionals committed to the field of nursing.

Conclusion

Ongoing changes in the health-care system will have a major impact on how and where nursing is practiced, and even on who practices it. Unless nurses become involved in decisions about the direction in which health care is going, band together

as a profession, and exert some of their tremendous potential power, politicians, physicians, hospital administrators, and insurance companies will ultimately be shaping their future. The move toward mandated staffing ratios is one way that nurses are demonstrating their power to achieve a goal when they band together and exert power as a group.

Nursing has taken great strides forward in achieving professional status in the health-care system. Currently, many nurses accept the premise that nursing is a profession and therefore are not very concerned about furthering the process. Even as nursing has matured and evolved into a field of study with an identifiable body of knowledge, the questions and problems that have plagued this profession persist. In addition, advances in technology, management, and society have raised new questions about the nature and role of nursing in the health-care system. Only by understanding and exploring the issues of professionalism will nurses be prepared to practice effectively in the present and meet the complex challenges of the future.

Issues in Practice

Mandatory Staffing Ratios: The California Experience

California was the first state that approved laws that mandate nurse-to-client staffing ratios (Table 1.2). Guidelines were developed in January 2002 and went into effect in January 2004.

Initial studies of the effects of the mandatory staffing ratios in California have disproved the California Hospital Association's claim that they would be too costly and cause the closing of hospital units, if not entire institutions. The estimated cost to meet the mandated ratios was between 1 and 1.7 percent, or approximately $217,000 per hospital. Although the cost estimates seem to be fairly accurate, the overall effect was only marginal for hospitals' bottom lines. It did not improve the profit margin but it did not significantly decrease it either.

It has been more difficult to come up with explanations of why this has occurred. Nursing groups claim that the better staffing ratios produce better client care, which in turn results in reduced costs for insurance and settlements from malpractice law suits. Others believe that hospitals, in meeting the mandatory staffing levels, are using fewer of the very expensive agency nurses. All groups

Table 1.2 California Proposed Nurse-to-Client Ratios (April 2002)

Hospital Unit	Ratio
Intensive care unit	1:2*
Operating room	1:1*
Neonatal ICU	1:2*
Intermediate care nursery	1:4
Well baby nursery	1:8*
Postpartum (multiple births never to exceed 8 per nurse)	1:8 (1:4 couples; 1:6 mothers only)
Labor and delivery	1:2
Postanesthesia care unit (recovery room)	1:2
Emergency departments	1:4 (1:2 critical; 1:1 trauma)
Burn unit	1:2
Pediatrics	1:4
Step-down/telemetry	1:4
Specialty care (oncology)	1:5
Telemetry unit	1:5
General medical–surgical	1:6 initially 1:5 phased in
Behavioral health psychiatric units	1:6
Mixed units	1:6 initially 1:5 phased in

*These units currently have minimum nurse-to-client ratios in statute and/or regulations.

Sources: Bochum, K: Ratio rationale: RNs explain why ratios matter. California Nurse 100(10):9–11, 2004; Garretson, S: Nurse-to-patient ratios in American health care. Nursing Standard 19(14):33–37, 2004; Spetz, J: California's minimum nurse-to-patient ratios: The first few months. Journal of Nursing Administration 34(12):571–578, 2004.

(continued)

Issues In Practice (continued)

seem to agree that increased staffing levels increase nurses' morale and, as a result, there is a reduction in turnover rates. Replacing RNs who quit because of poor staffing is very expensive. An average estimated cost to recruit and train a medical–surgical nurse is approximately $46,000. For a specialty nurse, as in intensive care or emergency, it may run as high as $64,000.

A slowly growing body of research demonstrates the connection between staffing levels and positive or negative health-care outcomes for hospitalized clients. Nursing associations and consumer groups feel that the quality of care is increased, along with client safety, with higher levels of RNs in the health-care setting. Although in the short run, mandatory staffing levels may seem to increase the nursing shortage, the long-term view is that it will help reduce the nursing shortage by addressing one of the leading causes of attrition among nurses— burnout from poor working conditions. If the health-care industry can keep more nurses in health care rather than having them leave for less stressful work settings, a major contribution will have been made to address the nursing shortage.

QUESTIONS FOR THOUGHT

1. Do you think the proposed staffing ratios are a good thing? Why or why not? How would they affect health care in your town?
2. Does your state have any proposed legislation regarding mandatory staffing ratios? If so, obtain copies of the bills, read them, and discuss them with your class.
3. Do you know who your legislator is? Have you contacted him or her about how you feel about mandatory staffing ratios? If not, call him or her today!

Sources: Bochum, K: Ratio rationale: RNs explain why ratios matter. California Nurse 100(10):9–11, 2004.
Dunton, N: Early evidence on California staffing ratios should be interpreted with caution. Policy, Politics & Nursing Practice 6(4):354–357, 2005.
Garretson, S: Nurse to patient ratios in American health care. Nursing Standard 19(14):33–37, 2004.
McLaughlin, M: Mandated staffing ratios: A view from both sides. Breathline 26(6):10–11, 2006.
Spetz, J: California's minimum nurse-to-patient ratios: The first few months. Journal of Nursing Administration 34(12):571–578, 2004.
Upenieks, V: Assessing nursing staffing ratios: variability in workload intensity. Policy, Politics & Nursing Practice 8(1):7–19, 2007.

Critical Thinking Exercises

- Distinguish between an occupation and a profession.
- Is nursing a profession? Defend your position.
- Discuss four ways in which nursing can improve its professional status.
- Name the three sources of power to which nurses have the most access. Discuss how nurses can best use these sources of power to improve nursing, nursing care, and the health-care system.

References

1. Alotaibi, M: Factors affecting nurses' decisions to join their professional association. International Nursing Review 54(2):160–165, 2007.
2. Kennedy, M: APNs: Improved outcomes at lower costs. American Journal of Nursing 104:9, 19, 2004.
3. Smith, GR: Spotlight on nurse staffing, autonomy, and control over practice. American Nurse Today, 2 (4):15–17, 2007.
4. Bellack, JP, and O'Neil, EH: Recreating nursing practice for a new century. Nursing and Health Care Perspectives 21(1):14–24, 2000.
5. Elango, B: Barriers to nurse entrepreneurship: a study of the process model of entrepreneurship. Journal of the American Academy of Nurse Practitioners 19(4):198–204, 2007.
6. Bolton, LB: Guest editorial. What Noah knew: why nursing must master the art of (professional) ark building. Nursing Administration Quarterly 31(2):97–98, 2007.
7. Vratny, A: A conceptual model for growing evidence-based practice. Nursing Administration Quarterly 31(2):162–170, 2007.
8. Fitzpatrick, ML: Prologue to Professionalism. Robert J. Brady, Bowie, MD, 1983.
9. O'Grady, ET: Health policy and politics. Nursing Economics 18(2):88–90, 2001.
10. American Nurses Association: Nursing Social Policy Statement ANA, Washington, DC, 1999.

Bibliography

Burke, RJ: The ripple effect: Staffing post restructuring. Nursing Management 33(2):41–43, 2002.

Callister, J, et al.: Inquiry in baccalaureate nursing education: Fostering evidence-based practice. Nursing Education 44(2):59–65, 2005.

Carter, M: The ABCs of staffing decisions. Nursing Management 35(6):16, 2004.

Ferguson, L, Day R: Evidence-based nursing education: Myth or reality. Nursing Education 44(3):107–116, 2005.

Freeman, LH, et al.: New curriculum for a new century. Nursing Education 41(1):38–40, 2002.

Irving, JA, and Sniper, J: Preserving professional values. Journal of Professional Nursing 18(1):5, 2002.

Kinsman, L, and James, EL: Evidence based practice needs evidence based implementation. Lippincott's Case Management 6(5):208–219, 2001.

Kovner, C, Harrington, C: CMS Study: Correlation between staffing and quality. American Journal of Nursing 102(9):65–66, 2002.

Manojlovich, M: Predictors of professional practice behaviors in hospital settings. Nursing Research 54(1):41–47, 2005.

Manthey, M: Continuing the case for the baccalaureate. Journal of Professional Nursing 18(1):7, 2002.

Narayan, MC, et al.: Searching for nursing's future. Nursing Management 33(1):26–30, 2002.

O'Bryan, L, et al.: Rework the workload. Nursing Management 33(3):38–40, 2002.

Thompson, D, and Burns, H: Work environment for nurses and the impact on protecting patients from health-care errors. Journal of Professional Nursing 20(3):145–147, 2004.

2

Historical Perspectives

Joseph T. Catalano

Learning Objectives

After completing this chapter, the reader will be able to:

- Explain why studying the history of health care and nursing is important to the profession of nursing.
- Name three "historical threads" found in the study of nursing history and discuss why they are important.
- Discuss Christian influences on health care and nursing.
- Discuss the influences of the Renaissance and Reformation on health care and nursing.
- Describe the major changes in health care and nursing that occurred during and immediately after World War II.

UNDERSTANDING OUR HISTORY

Knowledge about the profession's past can help us understand how nursing developed and even suggest solutions to problems that face the profession today. Several threads run throughout the history of nursing, including society's beliefs about the causes of illness, the value placed on individual life, and the role of women in society. The wars of modern history have also had a significant impact on nursing, particularly in influencing the development of technology and guiding the direction of health care. This chapter is not a treatise on the history of health care and nursing but presents some key historic milestones, which helped to form the foundations of health and nursing care.

ORIGINS OF NURSING

Before Nursing

Current nursing practice is a relatively recent development. The major concern of most early civilizations was the survival of the group, and because illness and injury threatened this survival, many primitive health-care practices grew from processes of trial and error. In prehistoric times, women tended to care for the ill and injured. Evil spirits were thought to be the cause of illness, and the medicine men and women who practiced witchcraft were considered religious figures.

Driving Out Demons

In ancient eastern civilizations, starting from about 3500 B.C., health care was intertwined with religion. Taoism emphasized balance and the driving of demons out of the ailing body. Acupuncture developed over the next several thousands of years, and medicinal herbs were used in preventive health care.

In Southeast Asia, Hinduism emphasized the need for good hygiene, and written records would soon chronicle a number of surgical procedures. This was also the first culture to document medical treatment outside the home, although women were prohibited from working. The rise of Buddhism around 530 B.C. caused a surge in health care, with public hospitals and high standards for doctors and other hospital workers and an emphasis on hygiene and prevention of disease. The development of medical knowledge was hindered to a degree by the refusal of the physicians to come in contact with blood and infectious body secretions and the prohibition against dissection of the human body.

Ancient Sciences

During the same period, the ancient Egyptians' belief that all disease was caused by evil spirits and punishing gods was changing. Health-care providers from that time showed a well-developed understanding of the basis of disease. Writings from 1500 B.C. refer to surgical procedures, the role of the midwife, bandaging, preventive care, and even birth control. Women enjoyed a higher status in Egyptian society and even worked in hospitals.[1] Physicians, however, were still men, who served in multiple roles as surgeons, priests, architects, and politicians.

The Babylonian Empire, united in 2100 B.C., was a civilization that focused on astrology. Its health-care practices included special diets, massage therapy, and rest to drive evil spirits from a body. People would go to the marketplace to seek advice on how to treat their ailments. During the height of the empire, strict guidelines governed doctors' fees and responsibilities in medical practice. There is also evidence from this period of child care and treatment for some diseases, but most care still took place in the home.

By 1900 B.C., the Hebrews had formed a nation along the Mediterranean and adopted many of the health practices of their neighbors. They integrated elements of the Egyptian sanitary laws to form the Mosaic Code that, as in many other cultures, mixed religion and medicine. Caring for widows, orphans, and other strangers in need was part of daily life. Hebrews had good knowledge of anatomy and physiology, especially the circulatory system. Physician-priests routinely performed operations such as cesarean sections (named later by the Romans), amputation, and circumcisions. They also enforced rules of purification, performed sacrifices, and conducted rituals related to food preparation.

The Father of Medicine

Ancient Greece was a culture that focused on appeasing the gods, and its medical practice was no exception. The god Apollo was devoted to medicine and good health. The Greeks performed sacrifices to appease the gods and practiced abortion and infanticide in an attempt to control the population. People took hot baths at spas to improve health, but the sick and injured were cared for at clinics. Although women were held in high esteem, they were not permitted to provide any health care outside the home.

Around 400 B.C., the writings of Hippocrates began to change medical practice in Greece. One of a roving group of physician-priests, Hippocrates was called "the father of medicine." His

> *The major concern of most early civilizations was the survival of the group, and because illness and injury threatened this survival, many primitive health-care practices grew from processes of trial and error.*

What Do You Think?

Is the study of history really necessary for nursing students? Why or why not?

beliefs focused on harmony with the natural law instead of on appeasing the gods. He emphasized treating the whole client—mind, body, spirit, and environment—and making diagnoses on the basis of symptoms rather than on an isolated idea of a disease. He was also concerned with ethical standards for physicians, expressed in the now-famous Hippocratic oath.

Health Care in the Roman Empire

Ancient Romans clung to superstitions and polytheism as the foundations for medical as well as religious practices. This dominant empire ruled from around 290 B.C. and absorbed useful elements of whatever culture they conquered—including the Greeks and Hebrews—into their own. They developed a quite advanced system of medicine and a pharmacology that included more than 600 medications derived from herbs and plants. Roman physicians were eventually able to distinguish among various conditions and performed many surgeries. They also did physical therapy for athletes; diagnosed symptoms of infections; identified job-related dangers of lead, mercury, and asbestos; and published medical textbooks.

> " *The term nurse is thought to have originated in this period, from the Latin word nutrire, meaning to nourish, nurture, or suckle a child.* "

The Romans' advances in creating an unlimited supply of clean water via aqueducts were critical in maintaining the good health of the citizens, as were central heating, spas and baths, and more advanced systems for sewage disposal. Because the great Roman armies were so crucial to the empire, they developed early hospitals to care for sick and injured soldiers. These were mobile and were staffed by female as well as male attendants, who performed duties that would today be thought of as nursing care: cleaning and bandaging wounds, feeding and cleaning clients, and providing comfort to the wounded and dying. In many ways, women enjoyed an equal place in society, and they provided home health care as well as midwifery.

Early Efforts at Nursing

The Sanctity of Life

The rise of Christianity, starting from 30 A.D., brought with it a strong belief in the sanctity of all human life. Christians considered practices such as human sacrifice, infanticide, and abortion—which had been common in Roman society—to be murder. Following the teachings of Jesus meant that caring for the sick, poor, and disadvantaged was of primary importance, and groups of believers soon organized to offer care for those in need.

Early writings of the Christian period record women's important role in ministering to the sick and providing food and care for the poor and homeless. Wealthy Roman women who had converted to Christianity established hospital-like institutions and residences for these caregivers in their homes. The term *nurse* is thought to have originated in this period, from the Latin word *nutrire,* meaning to nourish, nurture, or suckle a child. The majority of care was still provided by a family member in the home. Most early Christian hospitals were roadside houses for the sick, poor, or destitute, who were cared for by male and female attendants alike. The attendants learned from a process of trial and error and by observing others.

A Time of Disease

The Dark Ages, from roughly 500 to 1000 A.D., were marked by widespread poverty, illness, and death.

Plagues and other diseases such as smallpox, leprosy, and diphtheria ravaged the known world and killed large segments of populations. Health care at this time was almost nonexistent.

However, the strong beliefs of the Catholic Church, which was based in Rome, produced monasteries and convents that became centers for the care of the poor and the sick. By 500 A.D., there were several religious nursing orders in what is today England, France, and Italy. Men and women worked there and also traveled to rural areas where they were needed, combining religious rituals with home remedies as well as treatments such as bandaging, cautery, bloodletting, enemas, and leeching. The biggest contribution to health care in this period may have been the insistence on cleanliness and hygiene, which lessened the spread of infections. Medieval nurses did not have any formal schooling but learned through apprenticeships with older monks or nuns. Eventually hospitals came to be built outside of monastery grounds. Secular orders were also established, which could provide a wider range of services to the sick because they were not limited by religious restrictions and obligations.

Early Military Hospitals

At the end of the Dark Ages, there were a series of holy wars and invasions, including the Crusades, which produced many sick and injured who were far from home. Military nursing orders developed to care for the soldiers, but these were made up exclusively of men who wore suits of armor to protect themselves and their hospitals against attacks. These orders, with the emblem of the red cross, were extremely well organized and dedicated, and they existed well into the Renaissance.

Development of the Modern Nurse

Health Care in the Renaissance

In the intellectual reawakening of the Renaissance in Europe, starting in about 1350, nursing emerged in a recognizable form, although it did not grow steadily as a profession during this period. Inventions from this time include the microscope and thermometer, but the use of more modern diagnoses and treatment was viewed with skepticism. Monastic hospitals still regarded the restoration of health as secondary to the salvation of the soul.

Major political changes initiated by the Protestant Reformation in 1517 had the greatest effect on the health care of the period. In Catholic nation-states, including Italy, France, and Spain,

> *Medieval nurses did not have any formal schooling but learned through apprenticeships with older monks or nuns.*

health care remained generally unchanged from that of the Middle Ages, although the number of male nursing orders gradually decreased. By 1500, the majority of health care was provided by female religious orders.

What Do You Think?

Imagine yourself living in one of the historical periods discussed in this chapter. Given your or your family's health-care problems, how would your lives be different?

_____

_____

_____

_____

_____

_____

_____

_____

_____

_____

_____

_____

_____

A Nursing Hierarchy

In the nation-states that broke away from the Catholic Church, such as England, Germany, and the Netherlands, health care soon degenerated to a condition even worse than that of the Middle Ages. The role of women was reduced under Protestant leadership, and the male nurse all but disappeared. Secular nursing orders gradually took over the duties of the many substandard hospitals that had been established in metropolitan areas. The most famous of these was the Sisters of Charity, established in 1600.

These orders were the first to establish a nursing hierarchy. Primary nurses were called sisters and those assisting them were called helpers and watchers. It is at this time that people began to recognize the benefit of skilled nursing care. The first nursing textbooks appeared, and the use of midwives became widespread. Although hospitals were gaining importance, most clients still received health care at home.

The Industrial Revolution (1850–1950) caused a flood of people from rural areas throughout Europe into cities, and cramped living situations caused very bad health conditions and the spread of disease and plagues. Factory owners supported some forms of health care to keep their workers on the job, and this led to an early form of community health nursing. The Sisters of Charity expanded their care to include home care. Only a few male nursing orders survived the Protestant Reformation and Industrial Revolution, and several non-Catholic nursing orders were founded, including the famous Quaker Society of Protestant Sisters of Charity, which provided care primarily for prisoners and children.

> *Large numbers of women came out of their homes to work in the hospitals, and a number of African-American volunteers in the North paved the way for others to enter the health-care field in the future.*

NURSING IN THE UNITED STATES

Five hospitals existed in America before the Revolutionary War, housing the homeless and the poor and including rudimentary infirmaries. However, there were no identifiable groups of nurses for these infirmaries.[2] Health care in America at this time reflected that of the European countries the settlers had come from. Infant mortality rates were very high, ranging between 50 percent and 75 percent. One of the first schools of nursing was established in 1640 by the Sisters of St. Ursula in Quebec, and Spanish and French religious orders would establish hospital-based training schools in the New World over the next 100 years.

In Colonial Times

During the Revolutionary War, there was no organized medical or nursing corps, but small groups of untrained volunteers cared for the wounded and sick in their homes or in churches or barns. Benjamin Franklin founded Pennsylvania Hospital, the first U.S. hospital dedicated to treating the sick, in 1751.

Between the Revolutionary and Civil Wars, health care in the United States increased markedly with the influx of religious nursing orders from Europe. More early schools of nursing developed at this time. Despite the rapid increase in the number of hospitals, most nursing care was still given at home by family members. Hospitals were considered a last resort and still had very high mortality rates.

When the States Went to War

The Civil War caused more death and injury than any war in the history of the United States, and the demand for nurses increased dramatically. Women volunteers (as many as 6000 for the North and 1000 for the South) began to follow the armies to the battlefields to provide basic nursing care, although many of them were untrained. Navy Nurses, the American Red Cross, and the Army Nurse Corps all date from this period. Large numbers of women came out of their homes to work in the hospitals, and a number of African-American volunteers in the North paved the way for others to enter the health-care field in the future.

Technological developments in the 19th century included medications such as morphine and codeine for pain and quinine to treat malaria. The arrival of 30 million immigrants in this century meant that the need for health care increased accordingly. Hospitals sprang up, and many instituted their own schools of nursing. Still, home care was the preferred type of nursing.

After 1914

Untrained Nurses

At the beginning of World War I, there were only about 400 nurses in the Army Nurse Corps, but by 1917 that number swelled to 21,000. Because many hospitals were recruiting untrained women to provide basic care, a committee on nursing was formed to establish standards, and eventually the Red Cross began a training program for nurse's aides. This was supported by physicians but opposed by many nursing leaders, who were concerned that it relegated nursing to "women's work," which would be seen as something anyone could do with minimal training. Because nurse's aides were a cheap source of labor, they began to replace more trained nurses in hospitals. Unfortunately this also resulted in a lower quality of care.

Between Wars

After the war, a segment of the nursing profession began to focus intensely on improving the educational standards of nursing care. At this time, 90 percent of nursing care was still given at home, but nurses began to practice in industry and in branches of government outside of the military. The standards of nursing care were low, and external quality controls were nonexistent.

The Great Depression took its toll on health care and nursing, as jobs became scarce and many nursing schools closed. At this time, the federal government became one of the largest employers of nurses. The newly organized Joint Committee on Nursing recommended that jobs go to more qualified nurses and that the work day be reduced from 12 to 8 hours, although these measures were not widely implemented. During this period, hospitals became the primary source of health care, supported by hospital insurance programs. As the size of hospitals increased, more nursing jobs became available.

Establishing Standards

World War II produced another nursing shortage, and in response, Congress passed the Bolton Nurse Training Act, which shortened hospital-based training programs from 36 to 30 months. The new Cadet Nurse Corps established minimum educational standards for nursing programs and forbade discrimination on the basis of race, creed, or sex.[2] Many schools revised and improved their curricula to meet these new standards.

To encourage more nurses to enter the military, the U.S. government granted women full commissioned status and gave them the same pay as men with the same rank. By the end of the war, African-American and male nurses were also admitted to the armed services.

Modern Times: Emerging Specialties

A Team of Nurses

The advancements in health care made during World War II required that nurses receive more highly specialized education to meet clients' unique needs. After the war, many nurses left the profession to raise families, and the spaces were filled by graduates of new programs that trained licensed practical nurses (LPNs) and licensed vocational nurses (LVNs) in just 1 year. At this time, the concept of team nursing came to be widely accepted, although it removed the registered nurses (RNs) from direct client care, requiring them to serve as team leaders.

A Growing Need

Technical nursing programs, which granted associate degrees (associate degree nurse [ADN]) at 2-year community colleges, were developed to help with the nursing shortage. With the baby boom, the need for nurses continued to grow, and what had been a quick-fix solution began to take a stronger hold. By the mid-1960s, ADNs outnumbered the nurses with baccalaureate degrees (BSN) and the technical LPNs. Also, ADNs won the right to take the same licensing examinations as RN graduates from diploma and BSN programs.

Still, as the health-care system became increasingly complicated, some nursing leaders questioned whether 1- or 2-year LPN and ADN programs were adequate to meet the needs of the profession. Slowly the number of BSN programs and graduate-level programs began to increase.

Vietnam: Traveling Hospitals

The mobile army surgical hospital (MASH) units that had been developed during the Korean War were replaced during the Vietnam War with medical unit, self-contained transportable (MUST) hospitals, which were staffed by nurses as well as physicians. Some 5000 nurses served in this war, and for the first time, graduates of 2-year ADN programs were commissioned into the armed services. Several Navy nurses were injured in the line of duty, and one Army nurse was killed. Only recently have the efforts of these and other women who served been recognized at the Vietnam Women's War Memorial in Washington, dedicated in 1993.

THE EVOLUTION OF SYMBOLS IN NURSING

The Lamp

Pushing Back Darkness

The significance of the lamp is really the significance of light. Its origins can be traced back to the first attempts of human beings to control fire and use it as a tool of survival. These early humans soon found that fire was a source of warmth on cold nights, kept wild animals from attacking, and was useful for cooking.

Light, first in the form of torches and candles, and later in the form of the oil lamp, has been used by human beings for literally thousands of years to push back the darkness of night. It dispelled fear and allowed people to pursue learning long after the sun went down.

The lamp has long been used as a religious symbol. It often represents the eternal flame that dispels darkness and evil. Commonly found in Christian symbolism is the "Lady of Light," often depicted as radiant and glowing brightly and filled with goodness, purity, and wisdom. The lamp can also represent the flame of life, eventually extinguished by death.

As schools and universities developed during the Middle Ages, many adopted the lamp as a symbol of learning. The burning of the lamp signified the continual seeking of knowledge. It also symbolizes the enlightenment that accompanies knowledge. The coats-of-arms or logos used by many universities contain the image of a lamp.

> *The Civil War caused more death and injury than any war in the history of the United States, and the demand for nurses increased dramatically.*

A Sign of Caring

The lamp was first introduced as a symbol for the nursing profession at the time of Florence Nightingale. In addition to her fame as an early health-care reformer and pioneer, she became well known for her role in caring for injured soldiers during the Crimean War. She made history when she took her 38 nurses to Turkey to try to improve the squalid, filthy conditions she found in the primitive British field hospitals. As Nightingale and her nurses made their night rounds, caring for the wounded in unlit wards, they carried oil lamps to light the way. For the wounded and suffering, the sight of these lamps became signs of caring, comfort, and often the difference between life and death.

Nightingale's lamp was not the often-depicted "genie" or "Aladdin's" lamp. Rather, Nightingale would have used one of the many lamps in circulation around the wards, picking up whichever was closest at hand—an ordinary camp lamp or a Turkish candle lantern. She later became immortalized as the "Lady with the Lamp" in a poem written by Longfellow. In our modern society, oil lamps are sometimes used for atmosphere or nostalgic reminders of the past, although when the power goes out, they can be very handy. However, for graduate nurses, the lamp, or its close cousin the candle, retains its significance as a symbol of the ideals and selfless devotion of Florence Nightingale. It also signifies the knowledge and learning that the graduates have attained during their years in the nursing program. Even though the nursing graduates may not physically carry an oil lamp during pinning ceremonies, they symbolically carry the brightly burning lamp of their care and devotion as they minister to the sick and injured in their nursing practice.

The Nursing Pin

Unlikely as it may seem, the modern nursing pin can trace its origins to the heavy protective war shields used by soldiers as far back as the Greek and Roman Empires. The primary purpose of these shields was to protect the warriors from the spears, swords, and arrows of the opposing army. These ancient war shields, adorned with the emblems of the country the soldier was from and his particular unit in the army, also served as a quick way to distinguish friend from foe.

During the Crusades, the Knights Hospitallers of St. John of Jerusalem were formed to provide medical care for the wounded and sick. The Knights wore black tunics over their armor, carried no weapons, and wore a white Maltese cross on chains around their necks. Those wearing this cross became known for their skills in treating the injured and healing the wounded. Since that time, the Maltese cross has been recognized as a symbol of those who care for the sick. Although large by today's standards, the Maltese cross is often considered the first true nursing pin.

The shields of some medieval knights were painted with the coats-of-arms of the kings they were defending. Only the best knights, recognized for their skills in battle, strength, honesty, and dedication to the service of the king, were permitted to use the king's coat-of-arms on their shields. The coat-of-arms displayed to the world the characteristics by which the king wished to be known. A classic example is the symbol of the lion, found on the shields of the knights who served King Richard the Lion-Hearted, that indicated the King's fearlessness and power.

Similarly, during the Middle Ages when most of the population was illiterate, tradesmen and craft guilds began adopting symbols as pictorial representations of their services, skills, and crafts. Modern companies use trademarks and brand names in the same way today. Medieval schools and universities also began using symbols to represent their values and goals. The modern practice of "branding the university," or adopting an official symbol or logo for the school, can be traced back to these early practices. These symbols were embossed on clothing, buttons, badges, and pins that were worn by members of the group. Also traceable to this time in history are the "shields" and badges worn by firefighters and law enforcement officers. Although these shields offer little in the way of protection from arrows and spears, they symbolize official authority and identify the wearer as belonging to a unique, specially trained group.

The first modern nursing pin is attributed to Florence Nightingale. After receiving the medal of the Red Cross of St. George from Queen Victoria for her selfless service to the injured and dying in the Crimean War, Nightingale chose to extend the honor she had received to her most outstanding graduate nurses by awarding each of them a "badge of excellence." The badge or pin she designed for her school is a deep-blue Maltese cross. In the center of the cross is a relief image of Nightingale's head. As the number of nursing schools increased, each program designed a unique pin to represent its own particular values, philosophy, beliefs, and goals.

The pinning ceremony is part of a long tradition that acknowledges nursing graduates as belonging to a unique group and identifies them as new members of the health-care community. The historical origins of the pin remind nursing professionals of what it symbolizes. Like the badge worn by law enforcement officers, it is also a sign of their legal authority as licensed professionals. Nursing graduates wear their pins proudly in the work setting as evidence of their successful completion of the nursing program.

QUESTION:

Obtain a picture of your nursing school's pin. What do the various symbols on the pin signify?

The Cap

A Symbol of Service

It is rare to see a nurse wearing the traditional "nursing cap" in today's modern hospitals. However, the cap has a long, rich history. Although it may seem sexist by today's standards, throughout much of history, women were required to keep their heads covered with some type of garment. This practice was prevalent in the early Hebrew, Greek, and Roman cultures that served as the roots for modern western society and the current profession of nursing.

The origins of what we identify as modern nursing can be traced back to an early Christian era group of women, called "deaconesses." Deaconesses were set apart from other women of the period by their white head covering, which indicated that their primary service was to care for the sick. During the early centuries of Christianity, groups of deaconesses banded together and formed what later became the religious orders that were so prevalent in the Holy Roman Empire. The former deaconesses, now recognized as religious order nuns, remained the primary providers of care for the sick throughout the Middle Ages. The traditional garb of nuns, the long-robed habit with the wimple or veil, can be considered the first official nurse's uniform. Each religious order had its own unique style of habit and wimple. The order the nun belonged to could be easily identified from the habit or veil she was wearing.

Religious orders continued to be the primary source of care for the sick well into the 19th century. However, as the Industrial Revolution gained speed and the concept of the modern hospital developed, the care of the sick moved away from religious orders to care by lay people who did not wear the nun's robe and veil.

By the time Florence Nightingale trained in the Institute of Protestant Deaconesses in Germany, the veil had evolved into a white cap that signified "service to others." However, Florence Nightingale lived and practiced nursing during the Victorian era, which required "proper" women to keep their heads covered. The nursing cap Florence Nightingale wore was similar to the head garb worn by cleaning ladies of the day. It was hood-shaped with a ruffle around the face and tied under the chin. This early cap served multiple purposes. It met the requirements of the times for women to keep their heads covered; it kept the nurse's long hair, which was fashionable during the Victorian era, up and off her face; and it kept the hair from becoming soiled.

A Cap for Every School

In the United States, the first standardized nursing cap is generally attributed to Bellevue Training School in New York City around 1874. The cap's primary purpose was to keep the nurse's long hair from getting in the way, but it also identified nurses who had graduated from Bellevue. The Bellevue cap covered the whole head to just above the ears and resembled a modern knitted ski hat, except for being white linen with a rolled fringe at the bottom.

As the number of nursing schools increased, there was a corresponding increase in the need for unique caps. Each nursing school designed its own cap.

Nursing caps became very frilly, elaborate, and sometimes large and unwieldy. Some caps adopted the upside-down ice cream cone shape, similar to the cloth cone through which ether was given as an anesthetic. By looking at the cap, a person could still determine the school from which the nurse had graduated.

Traditionally, in the 3-year hospital-based schools of nursing, there were two separate ceremonies, one for capping and one for pinning. The capping ceremony usually took place after the student completed the initial 6 months of classroom education, which was considered the probationary period of the program. Capping indicated that the student was now off probation and that she had earned the right to wear the cap during clinical rotations in the hospital.

During nursing school, the cap was also used as a sign of rank and status. In the 3-year hospital-based nursing schools, first-year students wore plain white caps with no black bands anywhere. Second-year students had a vertical black band added to the edge of the cap, and third-year students were given a second vertical black band. When the student graduated, the vertical black bands were removed and a horizontal black band was placed across the front of the cap.

Unchanging Values

As shorter hair became an acceptable style for women in the 20th century, the nursing cap lost its function of controlling long hair. However, it continued as a status symbol and a source of pride and identity for the graduates of nursing schools into the 1970s. As technology increased in the health-care work environment, the traditional nursing cap became more and more of an obstacle for nurses in the practice setting. Also, research demonstrated that the cap, rather than protecting clients from infection by organisms from the nurse's hair, actually helped to colonize organisms. By the 1980s, health-care facilities no longer required nurses to wear caps as part of the uniform, and nursing schools eliminated the cap as a mandatory item of students' uniforms.

Most nursing programs have eliminated the capping ceremony as a throwback to an era that was repressive to women. However, the nursing cap connects graduates to a rich and long history. It retains its significance, from the time of Florence Nightingale, as a sign that the primary goal of nursing is "service to those in need." The nursing cap is a reminder of the unchanging values of wisdom, faith, honesty, trust, and dedication. These values are as important in today's modern, technology-filled hospitals as they were in the era when washing floors was a required basic nursing skill.

> **QUESTION:**
>
> Does your nursing school have a unique nursing cap used in the past? What is the symbolism of the cap's design?

NURSING LEADERS

The nursing profession as it is practiced today owes a great deal to a number of outstanding nurses who had a vision for the future. The few discussed here are representative of the great drive and dedication of the many individuals who created change and influenced the development of the nursing profession, even to this day.

Florence Nightingale (1820–1910)

Universally regarded as the founder of modern nursing, Florence Nightingale dedicated her long life to improving health care and nursing standards. Raised in England, Nightingale was considered highly educated for her time. Through travels with her family, she became aware of the substandard health care in many countries in Europe. In 1851, she attended a 3-month nurses' training program at the church-run hospital in Kaiserwerth, Germany. She was impressed with the program but came to believe that this brief training was insufficient. She later ran a private nursing home and realized that the only way to improve health care was to educate women to be reliable, high-quality nurses.

Volunteering Under Fire

Plans to develop a school of nursing in England were interrupted in 1854 by a cholera epidemic. Nightingale volunteered her services and learned a great deal about how to prevent the spread of disease. When the Crimean War broke out that same year, she obtained permission to take a group of 37 volunteer nurses into the battlefield area. British medical officers initially refused their assistance, but as conditions worsened they were admitted to the hospital.

After just 6 months of the nurses' cleaning and bandaging wounds, cooking, and cleaning the wards, the mortality rate dropped from 42 percent to 2 percent.[3] Nightingale expanded her reform to include supplies, a military post office, convalescent camps for long-term recovery, and residences for soldiers' families. She also began to help with the care given at the front lines. At the height of her work in the war, she supervised 125 nurses in several large hospitals, and her accomplishments were recognized by the Queen of England with an Order of Merit, the highest award given to English civilians.

Penicillin

What Do You Think?

What would current nursing practice and nursing education be like without the influences of Florence Nightingale?

Issues Now

Travel Nursing as a Career

As a nursing student, you may have heard of *travel nursing or traveling nurses*, but not really known what they were or if it might be something you would be interested in as a career. Much like the recruitment posters for the armed services, "See the World" seems to be an attractive slogan for those looking for new experiences and adventure. However, there may be some drawbacks to travel nursing.

Generally, travel nurse staffing companies require a BSN or higher degree. This standard allows the nurses to meet any staffing requirements of individual facilities, and research has demonstrated good client outcomes. Travel nurses differ from agency nurses in several ways. Travel nurses are usually committed to working for a facility for a predetermined length of time, usually around 3 months. To allow preparation for travel to the facility, they are scheduled for their time approximately 2 months before their start date. Agency nurses generally work on a per diem (by the day) basis and live near the facility. They work a few days at a time to meet a short-term staffing need. Travel nurses provide more continuity of care and fill in for long-term needs, such as extended illness, maternity leave, or even sabbatical leave.

Travel nurses can select where they want to work and the time period of the work schedule. They usually follow the schedule required by the facility, but have scheduled days off like any other nurses. Their salaries tend to be higher, and, depending on the company, the benefits may range from "bare bones" to what regular staffers would receive at a large health-care facility. The staffing agency also pays for the nurse's license and housing costs. Staffing agencies also have a group of employees who support the nurse and act as liaisons with the facilities to resolve any problems that may arise.

A nurse must be careful when selecting a travel nurse staffing company. The nurse should investigate the company carefully, talk to other nurses it employs, and examine the benefits closely. Generally, the larger the firm, the more locations it serves, and the better the benefits and support services. Some nurses use travel nurse employment to research locations in which they may be interned, and then permanently relocate when they find the ideal location.

So, if you want to be a travel nurse, the opportunities are out there. Travel nursing certainly provides a high degree of autonomy and control of your schedule and career. One of the key elements reported by nurses for career satisfaction is quality of life. The freedom of choice provided by travel nursing would certainly fulfill that need.

Sources: Duda, J: On the road again: Travel nursing. Nursing Spectrum 18A(15):32–33, 2006.
Shaffer, F: Travel nursing: Is it right for you? American Nurse Today 2(2):52–53, 2007.
Spotlight on travel nursing. Nursing 36 (11):72, 2006.

A Health-Care Reformer

The war experience strengthened Nightingale's convictions that nursing education required major reform. Believing that nursing schools should be run by nurses and be independent of hospitals and physicians, she advocated a program of at least 1 year that included basic biological science, techniques to improve nursing care, and supervised practice. She regarded nursing as a lifelong endeavor and felt that nurses should be in direct contact with clients rather than doing menial jobs such as cooking and cleaning. She worked tirelessly for the reform of health care and nursing and was appointed to many related committees and commissions. A prolific writer, she wrote extensively about improving hospital conditions, sanitation, nursing education, and health care in general.

Her famous Nightingale Training School for Nurses opened in 1860 and began to train nurses, who were in great demand throughout Europe and the United States. At this school, Nightingale advocated health maintenance and the concept that nursing was both an art and a science. She taught that each person should be treated as an individual and that nurses should meet the needs of clients, not the demands of physicians.

The school flourished, although it faced strong opposition from physicians who felt that nurses were already overtrained. Many early graduates went on to become important nursing leaders. Nightingale's ideas were somewhat diluted during the first half of the 20th century, but they have since resurfaced and are now evaluated in the light of a rapidly changing health-care system.

Isabel Adams Hampton Robb (1860–1910)

Isabel Adams Hampton Robb started out as a teacher in her home province of Ontario, Canada, but in 1881 she went to New York City to train to be a nurse. After graduation, she moved to Rome and became a superintendent of a hospital there. She had always focused on the academic rather than the clinical side of nursing, but in Italy her conviction grew that nurses needed a solid theoretical education—a belief that was not well accepted by the medical community of the time. From that point on, she dedicated her life to raising the standards of nursing education in the United States, first as director of the Illinois Training School for Nurses. The school that was unique for its time in that it was university based and emphasized academic learning. She later headed the new Johns Hopkins Training School for Nurses and would implement her ideas there as well.

Hampton Robb brought together leaders from key nursing schools to form the American Society of Superintendents of Training Schools for Nurses, and she served as its chairman. The group was the precursor to the National League for Nursing, which was dedicated to improving the standards for nursing education. In 1896, Hampton Robb became the first president of a group for staff nurses in active practice, called the Nurses Associated Alumnae of the United States and Canada, which would later become the American Nurses Association (ANA), dedicated to the improvement of clinical practice. She later helped develop the *American Journal of Nursing,* the first professional journal dedicated to the improvement of nursing, which is still the official journal of the ANA.

Lillian Wald (1867–1940)

Lillian Wald was raised in Ohio and graduated from the New York Hospital School of Nursing in 1901. After working as a hospital nurse, she entered medical school, but encounters with New York's poor and sick caused her to change direction. She instead opened the Henry Street Settlement, a storefront health clinic in one of the poorest sections of the city, which organized nurses to make home visits, focusing on sanitary conditions and children's health. Wald became a dedicated social reformer, an efficient fundraiser, and an eloquent speaker. Although women still did not have the right to vote, her political influence was felt worldwide.

> *The war experience strengthened Nightingale's convictions that nursing education required major reform. Believing that nursing schools should be run by nurses and be independent of hospitals and physicians, she advocated a program of at least 1 year that included basic biological science, techniques to improve nursing care, and supervised practice.*

Under Wald's auspices, Columbia University developed courses to prepare nurses for careers in public health. Wald also advocated wellness education, which the medical community did not value at the time. The Metropolitan Life Insurance Company saw the value in her beliefs, however, and asked her to organize its nursing branch. She is also credited with founding the American Red Cross's Town and Country Nursing Service and with initiating the concept of school nursing. In 1912, she founded and became the first president of the National Organization of Public Health Nursing. Many child health and wellness programs in use today are based on her efforts. Current proposals for health-care reform often include her ideas about public health nursing, independent clinics, and health maintenance.

What Do You Think?

Who is your favorite historical nursing leader? What are some of that person's characteristics that attracted you? Are there any current nurses or nurse educators who provide you with a role model? What are some of that person's characteristics that attract you?

_____

_____

_____

_____

_____

_____

_____

_____

_____

_____

_____

_____

Lavinia Lloyd Dock (1858–1956)

Lavinia Lloyd Dock left her home in Pennsylvania to attend New York's Bellevue Training School for Nurses in 1885. She noticed that many of her fellow students struggled to learn about all the medications that were becoming available, and she would later write the first medication textbook for nurses. She worked alongside Lillian Wald at the Henry Street Settlement and Isabel Hampton Robb at Johns Hopkins Hospital.

Like Wald, Dock believed that poverty and squalor contributed to poor health, and she dedicated herself to social reform to address these problems. However, she soon learned that she was limited in her influence because she was a woman, and she spent most of her career dedicated to the pursuit of equal rights. For 20 years she lobbied legislators at all levels about women's right to vote, believing that this was the only way to influence social reform and health care. An excellent example of the diverse ways that nurses can help achieve higher-quality health care, she is considered one of the most influential leaders in the early 20th century.

Annie W. Goodrich (1866–1954)

Annie Goodrich provided nursing care at Lillian Wald's Henry Street Settlement in New York after receiving her nursing degree. She was known as an outstanding nursing educator and ran a number of nursing schools in New York. In 1910, she was appointed a state inspector of nursing schools, a position that up to that time had been held only by physicians. After the U.S. Army asked her to survey its hospital nursing departments, Goodrich proposed that it organize its own nursing school. The school opened later that year, with her as its dean, and this school would serve as the model for others established at Army hospitals during World War I.

To respond to the need for nurses in the war, Goodrich also established a nursing training program at Vassar College, and after the war other colleges and universities slowly began to develop their own nursing programs. Goodrich had demonstrated that teaching theoretical information in a classroom was just as important in training highly skilled nurses as clinical practice. When the war was over, Goodrich returned to the Henry Street Settlement and then became a nursing educator, eventually serving as dean at the Yale University School of Nursing. Her many writings about nursing education and her experiences with military nursing have been a great contribution to the nursing profession.[4]

Issues in Practice

Case Study

Clara, who is 108 years old, is admitted through the hospital emergency department (ED) for nonspecific complaints of chest pain and dizziness. This is the third time that she has come to the hospital with this complaint in the past month. Although previous examinations and tests have shown no acute disease process, the ED physician thought that because of her age and long history of coronary artery disease, Clara should be monitored and evaluated more closely. Clara has no private insurance, but she is covered under Medicare, Parts A and B, with supplemental coverage from a small insurance company in her state.

Despite her age, Clara is mentally alert and competent. She lives by herself in a small apartment and manages basic daily care, including shopping and cleaning, with only minimal assistance from friends. She has no living family members, except for a few aging cousins in a distant state. She takes several medications at home: diltiazem (Cardizem) for her heart problems, ranitidine (Zantac) for a hiatal hernia, and papaverine (Pavabid) to increase her general circulation.

After a complete physical examination, including several laboratory tests and an electrocardiogram (ECG), she is scheduled for a cardiac catheterization. A significant block is seen in one of the major coronary arteries, and the physicians decide to perform an angioplasty on the artery. She is admitted to the intensive care unit (ICU) after the procedure, where she also receives two units of blood because she is anemic. She recovers without incident and is discharged 5 days after her admission. The total cost for her hospitalization, including tests and angioplasty, is more than $25,000.

Clara is not a typical client for her age group. Many medical experts would categorize the treatment given her as overtreatment because of the current emphasis on quality of life, death with dignity, and the futility of treating the hopelessly ill. Yet, as people in the United States continue to age, it is more likely that Clara will become the norm rather than the exception. Many issues—ethical, financial, and others—surround this case.

Critical Thinking Questions

1. As a general rule, should a complicated and expensive procedure, such us an angioplasty, always be approved for a 108-year-old client? If not, what should be the exceptions?

2. From a historical perspective, how would a client with Clara's health-care problems be treated in the Roman Empire? The Middle Ages? The United States in the 1800s? The United States in the 1950s?

3. The state where Clara lives has a severe budget shortfall, and substantial cuts in Medicaid benefits have taken place. The entire budget for immunizations of the state's children is only $10,000. What would you do as administrator of the state's Medicaid program if faced with the option of immunizing the children or paying for Clara's angioplasty?

4. The elderly, through various entitlement programs, consume a large proportion of the national budget. This cost is borne mainly by young and middle-aged workers through their taxes. Is it fair that the young be required to carry the burden for the care of the old? Is the government ever justified in rationing or limiting access to health care?

Conclusion

Many of the problems and difficulties with today's health-care system, and those of nursing in particular, are based in the historical development of the profession. Knowledge of these historic roots can help us understand why the profession of nursing is the way it is and even suggest solutions to problems that may seem unsolvable. For example, nursing today appears to be a profession with a high level of responsibility but a low level of power.

How did this situation develop? What can be done about it? A great deal of confusion exists about the education of nurses, unlike the situation in other health-care professions. Why does nursing have this problem, and how can this confusion be addressed? Those who belong to the nursing profession have a responsibility not only to learn about how these and other conditions developed, but also to relat e that knowledge to nursing's possibility for growth in the future.

References

1. Jenson, DM: History and Trends in Professional Nursing. CV Mosby, St. Louis, 1959.
2. Kalisch, PA, and Kalisch, BJ: The Advance of American Nursing. JB Lippincott, Philadelphia, 1995.
3. Woodham-Smith, C: Florence Nightingale. McGraw-Hill, New York, 1957.
4. Mason, DJ: Policy and Politics for Nurses. WB Saunders, Philadelphia, 1993.

Bibliography

Cristy, T: The first fifty years. American Journal of Nursing 9(9):1778–1784, 1971.
Cristy, T: Portrait of a leader: Lavinia Lloyd Dock. Nursing Outlook 17(6):72–75, 1969.
Cristy, T: Portrait of a leader: M. Adelaide Nutting. Nursing Outlook 17(1):20–24, 1969.
Cristy, T: Portrait of a leader: Isabel Hampton Robb. Nursing Outlook 17(3):26–29, 1969.
Cristy, T: Portrait of a leader: Isabel Maitland Stewart. Nursing Outlook 17(10):44–48, 1969.

D'Antonio, P: Women, nursing and baccalaureate education in 20th-century America. Journal of Nursing Scholarship 36(4):379–384, 2004.
Grypma, S: Critical issues in the use of biographic methods in nursing history. Nursing History Review 13:171–187, 2005.
Holder, V: From handmaiden to right hand: World War I and advancements in medicine. AORN Journal 80(5):911–923, 2004.
Jamieson, EM, et al.: Trends in Nursing History. WB Saunders, Philadelphia, 1968.
Lewenson, S: Integrating nursing history into the curriculum. Journal of Professional Nursing 20(6):374–381.
Murphy-Ende, K: Advanced practice nursing: Reflections on the past, issues for the future. Oncology Nursing Forum 29(1):26–33, 2002.
Newlson, S: The rhetoric of rupture: Nursing as a practice with a history? Nursing Outlook 52(5):255–261, 2004.
Selanders, LC: Florence Nightingale: Perseverance, power, possibilities. Maryland Nurse 4(3):1–2, 2001.
Smoyak, SA: Florence Nightingale, insane nurse. Journal of Psychosocial Nursing and Mental Health Services 39(10):6–8, 2001.

3

The Evolution of Licensure, Certification, and Nursing Organizations

Joseph T. Catalano

Learning Objectives

After completing this chapter, the reader will be able to:

- Identify the purposes and needs for nurse licensure.
- Distinguish between permissive and mandatory licensure.
- Explain why institutional licensure is unacceptable in today's health-care system.
- Evaluate the importance of nurse practice acts.
- Analyze the significance of professional certification.

MEETING EXPECTATIONS

Almost from the inception of nursing, societal needs and expectations have been the driving forces behind the establishment of the standards that guide the profession. In the early days of nursing, when health care was relatively primitive and society's expectations of nurses were low, there was little demand for regulations or controls over and within the profession. However, as technology and health care have advanced and become more complex, there has been a corresponding increase in societal expectations for nurses. All nurses now accept **licensure** and **certification** examinations as a given in today's health-care system. Where did these examinations come from, and what do they mean to the profession? This chapter explores the answers to these questions.

Rather than looking on the advent of sophisticated telecommunications, growing information technologies, redesigned health-care organizations, and increasing **health-care consumer** demands with fear and trepidation, nurses should consider this an exciting time of growth and opportunity. In today's health-care system, nurses have an almost unlimited number of ways to provide new and creative nursing care for clients in all settings. As society's needs and expectations change, so will the regulations and standards that help define nursing practice. Through their professional nursing organizations, nurses can help shape health-care regulations that establish the most freedom to provide effective care while maintaining the goal of protecting the public. It is likely that in the future state boards of nursing will look much different, just as the profession of nursing will differ from that of its past.

THE DEVELOPMENT OF NURSE PRACTICE ACTS

A nurse practice act is state legislation regulating the practice of nurses that protects the public, defines the scope of practice, and makes nurses accountable for their actions. Nurse practice acts establish state boards of nursing (SBNs) and define specific SBN powers regarding the practice of nursing within the state. Rules and regulations written by the SBNs become **statutory laws** under the powers delegated by the state **legislature.**

> *Through their professional nursing organizations, nurses can help shape health-care regulations that establish the most freedom to provide effective care while maintaining the goal of protecting the public.*

Regulatory Powers

Although nurse practice acts differ from one state to another, the SBNs have many powers in common. All SBNs have the power to grant licenses, to approve nursing programs, to establish standards for nursing schools, and to write specific regulations for nurses and nursing practice in general in that state.

Of particular importance is the SBNs' power to deny or revoke nurse licenses (Box 3.1).[1] Other functions of nurse practice acts include defining nursing and the scope of practice, ruling on who can use the titles registered nurse (RN) and licensed practical nurse/licensed vocational nurse (LPN/LVN), setting up an application procedure for

licensure in the state, determining fees for licensure, establishing requirements for renewal of licensure, and determining responsibility for any regulations governing expanded practice for nurses in that particular state.

The Need for Licensure

Imagine what the quality of health care would be if anyone could walk into a hospital, claim to know how to care for clients, and be given a job as a nurse. This situation might sound impossible in today's health-care system, but in the past, it was the norm rather than the exception.

Throughout the last half of the 19th century and the first half of the 20th century, rapid growth in health-care technology led to the increasing use of hospitals as the primary source of health care. Individuals who were qualified to provide this care, however, were in short supply. There were wide variations both in the abilities of those who claimed to be nurses and in the quality of the care they provided. Paradoxically, nursing leaders who had always advocated some type of **credentialing** for

Box 3.1

Reasons the State Boards of Nursing May Revoke a Nursing License

- Conviction for a serious crime
- Demonstration of gross negligence or unethical conduct in the practice of nursing
- Failure to renew a nursing license while still continuing to practice nursing
- Use of illegal drugs or alcohol during the provision of care for clients or use that carries over and affects clients' care
- Willful violation of the state's nurse practice act

nurses to ensure competency found that their attempts to initiate registration or licensure met with strong opposition from physician groups, hospital administrators, and practicing nurses themselves.

Early Attempts at Licensure

Although the idea of registering nurses had been in existence for some time, Florence Nightingale was the first to establish a formal list, or register, for graduates of her nursing school. In the United States and Canada, there was widespread recognition of the need for some type of credentialing of nurses as far back as the mid-1800s. The first organized attempt to establish a credentialing system was initiated in 1896 by the Nurses Associated Alumnae of the United States and Canada (later to become the American Nurses Association). As with other early attempts at licensure, it was met with resistance and eventually failed.[2]

Several early American nursing leaders, including Lillian Wald and Annie Goodrich, recognized the inconsistent quality of nursing care and the need for licensure to protect the public. In 1901, after an extensive and lengthy campaign to educate the public, physicians, hospital administrators, and nurses themselves about the need for licensure, the International Council of Nurses passed a resolution that required each state to establish a licensure and examination procedure for nurses. It took 3 years before the state of New York, through the New York Nurses Association, developed a licensure bill that passed the legislature (Box 3.2). Other states that followed New York's lead were North Carolina, New Jersey, and Virginia. Although these states had bills that were weaker than New York's nurse practice act, passage of such legislation was considered a major accomplishment for several reasons. Women did not even have the right to vote in general elections at the time these bills were passed. In addition, few licensure requirements and regulations of any type existed during this period in the history of the United States, even for the medical profession.

The Importance of Licensure Examinations

The thought of having to take an examination that can determine whether or not one can practice nursing can make even the best student anxious. Adding to the tension is the fact that the examination is given outside of the academic setting, by computer, and is created by individuals other than the

Box 3.2

Key Points in the New York State Licensure Bill (1904)

- Established minimum educational standards
- Established the minimum length of basic nursing programs at 2 years
- Required all nursing schools to be registered with the state board of regents (who oversee all higher education)
- Established a state board of nursing (SBN) with five nurses as members
- Formulated rules for the examination of nurses
- Formulated regulations for nurses that, if violated, could lead to the revocation of licensure

Source: Hirsh, IL: Statement on nursing's scope describes how two levels of nurses practice. American Nurse 20:13, 1988.

students' teachers. (See Chapters 10 and 11 for a detailed discussion of NCLEX-RN, CAT.)

A Measure of Competency

Some type of objective method, however, is necessary to prove that the individual is qualified to practice nursing safety; otherwise the public is not protected from unqualified practitioners. Early attempts at creating licensure examinations for nurses were met with strong resistance. Although all states had some form of licensure examination by 1923, the format and length of the examinations varied widely. Some states required both written and practical examinations to demonstrate safety of practice; others added an oral examination.

Although licensure was and is a state-controlled activity, the major nursing organizations in the United States eventually realized that, to achieve consistency of quality across the country, all nurses needed to pass a uniform examination. The American Nurses Association (ANA) Council of State Boards of Nursing was organized in 1945 to oversee development of a uniform examination for nurses that could be used by all state boards of nursing.

The NCLEX-RN, CAT

The National League for Nursing Testing Division developed a test that was implemented in 1950. Originally the test was simply called the State Board

Examination, but it was renamed the National Council Licensure Examination (NCLEX) in 1987. In 1994, the computerized version of the examination was implemented—the National Council Licensure Examination Computerized Adaptive Testing, for Registered Nurses (NCLEX-RN, CAT).

Licensure for nurses has undergone a major change. States are currently in the process of implementing the Mutual Recognition Model for Nursing Licensure, which will allow nurses licensed in one state to practice nursing in other states that belong to their regional agreement. The eventual goal is to have a "universal" nursing license that will allow nurses to practice in all states without having to become relicensed each time they cross a state border.

REGISTRATION VERSUS LICENSURE

The terms *registration* and *licensure* are often used interchangeably, although they are not synonymous. They serve a similar purpose, but some technical differences exist.

Registration

Registration is the listing, or registering, of names on an official roster after certain pre-established criteria have been met. Before mandatory licensure by the states became the norm, the only way a health-care institution could find out whether an applicant had met the standards for the position was by calling the applicant's school to see if the person had graduated or passed an examination. The school would tell the institution whether the applicant's name appeared on the official roster or register—hence the origin of the term *registered nurse*. With the advent of state board examinations, an institution merely has to contact the SBN to find out whether the individual is registered or licensed.

Licensure

Licensure is an activity conducted by the state through the enforcement powers of its regulatory boards to protect the public's health, safety, and welfare by establishing professional standards. Licensure for nurses, as for other professionals who deal with the public, is necessary to ensure that everyone who claims to be a nurse can function at a minimal level of competency and safety. There are several different types of licensure.

Permissive Licensure

Permissive licensure allows individuals to practice nursing as long as they do not use the letters "RN" after their names. Basically, permissive licensure only protects the "registered nurse" title but not the practice of nursing itself. Under a permissive licensure law, anyone could carry out the functions of an RN, regardless of their level of education, without having to pass an examination indicating competency.

Health-care administrators seem to support the concept of permissive licensure because it allows them to employ less-educated and lower-paid employees rather than the more highly educated and paid RNs. However, they also recognize that the quality of care decreases when the education level of health-care providers is lower. Although most early licensure laws were permissive, all states now have mandatory licensure.

What Do You Think?

Should permissive licensure be re-established because it will help reduce the cost of health care? Why? Why not?

_____

_____

_____

_____

_____

_____

_____

_____

_____

_____

_____

Mandatory Licensure

Mandatory licensure requires anyone who wishes to practice nursing to pass a licensure examination and become registered by the SBN. Because different levels of nursing practice exist, different levels of licensure are necessary. At the technical level, the individual must take and pass the LPN/LVN examination; at the professional level, the individual must take and pass the RN examination.

Mandatory licensure forced SBNs to distinguish between the activities that nurses at different levels could legally perform. The scope of practice defines the boundaries for each of the levels advanced practice nurse (APN), RN, and LPN/LVN. As more levels of nursing education (e.g., the associate degree in nursing [ADN]) have been added, however, lines dividing the different scopes of practice have become blurred. In the current health-care system, it is not unusual to find LPNs/LVNs performing activities that are generally considered professional.

A particularly confusing element in today's health-care system is the use of unlicensed individuals to provide health care. The advent of certified nursing assistants (CNA) and unlicensed assistive personnel (UAP) has led to widespread use of such individuals in all health-care settings. Although they must be supervised by an RN or LPN/LVN, these individuals are sometimes illegally assigned nursing tasks much more advanced than their levels of training. (See Chapter 14 for a more detailed discussion of delegation.) Even though permissive licensure is no longer legal, CNAs and UAP appear to fall under an unofficial type of permissive licensure.

Institutional Licensure

Cut Corners, Cut Costs

Although universally rejected by every major nursing organization, **institutional licensure** has become a reality for many other types of health-care workers, such as respiratory therapists and physical therapists. In some state legislatures, bills have been introduced to allow **foreign graduate nurses** and nurses who are licensed in foreign countries to work in specific institutions without taking the U.S. licensure examination. Up to this point, these bills have been stopped by the state nursing organizations before they could become law. Institutional licensure has been proposed periodically over the years as an alternative to governmental licensure.

Institutional licensure allows individual health-care institutions to determine which individuals are qualified to practice nursing within general guidelines established by an outside board. Although this type of licensure appeals to hospitals and nursing homes because it would allow them to

hire individuals with less education at a reduced cost, some serious difficulties are associated with it.

A Lack of External Control

Probably the most critical problem is the lack of any external control to determine a minimal level of competency. The designations of RN and LPN/LVN would be virtually meaningless under institutional licensure. These nurses would not be under the control of a state licensing board and thus would not be held to the same standards of practice as nurses who were licensed by the states.

A second problem is that nurses who wished to move to a new place of employment would have to undergo whatever licensure procedure the new institution had established before being allowed to work there. Currently, nurses who move from one state to another can obtain licensure by endorsement by having the state recognize their nursing license from the original state of licensure. This process is generally referred to as reciprocity.

CERTIFICATION

At first glance, it may appear that there is not much difference between certification and licensure. Strictly defined, licensure can be considered a type of legal certification. In the more widely accepted use of the term, however, certification is a granting of credentials to indicate that an individual has achieved a level of ability higher than the minimal level of competency indicated by licensure.[3] As technology increases and the health-care environment becomes more complex and demanding, nurses are finding a need to increase their knowledge and skill levels beyond the essentials taught in their basic nursing courses.

Certification acknowledges the attainment of increased knowledge and skills and provides nurses with a means to validate their own self-worth and competence. Some certification also carries with it a legal status, similar to licensure; but in many cases, certification merely indicates a specific professional status. The public, employers, and even nurses themselves have difficulty understanding what certification means.

Another element that adds confusion to the understanding of the process of certification is that a large number of groups can offer certification. These are usually professional specialty groups like the

National Association of Pediatric Nurse Associates and Practitioners (NAPNAP) and the American Association of Critical-Care Nurses (AACN), but they can also be national organizations like the National League for Nursing (NLN) or the ANA.

Individual Certification

The most common type of certification is called individual certification. When a nurse has demonstrated that he or she has attained a certain level of ability above and beyond the basic level required for licensure in a defined area of practice, that nurse can become certified. Usually some type of written and practical examination is required to demonstrate this advanced level of skill.

The ANA has its own certifying organization, the American Nurses Credentialing Center (ANCC) that offers widely recognized certifications in more than 40 areas. Almost all nurses with individual certification are required to maintain their skills and competencies through continuing education and a specified number of continuing education units (CEU). Recertification may be achieved through CEUs or retaking of the certification examination.

Organizational Certification

Organizational certification is the certification of a group or health-care institution by some external agency. It is usually referred to as accreditation and indicates that the institution has met standards established either by the government or by a nongovernmental agency. Often the ability of the institution to collect money from insurance companies or the federal government depends on whether or not the institution is certified by a recognized agency. Most hospitals are accredited by the Joint Commission on Accreditation of Healthcare Organizations (JCAHO) as a minimum level of accreditation. In most states, the State Health Department certifies health-care institutions, particularly nursing homes and extended care facilities.

Advanced Practice

Some state governments may either award or recognize certification granted to nurses in areas of advanced practice. In these cases, the certification becomes a legal requirement for practice at the APN level. Depending on the individual state's nurse practice act, nurses thus certified fall under regulations in the state's practice act that control the type of activities nurses may legally carry out when they perform advanced roles.[4]

For example, many states recognize the position of **nurse midwife** as an advanced practice role for nurses. In these states, a nurse midwife is allowed to practice those skills allowed under the nurse practice act of that state after obtaining certification. Generally nurse midwives are allowed to conduct prenatal examinations, do prenatal teaching, and deliver babies vaginally in uncomplicated pregnancies. They are not usually allowed to perform cesarean sections.

Varying Standards

An independent certification center was proposed in 1978 to establish uniform criteria and standards and to oversee all certification activities. Although it would eliminate much of the current confusion about certification and would help with the legal recognition of APNs, this proposal has not yet been acted upon because of opposition from physician and health-care administration groups.

Unfortunately, there is no uniformity among states in the recognition of certification of APNs.

Issues Now

Nurse Practitioners Lower Health-Care Costs While Improving Quality of Care

A number of studies have been conducted over the past few years on how advanced practice nurses (APN) fit into the health-care system and their overall effect on the quality of care. Initially, many physicians were opposed to APNs because they felt their level of training was inadequate to provide high-quality care and because they would be "cutting into" their practice and source of income.

These concerns have proven to be unwarranted. Advanced practice nurses tend to serve segments of the population that physicians generally do not treat, and the quality of care has been consistently judged to be at least at the level of physician care if not higher.

The University of Pennsylvania Study

The University of Pennsylvania conducted a study of hospitalized older adults suffering from congestive heart failure (CHF). Nationwide, CHF is a leading cause of morbidity and mortality among the elderly population. It is estimated that treatment of this disorder costs the health-care industry some $24 billion per year. It is logical to conclude that, if this group of elderly could avoid exacerbations of CHF requiring hospitalization, the costs for their care should decrease.

A group of master's-degree–prepared APNs received 2 months' additional training centered on care of the elderly population with cardiac-related problems. The elderly subjects were divided into two groups: a control group that received the usual hospital-based care and the test group that received care by the specially trained APNs. The study was conducted over a 1-year period. At the end of the year, the test group cared for by APNs had a 13.7% lower rate of death or hospitalization and an average reduction of cost of care of $4845.00 per client. Also, the test group went an average of 110 days longer without major complications associated with CHF than the control group.

Although there has not been any hard analysis of why these results occurred, there seem to be several underlying factors. First, as nurses, APNs have a basic orientation toward holistic and preventive care, rather than the narrow sick care model taught in most medical schools. By approaching clients' health-care needs from a broad focus that includes such elements as lifestyle, diet, and environment, the APNs' care not only treats present problems but affects those things that contribute to them.

Second, many clients, particularly the elderly, delay medical help in a hospital setting, particularly if they have to go through the emergency department, until they are severely ill. APN care is easier to access, and treating symptoms before they become acute is more cost effective and better for the client.

Third, APNs do not charge as much per visit as physicians do. They are inherently more cost-effective for primary health care.

(continued)

Issues Now (continued)

In the end, the same old problem still plagues nursing, even at the advanced practice level: lack of respect from the medical community. Studies such as the University of Pennsylvania study will help erase the underlying prejudices and increase the level of respect for nurses throughout the medical community.

Sources: Donnelly G: The essence of advanced nursing practice. Internet Journal of Advanced Nursing Practice, 8(1):1–12, 2007.

Kennedy, M: APNs: Improved outcomes at lower costs. American Journal of Nursing 104(9):19, 2004.

McConnell ES; Academic-practice partnerships to promote evidence-based practice in long-term care: oral hygiene care practices as an exemplar. Nursing Outlook 55(2):95–105, 2007.

The role of the advanced practice nurse in actualizing the best quality cost-effective health care in the acute care setting. National Association of Clinical Nurse Specialists National Conference Abstracts, Phoenix, February 28–March 3, 2007.

Some states recognize almost all certifications and have provisions in their nurse practice acts to help guide these practices. Other states have very little legal recognition of certification levels and thus few guidelines for practice. This confusion may result from so many organizations offering certification in different areas. In some advanced practice specialties, such as nurse practitioner, two or more organizations may offer certification for the same title. The certification standards vary from organization to organization, and the method of determining certification may also be different.

A More Significant Role

It is expected that advanced practice nurses will play a larger role in the rapidly evolving health-care system of the future. What that role will be depends on how well governmental organizations and the public understand the contributions practitioners can make as **primary care providers.** Without a uniform definition of this specialty, such nurses will not be utilized to their full potential.

Licensure and certification are both methods of granting credentials to demonstrate that an individual is qualified to provide safe care to the public. Without proof of competency, the profession of nursing would become chaotic, disorganized, and even dangerous. It is important for nurses to keep a watchful eye on pending legislation and practices that health-care institutions are initiating. Many of these proposals and practices are covert ways of reintroducing permissive and institutional licensure.

NURSING ORGANIZATIONS AND THEIR IMPORTANCE

Strength in Numbers

The establishment of a professional organization is one of the most important defining characteristics of a profession. Many professions have a single major professional organization to which most of its members belong and several specialized suborganizations that members may also join. Professions with just one major organization generally have a great deal of political power.

Nurses need and use power in every aspect of their professional lives, ranging from supervising unlicensed personnel to negotiating with the administration for increased independence of practice. Clearly, an individual nurse probably does not have much power; but for nurses as a group, the potential is increased exponentially by the organization. The dedication to high-quality nursing standards and improved methods of practice by the major nursing

> *"Clearly, an individual nurse probably does not have much power; but for nurses as a group, the potential is increased exponentially by the organization."*

organizations has led to improved care and increased benefits to the public as a whole.[6]

Speaking With One Voice

National nursing organizations need the participation and membership of all nurses in order to claim that they are truly representative of the profession. A large membership allows the organization to speak with one voice when making its values about health-care issues known to politicians, physicians' groups, and the public in general.

The National League for Nursing

Purposes

The primary purpose of the National League for Nursing (NLN) is to maintain and improve the standards of nursing education. The NLN is also a strong force in community health nursing, occupational health nursing, and nursing service activities. Its bylaws state that its purpose is to foster the development and improvement of hospital, industrial, public health, and other organized nursing services and of nursing education through the coordinated action of nurses, allied professional groups, citizens, agencies, and schools so that the nursing needs of the people will be met.

Membership

Although membership is open to individual nurses, the primary membership of the NLN comes in the form of agency membership, usually through schools of nursing. One of the major functions of this organization, through the National League for Nursing Accrediting Commission (NLNAC), is to accredit schools of nursing through a self-study process. The schools are given a set of criteria, or **essentials for accreditation,** and are then required to evaluate their programs against these criteria. After the evaluation report is written and sent to the NLNAC, site representatives visit the school to verify the information in the report and see whether the school has met the criteria. If the school meets the evaluation criteria, it is accredited for up to 8 years.

Accreditation of a school of nursing by the NLNAC indicates that the school meets national standards. In some work settings, it is a requirement that a nurse be a graduate of an NLNAC-accredited school of nursing before the nurse can be hired or accepted into many master's level nursing programs.

Other services and activities that the NLN carries out include testing, evaluating new graduate nurses, supplying career information and continuing education workshops and conferences for all levels of nursing, publishing a wide range of literature and videotapes covering current issues in health care, and compiling statistics about nursing, nurses, and nursing education.

The American Association of Colleges of Nursing

Purposes

The American Association of Colleges of Nursing (AACN) was established to help colleges with schools of nursing work together to improve the standards for higher education for professional nursing. The AACN, through the Commission on Collegiate Nursing Education (CCNE), has developed standards for the accreditation of baccalaureate schools of nursing and is poised to become a major accreditation agency, competing with the NLNAC. The AACN has developed and published a set of guidelines for the education of professional nursing students that is widely used as the theoretical basis for baccalaureate curricula.

Membership

Only deans and directors of programs that offer baccalaureate or higher degrees in nursing with an upper-division nursing major are permitted membership in the AACN.

The American Nurses Association

Purposes

The American Nurses Association (ANA) grew out of a concern for the quality of nursing practice and the care that nurses were providing. The major purposes for the existence of the ANA, as stated in its bylaws, include improvement of the standards of health and access to health-care services for everyone, improvement and maintenance of high standards for nursing practice, and promotion of the professional growth and development of all nurses, including economic issues, working conditions, and independence of practice.[6]

The American Association of Colleges of Nursing (AACN) was established to help colleges with schools of nursing work together to improve the standards for higher education for professional nursing.

Membership

Membership in the ANA is limited to 52 constituents: 50 state organizations, Washington, DC, and Puerto Rico. An individual joins a state organization and through the state organization indirectly is a member of the ANA. Certain discounts in membership are offered for new members and new graduate nurses. Various levels of membership are available for nurses who work part-time or those who are retired. The ANA makes every effort to encourage individual nurses to join the organization. Unfortunately, most nurses do not belong to this potentially powerful, politically active, and very influential organization.

Each state has the opportunity to determine what is needed from each member to run the state association; the amount of the dues that is sent to ANA is predetermined. Although dues are not inexpensive (they change a little from year to year, but are about $200 per year), the ANA offers various plans for payment, such as three equal payments over the course of a year or monthly payroll deductions. Because of the efforts of the ANA, nurses' salaries have risen to a point where this sum is affordable.

Other Services

When nurses pursue advanced education and levels of practice, as many are doing today, the ANA ANCC is essential for testing and certification of many of these practice levels. Although other organizations offer advanced practice certification, without the ANCC, there would be even less standardization for and less recognition of these practitioners by the public, physicians, or lawmakers.

Entry Into Practice. Another important issue that the ANA has been involved in is the entry-level education requirement for professional nurses. The ANA has supported the baccalaureate degree as the minimum educational requirement for nurses for the last 30 years. The ANA is in the forefront of the debate over **entry into practice,** which has continued into the 21st century.

Standards of Practice. Additional functions carried out by the ANA include the establishment and continual updating of standards of nursing practice. These standards are the yardstick against which nurses are measured and held accountable by **courts of law.** The ANA also established the official code of ethics that guides professional practice.

Legislation and Economics

Many of the political and economic activities of the ANA are carried out in the halls of legislatures and offices of legislators. The ANA Political Action Committee (ANA-PAC) is one of the most powerful in Washington, DC. (See Chapter 19 for a more detailed discussion.) Such activities have a profound effect on the role that nurses play and will continue to play in health care well into the 21st century.

Successful PAC activities require money and the power of a large, unified membership. The ANA-PAC seeks to influence legislation about nurses, nursing, and health care in general. It has been and will be a strong voice in the formulation of current national health-care reform.

Another important function of the ANA is economic. In many states, the ANA is the official **bargaining agent** for nurses in the negotiation of **contracts** with hospitals, nursing homes, and other health-care agencies that employ nurses. However, **collective bargaining** is done on a state-to-state basis—some states are **collective bargaining units** and others are not. (See Chapter 16 for a more detailed discussion.) Professional organizations represent professional groups better than a labor union that has little knowledge of professional activities or needs.

The National Student Nurses' Association

Purposes

The National Student Nurses' Association (NSNA) is an independent legal corporation established in 1953 to represent the needs of nursing students. Working closely with the ANA, which offers services, an official publication, and close communication, the NSNA consists of state chapters that represent student nurses in those particular states.

The main purpose of the NSNA is to help maintain high standards of education in schools of nursing, with the ultimate goal of educating high-quality nurses who will provide excellent health care. Students' ideas, concerns, and needs are extremely important to nursing educators. Most nursing programs have committees in which students are asked to participate, including curriculum development and evaluation techniques. It is important that students belong to these committees and actively participate in the committees' activities.

Membership

Membership consists of all nursing students in registered nurse programs. Students can join at the local, state, or national level or at all levels if desired. Dues are low, with a discount for the first year's membership.

Other Services

Additionally, the NSNA is concerned with developing and providing workshops, seminars, and conferences that deal with current issues in nursing and health care, with a wide range of subjects, from ethical and legal concerns to recent developments in pharmacology, test-taking skills, and professional growth. Student nurses who belong to the NSNA and who take an active part in its functions are much more likely to join the ANA after they graduate. Professional identity and professional behavior are learned. By beginning the process during the formal school years, student nurses develop professional attitudes and behaviors that they will maintain for the rest of their lives.

Benefits for Students

Many benefits exist for student nurses who belong to the NSNA. A number of scholarships are available through this organization to members of the NSNA. Members receive the official publication of the organization, *Imprint,* and the *NSNA News,* which keep the student nurse current on recent developments in health care and nursing.

The student member also has political representation on issues that may affect the student now or in the future. Some of these issues include educational standards for practice, standards of professional practice, and health insurance. The NSNA is also concerned with the difficulty that many nursing students from minority groups experience in the educational process. The Breakthrough Project is an attempt by the NSNA to help such students enter the profession of nursing.

Practicing Professionalism

Student nurses who join the NSNA experience firsthand the operation, activities, and benefits of a professional organization. In schools with active memberships, the NSNA can be a very exciting and useful organization for students.

Many NSNA chapters are involved in community activities that provide services at a local level and allow the student to practice "real" nursing. These services include providing community health screening programs for hypertension, lead poisoning, vision, hearing, and birth defects; setting up information and education programs; giving immunizations; and working with groups concerned with drug abuse, child abuse, drunken driving, and teen pregnancy. All nursing students should be encouraged to belong to this organization.

The International Council of Nurses

Membership in the International Council of Nurses (ICN) consists of national nursing organizations, and it serves as the international organization for professional nursing. The ANA is one member among 104 nursing associations around the world.

Each member nation sends delegates and participates in the international convention held every 4 years. The quadrennial conventions, or congresses, are open to all nurses and delegates from all nations.

The goal of the ICN is to improve health and nursing care throughout the world. The ICN coordinates its efforts with the United Nations and other international organizations when appropriate in the pursuit of its goals.

Some issues that have been the focus of concern of the ICN are social and economic welfare of nurses, the changing role of nurses in the present health-care environment, the challenges being faced by the various national nursing organizations, and how government and politics affect the nursing profession and health care. Overseeing the ICN is the Council of National Representatives. This body meets every 2 years and serves as the governing organization. ICN headquarters is located in Geneva, Switzerland.

Sigma Theta Tau

Sigma Theta Tau is an honors organization that was established in colleges and universities to recognize individuals who have demonstrated leadership or made important contributions to professional nursing. It is international, and candidates are selected from among senior nursing students or graduate or practicing nurses.

The organization has its headquarters in Indianapolis, where it has a large library open to members to use for scholarly activities and research. It also boasts the first online nursing journal, which can be accessed by any nurse with a computer anywhere in the world. Local chapters of Sigma Theta Tau collect and distribute funds to nurses who are conducting nursing research. The organization also holds educational conferences and recognizes those who have made contributions to nursing.

Grassroots Organizations

A growing trend in contemporary nursing has been the formation of grassroots nursing organizations. In reality, all nursing organizations start as the grassroots efforts of local nursing groups that are trying to solve a particular problem. Over time, these small grassroots organizations become more structured, larger, and eventually become national or international when they spread to other areas across the country or around the world. Unfortunately, the large organizations tend to lose sight of the fundamental issues they were

originally formed to solve, or they are unable to deal effectively with local problems.

Working to Bring About Change

Grassroots organizations usually have relatively small memberships; are localized to a town, city, or sometimes a state; and attempt to solve a problem or deal with an issue that the members feel is not being adequately handled by a large national organization. They may be created as a completely new and separate organization, or they may break away from a larger, established group. Because all the members of grassroots organizations are passionately concerned about only one or two issues at a time that affect them directly, they tend to work hard to effect change and can bring a great deal of concentrated power to bear upon people, such as legislators, who make the decisions about the issues.

Grassroots groups use a number of techniques that are often frowned upon by the more established organizations to attain their goals. In addition to the traditional techniques of writing letters, sending e-mail, and calling legislators, members of grassroots groups actively seek media attention, march on capitol buildings and state houses, introduce resolutions, and testify before committee hearings. Their success varies from issue to issue and location to location.

Successful Grassroots Efforts

Two examples of successful grassroots efforts are found in California and Pennsylvania. The California Nurses Association decided to break away from the ANA because it was not addressing some key state issues such as length of hospital stays, reduction in professional nursing staffs, and **managed care's** preoccupation with profit. The grassroots group in Pennsylvania formed a completely new organization, the Nurses of Pennsylvania (NPA), and focused their energies on the trend to replace licensed registered nurses with unlicensed technicians, sometimes called "downskilling."

Special-Interest Organizations

Why Do They Exist?

The historical origins of special-interest organizations in nursing are even older than those of the main national organizations. For example, the Red Cross, established in 1864, is one of the oldest special-interest organizations that nurses have been involved with. Like the Red Cross, most specialty organizations in nursing were founded when a group of nurses with similar concerns sought professional and individual support. These organizations usually start out small and informal, then increase in size, structure, and membership over a number of years. There were relatively few of these organizations until 1965, when an explosion in specialty organizations in nursing took place. During the next 20 years, almost 100 new organizations were formed, with the associated effect of diminishing membership levels in the ANA.

Clinical Practice. Specialty organizations are usually organized according to clinical practice area. Organizations exist for almost every clinical specialty and subspecialty known in nursing, such as obstetrics/gynecology, critical care, operating room, emergency department, and occupational health, as well as less known areas such as flight nursing, urology, and cosmetic surgery.

Education and Culture. Another focal area for these organizations is education and ethics. Organizations such as the American Association of Colleges of Nursing and the Western Interstate Commission for Higher Education fall into this category. Often organizations focus on the common **ethnic group,** cultural, or religious backgrounds of nurses. The National Association of Hispanic Nurses and the National Black Nurses Association represent this type of specialty organization.

Education and Standards. Although many of these organizations promote the personal and professional growth of their membership, they also carry out many other activities. Particularly important among these activities is establishing the standards of practice for the particular specialty area. Much as the ANA establishes overall standards of practice for

nursing in general, the specialty organizations establish standards for their particular clinical areas. Providing educational services for their members is another important activity of specialty organizations. Conferences, workshops, and seminars in the clinical area represented are important venues for nurses to keep current on new developments and to maintain high standards of practice.

Should They Matter to You?

How many of these specialty nursing organizations are there? No one really knows. Many such organizations are informal and run by volunteers. Organizations are continually being formed, and others are being disbanded.

Should nurses belong to these organizations? The answer is yes, but only after they belong to the ANA. Many of the larger specialty organizations have recognized this fact and have established close ties with the ANA. The ANA, in its turn, is well aware of the membership bleed-off from the specialty organizations and has initiated efforts to become more involved in the specialty nursing areas.

Before nurses join a specialty organization, they should determine whether its purposes are at odds with those of the ANA. Many of the large specialty organizations have their own lobbyists in both state and national legislatures. Because the legislators really do not know the differences between the various nursing organizations, they can easily become confused over health-care issues if they are receiving pressure from two nursing groups representing opposing sides of the same issue. At this point, legislators may simply surmise that nurses really do not know what they want and vote on an important issue without regard to nurses and nursing.

Conclusion

Nursing, in its journey toward professionalism, has been propelled and shaped by its nursing organizations, which were the main vehicles for the development of educational and practice standards, initiation of licensure, promotion of advanced practice, and general improvement in the level of care nurses provided. From their beginnings, nursing organizations have served as

channels of communication between nurses, consumers of health care, and other health-care professionals. In many cases, the nursing organizations have served as a focus of power for the profession to influence those important health policies that affect the whole nation. That continued unity is essential for the survival of nursing.

Issues in Practice

Juanita R, an RN at a large inner-city hospital, has been working on her off-hours as a volunteer in a storefront clinic to treat the indigent and underserved population of that part of the city. The clinic clientele is primarily Mexican-American, as are the majority of the 20 nurses working at the clinic. Because all the nurses, including a family nurse practitioner, volunteer their time and receive no pay, the small private grant that Juanita had managed to secure was adequate to cover the cost for rental of the building, basic supplies for the clinic, and a few medications. However, the grant is about to run out and is nonrenewable.

Juanita first tried to obtain money from the hospital to keep the clinic going, but she was told that the hospital was having its own financial problems because of managed care demands and could not spare any money. At a staff meeting of the nurses from the clinic, the nurses decided to band together and form a grassroots organization called the Storefront Clinic Nurses to focus their efforts on obtaining funds to keep the clinic open. They printed and passed out flyers, called local and city politicians, encouraged the patrons of the clinic to talk to people they knew, and even called the local television station for an interview about their plight.

Although most of the nurses' effort went unrewarded, a large pharmaceutical company became aware of their plight and wanted to provide a sizable financial stipend to the clinic, in addition to supplying free medications, for a period of at least 5 years. In addition to their philanthropic interests, the pharmaceutical company also wanted to gather long-term data about a newly developed antihypertensive medication. The company would provide the medication free to the clients at the clinic, the majority of whom had some degree of hypertension, and all the nurses would have to do is take and record the clients' blood pressure readings and complete "reported side effects" forms on each client. Client identifier codes, rather than names, would be used to maintain confidentiality. Juanita, as the group's coordinator, would be responsible for coordinating and preserving the data.

Although Juanita saw it as an answer to her prayers, she was concerned about the medication project. The pharmaceutical company said that no research consent forms were needed because the medication had already been through clinical trials and had received approval by the Food and Drug Administration. Juanita called another meeting of her nurses to discuss the issue. Without the grant, the clinic would close, but if they accepted the grant, they would have to participate in a medication research project that made Juanita feel uncomfortable.

1. What are the main issues in this case study?
2. What ethical principles are being violated? What is the ethical dilemma that Juanita is facing?
3. Are there any other solutions to this problem?

The tendency toward specialization has led to an ever-increasing number of nursing organizations, however, each focusing on a particular practice field within the profession. This trend has diluted the unity and ultimately lessened the power that nursing as a profession can exert in health care issues. Although it is important to recognize the complexity of today's health-care system and the pluralism inherent in nursing, unity of opinion on major issues is essential if nursing is to have any influence on the future of the profession.

The challenge for nurses in the future is to use the diversity in the profession as a positive force and to unite as a group on important issues. Awareness of earlier development of nursing organizations provides a perspective for the current situation and can act as a framework for planning the future.

What Do You Think?

What type of power does the individual nurse have? Cite examples of individual nurses who have used their power to effect changes in health care and nursing

Critical Thinking Exercises

- Develop a strategy for increasing the membership of the ANA.
- A labor union is attempting to organize the nurses at your hospital. Is it better for the professional nursing organization to represent the nurses? Why?
- A new graduate nurse is working in the intensive care unit (ICU) of a large hospital. She wants to join a nursing organization but only has a limited amount of money to spend. Her coworkers in the ICU want her to join the AACN, but she would also like to join the ANA. Basing her decision on economic and professional issues, which organization should she join?
- Compare and contrast certification and licensure. Should certification be legally recognized? Justify your answer.

References

1. Wendt, A: Monitoring entry-level practice: Keeping the National Council Licensure Examination for Registered Nurses current. Nurse Educator 32(2): 78–80, 2007.
2. Simpson, R: Small bytes for busy people. Multistate licensure: Regulating cross-country care. Journal of Clinical System Management 6(8/9):14, 2004.
3. Eisemon, N: "Raising the bar": Understanding the value and opportunities of professional nursing certification. Gastroenterology Nursing 30(2):149, 2007.
4. Carson-Smith, WY:Advanced practice nurses: A new skirmish in the continuing battle over scope of practice. Clinical Nurse Specialist: The Journal for Advanced Nursing Practice 21(1):52–54, 2007.
5. Manton, A, and Chamberlain, B: The importance of joining professional nursing organizations. Imprint 51:5,38–40, 2004.
6. American Nurses Association: Nursing's Social Policy Statement. ANA, Washington, DC, 1995.

Bibliography

Adams, D, and Miller, BK: Professionalism in nursing behaviors of nurse practitioners. Journal of Professional Nursing 17(4):203–210, 2001.

Barkley, TW, et al.: Practice issues: Credentialing, prescriptive authority, and liability. Nurse Practitioner Forum 2001 12(2):106–114, 2001.

Clowney, J: Moving ahead: Learning from experience: Renewing your vigour. Nursing Times 101(2):75, 2005.

Garncro, T: On solving the nursing shortage. Nurse Week (Special Edition) Feb 4, 2002, p 11.

Gingerich, B: Accreditation actions. Certification and licensure: CAM services providers. Home Health Care Management Practice 16(6):531–533, 2004.

Martin, B: Are you ready for certification, the mark of excellence? AACN NEWS 21(11):10, 2004.

Martin, SA: Network to promote advanced practice mentoring relationships. AACN News 19(3):5, 2002.

Mikos, C: Legal checkpoints: Inside the Nurse Practice Act. Nurse Manager 35(9):20, 22, 91, 2004.

Poe, L: Eleven answers about the Nurse Licensure Interstate Compact. Utah Nurse 13(3):18, 2004.

Results of a multistate licensure survey. AJN-2005 Career Guide: 40, 2005.

Salladay, S: Ethical problems. Nursing credentials: What's in a name (badge)? Nursing 34(8):11, 2004.

Sofer, D: Mandatory BSNs? New New York nurses could be required to eventually obtain baccalaureates. American Journal of Nursing 104(10):22, 2004.

Tahan, H: Guest column. Certification helps CMs meet today's challenges: Skills, knowledge, competency enhanced. Hospital Case Management 13(2):22, 31–32, 2005.

Whelan, J: "A necessity in the nursing world." The Chicago Nurses Professional Registry 1913–1950. Nursing History Review 13:49–75, 2005.

Your guide to certification: Here's what you need to know to pursue recognition of your expertise. American Journal of Nursing 2005 Career Guide:56–69, 2005.

4

Theories and Models of Nursing

Joseph T. Catalano

Learning Objectives

After completing this chapter, the reader will be able to:

- Explain why theories and models are important to the profession of nursing.
- Analyze the four key concepts found in nursing theories and models.
- Interrelate systems theory as an important element in understanding nursing theories and models.
- Evaluate how the four parts of all systems interact.
- Synthesize three nursing theories, identifying how the different nursing theorists define the key concepts in their theories.

CARING FOR REAL PEOPLE

For many nurses, and for most nursing students, the terms *theory* and *model* evoke images of textbooks filled with abstract, obscure words, and convoluted sentences. The visceral response is often "Why is this important? I want to take care of real people!" The simple answer is that understanding and using nursing theories or models will help you be a better nurse and provide better care to real people.

DIFFERENCES BETWEEN THEORIES AND MODELS

What is a Theory?

Although the terms *theory* and *model* are not synonymous, in nursing practice they are often used interchangeably. Strictly speaking, a theory refers to a speculative statement involving some element of reality that has not been proved. For example, the theory of relativity has never been proved, although the results have often been observed.

The nursing profession tends to use the term *theory* when attempting to explain apparent relationships between observed behaviors and their effects on a client's health. In this nursing context, the goal of a theory is to describe and explain a particular nursing action to make a **hypothesis** or predict its effect on a client's outcome, such as improved health or recovery from illness. For example, the action of turning an unresponsive client from side to side every 2 hours should help prevent skin breakdown and improve respiratory function.

In recent years, nursing has been moving toward using research findings to guide nursing practice. This approach, called evidence-based practice, is an important element in improving nursing care and proving many of the long-standing theories that the nursing profession has developed over the years.[1]

What Is a Model?

A model is a hypothetical representation of something that exists in reality. The purpose of a model is to attempt to explain a complex reality in a systematic and organized manner. For example, a hospital organizational chart is a model that attempts to demonstrate the interrelationships of the various levels of the hospital's administration.[2]

What Do You Think?

Do you consider yourself to be healthy? What factors make you healthy? What factors are indicators of illness?

_____

_____

_____

_____

_____

_____

_____

_____

_____

_____

_____

What Do Nurses Do?

Although a model tends to be more concrete than a theory, they both help explain and direct nursing actions. This ability, using a systematic and structured approach, is one of the key elements that raises nursing from a task-oriented job to the level of a real profession. With the use of a **conceptual model,** nurses can provide intelligent and thoughtful answers to the question "What do nurses do?" Consider this scenario:

> Mr. X had surgery for intestinal cancer 4 days ago. He has a colostomy and needs to learn how to take

care of it at home because he is going to be discharged from the hospital in 2 days. When the nurses attempt to teach him colostomy care, he looks away, makes sarcastic personal comments about the nurses, and generally displays a belligerent and hostile attitude.

Without an understanding of the underlying dynamics involved, the nurses' reactions to this client's behavior might be to become sarcastic and scold the client about his behavior or simply to minimize the amount of contact with him.[2] This type of response will not improve Mr. X's health status. If, however, the nurses knew about and understood the dynamics of the grief theory, they would realize that Mr. X was probably in the anger stage of the grief process. This understanding would direct the nurses to allow, or even to encourage, Mr. X to express his anger and **aggressiveness** without condemnation and to help him deal with his feelings in a constructive manner. Once Mr. X gets past the anger stage, he can move on to taking a more active part in his care and thus improve his health status. The **client goals** would then be achieved.

If a researcher were to stop 10 people at random on the street and ask the question, "What do nurses do?" he or she would likely get 10 different answers, but the confusion about nurses' activities extends far beyond the public at large. What if the researcher asked 10 hospital administrators, 10 physicians, or even 10 nurses the same question? It could be anticipated that the answers would vary almost as much as the answers from laypeople.

The Iowa Project

A Classification System

In an attempt to identify what exactly it is that nurses do, J. C. McCloskey and G. M. Bulechek, two nurse researchers at the University of Iowa, have been conducting a research project since 1990 to develop a **taxonomy** of the **interventions** that nurses use in their practice (Box 4.1). This research has been called Nursing Interventions Classification (NIC),

> _In recent years, nursing has been moving toward using research findings to guide nursing practice. This approach, called evidence-based practice, is an important element in improving nursing care and proving many of the long-standing theories that the nursing profession has developed over the years._

Box 4.1

What Constitutes Care?

At first glance, it would seem that everybody knows that nurses take care of clients. But what constitutes care? A study conducted by the faculty of the University of Iowa, called the Nursing Interventions Classification (NIC) or simply the Iowa Project, has identified 336 tasks or interventions that nurses are responsible for in their care of patients. Not all nurses carry out all 336 of these tasks all the time, but during an average career, a nurse would likely be involved in the majority of these tasks. Although this project was undertaken in the mid-1990s, it remains the benchmark study. Since the original study, several additional studies have been conducted that reaffirm the findings of the Iowa Project, and several researchers have undertaken projects to use the data generated by the Iowa Project in actual client care situations.

This project is an excellent example of how a nursing theory led to a research project that developed information that can be used by nurses in their daily practice. Based on the belief that nursing interventions are specific actions that a nurse can perform to bring about the resolution of a potential or actual health-care problem, the NIC attempted to identify and classify nursing interventions. It also attempted to rank those interventions according to the number of times a nurse was likely to perform one during a working day. The goal of the project was to develop a nursing information system that could be incorporated into the current information systems of all clinical facilities. By using the NIC system, hospital administrators, physicians, nurses, and even the public should be better able to recognize and evaluate the multiple interventions that nurses are responsible for in their daily work.

It is a generally acknowledged fact that nurses, as the largest single group of health-care providers, are essential to the welfare and care of most clients. Yet, in an age of health-care reform, nurses are finding it increasingly difficult to delineate the specific contributions they make to health care. If nurses are unable to define the care they provide, how are the reformers, politicians, and the public going to be able to identify the unique contribution made by nursing?

Unfortunately, many of the contributions that nurses make to health care are currently invisible because there is no method of classification for them in the computerized database systems now in use. Commonly used nursing interventions such as active listening, emotional support, touch, skin surveillance, and even family support cannot be measured and quantified by most current information systems.

The large number of interventions used daily by nurses demonstrates the complex and demanding nature of the profession. The breadth and depth of knowledge and skills demanded of nurses on a daily basis is much greater than is found in many other health-care professions. One study found that nurses working in general medical/surgical units during a 6-month period were likely to care for 500 clients with more than 600 individual diagnoses (many clients have multiple diagnoses). These researchers also found that the physical demands of the work were actually less difficult and tiring than dealing with the emotional and technical demands of handling the huge amounts of information generated by the care given.

Sources: Moorhead, S, et al.: Nursing outcomes classification (NOC): Iowa outcomes project, ed. 3. Mosby, St. Louis, 2004.

Haugsdal, C: Using the Nursing Interventions Classification to describe the work of the nurse practitioner. Journal of American Academy of Nurse Practitioners 15(2):87–94, 2003.

Hansen, M: Iowa Patient Safety Project update. Iowa Nurse Reporter 15(2):17, 2002.

Bulechek, GM, et al.: Nursing interventions used in nursing practice. American Journal of Nursing 94(10):59–61, 1994.

the Iowa Interventions Project, or simply the Iowa Project.[3–5]

The first results, published in 1994, categorized and ranked 336 interventions that nurses use when they provide care to clients. A follow-up study was conducted about 2 years after the original and published in 1996. This study categorized and ranked 433 interventions used by nurses. McCloskey and Bulechek[6] also investigated what nursing interventions were commonly used by nurses in specialty settings. Forty specialty areas responded, and the researchers were able to develop a table that lists what core skills are used by each organization.

This type of research helps identify the important contributions made by nursing to the health and well-being of clients. It also demonstrates the complex and demanding nature of the nursing profession. Although additional research has been conducted into this topic, the findings of McCloskey and Bulechek[4–6] continue to be considered the standard for all subsequent studies.

> *Although nursing models vary in terminology and approach to health care, there are four concepts that are common to almost all of them: client or patient (individual or collective), health, environment, and nursing.*

> *Nursing models tend to be holistic; they are concerned with curing disease and restoring a client's health, but they also focus on prevention of disease and maintenance of health. A healthy person is just as important to many nursing models as the person with a disease.*

Nursing Competencies

One way in which the nursing profession identifies what nurses do is by looking at **competencies.** In nursing, the word "competence" is often defined as the combination of skills, knowledge, attitudes, values, and abilities that support the safe and effective practice of the nurse. A nurse practices competently when he or she has mastered a range of skills and decision-making processes demonstrated in the care of clients. All the major nursing organizations have developed list of competencies for nurses. These are usually general, broad statements rather than catalogues of specific skills. (See Issues Now: Looking to the Future in this chapter.)

More recently, nursing researchers have attempted to develop specific lists of skills based on the general competency statements from the various nursing organizations. These skills lists help differentiate the various levels of nursing practice. One such list of skills is presented in Table 4.2 at the end of this chapter.

KEY CONCEPTS COMMON TO NURSING MODELS

Although nursing models vary in terminology and approach to health care, four concepts are common to almost all of them: client or patient (individual or collective), health, environment, and nursing. Each nursing model has its own specific definition of these terms, but the underlying definitions of the concepts are similar.

Client

The concept of client (or patient) is central to all nursing models, because it is the client who is the primary recipient of nursing care. Although the term *client* is usually used to refer to a single individual, it can also refer to small groups or to a large collective of individuals (for community health nurses, the community is the client).

A Complex Relationship. The concept of client has changed over the years as knowledge and understanding of human nature have developed and increased. A client constitutes more than a person who simply needs **restorative care** and comes to a health-care facility with a **disease** to be cured. Clients are now seen as complex entities affected by various interrelating factors, such as the mind and body, the individual and the **environment,** and the person and the person's family. When nurses talk about clients, the term *biopsychosocial* is often used to express the complex relationship between the body, mind, and environment.

Modeling a Healthy Client. A client, in many of the nursing models, does not have to have an illness to be the central element of the model (this explains the current preference of using the term *client* over the term *patient*). This is also one of the clearest distinctions between medical models and nursing models. Medical models tend to be restrictive and are almost exclusively devoted to curing diseases and to restoring health. Nursing models tend to be **holistic;** they are concerned with curing disease and restoring a client's health, but they also focus on prevention of disease and maintenance of health. A healthy person is just as important to many nursing models as the person with a disease.

Health

Like the concept of client, the concept of health has undergone much development and change over the years as knowledge has increased. Health was originally thought of as an absence of disease. A more current realistic view is that of health as a continuum, ranging from a completely healthy state, where there is no disease, to a completely unhealthy state, which results in death. At any given time in their lives, all people are located somewhere along the health continuum and may move closer to one side or the other depending on circumstances and health status.[7]

> *The culminating concept in all the various nursing models is nursing itself. After consideration of what it means to be a client, what it means to be healthy, and how the environment influences the client's health status either positively or negatively, the concept of nursing delineates the function and role nurses have in their relationships with clients.*

Health is difficult to define because it varies so much from one individual to another. For example, a 22-year-old bodybuilder who has no chronic diseases perceives health differently than an 85-year-old who has diabetes, congestive heart failure, and vision problems. The perception of health also varies from one culture to another and at different historical periods within the same culture. In some past cultures, a sign of health was pure white skin, whereas in the modern American culture, a dark bronze suntan has been more desirable as a sign of health—although there is an increasing recognition of the harmful effects of ultraviolet light on the skin.

Environment

The concept of environment is another element in most current nursing models. Nursing models often broaden the concept of environment from the simple physical environment to include elements such as living conditions, public sanitation, and air and water quality. Factors such as interpersonal relationships and social interactions are also included.

Some internal environmental factors that affect health include personal psychological processes, religious beliefs, sexual orientation, personality, and emotional responses. It has long been known that individuals who are highly self-motivated and internally goal directed (i.e., type A personality) tend to develop ulcers and have myocardial infarctions at a higher rate than the general population. Medical models, which are primarily illness oriented, although acknowledging this factor, may not consider it to be treatable. Nursing models that consider personality as one of the environmental factors that affect health are more likely to attempt to modify the individual's behavior (internal environment) to decrease the risk of disease.

Like the other key concepts found in nursing models, the concept of environment is used so that it is consistent within a particular model's overall context. Nursing models try to show how various aspects of environment interrelate and how they affect the client's health status. In addition, nursing models treat environment as an active element in the overall health-care system and assert that positive alterations in the environment will improve the client's health status.

Nursing

The Concept of Nursing

The culminating concept in all the various nursing models is nursing itself. After consideration of what it means to be a client, what it means to be healthy, and how the environment influences the client's health status either positively or negatively, the concept of nursing delineates the function and role nurses have in their relationships with clients.

Historically, the profession of nursing has been interested in providing basic physical care (i.e., hygiene, activity, and nourishment), psychological support, and relief of discomfort for clients. Modern nursing, although still including these basic elements of client care, has expanded into areas of health care that were only imagined a generation ago.

Client as Partner

In the modern nurse–client relationship, the client is no longer the passive recipient of nursing care. The relationship has been expanded to include clients as key partners in curing and in the health maintenance process. In conjunction with the nurse, clients set goals for care and recovery, take an active part in achieving those goals, and help in evaluating whether or not those actions have achieved the goals.[8]

What Do You Think?

How do you define nursing? What activities are important for the nurse to carry out?

Because of the broadened understanding of environment, several nursing models include manipulation of environmental elements that affect health as an important part of the nurse's role. The environment may be directly altered by the nurse with little or no input from the client, or the client may be taught by the nurse to alter the environment in ways that will contribute to curing disease, increasing comfort, or improving the client's health status.[9]

Four Key Concepts. To analyze and understand any nursing model, it is important to look for these four key concepts: client, health, environment, and nursing. These concepts should be clearly defined, closely interrelated, and mutually supportive. Depending on the particular nursing model, one element may be emphasized more than another. The resultant role and function of the nurse depend on which element is given greater emphasis.

GENERAL SYSTEMS THEORY

A widely accepted method for conceptualizing and understanding the world and what is in it is derived from a systems viewpoint. Generally understood as an organized unit with a set of components that interact and affect each other, a system acts as a whole because of the interdependence of its parts.[10] As a result, when part of the system malfunctions or fails, it interrupts the function of the whole system rather than affecting merely one part. Humans, plants, cars, governments, the health-care system, the profession of nursing, and almost anything that exists can be viewed as a system. The terminology and principles of systems theory pervade U.S. society.

A Basis in Thought

Manageable Fragments

Although general systems theory in its pure form is rarely, if ever, used as a nursing model, its process and much of its terminology underlie many nursing models. Elements of general systems theory in one form or another have found their way into many textbooks and much of the professional literature. General systems theory often acts as the unacknowledged **conceptual framework** for many educational programs. An understanding of the mechanisms and terminology of general systems theory is helpful in providing an orientation to understanding nursing models.

General systems theory, sometimes referred to simply as **systems theory,** is an outgrowth of an innate intellectual process. The human mind has difficulty comprehending large, complex entities as a single unit. As a result, the mind automatically divides that entity into smaller, more manageable fragments and then examines each fragment separately. This is similar to the process of deductive reasoning, in which a single complex thought or theory is broken down into smaller, interrelated pieces. All scientific disciplines, from physics to biology and the social sciences (e.g., sociology and psychology), use this method of analysis.

Reassembling the Fragments

Systems theory takes the process a step further. After analyzing or breaking down the entity, systems theory attempts to put it back together by showing how the parts work individually and together within the system. This interrelationship of the parts makes the system function as a unit. Often, particularly when the system involves biological or sociological entities, the system that results is greater than the sum of its parts.

For example, a human can be considered to be a complex, biosocial system. Humans are made up of a large number of smaller systems such as the endocrine system, neurological system, gastrointestinal system, urinary system, and so forth. Although each of these systems is important, in and of themselves they do not make a human. Many animals have the same systems, yet the human is more than the animal and more than the sum of the systems.

A Set of Interacting Parts

Although the early roots of general systems theory can be traced as far back as the 1930s, von Bertalanffy is usually credited with the formal development and publication of general systems theory around 1950.[11] His major achievement was to standardize the definitions of the terms used in systems theory and make the concept useful to a wide range of disciplines. Systems theory is so widely applicable because it reflects the reality that underlies basic human thought processes.

Very simply, a system is defined as a set of interacting parts. The parts that compose a system may be similar or may vary a great deal from each other, but they all have the common function of making the system work well to achieve its overall purpose.

A school is a good example of how the dynamics and interrelatedness of a system work.

A school as a system consists of a large number of units including buildings, administrators, teachers, students, and various other individuals (e.g., counselors, financial aid personnel, bookkeepers, and maintenance persons). Each of these individuals has a unique job but also contributes to the overall goal of the school, which is to provide an education for the students and to further the development of knowledge through research.

All systems consist of four key parts: the system itself (i.e., whether it is open or closed), input and output, throughput, and a feedback loop.

Open and Closed Systems

A system is categorized as being either open or closed. Very few systems are completely open or completely closed. Rather, they are usually a combination of both open and closed systems.

Open Systems

Open systems are those in which relatively free movement of information, matter, and **energy** into and out of the system exists. In a completely open system, there would be no restrictions on what moves in and out of the system, thus making its boundaries difficult to identify. Most systems have some control over the movement of information, energy, and matter around them. This control is maintained through the semipermeable nature of their boundaries, which allows some things in and keeps some things out, as well as allowing some out while keeping others in. This control of input and output leads to the dynamic equilibrium found in most well-functioning systems.

Closed Systems

Theoretically, a **closed system** prevents any movement into and out of the system. In this case, the system would be totally static and unchanging. Probably no absolutely closed systems exist in the real world, although there are systems that may tend to be closed to outside elements. A stone, for example, considered as a system, seems to be almost perfectly closed. It does not take anything in or put anything out. It does not change very much over long periods. In reality, though, it is affected by a number of elements in nature. It absorbs moisture when it is damp, freezes when cold, and becomes hot in the summer. Over long periods, these factors may cause the stone to crack, break down, and eventually become topsoil.

Systems that nurses deal with frequently are relatively open. Primarily, the client can be categorized as a highly open system that requires certain input elements and has output elements also. Other systems that nurses commonly work with (e.g., hospital administrators and physicians) are generally considered to be open systems, although their degree of openness may vary widely.

Input and Output

The processes by which a system interacts with elements in its environment are called *input* and *output*. Input is defined as any type of information, energy, or material that enters the system from the environment through its boundaries. Conversely, output is defined as any information, energy, or material that leaves the system and enters the environment through the system's boundaries. The end product of a system is a type of output that is not reusable as input. Open systems require relatively large amounts of input and output.

Throughput

A third term sometimes used in relationship to the system's dynamic exchange with the environment is *throughput*. Throughput is a process that allows the input to be changed so that it is useful to the system.

For example, most automobiles operate on some form of liquid fossil fuel (input) such as gasoline or diesel fuel. However, going to the gas station and pouring liquid fuel on the roof of the car will not produce the desired effects. If the fuel is put into the gas tank, it can be transformed by the carburetor or fuel injection system into a fine mist, which when mixed with air and ignited by a spark plug burns rapidly to produce the force necessary to propel the car. Without this internal process (throughput), liquid fuel is not a useful form of energy.

Feedback Loop

The fourth key element of a system is the *feedback loop*. The feedback loop allows the system to monitor its internal functioning so that it can either restrict or increase its input and its output and maintain the highest level of functioning.

Positive Feedback. Two basic types of feedback exist. Positive feedback leads to change within the system, with the goal of improving the system. Students in the classroom, for example, receive feedback from the teacher in several ways; it may be through direct verbal statements such as "Good work on this assignment" or through examination and homework grades. Feedback is considered positive if it produces a change in a student's behavior, such as motivating him or her to study more, spend more time on assignments, or prepare more thoroughly for class.

> *The feedback loop is an important element in systems theory. It makes the process circular and links the various elements of the system together.*

Negative Feedback. Negative feedback maintains stability; that is, it does not produce change. Negative feedback is not necessarily bad for a system. Rather, when a system has reached its peak level of functioning, negative feedback helps it maintain that level. For example, an athlete who has reached his or her peak level of performance through long hours of practice knows what type of practice is required to stay at that level of ability. Negative feedback—in the form of optimal times in the case of runners or number of pounds lifted in the case of weightlifters—indicates that no changes in practice patterns are required.

The feedback loop is an important element in systems theory. It makes the process circular and links the various elements of the system together. Without a feedback loop, it is virtually impossible for the system to have any meaningful control over its input and output.

Feedback loops are used at all levels in a hospital. Nurses get feedback about the care they provide both from clients and from their supervisors. The hospital administration gets feedback from clients and accrediting agencies. Physicians get feedback from clients, nurses, and the hospital administration. Systems theory is present, if sometimes unseen, in almost all health-care settings. Professional nurses need to be able to understand and identify the components of systems theory when they are encountered to improve their nursing practice and quality of care.

MAJOR NURSING THEORIES AND MODELS

At least 15 published nursing models (or theories) have been used to direct nursing education and nursing care.[12] The six nursing models discussed here (Table 4.1) have been selected because they are the most widely accepted and are good examples of how the concepts of client, health, environment, and nursing are used to explain and guide nursing actions. Discussion of these theories is not intended to be exhaustive, but rather to provide an overview

Table 4.1 Comparison of Selected Nursing Models

Nursing Theory	Client	Health	Environment	Nursing
Roy Adaptation Model	Human being—a dynamic system with input and output	A continuum with the ability to adapt successfully to illness	Both internal and external stimuli that affect behaviors	Multistep process that helps the client adapt and reach the highest level of functioning
Orem Self-Care Model	Human being—biological, psychological, social being with the ability for self-care	Able to live life to the fullest through self-care	The medium through which the client moves	Assistance in self-care activities to help the client achieve health
King Model of Goal Attainment	Person—exchanges energy and information with the environment to meet needs	Dynamic process to achieve the highest level of functioning	Personal, inter-personal, and social systems and the external physical world	Dynamic process that identifies and meets the client's health-care needs
Watson Model of Human Caring	Individual—has needs, grows, and develops to reach a state of inner harmony	Dynamic state of growth and development leading to full potential as a human being	The client must overcome certain factors to achieve health	Science of caring that helps clients reach their greatest potential
Johnson Behavioral System Model	Person—a behavioral system; an organized, integrated whole composed of seven subsystems	A behavioral system able to achieve a balanced, steady state	All the internal and external elements that affect client behavior	Activities that manipulate the environment and help clients achieve the balanced state of health
Neuman Health-Care Systems Model	An open system that constantly interacts with internal and external environment	An individual with relatively stable internal functioning of a high state of wellness (stability)	Internal and external stressors that produce change in the client	Identifies boundary disruption and helps clients in activities to restore stability

of the main concepts of the nurse theorist. It is important to understand the terms used in the theories as defined by their authors and to see the interrelationship between the elements in each theory as well as the similarities and differences among the various different models.

The Roy Adaptation Model

As developed by Sister Callista Roy, the Roy Adaptation Model of nursing is very closely related to systems theory.[13] The main goal of this model is to allow the client to reach his or her highest level of functioning through adaptation.

Client

The central element in the Roy Adaptation Model is man (a generic term referring to humans in general, or the client in particular, collectively or individually). Man is viewed as a dynamic entity with both input and output. As derived from the context of the four modes in the Roy Adaptation Model, the client is defined as a biopsychosocial being who is affected by various stimuli and displays behaviors to help adapt to the stimuli. Because the client is constantly being affected by stimuli, adaptation is a continual process.[13]

Inputs are called stimuli and include internal stimuli that arise from within the client's environment as well as stimuli coming from external environmental factors such as physical surroundings, family, and society. The output in the Roy Adaptation Model is the behavior that the client demonstrates as a result of stimuli that are affecting him or her.

Output, or behavior, is a very important element in the Roy Adaptation Model, because it provides the **baseline data** about the client that the nurse obtains through assessment techniques. In this model, the output (behavior) is always modified by the client's internal attempts to adapt to the input, or stimuli. Roy has identified four internal adaptational activities that clients use and has called them the four adaptation modes:

1. The physiological mode (using internal physiological process)
2. The self-concept mode (developed throughout life by experience)
3. The role function mode (dependent on the client's relative place in society)
4. The interdependence mode (indicating how the client relates to others)

Health

In the Roy Adaptation Model, the concept of health is defined as the location of the client along a continuum between perfect health and complete illness. Health, in this model, is rarely an absolute. Rather, "a person's ability to adapt to stimuli, such as injury, disease, or even psychological stress, determines the level of that person's health status."[13] For example, a client who was in an automobile accident, had a broken neck, and was paralyzed but who eventually went back to college, obtained a law degree, and became a practicing lawyer would, in the Roy Adaptation Model, be considered to have a high degree of health because of the ability to adapt to the stimuli imposed.

Environment

The Roy Adaptation Model's definition of environment is synonymous with the concept of stimuli. The environment consists of all those factors that influence the client's behavior, either internally or externally. This model categorizes these environmental elements, or stimuli, into three groups: (1) focal, (2) contextual, and (3) residual.

Focal stimuli are environmental factors that most directly affect the client's behavior and require most of his or her attention. **Contextual stimuli** form the general physical, social, and psychological environment from which the client emerges. **Residual stimuli** are factors in the client's past, such as personality characteristics, past experiences, religious beliefs, and social norms that have an indirect effect on the client's health status. Residual stimuli are often very difficult to identify because they may remain hidden in the person's past memory or may be an integral part of the client's personality.

Nursing

Assessment

In the Roy Adaptation Model, nursing becomes a multistep process, similar to the nursing process, to aid and support the client in the attempt to adapt to stimuli in one or more of the four adaptive modes. To determine what type of help is required to promote adaptation, the nurse must first assess the client.

The primary nursing assessments are of the client's behavior (output). Basically, the nurse should try to determine whether the client's behavior is adaptive or maladaptive in each of the four adaptational modes previously defined. Some first-level assessments of the pneumonia client might include a temperature of 104°F, a cough productive of thick green sputum, chest pain on inspiration, and signs of weakness or physical debility, such as the inability to bring in wood for the fireplace or to visit friends.

A second-level assessment should also be made to determine what type of stimuli (input) is affecting the client's health-care status. In the case of the client with pneumonia, this might include a culture and sensitivity of the sputum to identify the invasive bacteria, assessment of the client's clothes to determine whether they were adequate for the weather outside, and an investigation to find out whether any neighbors could help the client when he or she is discharged from the hospital.

Analysis

After performing the assessment, the nurse analyzes the data and arranges them in such a way as to be able to make a statement about the client's adaptive or maladaptive behaviors; that is, the nurse identifies the problem. In current terminology, this identification of the problem is called a **nursing diagnosis.** The problem statement is the first part of the three-part PES (problem–etiology–signs and symptoms) formulation that completes the nursing diagnosis (Fig. 4.1).

Setting Goals

After the problem has been identified, goals for optimal adaptation are established. Ideally, these goals should be a collaborative effort between the nurse and the client. A determination of the actions needed to achieve the goals is the next step in the process. The focus should be on manipulation of the stimuli to promote optimal adaptation. Finally, an evaluation is made of the whole process to evaluate whether the goals have been met. If the goals have not been met, the nurse must determine why, not how, the activities should be modified to achieve the goals.[11]

The Orem Self-Care Model

Dorothea E. Orem's model of nursing is based on the belief that health care is each individual's own responsibility. The model is aimed at helping clients direct and carry out activities that either help maintain or improve their health.[14]

Client

As with most other nursing models, the central element of the Orem model is the client, who is a biological, psychological, and social being with the capacity for self-care. Self-care is defined as the practice of activities that individuals initiate and perform on their own behalf to maintain life, health, and well-being. Self-care is a requirement both for maintenance of life and for optimal functioning.

Health

In the Orem Self-Care Model, health is defined as the person's ability to live fully within a particular physical, biological, and social environment, achieving a higher level of functioning that distinguishes the person from lower life forms.

Quality of life is an extremely important element in this model of nursing. A person who is

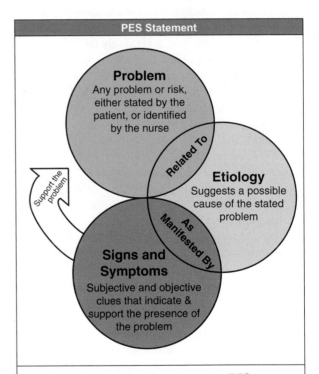

Together, these components make up the **PES** (**P**roblem, **E**tiology, **S**igns/symptoms) statement, which is demonstrated below

Pain, acute, may be *related to surgical wound, as manifested by facial grimacing, increased heart rate* and *verbal complaints* of pain at the incision site

F i g u r e 4 . 1 Together, these components make up the **PES** (**p**roblem–**e**tiology–**s**igns and **s**ymptoms) statement: *Pain, acute, may be related to surgical wound, as manifested by facial grimacing, increased heart rate,* and *verbal complaints* of pain at the incision site.

healthy is living life to the fullest and has the capacity to maintain that life through self-care. An unhealthy person is an individual who has a self-care deficit. This group of unhealthy individuals also includes adults with diseases and injuries, young and dependent children, the elderly, and the disabled. This deficit is indicated by the inability to carry out one or more of the key health-care activities. These activities have been categorized into six groups:

- Air, water, and food
- Excretion of waste
- Activity and rest
- Solitude and social interactions
- Avoiding hazards to life and well-being
- Being normal mentally under universal self-care

Universal Self-Care
In the Orem model, self-care is a two-part concept. The first type of self-care is called universal self-care and includes those elements commonly found in everyday life that support and encourage normal human growth, development, and functioning. Persons who are healthy, according to the Orem model, carry out the activities listed in order to maintain a state of health. To some degree, all these elements are necessary activities in maintaining health through self-care.[15]

The second type of self-care comes into play when the individual is unable to conduct one or more of the six self-care activities. This second type of self-care is called health deviation self-care. Health deviation self-care includes those activities carried out by individuals who have diseases, injuries, physiological or psychological stress, or other health-care concerns. Activities such as seeking health care at an emergency department or clinic, entering a drug **rehabilitation** unit, joining a health club or weight control program, or going to a physician's office fall into this category.

Environment
Environment, in the self-care model, is the medium through which clients move as they conduct their daily activities. Although less emphasized in this model, the environment is generally viewed as a negative factor in a person's health status because many environmental factors detract from the ability to provide self-care. Environment includes social interactions with others, situations that must be resolved, and physical elements that affect health.

Nursing
The primary goal of nursing in the Orem model is to help the client conduct self-care activities in such a way as to reach the highest level of human functioning. Because there is a range of levels of self-care ability, three distinct levels, or systems, of nursing care are delineated, based on the individual's ability to undertake self-care activities. As clients become less able to care for themselves, their nursing care needs increase.

Wholly Compensated Care
A person who is able to carry out few or no self-care activities falls into the wholly compensated nursing care category, in which the nurse must provide for most or all of the client's self-care needs. Examples of clients who require this level of care include comatose and ventilator-dependent clients in an intensive care unit, clients in surgery and the immediate recovery period, women in the labor and delivery phases of childbirth, and clients with emotional and psychological problems so severe as to render them unable to conduct normal activities of daily living.

Partially Compensated Care
Clients in the partially compensated category of nursing care can meet some to most of their self-care needs but still have certain self-care deficits that require nursing intervention. The nurse's role becomes one of identifying these needs and carrying out activities to meet them until the client reaches a state of health and is able to meet the needs personally. Examples of this level of nursing care include postoperative clients who can feed themselves and do basic activities of daily living (ADL) but are unable to care for a catheter and dressing, and clients with newly diagnosed diabetes who have not yet learned the technique of self-administered insulin injections.

> *The primary goal of nursing in the Orem model is to help the client conduct self-care activities in such a way as to reach the highest level of human functioning.*

Supportive Developmental Care

Clients who are able to meet all of their basic self-care needs require very little or no nursing interventions. These clients fall in the supportive developmental category of nursing care, in which the nurse's main functions are to teach the client how to maintain or improve health and to offer guidance in self-care activities and provide emotional support and encouragement.

What Do You Think?

Based on your experiences with the health-care system, write your own definition of client (patient). What factors led you to this definition?

_____

_____

_____

_____

_____

_____

_____

_____

_____

_____

_____

_____

_____

_____

Also, the nurse may adjust the environment to support the client's growth and development toward self-care or may identify community resources to help in the self-care process.[15] Conducting prenatal classes, arranging for discharge planning, providing child screening programs through a community health agency, and organizing aerobic exercise classes for postcoronary clients all are nursing actions that belong in the supportive developmental category of care.

A Three-Step Process

Nursing care is carried out through a three-step process in the Orem model. Step 1 determines whether nursing care is needed. This step includes a basic assessment of the client and identification of self-care problems and needs. Step 2 determines the appropriate nursing care system category and plans nursing care according to that category. Step 3 provides the indicated nursing care or actions to meet the client's self-care needs.

Five Methods

In the Orem model, step 3—the provision of nursing care (implementation phase)—is carried out by helping the client through one or a combination of five nursing methods:[12]

• Acting for or doing for another person
• Guiding another person
• Supporting another person (physically or psychologically)
• Providing an environment that promotes personal development
• Teaching another person

The King Model of Goal Attainment

The current widely accepted practice of establishing health-care goals for clients, and directing client care to meet these goals, has its origins in the King Model of Goal Attainment developed by Imogene M. King. It is also called the King Intervention Model.[16]

The King model also noted that nursing must function in all three system levels found in the environment: personal, interactional, and social. The primary function of nursing is at the personal systems level, whereby care of the individual is the main focus. However, nurses can effectively provide care at the interactional systems level, at which they deal with small to moderate-sized groups in activities such as group therapy and in health promotion classes. Finally, nurses can provide care at the social systems level through activities such as programs in community health. In addition, the role of nursing at the social systems level can be expanded to include involvement in policy decisions that have an effect on the health-care system as a whole.

Client

As in other nursing models, the focal point of care in the King model is the person or client. The client is viewed as an open system that exchanges energy and information with the environment—a personal system with physical, emotional, and intellectual needs that change and grow during the course of life. Because these needs cannot be met completely by the client alone, interpersonal systems are developed through interactions with others depending on the client's perceptions of reality, communications with others, and transactions to reduce stress and tension in the environment.

Environment

Environment is an important concept in the King model and encompasses a number of interrelated elements. The personal and interpersonal systems or groups are central to King's conception of environment. They are formed at various levels according to internal goals established by the client.

Personal Systems. At the most basic level are the personal systems, where an interchange takes place between two individuals who share similar goals. An example of such a personal system is a client–nurse relationship.

Interpersonal Systems. At the intermediate level are the interpersonal systems that involve relatively small groups of individuals who share like goals, for example, a formal weight-loss program in which the members have the common goal of losing weight. Human interactions, communications, role delineation, and stress reduction are essential factors at this level.

Social Systems. At the highest level are social systems, which include the large, relatively homogeneous elements of society. The health-care system, government, and society in general are some important social systems. These social systems have as their common goals organization, authority, power, status, and decision. Although the client may not be in direct interaction with the social systems, these systems are important because the personal and interpersonal systems necessarily function within larger social systems.

Evoking the principle of nonsummativity,* whenever one part of an open system is changed, all the other parts of the system feel the effect. For example, a decision made at the governmental level to reduce Medicare or Medicaid payments may affect when and how often a client can use health-care services such as doctor's office visits, group therapy, or emergency department care. The King model also includes the external physical environment that affects a person's health and well-being. As the person moves through the world, the physical setting

interacts with the personal system to either improve or degrade the client's health-care status.

Health

Viewed as a dynamic process that involves a range of human life experiences, health exists in people when they can achieve their highest level of functioning. Health is the primary goal of the client in the King model. It is achieved by continually adjusting to environmental stressors, maximizing the use of available resources, and setting and achieving goals for one's role in life. Anything that disrupts or interferes with people's ability to function normally in their chosen roles is considered to be a state of illness.

Nursing

The King model considers nursing to be a dynamic process and a type of personal system based on interactions between the nurse and the client. During these interactions, the nurse and the client jointly evaluate and identify the health-care needs, set goals for fulfillment of the needs, and consider actions to take in achieving those goals. Nursing is a multifaceted process that includes a range of activities such as the promotion and maintenance of health through education, the restoration of health through care of the sick and injured, and preparation for death through care of the dying.[11]

The process of nursing in the King model includes five key elements considered central to all human interactions:

- Action
- Reaction
- Interaction
- Transaction
- Feedback

The Watson Model of Human Caring

Although the concept of caring has always been an important, if somewhat obscure, element in the practice of nursing, the Watson Model of Human Caring defines caring in a detailed and systematic manner. In the development of her model, Jean Watson used a philosophical approach rather than the systems theory approach seen in many other nursing models. Her main concern in the development of this model was to balance the impersonal aspects of nursing care that are found in the technological and scientific aspects of

---

*Nonsummativity is the degree of interrelatedness among the systems parts. The higher the degree of nonsummativity, the greater the interdependence of parts.

Issues Now

Looking to the Future: The Pew Commission Final Report

Projected estimates of the nursing shortage based on data collected by the U.S. Bureau of the Census Current Population Survey, Division of Nursing, the Pew Commission, and the Buerhaus and Staiger data collection agency in 1998 are now considered woefully inadequate. Current projections of the nursing shortage range from 400,000 to as many as 1,000,000 by the year 2015. The Pew Commission's final report addressed the competencies that nurses in the future will need:

Twenty-One Competencies for the 21st Century

1. Embrace a personal ethic of social responsibility and service.
2. Exhibit ethical behavior in all professional activities.
3. Provide evidence-based, clinically competent care.
4. Incorporate the multiple determinants of health in clinical care.
5. Apply knowledge of the new sciences.
6. Demonstrate critical thinking, reflection, and problem-solving skills.
7. Understand the role of primary care.
8. Rigorously practice preventive health care.
9. Integrate population-based care and services into practice.
10. Improve access to health care for those with unmet health needs.
11. Practice relationship-centered care with individuals and families.
12. Provide culturally sensitive care to a diverse society.
13. Partner with communities in health-care decisions.
14. Use communication and information technology effectively and appropriately.
15. Work in interdisciplinary teams.
16. Ensure care that balances individual, professional, system, and social needs.
17. Practice leadership.
18. Take responsibility for quality of care and health outcomes at all levels.
19. Contribute to continuous improvement of the health-care system.
20. Advocate for public policy that promotes and protects the health of the public.
21. Continue to learn and help others to learn.

The Pew Commission also went on to identify five key areas for professional education:

1. Change professional training to meet the demands of the new health-care system.
2. Ensure that the health professions workforce reflects the diversity of the nation's population.
3. Require interdisciplinary competence in all health professionals.
4. Continue to move education into ambulatory practice.
5. Encourage public service of all health professional students and graduates.

The changes that will occur over the next decade may threaten some health-care professionals, but they will also open up a vista of opportunities for those willing to look creatively into the future. Nursing has to recognize that it will

Issues Now (continued)

grow only to the extent that it is able to contribute to the needs of an evolving health-care system. These needs will change with time. The Pew Report, although broad in scope, provides the nursing profession with a blueprint for dealing with these changes as they occur. It is a call to action that nurses and the nursing profession need to hear.

Sources: Bellack, JP, and O'Neil, EH: Recreating nursing practice for a new century: Recommendations of the Pew Health Professions Commission's Final Report, Nursing and Health Care Perspectives 21(1):14–21, 2000.

Brady, M, et al: A proposed framework for differentiating the 21 Pew Competencies by level of nursing education. Nursing and Health Care Perspectives 22(1):30–36, 2001.

Pontious, M: Where have all the nurses gone? The Oklahoma Nurse 47(1):1, 18, 2002.

More than one million new nurses needed by 2010. The American Nurse 34(1):5, 2002.

Critical Challenges: Revitalizing the Health Professions for the 21st Century. Pew Health Professions Commission, San Francisco, 1995.

practice with the personal and interpersonal elements of care that grow from a humanistic belief in life. Watson is also one of the very few theorists who openly recognize the client's and family's spirituality and spiritual beliefs as an essential element of health.[17]

Client

The concept of client or person in the Watson model is not well developed as separate from the concept of nursing. The individuality of the client is a key concern. The Watson model views the client as someone who has needs, who grows and develops throughout life, and who eventually reaches a state of internal harmony.

The client is also seen as a gestalt, or whole, who has value because of inherent goodness and capacity to develop. This gestalt, or holistic, view of the human being is a recurring theme in the Watson model; it emphasizes that the total person is more important to nursing care than the individual injury or disease process that produced the need for care. "The Watson model views the client as someone who has needs, who grows and develops throughout life, and who eventually reaches a state of internal harmony."

Environment

Environment in the Watson model is a concept that is also closely intertwined with the concept of nursing. Viewed primarily as a negative element in the health-care process, the environment consists of those factors that the client must overcome to achieve a state of health. The environment can be both external physical and social elements and internal psychological reactions that affect health.

Health

To be healthy according to the Watson model, the individual must be in a dynamic state of growth and development that leads to reaching full potential as a human. As with other nursing models, health is viewed as a continuum along which a person at any point may tend more toward health or more toward illness.

Illness, in the Watson model, is the client's inability to integrate life experiences and the failure to achieve full potential or inner harmony. In this model, the state of illness is not necessarily synonymous with the disease process. If the person reacts to the disease process in such a way as to find meaning, then that response is considered to be healthy. A failure to find meaning in the disease experience leads to a state of illness.

Nursing

Watson makes a clear distinction between the science of nursing and the practice of curing (medicine).[12] She defined nursing as the science of caring in which the primary goal is to assist the client to reach the greatest level of personal potential. The practice of curing involves the conduct of activities that have the goal of treatment and elimination of disease.

The process of nursing in the Watson model is based on the systematic use of the scientific problem-solving method for decision making. To best understand nursing as a science of caring, the nurse should hold certain beliefs and be able to initiate certain caring activities.

Values. Basic to the beliefs necessary for the successful practice of nursing in the Watson model is the formation of a humanistic altruistic system of values based on the tenet that all people are inherently valuable because they are human. In addition, the nurse should have a strong sense of faith and hope in people and their condition because of the human potential for development.

Caring. A number of activities are important in the practice of nursing according to Watson's caring way. These activities include establishing a relationship of help and trust between the nurse and the client; encouraging the client to express both positive and negative feelings with acceptance; manipulating the environment to make it more supportive, protective, or corrective for the client with any type of disease process; and assisting in whatever way is deemed appropriate to meet the basic human needs of the client.

The Johnson Behavioral System Model

By integrating systems theory with behavioral theory, Dorothy E. Johnson has developed a model of nursing that considers client behavior to be the key to preventing illness and to restoring health when illness occurs. Johnson holds that human behavior is really a type of system in itself that is influenced by input factors from the environment and has output that in its turn affects the environment.[12]

Client

Drawing directly on the terminology of systems theory, the Johnson model describes the person, or client, as a behavioral system that is an organized and integrated whole. The whole is greater than the sum of its parts because of the integration and functioning of its subsystems. In the Johnson model, the client as a behavioral system is composed of seven distinct behavioral subsystems. In turn, each of these seven behavioral subsystems contains four structural elements that guide and shape the subsystem.

Security. The first behavioral subsystem is the attachment, or affiliate, subsystem, which has security as its driving force. The type of activity that this subsystem undertakes is, for the most part, inclusion in social functions, and the behavior that is observed from this subsystem is social interaction.

Dependency. The second behavioral subsystem is the dependency subsystem, which has as its initiating force the goal of helping others. The primary type of activity involved is nurturing and promoting self-image. The observable behaviors that are a result of this activity include approval, attention, and physical assistance of the person.

Taking In. The third behavioral subsystem is called the ingestive subsystem, which has as its driving force the meeting of the body's basic physiological needs of food and nutrient intake. Correspondingly, its primary activity is seeking and eating food.

Eliminative Behavior. The fourth behavioral subsystem is the eliminative; its goal is removal of waste products from the system. Its primary activity is means of elimination, which is observed as the behavior of expelling waste products.

Sexual Behavior. The fifth behavioral subsystem is sexual behavior, which is found in the Johnson model's description of the person. The sexual subsystem has gratification and procreation of the species as its goals. It involves the complex activities of identifying gender roles, sexual development, and actual biological sexual activity. It manifests itself in courting and mating behaviors.

Self-Protection. The sixth behavioral subsystem is called the aggressive subsystem, and its driving force is the goal of self-preservation. All the actions that individuals undertake to protect themselves from harm, either internal or external, derive from this subsystem and are shown in actions toward others and the environment in general.

Achievement. The seventh, and final, behavioral subsystem is identified as achievement. Achievement has as its driving force the broad goal of exploration and manipulation of the environment. Gaining mastery and control over the environment is the primary activity of this subsystem; it can be demonstrated externally when the individual shows that learning has occurred and higher-level accomplishments are being produced.[18]

As with all open systems, the behavioral system that makes up the person seeks to maintain a dynamic balance by regulating input and output. This regulation process takes the form of adapting to the environment and responding to others. However, the Johnson model sees human behavior as being goal directed, which leads the person to constant growth and development beyond the maintenance of a mere steady state.

Health

A state of health exists, according to the Johnson model, when balance and steady state exist within the behavioral systems of the client. Under normal circumstances, the human system has enough inherent flexibility to maintain this balance without external intervention. At times, however, the system's balance may be disturbed to such a degree by physical disease, injury, or emotional crisis as to require external assistance. This out-of-balance state is the state of illness.

Environment

In the Johnson model, the environment is defined as all those internal and external elements that have an effect on the behavioral system. These environmental elements include obvious external factors, such as air temperature and relative humidity; sociological factors, such as family, neighborhood, and society in general; and the internal environment, such as bodily processes, psychological states, religious beliefs, and political orientation.

All seven behavioral subsystems of the client are involved with his or her relationship to the environment through the regulation of input and output. The client is continually interacting with the environment in the attempt to remain healthy by maintaining an internal dynamic balance.

Nursing

In the Johnson model, nursing is an activity that helps the individual achieve and maintain an optimal level of behavior (state of health) through the manipulation and regulation of the environment.[11] Nursing has functions in both health and illness.

Nursing interventions to either maintain or regain health involve four activities in the regulation of the environment:

- Restricting harmful environmental factors
- Defending the client from negative environmental influences
- Inhibiting adverse elements from occurring
- Facilitating positive internal environmental factors in the recovery process

As a professional, the nurse in the Johnson model provides direct services to the client. By interacting with, and sometimes intervening in, the multiple subsystems that are found in the client's environment, the nurse acts as an external regulatory force. The goal of nursing is to promote the highest level of functioning and development in the client at all times.

Nursing actions include helping the client act in a socially acceptable manner, monitoring and aiding with biological processes necessary for maintenance of a dynamic balance, demonstrating support for medical care and treatment during illness, and taking actions to prevent illness from recurring. In this model, nursing makes its own unique contribution to the health and well-being of individuals and provides a service that is complementary to that provided by other health-care professionals.

The Neuman Health-Care Systems Model

As envisioned by Betty Neuman, the Health-Care Systems Model focuses on the individual and his or her environment and is applicable to a variety of health-care disciplines apart from nursing. Drawing from systems theory, the Neuman model also includes elements from stress theory with an overall holistic view of humanity and health care.[16]

Client

In this model, the client is viewed as an open system that interacts constantly with internal and external environments through the system's boundaries. The client-system's boundaries are called lines of defense and resistance in the Neuman model and may be represented graphically as a series of concentric circles that surround the basic core of the individual. The goal of these boundaries is to keep the basic core system stable by controlling system input and output.

Neuman classifies these defensive boundaries according to their various functions. The internal lines of resistance are the boundaries that are closest to the basic core and thus protect the basic internal structure of the system. The normal lines of defense are outside the internal lines of resistance; they protect the system from common, everyday environmental stressors. The flexible line of defense surrounds the normal line of defense and protects it from extreme environmental stressors. The general goal of all these protective boundaries is to maintain the internal stability of the client.

Health

Health, then, in the Neuman model is defined as the relatively stable internal functioning of the client. Optimal health exists when the client is maintained in a high state of wellness or stability.

As in other nursing models, health is not considered an absolute state, but rather a continuum that reflects the client's internal stability while moving from wellness to illness and back. It takes a considerable amount of physical and psychological energy to maintain the stability of the person who is in good health.

> *In the Johnson model, nursing is an activity that helps the individual achieve and maintain an optimal level of behavior (state of health) through the manipulation and regulation of the environment.*

The opposite of a healthy state, illness exists when the client's core structure becomes unstable through the effects of environmental factors that overwhelm and defeat the lines of defense and resistance. These environmental factors, whether internal or external, are called stressors in this model.

Environment

The environment is composed of internal and external forces, or stressors, that produce change or response in the client. Stressors may be helpful or harmful, strong or weak.

Stressors are also classified according to their relationship to the basic core of the client-system. Stressors that are completely outside the basic core are termed extrapersonal stressors and are either physical, such as atmospheric temperature, or sociological, such as living in either a rural or an urban setting. Interpersonal stressors arise from interactions with other human beings. Marital relationships, career expectations, and friendships are included in this group of interpersonal stressors. Those stressors that occur within the client are called intrapersonal and include involuntary physiological responses, psychological reactions, and internal thought processes.

Nursing

Identifying Stressors

The nurse's role in the Neuman model is to identify at what level or in which boundary a disruption in the client's internal stability has taken place and then to aid the client in activities that strengthen or restore the integrity of that particular boundary. The Neuman model expands the concept of client from the individual to include families, small groups, the community, or even society in general.

Nursing's main concern in this model is either to identify stressors that will disrupt a defensive boundary in the future (prevention) or to identify a stressor that has already disrupted a defensive boundary, thereby producing instability (illness).[16] The Neuman model is based on the nursing process and identifies three levels of intervention: primary, secondary, and tertiary.

Types of Intervention

A **primary intervention** has as its main goal the prevention of possible symptoms that could be caused by environmental stressors. Teaching clients about stress management, giving immunizations, or encouraging aerobic exercise to prevent heart disease are examples of primary interventions.

A **secondary intervention** is aimed at treating symptoms that have already been produced by stressors. Many of the actions that nurses perform in the hospital or clinic (e.g., giving pain medications or teaching a client with cardiac disease about the benefits of a low-sodium diet) fall into this secondary intervention category.

Tertiary care actions seek to restore the client's system to an optimal state of balance by adapting to negative environmental stressors. Teaching a client how to care for a colostomy at home after discharge from the hospital is an example of nursing activities at the tertiary level.

TRENDS FOR THE FUTURE IN NURSING THEORY

Although the search for the perfect nursing model continues, the emphasis in recent years has shifted from developing new theories to applying existing theories to nursing practice. Also, the new theorists seem to be more interested in expanding existing nursing theories by including such concepts as cultural diversity, spirituality, family, and social change rather than starting all over again from the beginning. A good example of this trend is the cultural meaning–centered theory that was published by Mendyka and Bloom.[19] This theory expands the King model by adding a cultural perspective.

> *Although the search for the perfect nursing model continues, the emphasis in recent years has shifted from developing new theories to applying existing theories to nursing practice.*

A More Recent Theory
One of the more recent of the established nursing theories is the Man-Living-Health Model proposed by Rosemary Rizzo Parse. Although her original work started in 1981, a more developed form of her theory was published in 1987.[20–22] Parse's theory stresses the elements of experience, personal **values,** and lifestyle choices in the maintenance of health.

> *One of the hallmarks of a sound nursing theory or model is its flexibility and ability to adapt to new discoveries.*

A Matter of Choice
In this theory, the client can be any person or family who is concerned with the quality of their life situation. The client is viewed as an open, whole being who is influenced by past and present life experiences. The ability to make free choices is essential in this theory. The client, through choices he or she makes, interacts with the environment to influence health either positively or negatively.

Health, for Parse, is an ongoing process. Because clients make free choices, their health status is continually unfolding. In addition, health is determined by lived experiences, synthesis of values, and the way the client lives.[23]

Finding Meaning
The main role of nursing in the Parse model is to guide clients in finding and understanding the meaning of their lives. Once the client chooses a healthy life situation, the nurse can further increase the quality of the client's life and improve his or her health status. The ability to change the client's health-related values is an important skill for nurses to master in this model.

Parse never really defines the concept of environment in relationship to her theory. Specifically, it seems to be any health-related setting, but it can also be expanded to include past and present experiences.

New Challenges to Nursing Theory
As with any developing science, nursing will continue to change and respond to the dynamic trends of society. Older nursing models will be either replaced by new ones or modified to include developing concepts. Indeed, one of the hallmarks of a sound nursing theory or model is its flexibility and ability to adapt to new discoveries.

The increasing number of **independent nurse practitioners** and other advanced practice nurses are testing nursing theories as they have never been tested before. The theories that are flexible, realistic, and usable in practice will survive and remain as the pillars of professional nursing.[23] Those that are too theoretical or rigid will fall by the wayside and become mere footnotes in nursing texts.

Table 4.2 Competencies for Nursing Skills

Associate Degree RN	Baccalaureate Degree RN
Administering Blood Products	
Obtain and document baseline vital signs according to agency policies and procedures.	Same
Obtain blood transfusion history. Initiate administration of blood products according to agency policies and procedures.	Same
Evaluate and document client response to administration of blood products.	Same
Admission, Transfer, Discharge	
Admit client to a health-care facility following facility's policies and procedures.	Same
Transfer client within a health-care facility following facility's policies and procedures.	Same
Assist client to exit a health-care facility following facility's policies and guidelines.	Same
Assess client to determine readiness for discharge.	Manage the discharge planning process.
Facilitate the continuity of care within and across health-care settings.	Same
Assessment of Vital Signs	
Monitor and assess oral, rectal, and axillary temperature.	Same
Measure and record temperature using an electronic or tympanic thermometer.	Same
Monitor and assess peripheral pulses.	Same
Monitor and assess apical pulse.	Same
Monitor and assess apical-radial pulse.	Same
Monitor and assess blood pressure.	Same
Monitor and assess respiratory rate and character.	Same
Bowel Elimination	
Document characteristics of feces.	Same
Perform test for occult blood.	Same
Administer enemas for cleansing or retention.	Same
Remove a fecal impaction.	Same
Provide and teach colostomy and ileostomy care.	Same
Administer a rectal suppository.	Same
Administer a rectal tube.	Same
Develop client's bowel retraining protocol.	Same
Care of the Dying Client	
During dying process, provide measures to decrease client's physical and emotional discomfort.	Same
Evaluate final progress note on client's chart to determine completeness of information.	Same
Notify appropriate people and departments according to agency's policies and procedures.	Same

Associate Degree RN	Baccalaureate Degree RN
Evaluate family's response to client's death and make referrals as appropriate.	Develop services that support dying clients and their families.
Provide care for body after client's death according to agency's policies and procedures.	Same
Circulatory Maintenance Evaluate fetal heart rate pattern.	Same
Apply anti-embolism stockings.	Same
Obtain cardiopulmonary resuscitation certification.	Same
Client Teaching Assess and document client's and/or family member's knowledge of specific procedure or health problem.	Assesses client's readiness to learn.
Assess client and significant support person(s) for learning strengths, capabilities, barriers, and educational needs.	Develop materials to provide client and/or family member with information concerning procedure or health problem.
Develop an individualized teaching plan based on assessed needs.	Same
Modify teaching plan based on evaluation of progress toward meeting identified learning outcomes.	Same
Provide client and significant support person(s) with the information to make choices regarding health.	Same
Teach client and significant support person(s) the information and skills needed to achieve desired learning outcomes.	Same
Evaluate progress of client and significant support person(s) toward achievement of identified learning outcomes.	Using multiple teaching strategies, teach heterogeneous groups of clients, accounting for individual differences.
Implement teaching plan using individualized teaching and learning strategies with clients and/or groups in structured settings.	Implement teaching plan using individualized teaching and learning strategies with clients and/or groups in unstructured settings.
Communication Effectively use communication skills during assessment, intervention, evaluation, and teaching.	Same
Express oneself effectively using a variety of media in different contexts.	Same
Adapt communication methods to clients with special needs (e.g., sensory or psychological disabilities).	Same
Produce clear, accurate, and relevant writing.	Same
Use therapeutic communication within the nurse–client relationship.	Same
Maintain confidentiality of nurse–client interactions.	Same
Appropriately, accurately, and effectively communicate with diverse groups and disciplines using a variety of strategies.	Evaluate effectiveness of communication patterns.
Elicit and clarify client preferences and values.	Same
Evaluate dynamics of family interactions.	Same

(continued)

Table 4.2 Competencies for Nursing Skills (continued)

Associate Degree RN	Baccalaureate Degree RN
Evaluate data concerning coping mechanisms of client/family/support system.	Same
Provide emotional support to client/family/support system.	Same
Evaluate strengths of client and family/significant other.	Same
Evaluate need for alternative methods of communicating with client.	Same
Use assertive communication skills in interactions with clients and other health-care providers.	Teach assertive communication skills to clients, unlicensed assistive nursing personnel, and other licensed nurses.
Communicate data concerning client to appropriate members of the health-care team.	Same
Communicate the need for consultation/referral to interdisciplinary care team.	Identify and plan for services to assure continuity in meeting health-care needs during transition from one setting to another.
Collaborate with other health-team members to provide nursing care.	Collaborate with community members in planning care for the community.
Critical Thinking Within acquired knowledge base, create alternative courses of action, develop reasonable hypotheses, and develop new solutions to problems.	Same
Develop an awareness of personal values and feelings and examine basis for them.	Same
Evaluate credibility of sources used to justify beliefs.	Same
Examine assumptions that underlie thoughts and behaviors.	Same
Seek out evidence and give rationale when questioned.	Use critical thinking to further develop working hypotheses, using patterns and inconsistencies in data.
Delegation and Supervision Provide assistive personnel with relevant instruction to support achievement of client outcomes.	Specify aspects of nursing care that can appropriately be delegated to unlicensed health-care providers and assistive personnel.
Coordinate the implementation of an individualized plan of care for clients and significant support person(s).	Coordinate and/or implement plan of care for clients with multiple nursing diagnoses, especially both physiological and psychosocial diagnoses.
Delegate aspects of client care to qualified assistive personnel.	Delegate performance of nursing interventions.

Associate Degree RN	Baccalaureate Degree RN
Supervise and evaluate activities of assistive personnel.	Delegate nursing care given by others while retaining accountability for the quality of care given to the client.
	Supervise performance of nursing interventions.
	Supervise nursing care given by others while retaining accountability for the quality of care given to the client.
	Manage community-based care for a group of clients.
	Direct care for clients whose conditions are changing.
	Direct care for clients in situations with a potential for variation in client condition.
	Supervise implementation of a comprehensive client teaching plan.
Documentation	
Maintain privacy of client's record.	Same
Accurately document data according to agency's policies and procedures.	Same
Use common abbreviations and nomenclature for recording information in the client's record.	Same
	Establish a reporting and recording system to provide for continuity and accountability of programs in designated structured and unstructured settings (e.g., school health, occupational health, community).
Health Assessment	
Using a systematic process, perform a head-to-toe assessment.	Perform a holistic assessment of the individual across the lifespan.
Assess physical, cognitive, and psychosocial abilities of individuals in all developmental stages.	
Assess family structure, roles of family members, and family's strengths and weaknesses.	Perform a risk assessment of the individual and family, including lifestyle, family and genetic history, and other risk factors.
Evaluate an individual's capacity to assume responsibilities for self-care.	Same
	Perform assessment of using a family genogram.

(continued)

Table 4.2 Competencies for Nursing Skills (continued)

Associate Degree RN	Baccalaureate Degree RN
Assess community resources to determine possible referral sources.	Perform a community assessment for diverse populations.
	Perform an assessment of the environment in which health care is being provided.
	Establish processes to identify health risks in designated structured and unstructured settings (e.g., school health, occupational health, community).
	Integrate data from client, other health-care personnel, and other systems to which client is linked (e.g., work, church, neighborhood).
	Modify data collection tools to make them appropriate to client's situation (e.g., language and culture, literacy level, sensory deficit).
Use assessment findings to diagnose and evaluate quality of care, and to deliver high-quality care.	Perform family assessment.
Evaluate family's emotional reaction to client's illness (e.g., chronic disorder, terminal illness).	Same
Evaluate client's emotional response to treatment.	Same
Evaluate adequacy of client's support systems.	Same
Assist in diagnostic procedures used to determine client's health status.	Same
Health Promotion Facilitate parental attachment with newborn.	Same
Determine the need for a health promotion program.	Develop and implement a health promotion program.
Evaluate risk factors related to client's potential for accident/ injury/disease.	Same
Evaluate client's knowledge of disease prevention.	Same
Evaluate client's knowledge of lifestyle choices (e.g., smoking, diet, exercise).	Same
Heat and Cold Therapy Evaluate client's response to heat therapy.	Same
Evaluate client's response to cold therapy.	Same
Evaluate client's response to sitz bath.	Same
Monitor and evaluate client's response to hypothermia blanket.	Same
Monitor and evaluate infant's response to radiant warmer.	Same
Home Care Management Evaluate ability of family/support system to provide care for client.	Same

Associate Degree RN	Baccalaureate Degree RN
Evaluate client's home environment for self-care modifications (e.g., doorway width, accessibility for wheelchair, safety bars, etc.).	Develop criteria to evaluate client's home environment for self-care modifications (e.g., doorway width, accessibility for wheelchair, safety bars, etc.).
Infection Control	
Use aseptic practices: hand washing, donning and removing a face mask, gowning, donning and removing disposable gloves, bagging articles, managing equipment use for isolation clients, assessing vital signs.	Same
Use universal precautions.	Same
Use body substances isolation procedures.	Same
Evaluate client's immunization status.	Same
Use surgical aseptic practices: hand scrub, donning and removing a sterile gown, donning and removing sterile gloves, preparing and maintaining a sterile field.	Same
Assist with a sterile procedure.	Same
Information and Health-Care Technology	
Use technology, analyze information, and select resources effectively.	Use technology, synthesize information, and select resources effectively.
Demonstrate competence with current technologies.	Same
Use computers for record keeping and documentation in health-care facilities.	Same
	Use data management system to evaluate a comprehensive program for monitoring health of populations in designated structured and unstructured settings (e.g., school health, occupational health, community).
Intravenous Therapy	
Perform venipuncture to obtain blood specimens.	Same
Perform venipuncture with an over-the-needle device.	Same
Prime tubing and hang IV fluids.	Same
Load and discontinue a PCA pump.	Same
Administer and document IV piggyback medications.	Same
Administer and document IV push medications.	Same
Calculate IV flow rates.	Same
Document medications administered through IV.	Same
Discontinue an IV and document procedure.	Same
Monitor and maintain an IV site and infusion.	Same
Change IV tubing and container.	Same
Prime tubing and hang IV fluids.	Same
Determine amount of IV fluid infused and left-to-count each shift.	Same

(continued)

Table 4.2 Competencies for Nursing Skills (continued)

Associate Degree RN	Baccalaureate Degree RN
Assess implanted infusion devices.	Same
Maintain implanted infusion devices.	Same
Medication Administration Assess family members' knowledge of medication therapy: reasons for taking medication, daily dosages, side effects.	Same
Instruct clients and their families in the proper administration of medications.	Same
Accurately calculate medication dosages.	Same
Gather information pertinent to the medication(s) ordered: actions, purpose, normal dosage and route, common side effects, time of onset and peak action, nursing implications.	Same
Administer and document administration of enteral and parenteral medications per order.	Same
Administer and document administration of topical medications per order.	Same
Evaluate client's response to medication.	Same
Perform eye and/or ear irrigation according to agency guidelines.	Same
Meeting Mobility Needs Evaluate client's need for range-of-motion exercises.	Same
Evaluate client's level of mobility.	Same
Manage care of client who uses assistive devices.	Same
Provide client or family member with list of resources to contact when mobility or body alignment is impaired.	Evaluate client's need for range-of-motion exercises.
Evaluate client and/or family members' ability to perform range-of-motion exercises.	Evaluate client's level of mobility.
	Manage care of client who uses assistive devices.
	Provide client or family member with list of resources to contact when mobility or body alignment is impaired.
	Evaluate client and/or family members' ability to perform range-of-motion exercises.
Nursing Process Analyze collected data to establish a database for client.	Perform comprehensive assessment to determine client's ability to manage self-care, including physiological, psychosocial, developmental, and cognitive factors and their interaction with each other.

Associate Degree RN	Baccalaureate Degree RN
Identify client health-care needs to select nursing diagnostic statements.	Formulate individualized nursing diagnoses, based on a synthesis of knowledge from nursing, biological and behavioral sciences, and humanities, that reflect a health problem and its etiology.
	Consider complex interactions of actual and potential nursing diagnoses, e.g., 2 or more physiological and/or psychosocial nursing diagnoses.
Consider complex interactions of actual and potential nursing diagnoses.	Same
Identify client goals and appropriate nursing interventions.	Same
Develop and communicate nursing care plan.	Develop comprehensive plan of care in collaboration with client.
Implement and document planned nursing interventions.	Same
	Implement a care plan for individuals, families, and communities with complex health problems that have unpredictable outcomes.
	Use preventive, supportive, and restorative measures to promote client comfort, optimum physiological functioning, and emotional well-being.
	Base care planning on knowledge of primary, secondary, and tertiary levels of prevention.
Establish priorities for nursing care needs of clients.	Same
Evaluate and document the extent to which goals of nursing care have been achieved.	Participate in obtaining collective data concerning client outcomes.
	Deliver care that reflects an understanding of interactions among potentially conflicting nursing interventions.
	Initiate a comprehensive plan for discharge of client at time of admission.
	Care for clients in an environment that may not have established protocols.
	Care for clients in situations requiring independent decision making, e.g., community-based practice settings.
Pain Management Evaluate data from comprehensive pain history.	Same
Evaluate and document client's response to pharmacological and nonpharmacological interventions.	Same

(continued)

Table 4.2 Competencies for Nursing Skills (continued)

Associate Degree RN	Baccalaureate Degree RN
Document client's response to interventions used to prevent or reduce pain.	Same
Assess client when pain is not relieved through ordered pharmacological and nonpharmacological methods.	Collaborate with other members of healthcare team to identify alternative interventions.
Evaluate appropriateness of any pain medication taken by clients.	Same
Educate clients on correct use of medications.	Same
Manage and monitor client receiving epidural analgesia.	Same
Teach client to use a PCA device.	Same
Perioperative Care Preoperatively, assess client's risk for postoperative respiratory complications.	Same
Postoperatively, assess client's ability to perform respiratory exercises.	Same
Preoperatively, assess client's risk for postoperative thrombus formation.	Same
Postoperatively, assess client's ability to perform passive range-of-motion exercises.	Same
Preoperatively, assess client's willingness and capability to learn exercises.	Same
Preoperatively, assess family members' willingness to learn and to support client postoperatively.	Same
Postoperatively, assess client's condition during operative procedure, including range of vital signs, blood volume or fluid loss, fluid replacement, type of anesthesia, type of airway, and size and extent of surgical wound.	Same
Personal Hygiene of Clients Provide or assist with personal hygiene on developmental and/or chronological age basis.	Same
Provide or assist with personal hygiene needs as determined by physical limitations and/or diagnosis.	Same
Provide or assist with personal hygiene needs with respect to client's culture and/or religious values.	Same
Provide or assist with personal hygiene care in hospital, nursing home, or client's home.	Same
Assess and maintain chest tubes.	Same
Safety and Comfort Implement measures to protect the immunosuppressed client.	Same
Protect the client from injury.	Same
Verify identity of the client.	Same
Implement agency policies and procedures in the event of client injury.	Same
Follow policies and procedures for agency fires and safety measures.	Same

Associate Degree RN	Baccalaureate Degree RN
Follow procedures for handling biohazardous materials.	Same
Assess need for restraints or other safety devices.	Develop protocols for use of restraints or other safety devices.
Implement nursing measures to reduce the risk for falls, poisoning, and electrical hazards.	Same
Prepare for internal and external disasters.	Same
Develop a plan for reducing environmental stressors (e.g., noise, temperature, pollution).	Same
Evaluate client's orientation to reality.	Same
Evaluate need for measures to maintain client's skin integrity.	Same
Vascular Access Devices	
Assist with insertion of central venous catheters.	Same
Change a central venous catheter dressing.	Same
Monitor administration of medications/nutrients via a vascular access device.	Same
Measure and monitor central venous pressure.	Same
Maintain central vein infusions in adults and children.	Same
Change parenteral hyperalimentation dressing and tubing.	Same
Wound Care and Dressings	
Assess and manage wounds, including irrigation, application of dressings, and suture/staple removal.	Same

PCA = patient-controlled analgesia

Sources: Cowan, DT. Competence in nursing practice: A controversial concept—a focused review of literature. Accident & Emergency Nursing, 151(1)0: 20–26, 2007.

Dickey, C, et al.: Nursing Skills Identified as Required Competencies. Helene Fuld Educational Mobility Grant. Oklahoma Nursing Articulation Consortium, Kramer School of Nursing, Oklahoma City University.

Levett-Jones, TL: Facilitating reflective practice and self-assessment of competence through the use of narratives. Nurse Education in Practice, 7(2):112–119, 2007.

Conclusion

As nursing takes its rightful place among the other helping professions, nursing theory will take on additional importance. Nursing theory and models are the systematic conceptualizations of nursing practice and how it fits into the health-care system. Nursing theories help describe, explain, predict, and control nursing activities to achieve the goals of client care. By understanding and using nursing theory, nurses will be better able to incorporate theoretical information into their practice to provide new ways of approaching nursing care and improving nursing practice.

The development of nursing theory and models indicates a maturing of the profession. As the knowledge associated with the profession increases and becomes unique, more complex, and better organized, the general body of nursing science knowledge also increases. Only when nursing has a well-developed body of specialized knowledge will it be fully recognized as a separate scientific discipline and a true profession.

Critical Thinking Exercises

Mrs. M, an 88-year-old woman, has been a resident of St. Martin's Village, a lifetime care community, since her husband died 8 years ago. Her health status is fair. She has adult-onset diabetes controlled by oral medication and a scar from a tumor behind her left ear that was removed surgically. The wound from this tumor removal has never healed completely, and it has continuously oozed a serous fluid requiring a dressing.

At St. Martin's Village, Mrs. M has her own apartment, which she maintains with minimal assistance, receives one hot meal each day in a common dining room, and has access to a full range of services such as a beauty shop, recreational facilities, and a chapel. She is generally happy in this setting. She has no immediate family nearby, and the cost of the facility was covered by a large, one-time gift from her now deceased husband. Recently, she has become much weaker and has had difficulty walking, attending activities including meals, and changing the dressing on her ear. The nurse at St. Martin's Village is sent to evaluate this client.

- Select two nursing models and apply their principles to this case study. Make sure you include the concepts of client, health, environment, and nursing.

References

1. Ehrenberg, AC: Problem-based learning in clinical nursing education: integrating theory and practice. Nurse Education in Practice, 7(2):67–74 , 2007.

2. Algase, DL, et al.: Nursing theory across curricula. Journal of Professional Nursing 17(5):248–255, 2002.

3. Lu, D: Standardized nursing language in the systematized nomenclature of medicine clinical terms: A cross-mapping validation method. Computers, Informatics, Nursing 24 (5):288–296, 2006.

4. Clancy, TR: The benefits of standardized nursing languages in complex adaptive systems such as hospitals. Journal of Nursing Administration, 36(9):426–434.

5. Felton, G, et al: How does the NLNAC support the Pew Health Commission competencies? Nursing and Health Care Perspectives 21(1):53, 2000.

6. McCloskey, JC, et al.: Nursing interventions core to specialty practice. Nursing Outlook 46(3):67–76, 1998.

7. Mitchell, PR, and Grippando, GM: Nursing Perspectives and Issues. Delmar, Albany, NY, 1993.

8. McCann-Flynn, JB, and Heffron, PB: Nursing: From Concept to Practice. Robert J. Brady, Bowie, MD, 1984.

9. Riohl Sisca, JP: Conceptual Models for Nursing Practice. Appleton & Lange, E. Norwalk, CT, 1989.

10. Putt, A: General Systems Theory Applied to Nursing. Little, Brown, Boston, 1978.

11. Stevens, BJ: Nursing Theory: Analysis, Application, Evaluation. Little, Brown, Boston, 1984.

12. Fawcett, J: Analysis and Evaluation of Conceptual Models of Nursing. FA Davis, Philadelphia, 1989.

13. Sato, MK: Imagining nursing practice: The Roy adaptation model in 2050. Nursing Science Quarterly 20(1):47–50, 2007.

14. Allison, SE: Self-care requirements for activity and rest: an Orem nursing focus. Nursing Science Quarterly (1):68–76, 2007.

15. Leininger, MM (ed): Cultural Care Diversity and Universality: A Theory of Nursing. National League for Nursing, New York, 1992.

16. Beryl Pilkington, F: Envisioning nursing in 2050 through the eyes of nurse theorists: King, Neuman, and Roy. Nursing Science Quarterly 20(2):108–128, 2007.

17. Watson, J: Nursing: Human Science and Human Care; A Theory of Nursing. Appleton-Century-Crofts, E. Norwalk, CT, 1985.

18. Schaefer, KM, and Pond, JB: Levine's Conservation Model: A Framework for Nursing Practice. FA Davis, Philadelphia, 1991.

19. Khowaja, K: Utilization of King's interacting systems framework and theory of goal attainment with new multidisciplinary model: Clinical pathway. Journal of Advanced Nursing (2):44–50, 2007.

20. Aquino-Russell, C: Living attentive presence and changing perspectives with a Web-based nursing theory course. Nursing Science Quarterly 20(2):128-134, 2007.

21. Parse, RR: The lived experience of contentment: A study of the Parse Research Method. Nursing Science Quarterly 14(4):330–338, 2001.

22. Fawcett, J: Scholarly dialogue. The nurse theorists: 21st-century update: Rosemarie Rizzo Parse. Nursing Science Quarterly 14(2):126–131, 2001.

23. Manojlovich, M: The Nursing Worklife Model: Extending and Refining a New Theory. Journal of Nursing Management 15 (3):256–263, 2007.

Bibliography

Algase, DL, et al.: Nursing theory across curricula. Journal of Professional Nursing 17(5):248–255, 2002.

Baldwin A: Wagging the dog: An analysis of year 2000 workforce and education outcomes from recommendations of the 1995 Pew Commission report. Journal of Allied Health 30(3):160–167, 2001.

Determining cost of nursing interventions: Iowa Intervention Project. Nursing Economics 19(4):146–160, 2001.

More than one million new nurses needed by 2010. The American Nurse 34(1):5, 2002.

Narayan, MC, et al.: Searching for nursing's future? Nursing Management 33(1):26–30, 2002.

Nightingale, F: Notes on Nursing: What It Is and What It Is Not. Harrison, London, 1859 (Reprinted by JB Lippincott, Philadelphia, 1966).

Nursing shortage puts patients at risk and creates liability problems. Health Care Risk Management 23(6):61–65, 2002.

O'Connor, NA, et al.: Documenting patterns of nursing interventions using cluster analysis. Journal of Nursing Measurement 9(1):73–90, 2001.

Parse, RR: Man-Living-Health: Theory of Nursing. John Wiley, Philadelphia, 1987.

Pontious, JM. Where have all the nurses gone? The Oklahoma Nurse 47(1):1, 18, 2002.

SREB Study Indicates Serious Shortage of Nursing Faculty. Council On Collegiate Education for Nurses, 2002.

Stafford, J: Nursing students turned away: Faculty shortage limits enrollment nationwide. The Oklahoman, 2B, August 25, 2005.

5

The Process of Educating Nurses

Joseph T. Catalano

Learning Objectives

After completing this chapter, the reader will be able to:

- Compare the major differences between the diploma, associate degree nursing, and bachelor of science in nursing educational programs.
- Discuss at least three types of advanced nursing degrees.
- Distinguish between the different types of doctoral degrees available to nurses.
- Explain the concept of advanced practice for nurses.

EDUCATIONAL PATHWAYS

Unlike many other professions, nursing has several related, but unique, educational pathways that lead to licensure and professional status. Indeed, the current system of nursing education creates a great deal of confusion about nursing, not only among the public, but among nurses themselves. Perhaps the belief that "a nurse is a nurse is a nurse" developed because, even though registered nurses may be prepared in educational programs that vary in length, orientation, and content, the graduates all take the same licensing examination, and, superficially, all seem to be able to provide the same level of care. The licensure examination measures knowledge at the minimal level of safe practice. The workplace has not provided pay differences to distinguish levels of education despite studies showing performance differences.

PARADIGM SHIFTING

As in times past, the current profession of nursing faces many difficult challenges and extraordinary opportunities. Future trends in health care are being driven by a number of powerful societal forces that are producing an inevitable reshaping of health-care delivery. Traditionally somewhat insulated from the forces of change, nursing educators have been forced to recognize that graduates need to be prepared with knowledge and skills that are in tune with a rapidly evolving health-care system (Box 5.1). The most powerful of these forces of change are:

Box 5.1

Johnson & Johnson Promotes Nursing

The "Discover Nursing" ad campaign was initiated by the Johnson & Johnson Company in response to the nursing shortage in 1999 and is still a very active campaign. The goal is to bring more people into nursing. Working with nursing leaders and other concerned health-care organizations, the ad campaign is running a series of high-quality and catchy television commercials that feature nurses, both women and men, speaking about their work, its effect on society, and the rewards of a career in nursing.

A second element of the campaign is an associated Web site (www.discovernursing.com). The site has several sections that include answers to the question of "Why Nursing?"; details about the nursing market, benefits, and salaries; and nursing specialties. The "How?" section of the site contains information concerning nursing basics, a nursing program search with links to nursing programs across the country, a scholarship search program, and information about additional funds for nursing education. There are links on the Web page to almost any area of nursing and health care that the student could imagine.

The site also has profiles of nurses who share their stories of why they became nurses and elements of their careers that they find most rewarding.

Johnson & Johnson initially committed $25 million to this campaign for the television ads, maintenance of the Web site, and scholarship money for nursing students. Additional money has been added since that time. The campaign is an excellent example of how private industry, with the encouragement of the nursing profession, can work with nurses to benefit the health-care system.

- The movement toward a market-driven health-care economy
- The wider use of capitated managed care for financing coverage
- The increasing age and diversity of the U.S. population
- A shortage of registered nurses
- A shortage of qualified nursing faculty
- The rapid leaps forward in health-care and information technology

Since the year 2000, about 60 percent of nurses have been employed in acute care hospitals.[1] Hospitals have attempted to slow the drain to other employment settings by seeking Magnet Status certification, which identifies the facility as being "nurse friendly" and a place where nurse turnover rate is low.[2] The other 40% of nurses are employed in a wide variety of settings, including private practice, public health agencies, home health care, primary nursing school–operated nursing centers, **ambulatory care centers,** insurance and managed care companies, education, and health-care research. There is also an ever-growing group of **emerging health occupations** that have not yet been officially recognized by professional organizations.

What Do You Think?

Does an individual prepared in a technical course of study have enough knowledge to be a provider of professional nursing care in today's more complex health-care system? Do you think that the American Nurses Association (ANA) position statement on nursing education advocates a valid position? If yes, what can be done to bring nursing education into line with it?

The Pew Report

The Pew Health Professions Commission Report, sometimes referred to as the Pew Report, was published in the late 1990s. However, its recommendations for nursing education reform ring as true today as they did when the report was first issued.[3] Its 21 recommendations for all schools preparing health-care professionals are comprehensive and include:

- Expanding the scientific basis of the programs
- Promoting interdisciplinary education
- Developing cultural sensitivity
- Establishing new alliances with managed-care companies and government
- Increasing the use of computer technology and interactive software

The Pew Report also recommended a differentiated practice structure to simplify and consolidate the titles that are used for the different practitioner levels so that there is just one title for each level.

Nursing educators are continually challenged to evaluate whether the graduates of their programs are adequately prepared to meet the demands of all areas of care. Nursing educators also need to evaluate whether their own educational and skill preparation is sufficient to meet the needs of diverse health-care settings.

> *Perhaps the belief that 'a nurse is a nurse is a nurse is a nurse' developed because, even though registered nurses may be prepared in educational programs that vary in length, orientation, and content, the graduates all take the same licensing examination, and, superficially, all seem to be able to provide the same level of care.*

NURSES OF THE FUTURE

Nurses of the future will need to practice with self-reliance, independence, and flexibility. They will be required to have well-developed decision-making skills on the basis of critical-thinking ability, a working knowledge of community resources, and computer and technical competencies. Just as important, they will need to deliver high-quality client education and care while working within the constraints of a managed-care system with tight cost control measures.

Will nursing education ever be able to prepare a graduate who fulfills all the qualities required of nurses of the future? Nursing education responds with a "yes," but only with curricular revisions that provide graduates with the tools to continue to learn as they advance in their careers.

Hospital Skills and More

Hospital-based acute care nursing practice will always have an important place in any health-care system. Highly skilled acute care nurses will always find a place to practice. It is generally accepted that the older population requires more health care of all types—acute, chronic, and community based. Although the current system experienced a decrease in the use of acute care beds, a gradual reverse in this trend is beginning as the "baby boomers" become the senior citizens who require more care for acute problems.

Paradigm shifting in nursing education does not need to be an either/or proposition. It is sometimes felt that nursing education is either acute care focused or it is community focused. Nursing education needs to combine the two so that the graduate can practice with competence in either or both settings. The skills are similar, but the emphasis may be different. Although some hospital skills are being done by non-nurses at a cheaper cost, nursing education must still teach such important skills as critical thinking, therapeutic relationship, **primary care** and **case management,** as well as how to be comfortable with a consumer-driven health-care system.

Critical Thinking

Critical thinking has been an important element in nursing practice for many years. It is generally recognized as the ability to use basic core knowledge and decision-making skills in deciding and resolving situations with a relatively small amount of data and a high degree of risk and ambiguity. Although it has not always been called critical thinking, nursing has long been concerned with the ability to make good judgments and decisions about client care. (See Chapter 6 for a fuller discussion of critical thinking.)

Issues Now

Here to Stay: e-Nursing Education

As everyone is now aware, there is a nursing shortage, projected to only get worse over the next 10 to 20 years. Compounding the nursing shortage is a shortage of nursing faculty qualified to educate new nurses. One current trend viewed by some as a possible solution to the lack of nursing faculty is e-nursing education.

Almost all schools of nursing have been gradually incorporating more and more computer technology into their programs. However, full immersion into e-nursing education requires not only a total acceptance of technology, but a shift in fundamental thought processes that go beyond what is currently accepted for the age of information. As a general rule, nurses find change difficult, and nursing faculty like change even less. Fortunately, the changes in technology have come in small doses, which are much more palatable than major upheavals in knowledge.

Both nursing students and nursing instructors can look forward to several key technologies in the not-too-distant future. "Intelligent" assistive health-care devices have spurred the growth of new industries that did not exist even 5 years ago. Artificial limbs that respond to computer-mediated signals from the brain are being used by the victims of the violence in the Middle East. The elderly and those with mobility problems are being helped by intelligent walkers that not only help them ambulate, but aid them in changing position from sitting to standing and back. Nursing education will need to keep pace with these developments by teaching students how to use these devices and educate clients in their use.

All nursing faculty are aware that current nursing students are not like students of the past, even the recent past. Referred to as "Generation E" or "Millennials" and raised with computers and cell phones, these students do not respond well to sitting in lecture classes. They like to be more interactive and adapt readily to new technologies. They are masters at electronic multitasking and are nonlinear in their thought processes. The challenge for nursing educators is to develop and use technologies that keep these students engaged while ensuring that they master the vast amount of material required to practice nursing safely in today's complex health-care environment. Several educational software companies are beginning to develop simulators and electronic learning games that address this need.

One step beyond simulation learning is virtual reality. Still in its infancy as a learning methodology, it has great potential for education. It would allow students total participation in health-care scenarios, ranging from counseling sessions for clients with psychiatric disorders to advanced life support resuscitation of a client in cardiac arrest. Combined with simulation technology, it would allow students to use the equipment that they can expect to be familiar with in the work setting.

Wireless technology also has the potential to provide new learning opportunities and techniques. Access to the Internet is no longer tied to hard-wired devices. Through the cellular networks, anyone can access a whole world of information from e-mail to video streaming. Students enrolled in online programs can now access them from almost any place where they can make a cell phone call. A few book publishing companies have begun offering textbooks in electronic

(continued)

Issues Now (continued)

form (e-texts). Incorporated into these books are interactive exercises, videos, and simulation activities. Students can now "read" their textbooks anywhere they can take their wireless computers.

What will the nursing classroom of the future look like? It is a sure bet that the whole experience will be different. In reality, there may be no centrally located classrooms at all. Classroom lectures and interactive discussions will be conducted electronically over wireless devices. The way students learn will not be as important as what they learn, and learning will be measured through outcome testing. Nursing education will be asynchronous and available to anyone anywhere. In the far distant future, there may be only one nursing school for the whole country.

Sources: Connors, H: HIT plants SEEDS in healthcare education; Health information technology; Simulated E-Health Delivery System. Nursing Administration Quarterly 31(2):129–133, 2007.

Newman, L: Creating new futures in nursing education: Envisioning the evolution of e-nursing education. Nursing Education Perspectives 27(1):12–15, 2006.

Ornes, LL: Computer competencies in a BSN program. Journal of Nursing Education 46(2):75–78, 2007.

Spalla, TL: Technology. You've got mail: A new tool to help Millennials prepare for the National Council Licensure Examination. Nurse Educator 32(2):52–54, 2007.

At a fundamental level, the nursing process is a type of critical thinking. Unfortunately, in the health-care system of the future, a nurse's critical thinking skills will have to go far beyond those of the basic nursing process. Nursing education will need to prepare students for more advanced critical thinking by exposing them to real-life situations that require the use of creativity, intuition, analysis, and deductive and inductive reasoning. These situations are introduced in the classroom as case studies and are reinforced in the clinical setting through guided experiences and mentoring.

> "*Nursing education will need to prepare students for more advanced critical thinking by exposing them to real-life situations that require the use of creativity, intuition, analysis, and deductive and inductive reasoning.*"

The Therapeutic Relationship

Trust Is Essential

Therapeutic relationship skills have been long stressed by mental-health nursing faculty as a key element in the treatment of psychiatric problems. In reality, therapeutic relationship skills are essential for all

nurses to fulfill their roles as health-care providers and healers. Although these skills are currently being taught in a limited and focused way in most schools of nursing, they need to be expanded to involve directed services and relationship-centered nursing care.

Relationship-centered nursing care is client focused and revolves around the client's trust in, value of, and understanding of the nurse's skills and role in the healing process. The client must be able to feel comfortable with the nurse and share his or her understanding of both illness and health.

Follow-up Care

Currently, in many licensed practical nurse and licensed vocational nurse (LPN/LVN) programs and schools offering the associate degree in nursing, clinical experiences consist of one-time, 8-hour provision of care for an acute or chronically ill client. Little time is spent in follow-up care. However, many bachelors of nursing science (BSN) programs and some associate degree nursing (ADN) programs have expanded clinical experiences to include **discharge planning** and follow-up home health-care experiences.

To meet the demands of the future health-care system, all nursing education programs must be able to develop learning experiences for students that involve care for selected individuals or families over extended periods of time, perhaps ranging from several weeks to several semesters.

Case Management

A Growing Need

Care management is a general term that refers to a method of coordinating care either with an individual client or on a system-wide basis. **Case management,** in a health-care system driven by the demand for cost-effective care, usually is associated with coordinating care for an individual client as he or she moves from one level to another through the health-care system. Case management is now a certified specialty; however, there is an identified lack of qualified nurses trained in case management. Almost all the proposals for revisions in the health-care system include the **case manager** as an important element in the overall management of care.

Currently, case managers do not have to be registered nurses. Many individuals with degrees in social work and human resources as well as registered nurses are serving in the capacity of case managers. Perhaps the ideal situation would be to function as a **health-care team,** with both a registered nurse and a social worker coordinating all aspects of the client's care.

A Wide Range of Skills

As case managers, nurses are responsible for developing clinical pathways and for directing and guiding the overall health care of a specific group of clients. Case management includes not only overseeing the clients' care while they are in the hospital but also following clients through their rehabilitation at home, long-term follow-up, health-care practices, and developmental stages.

The knowledge and thinking required by an effective case manager go far beyond what is currently required of new graduates. Nurses must be able to understand not only the immediate disease process but also the long-term outcomes and factors that influence the disease. Case managers must also practice health-focused nursing and primary levels of intervention. Decisions will need to be made about care from a broad **database** as well as an understanding of the client's abilities, knowledge level, and even financial status.

Nursing education will be severely challenged to provide experiences to prepare students for this role. Students must be allowed to experience the authority, accountability, and responsibility of guiding a client's health care over an extended period. It might be beneficial to combine the learning experiences mentioned earlier in establishing the therapeutic relationship with the managed care experience.

The Consumer in Authority

A consumer-driven health-care system is at one and the same time the nurse's dream and nightmare. Many widely used nursing models or theories claim to be client centered, which translates into being consumer driven. Yet, when these models are put into practice, the care given is more provider driven than anything else.

> *A consumer-driven health-care system is at one and the same time the nurse's dream and nightmare.*

Care as Requested

A client/consumer-driven health-care system means that the care given is defined by the consumer and the outcomes are also determined by the consumer. The nurse must be able to accept the authority of the group or community as a determinant of health care. The nurse's role becomes one of a partner in guiding, implementing, and overseeing ways to deliver requested health care for a given community.

Many nursing programs, particularly baccalaureate programs, include a course in community health and home health-care nursing. A requirement of these courses is often to have the students perform a community survey in which they determine the needs of the community as they perceive them. Many of these courses have been modified so that the students learn from the community members what they perceive to be their own needs.

Paradigm shifting is never easy. Major paradigm shifts in thinking and acting are even more difficult. Nursing education is currently dealing with a huge paradigm shift. How educators are meeting these challenges will, to a large extent, shape the future of professional nursing.

ANA POSITION PAPER ON EDUCATION FOR NURSES

A Historical Perspective

After evaluating the changes that occurred in the health-care system during the 1950s and studying the projected educational needs for nurses, the American Nurses Association (ANA) published a paper in 1965 that took a stand on an issue that was, and still is, highly controversial. Although written more than 40 years ago, this document is still relevant to many of the issues in nursing education today.

For full appreciation of the significance of this paper, it must be examined from a historical perspective. The overall purpose of the ANA has always been to ensure high-quality nursing care to the public by fostering high standards of nursing practice. In addition, the ANA was concerned with furthering the professional and educational advancement of nurses as well as protecting their occupational welfare. To achieve these goals, the ANA took responsibility for establishing the scope of practice for nurses and for guaranteeing the competence of those who claim the title of nurse.

After World War II, there was an explosion of scientific and technological knowledge used in health care. The educational level of the population was also increasing, resulting in greater public demand for higher-quality health care. In re-evaluating the nature and scope of nursing practice, and the type and level of quality of education needed to meet these new demands, the ANA reached the conclusions that are presented in its position paper.

Support for the Bachelor's Degree

Since 1965, the ANA has upheld the belief that baccalaureate education should be the basic level of preparation for professional nurses. Specifically, the ANA concluded that:

> The education for all those who are licensed to practice nursing should take place in institutions of higher education; minimum preparation for beginning professional nursing practice at the present time should be the baccalaureate degree education in nursing; minimum preparation for beginning technical nursing practice at the present time should be associate degree education; education for assistants in the health care service occupations should be short, intensive preservice programs in vocational education institutions rather than on the job training.[4]

There were several assumptions on which the ANA based this position paper:

- Nursing is a helping profession and, as such, provides services that contribute to people's health and well-being.
- Nursing is of vital significance to the individual receiving services; it meets needs that cannot be met by the client, the family, or other persons in the community.
- The demand for the services of nurses will continue to increase.
- The professional practitioner is responsible for the nature and quality of all nursing care that clients receive.
- The services of professional practitioners of nursing will continue to be supplemented and complemented by the services of nurse practitioners who will be licensed.
- Education for those in the health-care professions must increase in depth and breadth as scientific knowledge expands.
- The health care of the public, in the amount and to the extent needed and demanded, requires the services of large numbers of health occupation workers, in addition to those licensed as nurses, to function as assistants to nurses. These workers are presently designated nurses' aides, orderlies, assistants, and attendants.
- The professional association must concern itself with the nature of nursing practice, the methods for improving nursing practice, and standards for membership in the professional association.[4]

Specialization and Interdependence

The rationale for taking such a strong stand on the future of nursing education derived from recognition by the profession of its heritage, its immediate problems, emerging social issues and trends, the nature of nursing practice, and the extent to which nurses could realistically enact changes for continued professional progress. The ANA drew on Florence Nightingale's vision of nursing and nursing education, which emphasized the value of education for the development of the profession. It was important to Nightingale that schools of nursing be independent of hospitals and have a strong theoretical component on which to base clinical practice.

By recognizing the increasing complexity of society, the ANA realized that nursing was not only becoming more specialized but was also moving toward greater interdependence with other groups in society. One of these key groups was the U.S. federal government. As the government began increasing aid for nursing education, educational facilities expanded, providing greater opportunities for professional advancement. Larger numbers of students with more varied backgrounds were recruited into the profession, requiring greater flexibility in nursing education programs to accommodate their needs.

Schools of nursing were, at the same time, also hard pressed to meet the attendant demands of science and technology that were changing the traditional role of nurses. In addition to expanding roles for nurses, greater consumer awareness and expectations were placing new demands on nurses' abilities.

Even in 1965, the ANA recognized that nurses were required to master a very large and extremely complex body of knowledge. In addition, nurses were being increasingly called upon to make critical and independent decisions about client care.

Effects of the ANA Paper

The implications of the ANA paper were far-reaching and highly controversial. This paper affected many different elements of society and the health-care industry.

A Changing Role for Hospitals. Hospitals recognized that they would no longer retain their traditional role of preparing nurses for practice. Even though pressure to move nursing education from hospital-based diploma schools to institutions of higher education had been building for some time, in the mid-1960s, 75 percent of the graduating nurses were from hospital-based diploma programs.[5]

Colleges Under Pressure. Colleges and universities were hard pressed to quickly develop undergraduate and graduate curricula for increasing numbers of nursing majors. The relatively few baccalaureate programs in existence at the time were generally small and found it difficult to expand rapidly. It also became evident that a clear distinction between technical and professional programs needed to be made.

The Debate Continues

To this day, the ANA remains firmly committed to its stand that all nursing education should be housed in institutions of higher learning. More than 40 years have elapsed since this statement was made, and the profession of nursing is still trying to reach a consensus on the issue of basic educational preparation for entry into practice.

An examination of the current entry into practice debate from an educational perspective reveals a number of similarities in the social and political pressures felt by nursing in 1965. Not only do these same challenges exist in today's health-care system, but many new challenges have developed because of fast-paced technology developments and social changes.

Defining a Profession

A similar resolution defining entry into practice was proposed by the ANA in 1985, but it also met strong opposition and was never enacted. In 1996, the American Association of Colleges of Nursing (AACN) presented its own position paper emphasizing the belief that the baccalaureate degree should be the minimal requirement for entry into the nursing profession. The discussion remains ongoing with seemingly little hope for resolution. The most influential reasons these proposals have not been adopted are economic, not conceptual. Although some experts believe it is time to leave the old debate behind and work toward developing a better-educated profession in general, many others see the issue as important to the definition of nursing as a profession.

Continuing discussion and efforts to bring about collaborative agreement on nursing education is a goal that the profession must work toward. Only after the issue of basic entry-level education for professional nursing is resolved, and when nurses, like all other professionals, obtain their knowledge from recognized schools of higher education, will

> *Continuing discussion and efforts to bring about collaborative agreement on nursing education is a goal that the profession must work toward.*

nursing as a profession be able to resolve its other important problems. Advancement of clinical practice, preparation for advanced practice roles, and an increased body of nursing knowledge all depend on baccalaureate entry-level education for professional nurses.

DIPLOMA SCHOOLS

No Academic Degree

The Nightingale School of Nursing was a diploma school in the strict use of the term. When nurses graduated from this school they were given a certificate or diploma noting their graduation, but no academic degree. The first graduates from the Nightingale School soon began to establish their own schools of nursing based on the Nightingale model and adhered to her philosophy of nursing education. These were also diploma schools.

> 66 *In early hospital-based diploma schools of nursing, hospitals used the student nurses as a major source of free labor for their facilities. There was little or no classroom or theoretical study.* 99

An Improvement in Care

After an initial period of uncertainty and trepidation, both physicians and hospital administrators began to recognize that when the education of nurses improved, so too did the overall quality of the care provided by their hospitals. They also understood that these types of schools that were closely associated with hospitals could provide a source of free, or inexpensive, labor in the form of nursing students.

Diploma schools sprang up throughout Europe so that, in time, each hospital had its own school of nursing. Many of Nightingale's principles and concerns about nursing education were abandoned during this period of growth.

Catching up to Europe

In the United States, developments in nursing education, as with health care in general, lagged behind those in Europe. It was not until the mid-1870s that the first school of nursing was established in the United States. This was a diploma school attached to the New England Hospital for Women.[6]

As in Europe, the idea of diploma schools quickly caught on, and within 10 years almost every large hospital in the United States had its own diploma school of nursing. These schools had very little in common with the Nightingale School of Nursing. There was no uniformity in curriculum, length of program, or requirements. To guarantee adequate enrollment, candidates were again being recruited from the lowest levels of society.

Learning on The Job

A Source of Cheap Labor

In early hospital-based diploma schools of nursing, hospitals used the student nurses as a major source of free labor for their facilities. There was little or no classroom or theoretical study. The students learned exclusively by hands-on experience during their 12- to 14-hour, 7-day-a-week work shifts.

Most of the students were young, single women recruited just after they graduated from high school. They were confined to dormitories on the hospital property. The dormitories were monitored closely by a housemother who enforced the rigorous rules of behavior covering all aspects of the students' lives and dismissed students for even minor infractions of the rules. The early diploma schools of nursing were organized and administered on a model that was similar to the strictest of the religious orders.

Submission to Authority

The nurses who graduated from these schools were proficient in basic nursing skills and could assume positions in the hospital where they were trained or in home nursing, where they worked on a case-by-case basis without any additional orientation or education. Because of the 24-hour-a-day, 7-day-a-week socialization process administered by these schools, diploma graduate nurses tended to be very submissive to authority and willing to carry out any duty to please the physician, administrator, or head nurse. Before the advent of licensure examinations and standardization of practice, nurses from diploma schools were often limited to employment in their own training institutions or in home health-care settings.

A Move Toward Accreditation

Diploma schools of nursing remained relatively unchanged in the United States until 1949, when the National Nursing Accrediting Service, working under the guidance of the National League for Nursing Education, became the licensing body for all schools of nursing that voluntarily sought accreditation. The first formal accreditation of nursing schools occurred in the early 1950s. In 1952, the National League for Nursing (NLN) assumed accrediting responsibilities for all schools of nursing.[7] Accreditation by the National League for Nursing Accrediting Commission (NLNAC) has always been and remains a voluntary undertaking.

Outcome Criteria

To be accredited by the NLN, schools of nursing had to meet specific **outcome criteria** and teach specific content in their curricula. Many of the diploma schools of nursing could not or would not comply with these criteria and eventually closed. Some of the requirements for the schools that did choose to comply with the NLN included:

- Implementing a 3-year course of study meeting the criteria established by the state board of nursing using only faculty with baccalaureate or higher degrees in nursing
- Developing a philosophy and demonstrating how that philosophy was implemented through learning objectives, course objectives, and outcome criteria
- Showing an adequate pass rate on the State Board or National Council Licensure Examination (NCLEX)

A Jump in Expense

One of the key factors that all state boards of nursing were concerned about was that the school be able to demonstrate that the students were not being used as unpaid hospital personnel while they were in their education and training programs. When students could no longer be used as free labor, diploma nursing schools went from being virtually free to the hospital to being very expensive.

Not only did the hospitals still have to pay for the room and board of the students, but they also now had to hire and pay additional staff because the students could no longer be included in the overall staff numbers. Even more diploma schools closed because of the financial burdens to the hospitals. The schools that stayed open began increasing their tuition rates to the point that they were as expensive as programs granting academic degrees.

CONVERTING THE CURRICULUM

During the 1960s and 1970s, many diploma schools became associated with universities and converted their curricula into degree-granting programs. According to recent data published by the NLN, approximately 100 accredited diploma programs remain open in the United States. They are of universally high quality and meet all the standards necessary for NLN accreditation. The main emphasis remains on preparing nurses who are highly competent in technical nursing skills through extensive, hands-on practice in the clinical setting, but elements of leadership, humanities, and general sciences are also included in the classroom setting.[8]

ASSOCIATE DEGREE NURSING

The **associate degree nursing (ADN) program** was developed by Mildred Montague as a short-term solution to the nursing shortage experienced after World War II.[9] Originally designed to prepare students for technical nursing practice, the 2-year ADN programs were offered through community colleges with an emphasis on developing the skills necessary to provide high-quality bedside care in less time than BSN programs.

Technical Orientation

A successful pilot program for ADNs was conducted by Montague at Teachers' College in Columbia University in New York City in 1952 to prepare technical nurses who could assist professional nurses. It demonstrated that community college-based programs could attract large numbers of students, prove cost effective, and produce skillful technical nurses in half the time required for BSN programs.[10]

Which Exam to Take? Early on, there was some heated debate concerning licensure and titling for this group of nurses. The technical orientation of the curriculum was, and remains, very similar to that found in programs that prepare LPNs, but the location of the programs in the community college setting and the increased theoretical orientation seemed to elevate these programs to a higher educational plane. It was finally decided that the ADN graduates should take the registered nurse (RN) licensure examination rather than the LPN/LVN examination.

A Proven Track Record

The emphasis on technical skills of the ADN programs met a need in the health-care system of the 1960s and 1970s. By the early 1980s, there were more than 800 ADN programs across the United States; as of 2007, the number was close to 900, with more than 63,000 students attending.[11] Graduates from these programs soon exceeded the number of graduates from all the diploma, BSN, and LPN/LVN programs combined.

Although it is possible to complete the requirements for an ADN in 2 academic years, most programs take at least 3 years to complete for a new student who has no prior college credit.[11] ADN graduates have a proven track record for providing safe bedside care for clients from the first day they are hired. They function well as team members and, after a period of orientation, can assume responsibility for the care of clients who are more acutely ill.

BACCALAUREATE EDUCATION

A Slow Increase

The development of schools of nursing in the university and college setting was a gradual process that extended over several decades. Only a few collegiate nursing programs were established during the years when the diploma programs were expanding. Some of these early collegiate programs were a hybrid mixture of college-level classes and diploma school clinical experiences that still granted only a diploma rather than an academic degree.

Early attempts at college-level nursing programs sometimes took the form of "pre-nursing" courses over a 1- or 2-year period that prepared students to enter upper division schools of nursing. Generally acclaimed as the first university program to be completely conducted in the higher education setting, the University of Minnesota School of Nursing was opened in 1909. In 1923, the Yale School of Nursing began accepting students; it is considered the first autonomous college of nursing in the United States.

The number of university-based nursing programs gradually increased over the years, and by the beginning of World War II there were 76 programs granting baccalaureate degrees in nursing. These programs tended to specialize in preparing nurses for public health nursing, teaching, administration, and supervisory positions in hospitals. Although all these programs included a clinical component, the emphasis was more on theoretical knowledge, development of decision-making skills, and leadership.

Universities in general enjoyed rapid growth immediately after World War II, and higher-education nursing programs expanded along with the universities. Many military nurses, prepared by the Cadet Nurse Corps during World War II, went back to school under the G. I. Bill to complete their baccalaureate degrees.

Training for a Profession

During this rapid growth period, these **baccalaureate degree nursing programs** were plagued with problems similar to those found in the diploma programs during their own rapid expansion period. Primarily, the lack of uniformity in content, curriculum, and even length of programs was problematic. It was difficult to find qualified faculty because most of the nurses up to this time had received their education in diploma programs. No doctorate degrees existed in nursing, few nurses had master's degrees, and only a smattering of nurses had baccalaureate degrees.

During the late 1940s and early 1950s, awareness began to develop that there was a need to stratify nursing education programs into technical levels and professional levels. It became apparent that all health-care professionals should have, at minimum, a baccalaureate degree.[12]

The NLN began to develop strict criteria for the accreditation of baccalaureate nursing programs. These criteria included courses in general education, general sciences, humanities, and language as well as specific nursing courses. They required a certain number of hours to be spent in the clinical setting practicing nursing skills, a faculty prepared at the master's degree level, and the availability of laboratory and library facilities for the students. Faculty-to-student ratios were limited, particularly in the clinical setting, and outcome criteria were required for the students.[13]

> *During the late 1940s and early 1950s, awareness began to develop that there was a need to stratify nursing education programs into technical levels and professional levels. It became apparent that all health-care professionals should have, at minimum, a baccalaureate degree.*

Different Approaches

Although all university-level baccalaureate degrees in nursing have the same number of required credit hours and educational requirements for baccalaureate degrees, there are three avenues for attaining this degree.

> *The practical/vocational nurse, in one form or another, has been a part of the health-care system in the United States for more than 100 years.*

The Professional Degree. The BSN degree fulfills the criteria of a professional degree. It meets the overall requirements for a college baccalaureate degree (124 credit hours, 65 hours of nursing major, and most of the general education requirements), but does not meet all the general education requirements for an academic bachelor of science (BS) degree. Although this degree is usually obtained in a traditional college setting, it can also be obtained through an **external degree** program where the student has to meet the criteria for the BSN.

The Full Academic Degree. The second approach is found in programs that offer a bachelor of science degree with a major in nursing (BS Nursing). This degree is the full academic college degree and guarantees that the person holding it has met all of the general education, science, and major subject requirements. According to statistics published by the NLN for academic year 2007, there were more than 535 accredited programs offering baccalaureate degrees in nursing.

A third avenue that may be pursued is sometimes called the career ladder program (see section on ladder programs in this chapter).

PRACTICAL/VOCATIONAL NURSING

The practical/vocational nurse, in one form or another, has been a part of the health-care system in the United States for more than 100 years. Although the earliest formal schools of practical/vocational nursing were started around 1890, informal training programs for this level of nursing probably existed well before that time—for example, in the Young Women's Christian Association (YWCA), particularly in New York City.

A Useful Trade

These programs took uneducated girls who had migrated from rural areas and farms to the cities in search of employment and taught them a useful trade with which they could support themselves. With no regulation or accreditation for the early practical/vocational nurse programs, there were wide variations in the quality, length, and focus of what was being taught. Generally, the students were taught to provide home care, similar to that given by private duty nurses, for clients ranging from newborns to the elderly and invalids.

The number of **practical/vocational nursing programs** gradually increased during the next 50 years. Graduates of these 3-month programs were beginning to find employment in hospitals and nursing homes as well as in areas of private duty. During the nurse shortage after World War I, many hospitals found that these relatively undereducated nurses, after receiving on-the-job training in the hospital, could function at a fairly high level of skill, and at a much reduced cost. The word got around, and soon the number of these unlicensed nurses grew.

Compulsory Licensure

By the late 1930s, the ANA saw the need to regulate the quality of the practical/vocational nursing programs to protect public safety. It was not until 1938 that the state of New York took seriously the ANA's recommendation for compulsory licensure for practical/vocational nurses and enacted the first law requiring such licensure.

In 1960, all practical/vocational nurses were required to pass a licensure examination before they could practice. These nurses are now referred to as licensed practical nurses (LPNs). In Texas and California, these nurses are called licensed vocational nurses (LVNs).

The Importance of Technique

Although education for LPNs and LVNs varies slightly from one state to another, there are some common characteristics. Most of the programs are from 9 to 12 months and are measured in clock hours rather than academic hours. They are often offered in hospitals, high schools, vocational schools, or trade schools, although some programs are conducted in community colleges or even in universities.

Orientation of the curricula in these programs is highly technical and emphasizes the learning of skills in the setting of a hospital or nursing home with less emphasis on theoretical knowledge. Because they are **technicians,** it is much more important for practical/vocational nurses to learn how to do something than why it is being done.

Filling a Shortage

The stated scope of practice for the practical/vocational nurse involves providing care for clients in hospitals, nursing homes, or the home setting for those who have stable conditions. LPNs/LVNs are to be under the supervision of an RN or a licensed physician.

However, in the real world, LPNs/LVNs are often required to provide care well outside their scope of practice, often functioning in leadership roles or providing care in acute settings with highly unstable clients. LPNs/LVNs are often hired when there are shortages of RNs to fill the gaps in client care.

Many associate degree RN programs have developed a ladder curriculum whereby an LPN/LVN can go back to school for a shorter period, often receiving credit for years of experience, complete the program in 1 year, and then take the RN licensure examination.

LADDER PROGRAMS

Upward Mobility

Career ladder, educational ladder, **articulation,** or educational mobility programs have become increasingly popular as a result of an interest in **upward mobility,** educational articulation, and **career**

mobility. A ladder program allows nurses to upgrade their education and move from one educational level to another with relative ease by granting credit for previous course work and experience and without loss of credits from previous education.

Each ladder program is developed according to the philosophy of the particular nursing school, may use any one of a number of curricular patterns, uses one of several means of **advanced placement** or credit granted for previous education, and must meet NLNAC accreditation standards.

Ladder programs take several different forms. Some ladder programs provide a **competency-based education** that allows the students to proceed at their own pace as long as they fulfill required educational outcomes. Ladder programs have become increasingly popular as colleges move toward Web-based courses and programs.

The Associate Ladder

The LPN/LVN-to-ADN ladder allows individuals who have been licensed as LPNs/LVNs to take a minimal number of courses in an associate degree program to obtain their ADN and then take the NCLEX-RN, CAT to become licensed as registered nurses. Programs vary widely as to how many credits they will accept from the LPN/LVN programs and how many courses the students take to complete the degree. Some of the requirements for number of hours are out of the control of the nursing programs, because they have been established as general education requirements of the college or are state regent's requirements. These programs are highly compatible because of the similarity of curricula and the technical orientation of both types of programs.

The Baccalaureate Ladder

Some LPN/LVN-to-BSN ladder programs either allow licensed LPNs/LVNs to challenge a number of courses, or grant them credit for nursing courses on the basis of previous experience and demonstrated competency. Students who enter these types of ladder programs usually spend more time in school than those in the LPN/LVN-to-ADN programs. In addition to meeting the requirements of the BSN, they also have to meet the general education requirements for a baccalaureate degree and complete 124 hours of college-level courses. One problem in developing these types of ladder programs is that many states' boards of

regents do not recognize courses taken at the vocational-technical level as higher education courses and therefore will not transfer them into the college setting.

Two Plus Two

Nursing education has seen a marked increase in the number of ADN-to-BSN and diploma-to-BSN ladder programs, sometimes called **two plus two (2 + 2) programs.** These programs admit individuals who are already licensed as registered nurses but who have either a diploma or an associate degree.

These programs may take several different forms. Upper division baccalaureate programs work exclusively with RNs, have no generic students, and are designed exclusively to meet the educational needs of students who are already RNs. Many of these programs have adopted or are moving toward an almost totally online format; students take most of the classes on their home computers, with only minimal requirements for class attendance on campus. These types of classes work particularly well for students who work full time and may have family responsibilities.

Other programs accept ADN or diploma graduates as students, in addition to generic students. These schools often have separate programs for ADNs or diploma RNs that allow them to take examinations to prove educational knowledge and nursing proficiency (**challenge examinations**) in specific classes, thus granting credit for their nursing experience. The RNs then take advanced-level nursing courses, such as Community Health/Home Health Care, Leadership, and Critical Care, which are not commonly found in diploma or ADN programs. Many of these programs also are online.

In either case, on completion of the degree requirements, these nurses are granted a baccalaureate degree. Some of these programs have an **open curriculum** that allows students to enter and leave the program freely. There are 418 such programs accredited by the NLNAC.[11]

The Master's Ladder

For the ADN

A growing trend in educational ladder programs is the ADN-to-MSN programs. Schools that offer this type of ladder must have an MSN program in place. The ADN students who enter these programs are given credit for prior classes and work experience and take both undergraduate- and graduate-level courses, receiving a BSN along the way to obtaining the MSN.

These programs vary a great deal from school to school and may require from three to five semesters of classes. Often they are offered on a part-time basis, with many evening and weekend classes or Web-based classes to meet the needs of working students.

For the Nurse Practitioner

Another type of educational ladder program that is less common is the nurse practitioner (NP)-to-MSN program. These programs admit nurse practitioners who graduated from programs that allowed the student to become certified but did not include enough credit hours for a master's degree. Again, the students are granted credit for past classes and work experience and often are allowed to challenge a certain number of core courses. Then they take the remaining required courses and are granted an MSN at graduation.

MASTER'S- AND DOCTORAL-LEVEL EDUCATION

The baccalaureate degree is considered a generalist degree that exposes a student to a wide range of subjects during the 4 years spent in college. The master's degree, on the other hand, is a specialist's degree.[14] Students who pursue a master's degree concentrate their study in one particular subject area and become expert in that given area.

Master's Degree Programs

Master's degree nursing programs have been in existence almost from the time baccalaureate-level nursing programs were started. Some early and current nurse leaders have stated that the master's degree in nursing should be the entry-level degree. The early master's degrees in nursing programs were designed for students who had baccalaureate degrees in other majors, such as biology, and wanted to become nurses. After completion of an additional 36 to 42 credit hours in nursing courses only, these students were awarded the MSN, and could then take the licensure examination for registered nurses.

Experience Required

Today, most master's degrees in nursing programs are restricted to registered nurses who have the baccalaureate degree. Many of these programs require at least 1 year of clinical practice after the BSN and require an additional 36 to 46 college credit hours. Most students who enter master's degree programs attend classes on a part-time basis while they are working and may take up to 5 years to complete the requirements. Many universities have recognized this trend and have tailored their programs to meet the needs of these part-time students; universities now offer courses over the Internet, by distance education in the evening, on weekends, or 1-day-a-week programs. There are 296 accredited master's degree programs in the United States.[11]

There are a number of available areas of study for those pursuing master's degrees in nursing. Some of the more popular areas include nursing administration, community health, psychiatric mental health, adult health, maternal–child health, gerontology, rehabilitation care, nursing education, and some more advanced areas of practice, such as anesthesiology, pediatric nurse practitioner (PNP), family nurse practitioner, geriatric nurse practitioner (GNP), and obstetrical–gynecological nurse practitioner.[15] Most of these programs require the student to pass a comprehensive written or oral examination, and some courses require the student to write an extensive research thesis before graduation.

Professional and Academic Degrees

There are two basic types of master's degrees in nursing. The master's of science in nursing (MSN) is the professional degree, and the master's of science with a major in nursing degree (MS Nursing) is the formal academic degree.[16] In practice, however, little differentiation is made between the two. Almost all master's programs accredited by the NLNAC require the applicant to have at least a 3.0 grade point average (GPA) and to demonstrate academic proficiency by achieving a satisfactory score on the Graduate Record Examination (GRE) or the Miller's Analogy Test before admission. The GRE is also used to recommend remedial coursework needed to correct deficiencies before the master's program is undertaken.

What Do You Think?

Have you ever been to an advanced practice nurse for care? How would you rate the quality of that care? If you have not been to an advanced practice nurse, would you consider going to one for care? Why or why not?

_____

_____

_____

_____

_____

_____

_____

_____

_____

Doctoral Programs

In the evolution of the various levels of education, the baccalaureate degree is a generalist's degree, the master's degree is a specialist's degree, and the doctoral degree is a generalist's degree, although at a much higher academic level than the baccalaureate degree. The major purpose of early doctoral degrees was to prepare the individual to conduct advanced research in a particular area of interest.

A Wide Range of Choices

Currently there is a wide range of available doctoral degrees for nurses. The doctor of philosophy (PhD) degree is the most accepted academic degree and is designed to prepare individuals to conduct research. The doctor of education (EdD) degree is considered to be a professional degree, although in many programs there is little difference between the courses of study taken by the EdD and PhD candidates. In other programs, the PhD focuses

> *In the evolution of the various levels of education, the baccalaureate degree is a generalist's degree, the master's degree is a specialist's degree, and the doctoral degree is a generalist's degree, although at a much higher academic level than the baccalaureate degree.*

primarily on research, whereas the EdD focuses more on administration in the educational setting. The classes and research credits differ somewhat between the two degrees.

Since the 1970s, other doctoral programs for nurses have been developed that stress the clinical rather than the academic nature of nursing.[17] These include the doctor of nursing science (DNSc) and the doctor of science in nursing (DSN), which is a clinically oriented nursing degree. The doctor of nursing (DN or ND) degree is for the person with a BS or MS in a field other than nursing who wants to pursue nursing as a career. It is a generalist's degree at a basic level of education.

In recent years, there has been some discussion of making these degrees the basic entry degree into the profession of nursing. An additional degree for nurses who wish to pursue a career in higher education, the doctor of nursing education (DNEd) degree, is available.

Few Programs, Tough Requirements

Despite the wide range of doctoral degrees in nursing, there are relatively few programs across the United States that offer these degrees. Many nurses who seek them may obtain them in fields such as higher education, psychology, college teaching, and adult education. Fewer than 2 percent of nurses hold doctoral degrees.

The requirements for all doctoral education degrees are similar, even though the specific degrees being sought may be different. The student must have attained a master's degree and must have achieved a satisfactory score on the GRE. Often there is an admission interview and preprogram examination that must be passed before the candidate can be formally admitted to the program. Doctoral programs are at least 60 college credit hours in length, require many statistics and research courses, and often have a residency requirement. Before the doctoral degree can be granted, the student must successfully complete both oral and written comprehensive examinations, as well as write a doctoral dissertation explaining the conducting of a major research project.

References

1. Freeman, LH, et al.: New curriculum for a new century. Nursing Education 41(1):38–40, 2002.
2. Halfer, D: Graduate nurse perceptions of the work experience. Nursing Economic 24(3):150–155, 2006.
3. Bellack, JP, and O'Neil, EH: Recreating nursing practice for a new century: Recommendations and implications of the Pew Health Professions Commission's Final Report. Nursing and Health Care Perspectives 21(1):14–21, 2002.
4. American Nurses Association: Position Paper on Education. ANA, Kansas City, MO, 1965.
5. Fitzpatrick, ML: Prologue to Professionalism. Robert J. Brady, Bowie, MD, 1983.
6. Jamieson, EM, et al.: Trends in Nursing History. WB Saunders, Philadelphia, 1968.
7. Hegner, BR, and Caldwell, E: Nursing Assistant: A Nursing Process Approach, ed. 6. Delmar, Albany, NY, 1995.
8. National League for Nursing: Trends in Education, 2007. Available at www.nln.org.
9. Reber-Frantz, A: Needed: Nursing education overhaul... "Bush budget threatens cut for advanced nursing programs." NurseWeek 10:19, 2007.
10. Lahaie, U: WebQuests: A New Instructional Strategy for Nursing Education. Computers, Informatics, Nursing 25(3):148–156, 2007.
11. National League for Nursing: Statistics on Education, 2007. Available at www.nln.org.
12. McLoughlin, M: Peeling back the layers of learning: a classroom model for problem-based learning. Nurse Education Today 27(4):271–277, 2007.
13. Felton, G, et al.: How does NLNAC support the Pew Health Commission Competencies? Nursing and Health Care Perspectives 21(1):53, 2000.
14. Mills AC: Evaluation of online and on-site options for master's degree and post-master's certificate programs. Nurse Educator 32(2):73–77, 2007.
15. Williamson, GR: Change on the horizon: Issues and concerns of neophyte advanced healthcare practitioners. Journal of Clinical Nursing 15 (9):1091–1098, 2006.
16. Hathaway, D: The practice doctorate: perspectives of early adopters. Journal of Nursing Education 45(12):487–496, 2006.
17. Jolley, J: Choose your doctorate. Journal of Clinical Nursing 16(2):225–233, 2007.
18. Distler, JW: Critical thinking and clinical competence: Results of the implementation of student-centered teaching strategies in an advanced practice nurse curriculum. Nurse Education in Practice 7(1):53–59, 2007.

Bibliography

Bosher, S: Linguistic bias in multiple-choice nursing exams. Nursing Education Perspectives 24(1):15–34, 2003.

Brady, M, et al.: A proposed framework for differentiating the 21 Pew competencies by level of nursing education. Nursing and Health Care Perspectives 22(1):30–35, 2002.

Callister, S, et al.: Inquiry in baccalaureate nursing education: Fostering evidence-based practice. Nursing Educator 44(2):59–65, 2005.

Emerson, R, and Records, K: Nursing profession in peril. Journal of Professional Nursing, 21(1):5–9, 2005.

Ferguson, L, and Day, R: Evidence-based nursing education: Myth or reality? Nursing Education 44(3):107–116, 2005.

Fondiller, SH: The advancement of baccalaureate and graduate nursing education 1952–1972. Nursing and Health Care Perspectives 21(1):10–13, 2002.

Freeman, LH, et al.: New curriculum for a new century. Nursing Education 41(1):38–40, 2002.

Hoffman, L, et al.: Outcomes of care managed by an acute care nurse practitioner vs attending physician team in a subacute medical intensive care unit. American Journal of Critical Care 14(2):121–130, 2005.

Jeffries, P: Technology trends in nursing education: Next steps. Nursing Education 44(1):3–5, 2005.

Katz, T, et al.: Essential qualifications for nursing students. Nursing Outlook 52(6):277–289, 2004.

Long, K: Preparing nurses for the 21st century: Re-envisioning nursing education and practice. Journal of Professional Nursing 20(2):1–4, 2004.

Manojlovich, M: Predictors of professional practice behaviors in hospital settings. Nursing Research 54(1):41–47, 2005.

Medley, C, and Home, C: Using simulation technology for undergraduate nursing education. Nursing Education (44):131–135, 2005.

Miller, J, et al.: A study of personal digital assistants to enhance undergraduate clinical nursing education. Nursing Education 44(1):19–27, 2005.

Rosenstein, A, and O'Daniel, M: Disruptive behavior & clinical outcomes. Nursing Management 36(1):18–28, 2005.

Stewart, S, and Dempsey, L: A longitudinal study of baccalaureate nursing student's critical thinking dispositions. Nursing Education 44(2):81–85 2005.

Study looks at impact of nurses' education level. American Nurse 35(6):5–6, 2005.

6

Critical Thinking

Joseph T. Catalano

A DECISION PROCESS

The Art of Thinking

One of the most important responsibilities that nurses have is to make correct and safe decisions in a variety of client-care situations. The decisions made by nurses affect the health status, recovery time, and even the survival or death of a client. For example, the critical care nurse must decide when to give certain medications on the basis of changes in the client's condition. The emergency department nurse must decide which clients to treat first by assessing the extent of their injuries. The hospital staff nurse must decide what prn medication to give for which set of symptoms. The home health nurse must decide when to call the physician about a change in a client's condition.

The process by which these decisions are made involves the use of critical thinking. Critical thinking is based on reason and reflection, knowledge, and instinct derived from experience. It has also been defined as "the art of thinking about thinking." It is both an attitude about and an approach to solving problems. Critical thinking helps nurses make decisions about problems for which there are no simple solutions. Often nurses have to make these decisions with less than complete information.

An Essential Element

Although critical thinking has always been used by nurses to some degree and is recognized as important in the provision of care, its status increased greatly when the National League for Nursing Accrediting Commission (NLNAC) designated critical thinking as

Nurses also need to learn about and evaluate the value systems of those with whom they are working. Even though they may not agree with those values, it is important to recognize them and work with them when attempting to affect health. For example, when teaching a group of high-school students about STDs, it would be essential to know what their attitudes toward sex and health are. In all likelihood, these attitudes would be different from those of the nurse. An education program organized around only the nurse's belief and value system would be doomed to failure. Presenting the information from the students' viewpoint would help them better understand and perhaps be more willing to accept it.

> *Nurses also need to learn about and evaluate the value systems of those with whom they are working. Even though they may not agree with those values, it is important to recognize them and work with them when attempting to affect health.*

Imagine and Explore Alternatives Creatively

Once the nurse has identified the problem and explored the assumptions and rituals, he or she needs to consider the possible alternatives to care delivery. However, the nurse does not need to do this alone. This information can be obtained from a variety of sources, such as written reports, surveys, and published articles. Information may also be obtained informally from others, such as in discussions with individuals who work in the field or have dealt with a similar problem before, or via feedback from the clients who are receiving the care. No matter what the source of information, it needs to be evaluated critically for accuracy, consistency, cause and effect, and biases.[4]

A nurse using critical thinking will often be able to identify more than one solution to a problem. For example, possible solutions to the teenage STD problem may include providing condoms for all high-school students, performing tubal ligations on sexually active girls, or establishing strict nighttime curfews.

> *Critical thinking, when applied to the nursing process, makes it a powerful client problem-solving tool.*

> *A nurse using critical thinking will often be able to identify more than one solution to a problem.*

Although all these solutions may be effective, the nurse would have to evaluate the cause-and-effect relationship, value, and consequences of each of these courses of action. A nurse who is a critical thinker would consider each one of these before implementing a course of action.

CRITICAL THINKING IN DECISION MAKING

Although critical thinking is used in all aspects of decision making, it is particularly important in the nursing process. It is important to remember that although the nursing process and critical thinking are interrelated and interdependent, they are not identical.

As a way of looking at the world, critical thinking allows the nurse to consider new ideas and then evaluate those ideas in light of accepted information as well as client and personal value systems. Nurses are constantly making decisions in both their professional and personal lives. By viewing critical thinking as a purposeful mental activity in which ideas are evaluated and decisions reached, nurses will be able to make ethical, creative, rational, and independent decisions related to client care.[5]

Critical thinking, when applied to the nursing process, makes it a powerful client problem-solving tool. Critical thinking expands the usual linear nursing process into a gestalt that allows the nurse to sort through the multiple variables that are often encountered in client care. Effective use of critical thinking within the nursing process is evident when the nurse successfully applies knowledge from other disciplines in the resolution of client problems, deals with stressful environments, and creatively resolves unique nursing care problems.

Conclusion

Nurses practicing in today's health-care system are required to master many skills. Critical thinking underlies many of these skills. By examining assumptions, beliefs, propositions, and meanings, nurses are able to make sound and valid decisions about client care. Critical thinking both underlies and expands the nursing process in the practical provision of nursing care. When students and nurses master critical thinking concepts and skills, they open their perspectives on client care. An important transformation occurs when students are taught how to think rather than what to think.

The profession of nursing is in an active state of change, continually developing new theories, redefining its practice, and adapting to changing public policy and social mandates. Nurses who use critical thinking in making nursing judgments tend to consider the client's human rights and be effective client advocates. These nurses will also be able to adapt the rules of the nursing process to meet a wide range of client needs.

Issues in Practice

Long Shifts = More Mistakes

Working Past the Limit

It would seem that any person with some common sense and the basic ability to reason logically would conclude that if nurses work longer and/or more frequent shifts, their chance for making errors in client care will increase. However, in an age when "evidence-based practice" is the buzz phrase and nobody seems to rely much on common sense, there has to be scientific proof of a cause-and-effect relationship between the two elements.

Aiken and associates[1] demonstrated in a longitudinal study over 6 years that the death rate of postoperative clients increases when nurses' client loads exceed four surgical clients (along with increases in nurse dissatisfaction and turnover rates). In much the same way, a recent study by researchers in Pennsylvania concluded that there is a threefold increase in the incidence of errors among nurses who work for more than 12.5 hours in any given shift.

Ann Rogers, the study's lead author, in conjunction with her colleagues at the University of Pennsylvania, followed and analyzed the work habits of 393 hospital nurses over a 4-week period. The research was funded by the federal Agency for Healthcare Research and Quality and the Robert Wood Johnson Foundation, a philanthropy devoted to health issues.

The "Longest Shift" Prize

The researchers looked at data from 5317 shifts worked by the nurses they studied. The nurse who took home the "Longest Shift" prize worked a shift that lasted an amazing 23 hours and 40 minutes. During the study period, they found that overall, the nurses in the study worked shifts longer than 12.5 hours more than 40 percent of the time. Usually the overtime was not scheduled in advance and the nurses in the study worked an average of 55 minutes longer than was scheduled. One third of the nurses worked overtime every day they worked during the 4-week study period.

Although there have been approximately 50 studies on the effects of long shifts and sleep deprivation among medical students and physicians, very few studies have centered on how long nursing shifts affect nurses, who compose the largest single group of health-care professionals. In addition to hiring less qualified workers to fill in the gap left by the RN shortage, hospitals and other health-care facilities have been extending the lengths of nurses' shifts and having nurses working more shifts per week.

With health-care's current focus on understanding why medication errors occur and how to prevent them, the data from the study found that the nurses in the study made 199 medical errors. The researchers also found 213 medication near-errors, in which nurses caught themselves before they administered the wrong medication. The researchers concluded that all the nurses in the study had an increased probability of making at least one medication error whenever they worked past the scheduled 12-hour limit.

Issues in Practice (continued)

The researchers also concluded that there should be limited use of 12-hour shifts and that overtime associated with 12-hour shifts be eliminated completely. Similarly, the Institute of Medicine, an independent organization that advises the federal government on medical matters, also has recommended reducing the length of nurses' shifts, including limiting their workday to 12 hours.

Sources: Assadian, O: Implications of staffing ratios and workload limitations on healthcare-associated infections and the quality of patient care. Critical Care Medicine 35(1):296–298, 2007.

Hamilton, KE: Nurse staffing in relation to risk-adjusted mortality in neonatal care. Archives of Disease in Childhood—Fetal & Neonatal Edition 92(2): 99–103, 2007.

Welton, JM: Nurse staffing, nursing intensity, staff mix, and direct nursing care costs across Massachusetts hospitals. Journal of Nursing Administration 36(9):416–425, 2006.

Reuters, CNN.Com, Wednesday, July 7, 2004.

Critical Thinking Exercises

Use the steps in the nursing process to provide a plan of care, including at least two nursing diagnoses, for the following client situation:

Mr. Y is 49 years old and has been complaining of chest pain starting in the center of his chest and radiating to his left arm and hand for 2 hours. He is having trouble breathing, is very pale, and has cool and moist skin. His pulse is 134 beats per minute and irregular, his blood pressure is 92/50 mm Hg, and his respiratory rate is 24 breaths per minute. He is very anxious and expresses concern about having to leave his job as an accountant because of these symptoms. He is diagnosed as having an acute anterior myocardial infarction and is admitted to the intensive care unit.

- What key assessment does the nurse need to identify as essential to this client's problem?
- What problems does this client have that a nurse can treat independently? Write nursing diagnoses for these problems.
- What can be accomplished in the nursing treatment of this client's problems (goals)?
- What type of activities can the nurse undertake to achieve the goals (intervention)?
- What does the nurse need to look for to see whether the interventions have worked (evaluation)?

References

1. Shin, KR: Critical thinking dispositions in baccalaureate nursing students. Journal of Advanced Nursing 56(2):182–189, 2006.
2. Eisenhauer, LA: Nurses' reported thinking during medication administration. Journal of Nursing Scholarship 39(1):82–87, 2007.
3. Tanner, C: What have we learned about critical thinking in nursing? Nursing Education 44(2):47–49, 2005.
4. Suliman, WA: Critical thinking, self-esteem, and state anxiety of nursing students. Nurse Education Today 27(2):162–168, 2007.
5. Distler, JW: Critical thinking and clinical competence: Results of the implementation of student-centered teaching strategies in an advanced practice nurse curriculum. Nurse Education in Practice 7(1):53–59, 2007.

Bibliography

Ali, N, et al.: Validation of critical thinking skills in online responses. Nursing Education 44(2):90–95, 2005.

Allen, G, et al.: Reliability of assessment of critical thinking. Journal of Professional Nursing 20(1):15–23, 2004.

Anderson, K: Teaching cultural competencies using an exemplar from literal journalism. Nursing Education 43(6):254–260, 2004.

Case, J et al.: A qualitative tool for critical thinking skill development. Nurse Educator 29(4):147–152, 2004.

Daily, WM: The development of an alternative method in the assessment of critical thinking as an outcome of nursing education. Journal of Advanced Nursing 36(1):120–130, 2001.

Giddens, J, and Gloeckner, G: The relationship of critical thinking to performance on NCLEX. Nursing Education 44(2):85–90, 2005.

Martin, C: The theory of critical thinking of nursing. Nursing Education Perspectives 23(5):243–247, 2002.

Maslow, AH: Motivation and Personality. Harper & Row, New York, 1971.

Nokes, K, et al.: Does service-learning increase cultural competency, critical thinking and civil engagement? Nursing Education 44(2):65–71, 2005.

Smith, Q: 5 competencies needed by new baccalaureate graduates. Nursing Education Perspectives 25(4):166–175, 2004.

Twibell, R, et al.: Faculty perceptions of critical thinking in student clinical experience. Nursing Education 44(2):271–281, 2005.

Winningham, ML, and Preusser, BA: Critical Thinking in Medical-Surgical Settings. Mosby, St. Louis, 2001.

2

Making the Transition
to Professional

ETHICS COMMITTEES

Physicians, nurses, and other staff members often encounter ethical conflicts they are unable to resolve on their own. In these cases, the interdisciplinary ethics committee can help the health-care provider resolve the dilemma. An increasing number of health-care facilities, particularly hospitals, have instituted ethics committees that make their consultation services available to health-care providers.

The people who belong to the ethics committee vary somewhat from one institution to another, but almost all include a physician, a member of administration, an RN, a clergy person, a philosopher with a background in ethics, a lawyer, and a person from the community. Members of ethics committees should not have any personal agenda that they are promoting and should be able to make decisions without prejudice on the basis of the situation and ethical principles.

Depending on the institution, the scope of the ethics committee's duties can range widely, from very limited activity with infrequent meetings on an ad hoc basis to active promotion of ethical thinking and decision making through educational programs. Other common functions of ethics committees include evaluating institutional policies in the light of ethical considerations, making recommendations about complex ethical issues, and providing education programs for medical and nursing schools as well as the community. It is extremely important that nurses participate in these committees and that the ethical concerns of the nurses are recognized and addressed.

Case Study

When to Tell

A 48-year-old woman was scheduled for a below-the-knee amputation due to complications from diabetes. She was admitted to the preoperative area, signed a number of surgical permits, and was given her preoperative sedative medication. Because clients undergoing this type of surgery usually lose a significant amount of blood, several units of blood had been typed and cross-matched and placed on standby for her. After she was moved to the operating room and anesthetized, the nurse anesthetist rapidly administered the first unit of blood in preparation for the anticipated blood loss during surgery.

The circulating nurse was checking the paper work prior to the beginning of the operation and noticed that there was no consent signed for the administration of blood products. In examining the chart further, she noted that under the "Religion" section was listed "Jehovah's Witness." The Jehovah's Witness religion does not allow blood transfusions or transplantation of any tissue or organs. The circulating nurse told the nurse anesthetist about the client's religion and his response was, "Holy cow—I can't believe this is happening!"

The family did not know about the blood transfusion and obviously the client, who was under anesthesia, did not know she had received a unit of blood. The nurse anesthetist announced that it was not his fault because he was never told about the client's religion and was not going to tell the family or client about the mistake. The circulating nurse felt that because she did not administer the blood, she should not be the one to inform the family. The unit manager was called in, and the consensus was that she should be the one to reveal the information because she was ultimately responsible for what occurred in the surgical unit. Her feeling was that because no physical harm was done to the client, the whole incident should just be kept quiet.

Questions:

1. Using the ethical decision-making model (above), work through the decision-making process for this ethical dilemma.
2. What are the key ethical principles involved in this dilemma?
3. What are the possible solutions to the dilemma and their consequences?
4. How would you resolve the dilemma? How would you defend your decision?

ETHICAL SYSTEMS

An ethical situation exists every time a nurse interacts with a client in a health-care setting. Nurses continually make ethical decisions in their daily practice, whether or not they recognize it. These are called normative decisions.

Normative Ethics. **Normative ethics** deal with questions and dilemmas that require a choice of actions when there is a conflict of rights or obligations between the nurse and the client, the nurse and the client's family, or the nurse and the physician. In resolving these ethical questions, nurses often use just one ethical system, or they may use a combination of several ethical systems.

The two systems that are most directly concerned with ethical decision making in the health-care professions are utilitarianism and deontology. Both apply to bioethical issues: the ethics of life (or, in some cases, death).

Bioethics. **Bioethics** and **bioethical issues** are terms that are in common use. These terms have become synonymous with health-care ethics and encompass not only questions concerning life and death but also questions of quality of life, life-sustaining and life-altering technologies, and biological science in general. It is in the context of bioethics that the following discussion of these two systems of ethics is undertaken.

Utilitarianism

Ethical Precepts
Utilitarianism (also called **teleology,** consequentialism, or situation ethics) is referred to as the ethical system of utility. As a system of normative ethics, utilitarianism defines good as happiness or pleasure. It is associated with two underlying principles: "the greatest good for the greatest number" and "the end justifies the means." Because of these two principles, utilitarianism is sometimes subdivided into rule utilitarianism and act utilitarianism.

Rule Utilitarianism
According to rule utilitarianism, the individual draws on past experiences to formulate internal rules that are useful in determining the greatest good. With act utilitarianism, the particular situation in which a nurse finds himself or herself determines the rightness or wrongness of a particular act. In practice, the true follower of utilitarianism does not believe in the validity of any system of rules because the rules can change depending on the circumstances surrounding whatever decision needs to be made.

Act Utilitarianism
Situation ethics is probably the most publicized form of act utilitarianism. Joseph Fletcher, one of the best-known proponents of act utilitarianism, outlines a method of ethical thinking in which the situation itself determines whether the act is morally right or wrong. Fletcher views acts as good to the extent that they promote happiness and bad to the degree that they promote unhappiness. Happiness is defined as the happiness of the greatest number of people, yet the happiness of each person is to have equal weight.

Abortion, for example, is considered ethical in this system in a situation where an unwed mother on welfare with four other children becomes pregnant with her fifth child. The greatest good and the greatest amount of happiness are produced by aborting this unwanted child.

Because utilitarianism is based on the concept that moral rules should not be arbitrary but should rather serve a purpose, ethical decisions derived from a utilitarian framework weigh the effect of alternative actions that influence the overall welfare of present and future populations. As such, this system is oriented toward the good of the population in general and toward the individual in the sense that the individual participates in that population.

Advantages
The major advantage of the utilitarian system of ethical decision making is that many individuals find it easy to use in most situations. Utilitarianism is built around an individual's needs for happiness in which the individual has an immediate and vested interest. Another advantage is that utilitarianism fits well into a society that otherwise shuns rules and regulations.

A follower of utilitarianism can justify many decisions based on the happiness principle. Also, its utility orientation fits well into Western society's belief in the work ethic and a behavioristic approach to education, philosophy, and life.

Telling a Sad Truth?
The follower of utilitarianism will support a general prohibition against lying and deceiving because ultimately the results of telling the truth will lead to greater happiness than the results of lying. Yet truth telling is not an absolute requirement to the follower of utilitarianism. If telling the truth will produce widespread unhappiness for a great number of people and future generations, then it would be ethically better to tell a lie that will yield more happiness than to tell a truth that will lead to greater unhappiness.

Although such behavior might appear to be unethical at first glance, the strict follower of act utilitarianism would have little difficulty in arriving at this decision as a logical conclusion of utilitarian ethical thinking.

Disadvantages

Who Decides?

Some serious limitations exist in using utilitarianism as a system of health-care ethics or bioethics. An immediate question is whether happiness refers to the average happiness of all or the total happiness of a few. Because individual happiness is also important, one must consider how to make decisions when the individual's happiness is in conflict with that of the larger group.

> *Another advantage is that utilitarianism fits well into a society that otherwise shuns rules and regulations. A follower of utilitarianism can justify many decisions based on the happiness principle.*

More fundamental is the question of what constitutes happiness. Similarly, what constitutes the greatest good for the greatest number? Who determines what is good in the first place? Is it society in general, the government, governmental policy, or the individual? In health-care delivery and the formulation of health-care policy, the general guiding principle often seems to be the greatest good for the greatest number. Yet where do minority groups fit into this system?

Also, the tenet that the ends justify the means has been consistently rejected as a rationale for justifying actions. It is generally unacceptable to allow any type of action as long as the final goal or purpose is good. The Nazis in the 1930s and 1940s used this aphorism to justify many actions that may be viewed by others to be considerably less than good.

What is Good?

The other difficulty in determining what is good lies in the attempt to quantify such concepts as good, harm, benefits, and greatest. This problem becomes especially acute in regard to health-care issues that involve individuals' lives. For example, an elderly family member has been sick for a long time, and that course of illness has placed great financial hardship on the family. It would be ethical under utilitarianism to allow this client to die or even to euthanize her to relieve the financial stress created by her illness.

Utilitarianism as an ethical system in the health-care decision-making process requires use of an additional principle of distributive justice as an ultimate guiding point. Unfortunately, whenever an unchanging principle is combined with this system, it negates the basic concept of pure utilitarianism.

Pure utilitarianism, although easy to use as a decision-making system, does not work well as an ethical system for decision making in health care because of its arbitrary, self-centered nature. In the everyday delivery of health care, utilitarianism is often combined with other types of ethical decision making in the resolution of ethical dilemmas.[5]

Deontology

Ethical Precepts

Deontology is a system of ethical decision making based on moral rules and unchanging principles. This system is also termed the formalistic system, the principle system of ethics, or duty-based ethics. A follower of a pure form of the deontological system of ethical decision making believes in the ethical absoluteness of principles regardless of the consequences of the decision.

The Categorical Imperative. Strict adherence to an ethical theory, in which the moral rightness or wrongness of human actions is considered separately from the consequences, is based on a fundamental principle called the categorical imperative. It is not the results of the act that make it right or wrong, but the principles by reason of which the act is carried out. These fundamental principles are ultimately unchanging and absolute and derived from the universal values that underlie all major religions. Focusing on a concern for right and wrong in the moral sense is the basic premise of the system. Its goal is the survival of the species and social cooperation.

Unchanging Standards

Rule deontology is based on the belief that standards exist for the ethical choices and judgments made by individuals. These standards are fixed and do not change when the situation changes. Although the number of standards or rules is potentially unlimited, in reality—and particularly in dealing with bioethical issues—many of these principles can be grouped together into a few general principles.

These principles can also be arranged into a type of hierarchy of rules and include such maxims as the following: People should always be treated as ends and never as means; human life has value; one is always to tell the truth; above all in health care, do no harm; humans have a right to self-determination; and all people are of equal value. These principles echo such fundamental documents as the Bill of Rights and the American Hospital Association's Patient's Bill of Rights.

Advantages

The deontological system is useful in making ethical decisions in health care because it holds that an ethical judgment based on principles will be the same in a variety of given similar situations regardless of the time, location, or particular individuals involved. In addition, deontological terminology and concepts are similar to the terms and concepts used by the legal system.

The legal system emphasizes rights, duties, principles, and rules. Significant differences, however, exist between the two. Legal rights and duties are enforceable under the law, whereas ethical rights and duties are usually not. In general, ethical systems are much wider and more inclusive than the system of laws that they underlie. It is difficult to have an ethical perspective on law without having it lead to an interest in making laws that govern health care and nursing practice.

Disadvantages

The deontological system of ethical decision making is not free from imperfection. Some of the more troubling questions include the following: What do you do when the basic guiding principles conflict with each other? What is the source of the principles? Is there ever a situation where an exception to the rule will apply?

Although various approaches have been proposed to circumvent these limitations, it may be difficult for nurses to resolve situations in which duties and obligations conflict, particularly when the consequences of following a rule end in harm or hurt

> *Ethical theories do not provide recipes for resolution of ethical dilemmas. Instead, they provide a framework for decision making that the nurse can apply to a particular ethical situation.*

being done to a client. In reality, there are probably few pure followers of deontology, because most people will consider the consequences of their actions in the decision-making process.

APPLICATION OF ETHICAL THEORIES

Ethical theories do not provide recipes for resolution of ethical dilemmas. Instead, they provide a framework for decision making that the nurse can apply to a particular ethical situation.

A Framework for Decisions

At times, ethical theories may seem too abstract or general to be of much use to specific ethical situations. Without them, however, ethical decisions may often be made without reasoning or forethought and may be based on emotions. Most nurses in attempting to make ethical decisions combine the two theories presented here.

What Do You Think?

Identify a situation in which you were faced with an ethical dilemma. Which system of ethical decision making did you use? Why did you select that system?

_____

_____

_____

_____

_____

_____

_____

_____

_____

_____

Nursing Code of Ethics

A code of ethics is generally defined as the ethical principles that govern a particular profession. Codes of ethics are presented as general statements and thus do not give specific answers to every possible ethical dilemma that might arise. These codes do, however, offer guidance to the individual practitioner in making decisions.

A Periodic Review

Ideally, codes of ethics should be reviewed periodically to reflect necessary changes in the profession and society as a whole. Although codes of ethics are not judicially enforceable as laws, consistent violations of the code of ethics by a professional in any field may indicate an unwillingness to act in a professional manner and will often result in disciplinary actions ranging from reprimands and fines to suspension of licensure.

Although they are similar, there are several different codes of ethics that nurses may adopt. In the United States, the American Nurses Association (ANA) Code of Ethics is the generally accepted code. After several years of work, the ANA revised the Code of Ethics in 2001 to be more reflective of the health-care challenges in the new century (Box 7.1). There is also a Canadian Nurses Association Code of Ethics.

Clearly Stated Principles

The ANA Code of Ethics has been acknowledged by other health-care professions as one of the most complete. It is sometimes used as the benchmark against which other codes of ethics are measured. Yet, a careful reading of this code of ethics reveals only a set of clearly stated principles that the nurse must apply to actual clinical situations.

Box 7.1

The American Nurses Association Code of Ethics

1. The nurse in all professional relationships practices with compassion and respect for the inherent dignity, worth, and uniqueness of every individual, unrestricted by considerations of social or economic status, personal attributes or the nature of health problems.
2. The nurse's primary commitment is to the patient, whether an individual, family, group, or community.
3. The nurse promotes, advocates for, and strives to protect the health, safety, and rights of the patient.
4. The nurse is responsible and accountable for individual nursing practice and determines the appropriate delegation of tasks consistent with the nurse's obligation to provide optimum patient care.
5. The nurse owes the same duties to self as to others including the responsibility to preserve integrity and safety, to maintain competence, and to continue personal and professional growth.
6. The nurse participates in establishing, maintaining, and improving health-care environments and conditions of employment conducive to the provision of quality health care and consistent with the values of the profession through individual and collective action.
7. The nurse participates in the advancement of the profession through contributions to practice, education, administration, and knowledge development.
8. The nurse collaborates with other health professionals and the public in promoting community, national, and international efforts to meet health needs.
9. The profession of nursing, as represented by associations and their members, is responsible for articulating nursing values, for maintaining the integrity of the profession and its practice, and for shaping social policy.

Source: Code for Nurses with Interpretive Statements. American Nurses Publishing, American Nurses Foundation/American Nurses Association, Washington, DC, 2001, p 1. with permission.

For example, the nurse involved in resuscitation will find no specific mention of **no-code orders** in the ANA Code of Ethics. Rather, the nurse must be able to apply general statements to the particular situation. For example:

The nurse . . . practices with compassion and respect for the inherent dignity, worth, and uniqueness of every individual, unrestricted by considerations of social or economic status, personal attributes or the nature of health-care problems.

The nurse is responsible and accountable for individual nursing practice and determines the appropriate delegation of tasks consistent with the nurse's obligation to provide optimum patient care.

The ANA Code Revised

The revised Code of Ethics restates and reinforces the basic values and commitments that have been and remain essential to the profession of nursing. Traditional ethical principles such as veracity, justice, beneficence, and autonomy are re-emphasized. The nurse is still expected to practice with cooperation, wisdom, compassion, honesty, courage, and respect for the client's privacy. However, the revised code, in response to current health-care practices, defines new boundaries of duty and loyalty. Ethical challenges, such as cost containment, delegation, and information technology, require nurses to look at health care from new perspectives.

The revised code supports nurses in their attempts to upgrade their employment conditions and environment through measures such as collective bargaining. The revised code addresses and supports nurses who are involved in whistle-blowing when dealing with health-care team members who may be chemically impaired or otherwise incompetent in practice. It also supports nurses in their right to refuse to practice in treatments that violate their beliefs.

The revised code also expands nursing duties beyond individual nurse–client interactions. It recognizes that professional nurses now work in multiple practice areas; therefore, they are responsible for developing and using their knowledge in these expanded areas through research and collaborative practice. The 2001 Code for Nurses is an important document that nurses need to be familiar with, both to help ensure ethical practice and to shape an improved future for the profession of nursing.

THE DECISION-MAKING PROCESS

Nurses, by definition, are problem solvers, and one of the important tools that nurses use is the nursing process. The nursing process is a systematic step-by-step approach to resolving problems that deal with a client's health and well-being.

Although nurses deal with problems related to the physical or psychological needs of clients, many feel inadequate when dealing with ethical problems associated with client care. Nurses in any health-care setting can, however, develop the decision-making skills necessary to make sound ethical decisions if they learn and practice using an ethical decision-making process.

Modeling the Nursing Process

An ethical decision-making process provides a method for nurses to answer key questions about ethical dilemmas and to organize their thinking in a more logical and sequential manner. Although there are several ethical decision-making models, the problem-solving method presented here is based on the nursing process. It should be a relatively easy transition from the nursing process used in the resolution of a client's physical problems to the ethical decision-making process for the resolution of problems with ethical ramifications.

The chief goal of the ethical decision-making process is to determine right and wrong in situations where clear demarcations are not readily apparent. This process presupposes that the nurse making the decision knows that a system of ethics exists, knows the content of that ethical system, and knows that the system applies to similar ethical decision-making problems despite multiple variables. In addition to identifying their own values, nurses also need an understanding of the possible ethical systems that may be used in making decisions about ethical dilemmas.

The following ethical decision-making process is presented as a tool for resolving ethical dilemmas (Fig. 7.1).

Step 1: Collect, Analyze, and Interpret the Data

Obtain as much information as possible concerning the particular ethical dilemma. Unfortunately, such information is sometimes very limited. Among the important issues are the client's wishes, the client's family's wishes, the extent of the physical or

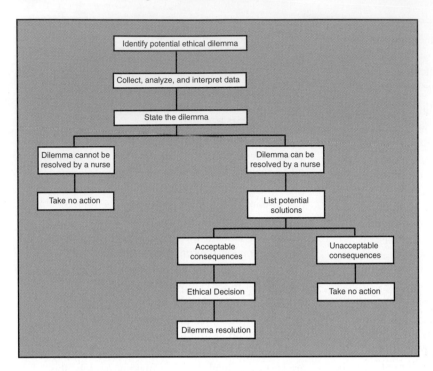

Figure 7.1 Ethical decision-making algorithm. (Adapted with permission from Catalano, JT: Ethical decision making in the critical care patient. Critical Care Nursing Clinics of North America 9(1):45–52, 1997.)

What Do You Think?

Identify a health-care–related ethical situation that is currently in the news. What are the key elements of the dilemma? Discuss how to resolve it with your classmates.

_____

_____

_____

_____

_____

_____

_____

_____

_____

_____

_____

_____

_____

_____

emotional problems causing the dilemma, the physician's beliefs about health care, and the nurse's own orientation to issues concerning life and death.

Many nurses, for example, face the question of whether or not to initiate resuscitation efforts when a terminally ill client is admitted to the hospital. Physicians often leave instructions for the nursing staff indicating that the nurses should not resuscitate the client but should, instead, merely go through the motions to make the family feel better, which is sometimes referred to as a **slow-code order.** The nurse's dilemma is whether to make a serious attempt to revive the client or to let the client die quietly.

Important information that will help the nurse make the decision might include:

• The mental competency of the client to make a no-resuscitation decision
• The client's desires
• The family's feelings
• Whether the physician previously sought input from the client and the family
• Whether there is a living will or DPOAHC

Many institutions have policies concerning no-resuscitation orders, and it is wise to consider these during data collection. After collecting information, the nurse needs to bring the pieces of information together in a manner that will give the clearest and sharpest focus to the dilemma.

Step 2: State the Dilemma

After collecting and analyzing as much information as is available, the nurse needs to state the dilemma as clearly as possible. In this step, it is important to identify whether the problem is one that directly involves the nurse or is one that can be resolved only by the client, the client's family, the physician, or the DPOAHC.

Recognizing the key aspects of the dilemma helps focus attention on the important ethical principles. Most of the time, the dilemma can be reduced to a few statements that encompass the key ethical issues. Such ethical issues often involve a question of conflicting rights, obligations, or basic ethical principles.

> *Recognizing the key aspects of the dilemma helps focus attention on the important ethical principles. Most of the time, the dilemma can be reduced to a few statements that encompass the key ethical issues.*

In the case of a no-resuscitation order, the statement of the dilemma might be "the client's right to death with dignity versus the nurse's obligation to preserve life and do no harm." In general, the principle that the competent client's wishes must be followed is unequivocal. If the client has become unresponsive before expressing his or her wishes, then the family members' input must be given serious consideration. Additional questions can arise if the family's wishes conflict with those of the client.

Step 3: Consider the Choices of Action

After stating the dilemma as clearly as possible, the next step is to attempt to list, without consideration of their consequences, all possible courses of action that can be taken to resolve the dilemma. This brainstorming activity, in which all possible courses of action are considered, may require input from outside sources such as colleagues, supervisors, or even experts in the ethical field. The consequences of the different actions are considered later in this chapter.

Some possible courses of action for the nurse in the resuscitation scenario might include the following:

- Resuscitating the client to the nurse's fullest capabilities despite what the physician has requested
- Not resuscitating the client at all
- Only going through the motions without any real attempt to revive the client
- Seeking another assignment to avoid dealing with the situation
- Reporting the problem to a supervisor
- Attempting to clarify the question with the client
- Attempting to clarify the question with the family
- Confronting the physician about the question
- Consulting the institution's ethics committee

For nurses who are unsure about which issues can be referred to the ethics committee, the facility's policy and procedure manual can give direction.

Step 4: Analyze the Advantages and Disadvantages of Each Course of Action

Some of the courses of action developed during the previous step are more realistic than others. The identification of these actions becomes readily evident during this step in the decision-making process, when the advantages and the disadvantages of each action are considered in detail. Along with each option, the consequences of taking each course of action must be thoroughly evaluated.

Consider whether initiating a discussion might anger the physician or cause distrust of the nurse involved. Both these responses may reinforce the attitude of submission to the physician, and either could create difficulty in continuing to practice nursing at that institution. The same result might occur if the nurse successfully resuscitates a client despite orders to the contrary. Failure to resuscitate the client has the potential to produce a lawsuit unless a clear order for no resuscitation has been given. Presenting the situation to a supervisor may, if the supervisor supports the physician, cause the nurse to be considered a troublemaker and thus have a negative effect on future evaluations. The same process could be applied to the other courses of action.

When considering the advantages and disadvantages, the nurse should be able to narrow the realistic choices of action. Other relevant issues need to be examined when weighing the choices of action.

A major factor would be choosing the appropriate code of ethics. The ANA Code of Ethics should be part of many client-care decisions affected by ethical dilemmas.

Step 5: Make the Decision and Act on It

The most difficult part of the process is actually making the decision, following through with action, and then living with the consequences. Decisions are often made with no follow-through, because nurses are fearful of the consequences of their decisions. By their nature, ethical dilemmas produce differences of opinion, and not everyone will be pleased with the decision.

In the attempt to solve any ethical dilemma, there will always be a question of the correct course of action. The client's wishes almost always supersede independent decisions on the part of health-care professionals. A collaborative decision made by the client, physician, nurses, and family about resuscitation is the ideal situation and tends to produce fewer complications in the long-term resolution of such questions.

Conclusion

Ethical dilemmas, by definition, are difficult to resolve. Rarely will a nurse find ethical dilemmas covered in policy, procedure, and protocol manuals, but nurses can develop the skills necessary to make appropriate ethical decisions. The key to developing these skills is the recognition and frequent use of an ethical decision-making model and application of the appropriate ethical theories to the dilemma. As an

orderly approach in solving the often disorderly aspects of ethical questions encountered in nursing practice, the decision-making model presented in this chapter can be applied to almost every type of ethical dilemma. Although each situation is different, ethical decision making based on ethical theory can provide a potent tool for resolving dilemmas found in client-care situations.

Critical Thinking Exercises

1. Ask the facility where you work or have clinical rotations what code of ethics they use. How does that differ from the ANA Code?
2. Ask your faculty what code of ethics is used for your evaluation.
3. Compare and contrast ethics with laws by delineating the purposes, scopes, and methods of enforcement of each.
4. Distinguish between the two types of obligations.
5. Compare the three categories of rights.
6. Analyze the following ethical dilemma case study using the ethical decision-making process:
   - What are the important data in relation to this situation?
   - State the ethical dilemma in a clear, simple statement.
   - What are the choices of action and how do they relate to specific ethical principles?
   - What are the consequences of these actions?
   - What decision can be made?

Bill L, a veteran emergency department (ED) nurse, called the resident physician about a client just admitted to the ED after a fall from a ladder. The client, a 52-year-old man, had been fixing his roof when the accident occurred. He had suffered a minor head injury, a twisted ankle, and a badly bruised arm. He also had a long history of asthma and heavy smoking. Not long after his admission to the ED, the client became cyanotic, dyspneic, and semiconscious. By the time the resident physician arrived, the nurse had prepared the client for endotracheal intubation and had already notified the personnel in the medical intensive care unit (MICU) that they would be receiving this client.

After a hasty evaluation of the client, the resident decided to perform an emergency tracheostomy before transporting the client to the MICU. While performing the tracheostomy, the physician severed a major blood vessel and the client hemorrhaged profusely. After several tense minutes, the endotracheal tube was inserted, and the client was quickly transported to the MICU. The client remained cyanotic and had great difficulty breathing. Shortly after he left the ED, the nurse realized that the oxygen tank that the client had been connected to was empty. The client never regained consciousness and died 3 days after admission. His death was due to respiratory failure and not to the injuries sustained in the fall.

When the client's wife came to the unit to collect the deceased's belongings, the nurse was torn between telling her about the mistakes that were made in the treatment of her husband and remaining silent. What are the key ethical principles involved in this situation? Are there any statements in the ANA Code of Ethics that may help resolve this dilemma? What would be the consequences of informing the client's wife of the truth? What are the consequences of not informing her?

References

1. Memarian, R: Professional ethics as an important factor in clinical competency in nursing. Nursing Ethics 14(2):203–214.
2. Day, L: Foundations of clinical ethics: Disengaged rationalism and internal goods. American Journal of Critical Care 16(2): 79–183, 2007.
3. Chaloner, C: An introduction to ethics in nursing. Nursing Standard 21(32):42–46, 2007.
4. Erlen, JA: Patient safety, error reduction, and ethical practice. Orthopaedic Nursing, 26(2):130–133, 2007.
5. Racher, FE: The evolution of ethics for community practice. Journal of Community Health Nursing 24(1):65–76, 2007.

Bibliography

DePalo, V, et al.: Do-not-resuscitate and stratification-of-care forms in Rhode Island. American Journal of Critical Care 12(3):239–241, 2003.

Engelhardt, HT, and Cherry, MJ: Allocating Scarce Resources. Georgetown University Press, Baltimore, 2002.

Erlen, J: HIPAA: Clinical and ethical considerations for nurses. Orthopedic Nursing 23(6):410–413, 2004.

Irving, JA, and Sniper, J: Preserving professional ethics. Journal of Professional Nursing 18(1):5, 2002.

Kennedy, W: Beneficence and autonomy in nursing: A moral dilemma. British Journal of Perioperative Nursing 14(11):500–506, 2004.

Mathes, M: Ethics, law, and policy: Ethical decision making and nursing. Medical Surgical Nursing 13(6):429–431, 2004.

Milton, C: Ethical issues: The ethics of respect in nursing. Nursing Science Quarterly 18(1):20–23, 2005.

Oxtoby, K: Consent: Obtaining permission to care. Nursing Times 101(1):22–24, 2005.

Quinn, S: Health policy and ethics forum. Ethics in public health research: Protecting human subjects: The role of community advisory boards. American Journal of Public Health 94(6):918–922, 2004.

8

Bioethical Issues

Joseph T. Catalano

THE CLIENT'S WELL-BEING

In the recent history of nursing, numerous biomedical and ethical dilemmas have arisen. Historically, nurses have been concerned with moral responsibility and ethical decision making. The nursing code of ethics and its frequent revisions demonstrate the profession's concern with providing ethical health care.

The earliest codes of ethics made obedience to the physician the nurse's primary responsibility. The present code of ethics recognizes that the primary responsibility of the nurse is the client's well-being. This change in emphasis reflects the profession's increased self-awareness, independence, and growing accountability for its actions. Unfortunately, this new attitude has also heralded an era of increased tension, self-doubt, and ethical confusion. By examining the issues and identifying the key moral and ethical conflicts, nurses will be able to accept their moral responsibilities and make good ethical decisions.

In the course of their careers, nurses are likely to encounter any number of ethical dilemmas. Although a complete analysis of every issue is beyond the scope of this book, some of the more common situations and their important ethical features are presented as examples of ways to analyze such dilemmas and to make informed decisions. The resolution of ethical dilemmas is never an easy task, and it is likely that someone may disagree with the decision.

ABORTION

A Polarizing Issue

Few issues evoke as strong an emotional reaction as abortion. Because of its religious, ethical, social, and legal implications, the abortion issue touches everyone in one way or another. There seems to be very little middle ground. People are either strongly in favor of abortion or oppose it completely. Even in presidential elections, abortion has become a central issue and the outcomes of some elections may very well be decided by the candidates' positions on the law that supports the practice.

What Do You Think?

Do you support or reject elective abortion? On what ethical principles do you base your belief? What advice would you give to a pregnant teenager who wanted to have an abortion?

_____
_____
_____
_____
_____
_____
_____
_____
_____
_____
_____
_____

A Matter of Convenience?

Elective abortion is the voluntary termination of a pregnancy before 24 weeks of gestation. An elective abortion may be either therapeutic or self-selected. Late term abortions are the termination of a pregnancy after 24 weeks of gestation up to the day of delivery. Strictly speaking, a therapeutic abortion would be one performed in consultation with and on the recommendation of a physician or psychiatrist, based on the conclusion that the mother's health or psychological state would be damaged without the abortion.

Self-selected, or elective, abortions are those performed solely on the mother's own decision, without consultation with a physician or psychiatrist, usually for economic or convenience reasons. In the case of *Roe v. Wade* in 1973, the Supreme Court changed the legal status of elective abortion in the United States, but the ethical basis and moral status of this decision remain controversial.

A careful reading of the court's decision in *Roe v. Wade* reveals that the justices made no

decision about the ethics or morality of elective abortion. Rather, the court said that, according to the U.S. Constitution, all people have a right to determine what they can do with their bodies (i.e., the right to self-determination) and that such a right includes termination of a pregnancy.

A Conflict of Rights?

The fundamental issues at the heart of the abortion debate center on the question of when life begins and the right of freedom of choice. Those who argue against abortion believe that life begins at the moment of conception and therefore hold that abortion is an act of killing. Proponents of abortion argue that the fetus is not really human until it reaches the point of development when it can live outside the mother's body (i.e., the age of viability, about 20 weeks). From a deontological standpoint, abortion represents a basic conflict of rights.

On one hand, a woman's rights to privacy, self-determination, and freedom of choice are at issue. In the United States, these rights are fiercely held and are considered to be issues of public policy and **constitutional law.** Indeed, these rights form the basis of the *Roe v. Wade* decision.

The conflicting right from the antiabortion side of the dilemma is the fetus's right to life. In most Western civilizations, particularly those that are based on Judeo-Christian beliefs, the casual and intentional taking of a human life is strongly prohibited. Life is the most basic good, because without it there can be no other rights. In general, the right to life is considered to be the most profound of the rights and is absolute in most situations.

When one is attempting to resolve the ethics and morality of abortion, these two conflicting rights need to be weighed against each other. Nurses are often placed in situations where they must help clients make decisions about abortion. Just as frequently, they are asked to participate in the procedure itself.

Where Your Values Fit In

In practice, ethical issues are always affected by the health-care provider's moral values. In the dilemma over abortion, nurses must analyze their own values and perceptions of their roles to make the best decisions. As a client **advocate,** should a nurse be for or against abortion? How can a nurse avoid influencing the woman's decision about abortion? Can a nurse ethically and legally refuse to assist at abortions? Should the client's reason for wanting an abortion or her stage of pregnancy (i.e., first or second trimester, or later, requiring a partial-birth procedure) have any influence on the nurse's decision?

These questions are not easily answered, but understanding the underlying principles involved in the issue may help defuse some of the emotional impact that often surrounds this topic. As in all complicated ethical dilemmas, the nurse needs to remember that the client must receive competent, high-quality care regardless of the nurse's own personal values or moral beliefs.

GENETICS AND GENETIC RESEARCH

The ability to alter genetic material to produce organisms that differ greatly from their original form is now a reality. Scientific and popular literature is filled with reports of new ways to identify and change the genetic material of all types of living creatures.

The Future is Now

Currently, genetically altered bacteria (e.g., *Escherichia coli*) are used to produce various medications, including a purer form of insulin. Genetically altered corn is now growing in very hot, dry places and is resistant to most insects. Abnormal genes that indicate individuals who are at risk for various types of cancer, Alzheimer's disease, Parkinson's disease, and Down syndrome have been identified.

In the 20th century, society became so accustomed to the idea that science should be allowed to do whatever it is capable of doing that very few questions were asked about the ethics of genetic engineering and research. As with most scientific research and techniques, the techniques of genetic engineering are ethically neutral. Procedures such as refining recombinant DNA, gene therapy, altering germ cells, and cloning other cells are neither good nor bad in themselves. The potential for misuse of these procedures is so great, however, that it may permanently alter or even destroy the human species.

In practice, ethical issues are always affected by the health-care provider's moral values. In the dilemma over abortion, nurses must analyze their own values and perceptions of their roles to make the best decisions.

Ethics of Genetic Research

Several ethical issues need to be considered when genetic engineering and research are being conducted, including those involving the safety of genetic research, the legality and morality of genetic screening, and the proper use of genetic information.

Recently proposed laws attempt to regulate genetic research to prevent the production of a supervirus or superbacterium that could exterminate the entire human population.[1]

Mandatory Screening

With current technology, it is possible to detect genetic patterns in newborn infants that are linked to breast and colon cancer, heart disease, Huntington's disease, and Parkinson's disease. The advantage to insurance companies, which could screen individuals as early as infancy for costly and potentially lethal diseases later in life, is obvious: these individuals could be excluded from health and life insurance coverage, thus saving the insurance companies a great deal of money.

Although this practice would most likely be unethical, the concept of mandatory genetic screening is not unrealistic. Because it requires just one blood sample from a person at some point during that person's life, it is possible that this type of screening could even be done without the individual's knowledge or consent.

Informed Consent

Informed consent is permission granted by a person based on full knowledge of the risks and benefits of what is being done. The basic question is: Do parents violate the right of informed consent if they give permission to have gene testing performed on their newborn and have the results released to an insurance company? Do insurance companies violate informed consent if they somehow obtain the information without the knowledge of the client? (Informed consent is discussed in detail in Chapter 9.)

Confidentiality

Similarly, confidentiality is at great risk of being violated by genetic screening. The confidentiality, trust, and fidelity that exist between the health-care provider and the client have been the basis of the therapeutic relationship. In some cases, individuals may be denied employment because of the results of genetic testing. In this time of the information

superhighway and vast computerized databases, very little of a client's health history remains confidential.[2] Recently, various state and federal law enforcement agencies have compiled DNA data bases for identifying criminals. It is only a short step from using genetic samples for disease screening to placing DNA samples in a national database.

Emotional Impact

An important ethical implication for nurses is the emotional impact that genetic information may have on the client. Knowledge of the possible long-term outcome of one's health, particularly if that knowledge is negative, may cause a client **anxiety,** or the person may become depressed or suicidal. Nurses must further hone their teaching and counseling skills to assist clients in dealing with the implications of this type of information.

Obstetric nurses have been involved with genetic screening procedures for years. Some of the most important information obtained from amniocentesis deals with the genetic composition of the fetus. It is important that the mother understand the procedure and the type of information it may yield and that she give informed consent for this procedure.

Self-Determination

Nurses have a strict ethical obligation to refuse to participate in mandatory, involuntary screening programs, as well as a strict prohibition about revealing genetic test results to unauthorized individuals. Forcing testing on clients who are strongly opposed to finding out information about their genetic status is clearly a breach of those clients' right to self-determination.

However, much as the current practice of routine screening for diseases such as tuberculosis, hepatitis, and blood lead levels promotes the general health of the population, so does the screening for genetic diseases. Clients who are strongly opposed to such genetic screening must be allowed the option to refuse it to maintain their right to self-determination.

Promise or Threat?

Now that the human genome has been decoded, a whole new world of possibilities—both positive and negative—has been opened for health-care providers. The impact of the Human Genome Project, cloning research, and other related genetic procedures is on par with the discovery of bacteria and antibiotics. The potential for the cure of almost all known diseases, ranging from viral infections to cancer to the regeneration of spinal cord nerves, is now possible.

On the other side of the issue, there is the potential for the development of superviruses that could wipe out the population of the earth. Nurses need to watch each development very closely and call their legal representatives when they believe science is moving into dangerous areas.[3]

USE OF FETAL TISSUE

Fetal tissue research has been conducted since at least the early 1990s. Traditional fetal tissue research has been generally limited to taking living cells from an aborted fetus and transplanting them into people who have chronic or severe diseases. The procedure has been found to be helpful to a limited extent in the treatment of Alzheimer's disease, Parkinson's disease, and spinal cord regeneration after traumatic injuries.

Growing Tissue on Demand

Artificial Conception. From 1997 to 2000, the Human Genome Project added a new twist to this research. Rather than using tissue from aborted fetuses, scientists are now growing their own fetal tissue in the laboratory through **artificial insemination** and in vitro fertilization procedures. These test-tube fetuses are then dissected. Various fetal tissues are used for genetic and other types of research. The legal system became aware of the potential abuses of these procedures and has passed legislation to control their use, including limiting the age of in vitro fetuses to 6 weeks. After 6 weeks, such fetuses will have to be destroyed.

Stem Cell Research. Stem cell research is a closely related issue. Stem cells are the very early cells present in the developing fetus that have not yet begun to differentiate; that is, all the cells are identical and contain all the genetic material needed to reproduce an identical individual. Stem cells can be separated and then placed in an environment where they will form more stem cells; or the genetic material from the stem cell can be removed and replaced; or the genetic material can be removed, manipulated, and then replaced. Federal administrative decisions made by the Bush administration have severely limited federal funding for stem cell research; however there are no restrictions on privately funded stem cell research.[4]

Recent research in stem cell technology has found that umbilical cord blood contains significant levels of stem cells. Because the placenta and umbilical cord are discarded after a baby is born, this would seem to be a source of stem cells without the ethical implications of in vitro fertilization and embryonic research that requires the destruction of embryos. However, several ethical questions to consider are: Who owns the placenta and umbilical cord after the baby is born? Does the mother own it? Should she receive payment for it? Is it the baby's? Or is it just considered medical waste, like a tumor that has been removed?

Like stem cells, fetal tissue is highly desirable for research and transplantation because it lacks some of the genetic material that makes more mature tissues and organs more likely to cause rejection in the host. These fetal tissues are also in a rapid growth mode and naturally develop more quickly than do tissues from other sources. Scientists involved in this research see fetal tissue as one of the most important means of curing diseases.

The Source of the Material

Even a superficial consideration of these procedures necessarily raises many important ethical issues. The source of the research material is basic to the ethics of this type of research. In the past, much of the material came from elective abortions.

Potential for Abuse. Because of the immaturity and lack of differentiation of cells during the first trimester of pregnancy, the best fetal tissue comes from fetuses aborted during the second trimester. Most scientists agree that second-trimester fetuses have well-developed nervous, cardiovascular, gastrointestinal, and renal systems and are capable of feeling pain. Even though fetal tissue research has not led to an increase in abortions, the potential for abuse is tremendous.

Paying for Fetuses? It is also not definite whether the fetal tissue research scientists are paying others for these aborted fetuses. If payment is being made for aborted fetuses, it would seem to violate both the laws that prevent payment for organs used in transplantation and the moral respect for humanity. Questions also arise concerning who is giving permission for the use of fetuses in transplantation procedures. Does anyone really own them?

In Vitro Fertilization. Another important ethical issue concerns the use of in vitro fertilization as a source for fetal tissue. Many religious groups question the morality of the procedure itself. Even if in vitro fertilization is considered ethical for procedures such as surrogate motherhood, is it ethical to create fetuses that are going to be used only for research and transplantation? From whom are the ova and sperm coming? Have the people from whom these have been obtained given permission for such use of their tissues? What about the rights of a fetus that was created in a test tube without ever having a hope of a normal life?

The Nurse's Role

The 1988 directive, which was extended indefinitely in 1990 to prevent the Department of Health and Human Services from using federal money for fetal tissue research, was amended in 2001 to allow this type of research on a very limited basis with federal funding. Local biomedical ethical panels can make decisions about this type of research. Many of these panels, which consist mainly of research scientists, have ruled in favor of continuing research.

Nurses may have an important role to play in issues involving fetal tissue research. Although they will not likely be involved directly in research, nurses are often employed in facilities where elective abortions are performed. Nurses employed in such places must become aware of the issues involved in abortion. They also should know where the aborted fetuses are taken and how they are disposed of. Nurses should also remain informed about developing procedures and techniques regarding fetal tissue research; they should support legal and ethical efforts to control its abuses.

ORGAN TRANSPLANTATION

Despite widespread public and medical acceptance of organ transplantation as a highly beneficial procedure, ethical questions still remain. Whenever a human organ is transplanted, many people are involved, including the donor, the donor's family, medical and nursing personnel, and the recipient and his or her family. Transplantation is the only health-care field in which actions taken by a group of medical professionals in one part of the country affect their counterparts in another part of the country. Society as a whole is affected by organ transplantation, mainly because of

the high cost of the procedures, which usually are covered by federal funding from taxes or reimbursement from private insurance, which in turn increases insurance premiums. Each one of these persons or groups has rights that may directly conflict with the rights of others.

The Good of the Donor

Currently, the three primary sources for organ and tissue donations are living related donors, living unrelated donors, and **deceased, formerly called cadaveric, donors.** Transplant centers and organizations involved in obtaining organs and tissues have developed complex procedures to cope with the ethical and legal issues involved in transplantation. Despite these efforts, some ethical uncertainties still surround the issue of organ transplantation.

When the Donor Is a Child

Living pediatric organ donors exemplify a particularly sensitive issue, for example, when one sibling donates a kidney to another sibling, a procedure that poses some serious risk for both donor and recipient. Parents are required to give consent for medical procedures for their children. By legal definition, a child younger than 18 years of age cannot give informed consent to such a procedure. It can be argued, however, that ethically the donor child, as a participant, should have input in making such a decision. At what age can a child have a say in the decision? Can a child be forced, for example, to donate a kidney even if he or she refuses? (See the discussion of children's ethics later in this chapter.)

One situation that illustrates this dilemma is that of a teenage girl who developed leukemia. The only way to save her life was to find a bone marrow donor who matched her genetic type. When no donor could be found, the parents decided to have another baby in the hope that the bone marrow of the second child would match that of the first child. After the baby was born, it was found that the bone marrow did indeed match, and when the child was old enough to donate safely, the bone marrow was taken and transplanted into the older child.

> *Whenever a human organ is transplanted, many people are involved, including the donor, the donor's family, medical and nursing personnel, and the recipient and his or her family.*

When Does Death Occur?

Despite the best efforts of the medical and legal community to establish criteria for death, some ethical questions still linger about what constitutes death. Because organs such as the heart, lungs, and liver, should ideally come from a donor whose heart is still beating, some clinicians fear that there will be a tendency for physicians to declare that a person is dead before death actually occurs. Many people also mistakenly believe that if they indicate they would like to be organ donors, and become sick or injured and admitted to the hospital, physicians will not work as hard to "save their lives."

The most widely accepted criterion for determining death in deceased donors is **death by neurological criteria,** formerly called brain death. The definition of death by neurological criteria in conjunction with organ donation is very clear, and health-care professionals use proven procedures to test for and determine death by neurological criteria. Some researchers, however, question whether death by neurological criteria actually means that a person ceases to exist as a human. Are there some other criteria that ought to be examined in conjunction with death by neurological criteria?

Selecting the Recipient

One of the most difficult ethical issues involved in organ transplantation is the selection of recipients. Because fewer organs are available than the numerous people who need them, the potential ethical dilemmas are great.

Legislating Donation

The Uniform Anatomical Gift Act, passed in 1968, made the donation of organs, eyes, and tissue for transplant a legal transaction involving a prespecified recipient. Later legislation prohibited prespecification of recipients by creating a federal entity to regulate the transplantation industry, and made the sale of human organs illegal. This legislation, the National Organ Transplant Act, also led to the creation of the United Network for Organ Sharing (UNOS), which regulates organ allocation and maintains the national organ transplant waiting list. UNOS created a database of all people wait-listed for an organ, and attempted to rank all people waiting for organs on a need-based list in a nondiscriminatory manner. Each organ has its own allocation and ranking policies. However, some important criteria for ranking include need, length of time on the list, potential for survival, prior organ transplantation, value to the community, and tissue compatibility. The UNOS allocation policy is designed to provide organs for clients who have the greatest need as well as the best projected outcome for a successful transplant.

Nurses can be, and often are, involved in some aspect of the organ donation process. Many states have passed laws that requiring health-care workers to refer all potential organ donors to the local organization responsible for organ recovery. Many organ recovery agencies also provide continuing education for nurses, so they are trained in the proper ways to ask the family members of potential organ donors whether they have ever thought about their dead or dying loved one being an organ donor (Box 8.1).

Box 8.1

Organ Donation

Seven Questions That Families Often Ask About Organ Donation and How You Should Answer Them

Many families refuse to donate a loved one's organs simply because they do not fully understand organ donation. By being prepared to address their concerns, you can help them make a decision they are comfortable with.

Here are the most common questions families ask about organ donation. Review them along with the answers so that you are prepared the next time that you need to counsel a family on this sensitive issue.

1. *Whose consent is needed to allow organ donation?*

   Consent must come from the patient's legal next of kin, even if the patient has a signed donor card or an organ donation sticker on his or her driver's license.

(continued)

Issues in Practice

In the current health-care environment, nurses may encounter elderly clients who function independently at home and have not officially or legally been declared incompetent, but whose behavior might indicate that they are unable to make rational decisions about their care. Consider the following situation:

A 74-year-old client, Buster Mack, had been a long-haul truck driver for most of his life and was still driving his big rig into his 60s. He had been in relatively good health until 5 years ago, when he was diagnosed with lung cancer. A lobectomy was performed at that time, and he was treated with follow-up radiation and chemotherapy, but the cancer had slowly metastasized to the bone. His current hospitalization was because of a syncopal episode witnessed by a neighbor in the front yard of Mr. Mack's home, where he lives by himself.

During the admission assessment, the nurse observed that Mr. Mack had trouble focusing on the questions, and often the answer was unrelated to the question or in the form of a long rambling account of something that happened many years ago. Although he knew he was in a hospital (he could not remember the name), he had no idea where it was or what the date was. His demeanor was cooperative and pleasant, and he laughed easily when the nurse joked with him. He could not remember whether he had any family left living, although the name and address of a son in a distant city were listed on the old records.

Mr. Mack signed all the admission papers and consent forms placed in front of him for a number of neurological tests. His physician was fearful that the cancer might have spread to his brain and wanted to do a magnetic resonance imaging (MRI) test, spinal tap, and brain scan. The MRI and brain scan showed a small tumor in an area of the brain where it could be removed rather easily. Mr. Mack's physician, in consultation with a neurosurgeon, felt that an immediate craniotomy with removal of the tumor was required. After explaining the procedure to Mr. Mack, the physicians placed the consent-to-operate form on his over-the-bed table and gave him a pen. He promptly signed and gave it back.

Later on that day during her shift assessment, the nurse checked on Mr. Mack. The neighbor who had found him unconscious was visiting at the time. When the nurse asked Mr. Mack whether he was ready for the surgery scheduled for the next morning, he had a blank look on his face. On further questioning, the nurse concluded that Mr. Mack had no idea about what was going to happen to him the next day. The neighbor, who helped Mr. Mack with his bills and other paper work at home, stated: "He'll pretty much sign anything that you put in front of him." At this point the nurse felt that Mr. Mack was incapable of making an informed decision about the craniotomy.

The nurse called both the primary physician and the neurosurgeon about her observations. She was told bluntly that the consent had been signed and that they were going to operate on Mr. Mack the next day for his own good. If she wanted what was best for the client, she would just drop the issue.

Should the nurse just drop the issue? Is there anything she could do to resolve the problem? What ethical principles are involved with this situation?

from the beneficence and nonmaleficence viewpoints, living wills seem to violate the principle of providing benefit to the client. This perception makes many health-care providers ethically uncomfortable. In some situations, the implementation of a living will might actually involve the termination of some modes of treatments already in use. Termination of treatments would seem to constitute harm to the client.

In either case, respecting a living will might often appear to health-care providers to be a violation of their duty to help clients and preserve life. Nurses, as well as other health-care providers, often experience a sense of frustration when they are not allowed to use all the skills they have learned to preserve life.

Lack of Clarity

A third difficulty nurses and other health-care workers may have with living wills is their formulation and legal enforcement. In general, the language used in the standard living will document is broad and vague. Living wills are often not specific enough to include all the forms of treatments that are possible for the many types of illnesses that might render a person incompetent to make decisions. Health-care providers may have little direction as to the care they are to give if the circumstances at the time the living will was formulated are significantly different from the declared wishes of the client.

Furthermore, unless the particular state has enacted into law a special type of living will called a natural death act, the living will has no mechanism of legal enforcement. Also, when a client travels from one state to another, the legal effect of the living will may be in question. Does the nonresident state have an obligation to honor it?

In some states, a living will is considered only advisory, and the physician has the right to comply with the living will or treat the client as the physician deems most appropriate. There is no protection for nurses or other health-care practitioners against criminal or civil liability in the execution of living wills in states without a natural death act. Once a valid living will exists, it only becomes effective when the person who formulated it meets the qualifications for the natural death act. In most states, the individual must be diagnosed as having a terminal condition where the continuation of treatment and life support would only prolong the

client's dying process, but there is no clear consensus on the definition of *terminal condition*.

A Guide for the Care Provider

Despite all these difficulties, living wills are still a good way for a client to make health-care wishes known to health-care providers. Documents that are specific about treatment modalities, are written in a "legal" format, and are signed by two or more witnesses tend to be treated with an increased level of respect by health-care providers (Fig. 8.1).

Nurses can help clients plan ahead for their care should they become unable to make decisions for themselves. Although the nurse should not make the decisions for the client, the nurse can provide important information about the various treatment modalities that the client is considering. The nurse also can help clients clarify their wishes and guide them through the process of formulating an advance directive.

EUTHANASIA AND ASSISTED SUICIDE

Although the term *euthanasia* simply means a "good" or peaceful death, it has taken on the connotation of some type of action that produces death. A distinction needs to be made between passive and active euthanasia. Passive euthanasia usually refers to the practice of allowing an individual to die without any extraordinary intervention. This umbrella definition includes practices such as DNR orders, living wills, and withdrawal of ventilators or other life support.

Active Euthanasia

Active euthanasia usually describes the practice of hastening an individual's death through some act or procedure. This practice is also sometimes referred to as mercy killing and takes many forms, ranging from use of large amounts of pain medication for terminal cancer clients to use of poison, a gun, or a knife to end a person's life.

The Case of Dr. Kevorkian

Assisted suicide—brought to public attention by Dr. Jack Kevorkian, a Michigan physician who publicly practiced it for many years—can be considered a type of active euthanasia or mercy killing. The central issue that Dr. Kevorkian demonstrated was whether it is ever ethically and legally permissible

PENNSYLVANIA DECLARATION

INSTRUCTIONS	
PRINT YOUR NAME	I, _____, being of sound mind, willfully and voluntarily make this declaration to be followed if I become incompetent. This declaration reflects my firm and settled commitment to refuse life-sustaining treatment under the circumstances indicated below. I direct my attending physician to withhold or withdraw life-sustaining treatment that serves only to prolong the process of my dying, if I should be in a terminal condition or in a state of permanent unconsciousness. I direct that treatment be limited to measures to keep me comfortable and to relieve pain, including any pain that might occur by withholding or withdrawing life-sustaining treatment.

CHECK THE OPTIONS WHICH REFLECT YOUR WISHES	In addition, if I am in the condition described above, I feel especially strongly about the following forms of treatment:
	    I ( ) do ( ) do not want cardiac resuscitation.
	    I ( ) do ( ) do not want mechanical respiration.
	    I ( ) do ( ) do not want tube feeding or any other artificial or
	         invasive form of nutrition (food) or hydration (water).
	    I ( ) do ( ) do not want blood or blood products.
	    I ( ) do ( ) do not want any form of surgery or invasive
	         diagnostic tests.
	    I ( ) do ( ) do not want kidney dialysis.
	    I ( ) do ( ) do not want antibiotics.
	
	I realize that if I do not specifically indicate my preference regarding any of the forms of treatment listed above, I may receive that form of treatment.

ADD PERSONAL INSTRUCTIONS (IF ANY)	Other instructions:
© 2000 PARTNERSHIP FOR CARING, INC.	

Figure 8.1 Sample advance directive. Because the laws on advance directives vary widely from state to state, there is no standard advance directive whose language conforms exactly with all states' laws. (Reprinted with permission of Partnership for Caring, formerly Choice in Dying, 200 Varick Street, New York. For more information visit www.partnershipforcaring.org.)

for health-care personnel to assist in taking a life. In most states the practice is illegal. The legal definition of homicide—bringing about a person's death or assisting in doing so—seems to fit the act of assisted suicide. In the past, there has been a great deal of hesitation on the part of the legal system to prosecute persons who are involved in assisted suicide, and on the part of juries to convict physicians who participate in the activity.

> " *The central issue that Dr. Kevorkian demonstrated was whether it is ever ethically permissible for health-care personnel to assist in taking a life.* "

A Killing on TV

In the fall of 1998, Dr. Kevorkian raised the legal and ethical stakes. On a nationally broadcast network news show, *60 Minutes,* he not only admitted to administering a lethal medication to a client without the client's assistance, but he also played a videotape that showed the whole episode.

The client, who had Lou Gehrig's disease (amyotrophic lateral sclerosis), had requested that

APPOINTING A SURROGATE	PENNSYLVANIA DECLARATION PAGE 2 OF 2

Surrogate decisionmaking:

I ( ) do ( ) do not want to designate another person as my surogate to make medical treatment decisions for me if I should be incompetent and in a terminal condition or in a state of permanent unconsciousness.

PRINT THE NAME, ADDRESS AND PHONE NUMBER OF YOUR SURROGATE

Name: _____

Address : _____

Phone: _____

PRINT THE NAME, ADDRESS AND PHONE NUMBER OF YOUR ALTERNATE SURROGATE

Name and address of substitute (if surrogate designated above is unable to serve):

Name: _____

Address: _____

Phone: _____

PRINT THE DATE

I made this declaration on the _____ day of _____ .
                                (day)   (month, year)

SIGN THE DOCUMENT AND PRINT YOUR ADDRESS

Declarant's signature: _____

Declarant's address: _____

WITNESSING PROCEDURE

The declarant, or the person on behalf of and at the direction of the declarant, knowingly and voluntarily signed this writing by signature or mark in my presence.

YOUR TWO WITNESSES MUST SIGN AND PRINT THEIR ADDRESSES

Witness's signature: _____

Witness's address: _____

Witness's signature: _____

Witness's address: _____

© 2000
PARTNERSHIP
FOR CARING, INC.

Courtesy of **Partnership for Caring, Inc.**   6/96
1620 Eye Street, NW. Suite 202, Washington, DC 20006 800-989-9455

Figure 8.1 (*continued*)

Dr. Kevorkian help him end his life. The client had signed a **consent** form and release and was even given an extra 2 weeks to "think about it." The client waited only for 3 days before making his final request for the lethal medication.

Under Michigan law, Dr. Kevorkian could have been charged with **manslaughter** or even first-degree murder. Dr. Kevorkian admitted that his **motivation** for the act was to be tried under these laws as a test case for active euthanasia. He was arrested 2 weeks after the tape was broadcast, on a charge of first-degree murder. However, he believed that a jury would never convict him. The trial verdict

was guilty of second-degree murder and he served 10 years of a 25 years-to-life prison term. He was released on probation in 2007. This verdict reinforced the belief of most health-care professionals that mercy killing or assisted suicide is always ethically wrong.

The unfortunate fallout from Dr. Kevorkian's conviction is that many physicians have become even more reluctant to write DNR orders or comply with clients' and/or families' wishes to allow clients to be removed from life support. Clearly they do not understand the distinctions between active and passive euthanasia.

An Issue of Self-Determination

A Last Act of Control?

The fundamental ethical issue in these situations is the right to self-determination. In almost every other health-care situation, a client who is mentally competent can make decisions about what care to accept and what care to refuse. Yet, when it comes to the termination of life, this right becomes controversial. Supporters of the practice of assisted suicide believe that the right to self-determination remains intact, even with regard to the decision to end one's life. It is the last act of a very sick individual to control his or her own fate. Many believe that medical personnel should be allowed to assist clients in this procedure, just as they are allowed to assist clients in other medical and nursing procedures.

An Unacceptable Practice?

Those who oppose assisted suicide find these arguments unconvincing. Legally, ethically, and morally, suicide in U.S. society has never been an accepted practice. Health-care staff goes to great lengths to prevent suicidal clients from injuring themselves. In addition, it would seem that individuals in the terminal stages of a disease, who are overwhelmed by pain and depressed by the thought of prolonged suffering, might not be able to think clearly enough to give informed consent for assisted suicide. Also, because the termination of life is final, it does not allow for spontaneous cures or for the development of new treatments or medications.

Nonmaleficence is the term that describes the obligation to do no harm to clients. Whether assisting in or causing the death of a client is a violation of this principle is most likely to be an issue that will continue to be debated for some time. Several states have passed laws permitting assisted suicide, but these states have very strict guidelines. The American Nurses Association (ANA) and other nurses' organizations oppose assisted suicide as a policy and believe that nurses who participate in it are violating the code of ethics. For similar reasons, the ANA opposes nurses participating in executions of convicted criminals.

> *Most acute care facilities will make some exceptions for the treatment of clients with AIDS, for example if the nurse is pregnant, is receiving chemotherapy, or has had other immunity problems. In most situations, however, the nurse is obligated to provide the best nursing care possible for all clients, including those with AIDS.*

HUMAN IMMUNODEFICIENCY VIRUS AND ACQUIRED IMMUNODEFICIENCY SYNDROME

After several years of decrease, the number of human immunodeficiency virus (HIV) and acquired immunodeficiency syndrome (AIDS) cases continues to rise again in the United States despite educational efforts on its prevention and spread. Several Asian countries are also seeing a recent dramatic increase in cases of HIV/AIDS. In some parts of Africa, it is estimated that as much as 60 percent of the population is infected with the virus.

An Emotional Issue

HIV and AIDS have evoked strong emotions both in the public and in the medical community. Nurses, who for years held strongly to the ethical principle that all clients regardless of race, sex, religion, age, or disease process should be cared for equally, are questioning their obligation to take care of clients who have AIDS.

The Right to Privacy

Several ethical issues underlie the HIV/AIDS controversy. One of the most important is the right to privacy. Although there is a general requirement to report infection with HIV/AIDS to the Centers for Disease Control and Prevention (CDC), many states have strict laws regarding the confidentiality of the diagnosis. Unauthorized revelation of the diagnosis of HIV/AIDS brings the possibility of a lawsuit against the health-care provider or institution. However, the right to privacy is not absolute. Diseases such as tuberculosis, gonorrhea, syphilis, and hepatitis, which are highly contagious and sometimes fatal, must be reported to public health officials.

If the right to privacy can be violated when the public welfare is at stake, does HIV/AIDS represent this type of threat? Is it unjust to ask health-care providers to care for clients with this disease without knowing that the client has it? Is it just to violate a client's privacy when the disease carries with it a potential for social stigma and isolation? Does the client have a right to know that a health-care provider is infected with HIV/AIDS?

The Right to Care
Another important ethical issue is the right to care. Can a nurse refuse to care for a client with HIV/AIDS? Obviously, a fundamental right of a client is to receive care, and a fundamental obligation of a nurse is to provide care.

The Nurse's Own Interest
The first statement of the ANA Code of Ethics for Nurses is that a nurse must provide care unrestricted by any considerations. Most acute care facilities will make some exceptions for the treatment of clients with HIV/AIDS, for example if the nurse is pregnant, is receiving chemotherapy, or has had other immunity problems. In most situations, however, the nurse is obligated to provide the best nursing care possible for all clients, including those with HIV/AIDS.

What Cost to Society?
What about the tremendous cost involved in treating individuals who have HIV/AIDS? The medical cost of treating a client with HIV/AIDS from the time of diagnosis to the time of death can run into the millions of dollars. In the face of this crisis, governmental agencies, which bear the brunt of paying for HIV/AIDS treatment, will have to make some difficult decisions concerning this issue. With more than 2 million U.S. citizens already infected with this disease, the cost to American society is becoming astronomical.

Nurses have the obligation to care for all clients, including those with HIV/AIDS, but should physicians, hospitals, or governmental agencies also be held to this same precept? Should our society regard health care as a right or a privilege?

ETHICS INVOLVING CHILDREN

Although children are universally acknowledged as the hope of the future, many children remain poorly fed, clothed, housed, and educated and are in dire need of all types of health care, even in affluent countries such as the United States. In the past few years, there has been a marked increase in the reporting of incidents of child neglect and abuse by parents.

The Power of Parents
Our society generally acknowledges the tremendous decision-making power that parents have on behalf of their children; however, there are limits to how parents may decide to act. These limits are sometimes obvious, such as in cases of physical abuse and cruelty to children; however, they may also be less conspicuous, such as in cases of neglect or decisions about withholding medical care for religious reasons. Health-care professionals often find themselves trying to make decisions about the appropriateness of a parent's actions toward a child.

The legal and ethical factors surrounding the decisions that health-care providers must make about child health issues are complicated and sometimes contradictory, ranging from laws about reporting suspected abuse to obtaining permission for treatment. This section focuses on child abuse and the ethical issues that it creates for nurses, and the issues of informed consent as it pertains to children.

Issues involving children have always been an important consideration in our society. Whereas the political attention seems to focus on education, drug and alcohol abuse, and child health-care issues, ethical concerns in **pediatrics** are never forgotten and often serve as the unspoken basis for the more visible issues.

Child health ethical issues are numerous and diverse, ranging from mass screening for diseases to withholding permission for treatment.

Child Abuse

Case Study

Emily, who is 8 months old, was brought to the hospital by her 17-year-old unemployed mother, who stated that the baby refused to eat at home and vomited a lot. Emily was very small for her age and was below the growth curve for weight. She was also neurologically introverted and showed little interest in her surroundings. She slept a great deal of the time. She was admitted to the hospital with a diagnosis of nonorganic failure to thrive.

During her stay in the hospital, Emily ate well and gained a significant amount of weight. Her neurological status also improved.

One nurse suspected that this was a case of neglect (a form of child abuse) and suggested to the physician that child protective services be notified to evaluate the case. The physician resisted because there was not enough evidence to make a definitive case and thought that it was unfair to the parents to make such a claim. The other nurses felt that by reporting the case they would lose the trust of the mother and cause her to avoid health care for Emily in the future. They also cited a case in which nurses and the hospital were sued when they reported a teenage mother for neglect; the accusation later proved to be false.

Emily was sent home after 3 weeks but was readmitted 1 month later with the same complaints of poor feeding. She had lost weight since her discharge from the hospital, and she was again neurologically withdrawn. The physician still refused to notify child protective services because of the lack of hard evidence. He thought that the available data did not warrant an investigation and possible removal of the child from the home. The nurse still believed that the mother should be reported on the basis of suspicions that could be substantiated legally.

Ethics Regarding Child Abuse

There is a general legal requirement in most states that suspected child abuse must be reported by health-care providers as well as by anyone who suspects that child abuse has occurred. Abuse is more obvious when the child has physical injuries that do not fit the medical history or are atypical for the age group. However, in cases of neglect, the evidence may be very minimal or even nonexistent. Often nurses and physicians who specialize in the care of children rely on their experience in making decisions about reporting or not reporting suspected abuse.

A conflicting ethical principle that is sometimes forgotten in the reporting of suspected child abuse is the family's right to privacy and self-determination. It is an equally fundamental right that Emily's parents be allowed to live their lives according to their own values, free from intrusions.

Decisions about reporting suspected child abuse or neglect rest on the underlying ethical principles of beneficence and protection of the best interests of the child. It is always difficult to decide how far ranging these concerns for "best interest" should be. Physicians tend to focus on solving the immediate problem. Nurses have a more holistic viewpoint and tend to see children in relationship to their environments as well as the environments of the parents. Nurses also tend to think of themselves as saviors, protecting the unfortunate or disadvantaged from a malignant social system and often making value judgments about the lifestyles of others from their middle-class vantage point.

A conflicting ethical principle that is sometimes forgotten in the reporting of suspected child abuse is the family's right to privacy and self-determination. However, when the child is a client in the hospital, beneficence usually outweighs fidelity and veracity.

Resolving the Dilemma

How is the nurse going to resolve this dilemma? Should she report the case and go against the physician's decision? Should she just agree with the physician and defer to his greater experience and better judgment? Should she submit the problem to the hospital ethics committee? Are there any other possible options for action in this case?

It is likely that the physician was correct in his decision about this case, although his ethical reasoning may leave something to be desired. Legally, it is unlikely that there would be sufficient proof to remove the infant from the mother because home monitoring could achieve the same results. Therefore, how can the ethical obligations for the best interest of the child be met?

One very plausible solution is to monitor the child closely through frequent follow-up either at the physician's office or at the local health department. In addition, a follow-up and home evaluation could be arranged through a home health-care agency, which could also make available other community resources to help in Emily's care. If the infant continued to fail to gain weight, or if it was later determined that Emily's mother was indeed unable to care adequately for her, the case could then be referred to child protective services.

The role of the nurse who cares for the very young or abused child is one of client advocate. These children need help and protection, and at times, for their very survival, must be taken out of an abusive home setting. Nurses need to be aware of and use all the assets available in these situations, including the police, child protective services, welfare, and home health-care agencies.

Informed Consent and Children

Case Study

Peter, one of a pair of 7-year-old identical twins, developed severe bilateral glomerulonephritis after Strep throat infection. The renal involvement was so severe that it did not respond to any medical treatment, and both of his kidneys had to be removed. Paul, Peter's identical twin, was evaluated for kidney donation and, as expected, matched on all six antigens as well as blood type and size. Paul seemed to understand what had happened to his brother and agreed to donate one of his kidneys to keep his brother alive.

However, the children's parents were having some trouble agreeing on whether Paul should donate a kidney to Peter. The twins' mother felt that the donation and transplant should be permitted because it would indeed help keep Peter alive and would also make Paul feel that he was an important part of the process. She argued that if Peter ever did die, Paul would be overcome with guilt knowing that he could have saved his brother but did not.

The twins' father was not as certain about the transplant procedure. He thought that Paul was too young to make a truly free decision of that type and that he did not really understand the serious nature of a kidney removal operation. He thought that Paul, because he was so young, might have been unduly influenced by subtle yet powerful pressures from his family. No one had directly told Paul that he *must* donate one of his kidneys, yet the

Determining the Greatest Good

Sherry is an RN who works for a rehabilitation center that deals mainly with developmentally delayed children. For several years, Sherry has been following the case of Margie N, who is now 8 years old and has Down syndrome and moderate retardation. Margie has made steady, if slow, progress in achieving basic motor and cognitive skills but still requires close supervision of all activities and care for all basic hygiene needs. Margie is still not advanced enough to participate in group activities at the center's day clinic.

Mrs. N, Margie's mother, a 42-year-old widow, has been providing a high level of care for Margie at home as well as meeting the child's demands for love and attention. Recently, Mrs. N has been diagnosed with systemic lupus erythematosus (SLE), which has displayed as its primary symptoms severe joint pain and stiffness. During the past several months, Mrs. N has been finding it increasingly difficult to care for Margie because of the progressive nature of the SLE.

Mrs. N is trying to make a decision about long-term care for Margie. She trusts Sherry's judgment completely and often relies on the information and teaching given by the nurse to make changes in Margie's care. Sherry is uncertain about what advice she should give. She recognizes that the high level of care and comfort provided by Mrs. N has been an essential part in the advances Margie has made up to this point, but she also recognizes that Mrs. N may soon reach a point at which that care can no longer be provided. It seems that to do what is good for Mrs. N (i.e., placing Margie in an institution) would be harmful to Margie, whereas doing what is good for Margie (i.e., leaving her at home) would be harmful to Mrs. N. What is the best course of action in this situation? Are there any alternative solutions to this dilemma?

References

1. Jenkins, J: Establishing the essential nursing competencies for genetics and genomics. Journal of Nursing Scholarship 39(1): 10–16, 2007.
2. Conley, YP: The future of genomic nursing research. Journal of Nursing Scholarship 39(1):17–24, 2007.
3. Heller, BR: 10 Trends to watch. Health Care Perspectives 24(1): 9–14, 2002.
4. Saria, MG: Hematopoietic stem cell transplantation: Implications for critical care nurses. Clinical Journal of Oncology Nursing 11(1):53–63, 130–134, 2007.
5. Tissue-tracking requirements: Putting all the pieces together. Operating Room Manager, 23(2):1, 15–17, 2007.
6. Gallagher, A: Terminal sedation: Promoting ethical nursing practice: Art and science ethical decision-making. Nursing Standard 21(34):42–46, 2007.
7. Duke, G: Knowledge, attitudes and practices of nursing personnel regarding advance directives. International Journal of Palliative Nursing 13(3):109–115, 2007.
8. Murphy, P: Ethics in practice: How to avoid DNR miscommunications. Nursing Management 38(3):17, 20, 2007.

Bibliography

Berger, J: Ethical challenges of partial do-not-resuscitate (DNR) orders: Placing DNR orders in the context of a life-threatening conditions care plan. Archives of Internal Medicine 163(19):2270–2275, 2003.

Clendinen, D: "My father wasn't there." The care of Terri Schiavo has universal and personal resonance. The New York Times, October 26, 2003, 12.

Conway, A: Ethical issues in the neonatal intensive care unit. Critical Care Nursing Clinics of North America 16(2):271–278, 2004.

Engelhardt, HT, and Cherry, MJ: Allocating Scarce Resources. Georgetown University Press, Baltimore, 2002.

Ewing, A, and Catlin, A: Pediatric ethics, issues, & commentary. Pediatric Nursing 30(6):471–472, 2004.

Fontanarosa, P: Controversies: Surrogate consent for living related organ donation. JAMA 291(6):728–731, 2004.

Grace, P: Patient safety and the limits of confidentiality. American Journal of Nursing 104(11):33–37, 2004.

Jenkins, J: Ethical implications of genetic information. Online Journal of Issues in Nursing February 9, 2001.

Horner, S: Ethics and genetics: Implications for CNS practice. Clinical Nurse Specialist 18(5):228–231, 2004.

Husted, G: When is a health care system not an ethical health care system? Suspending the do-not-resuscitate order in the operating room. Critical Care Nursing Clinics of North America 12(2):157–163, 2004.

Koppelman, E: The dead donor rule and the concept of death: Severing the ties that bind them. American Journal of Bioethics 3(1):1–9, 2003.

McNeil, D: Vegetative or minimally conscious? The New York Times, October 26, 2003.

Offit, K, and Gostin, L: Health law and ethics: The "duty to warn" a patient's family members about hereditary disease risks. JAMA 292(12):1469–1473, 2004.

Paul, R, and Elder, L: Ethical Reasoning. The Foundation for Critical Thinking, 2003 (www.crticalthinking.org).

Rushton, C, and Ferrell, B: Ethics and palliative care in pediatrics: When should parents agree to withdraw life-sustaining therapy for children? American Journal of Nursing 104(4):54–64, 2004.

9

Nursing Law and Liability

Mary Evans and Tonia Aiken

Learning Objectives

After completing this chapter, the reader will be able to:

- Distinguish between statutory law and common law.
- Differentiate civil law from criminal law.
- Explain the legal principles involved in:
  Unintentional torts
  Intentional torts
  Quasi-intentional torts
  Informed consent
  Do-not-resuscitate (DNR) orders
- Describe the trial process.
- List methods to prevent litigation.
- Identify the elements in delegation.

THE LEGAL SYSTEM

For many nurses, the mere mention of the word *lawsuit* provokes a high level of anxiety. At first glance, the legal system often seems to be a large and confusing entity whose intricacies are designed to entrap the uninitiated. Many nurses feel that even a minor error in client care will lead to huge settlements against them and loss of their nursing license. In reality, even though the number of lawsuits against nurses has been increasing since the early 1990s, the number of nurses who are actually sued in court remains relatively small. However, many cases are settled out of court often before any official legal action has been taken.

It is important to remember that the legal system is just one element of the health-care system. Laws are rules to help protect people and to keep society functioning. The ultimate goal of all laws is to promote peaceful and productive interactions between and among the people of that society.

An understanding of basic legal principles will augment the quality of care that the nurse delivers. In our litigious society, it is important to comprehend how the law affects the profession of nursing and the individual nurse's daily practice.

SOURCES OF LAW

There are two major sources of laws in the United States: statutory law and common law (Box 9.1). Most laws that govern nursing are state-level statutory laws because licensure is a function of the state's authority.

Statutory Law
Statutory law consists of laws written and enacted by the U.S. Congress, the state legislatures, and other governmental entities such as cities, counties, and townships. Legislated laws enacted by the U.S.

Box 9.1

Division and Types of Law

I. Statutory Law
   A. Criminal Law
      1. Misdemeanor
      2. Felony
   B. Civil Law
      1. Tort Law
         a. Unintentional tort
         b. Intentional tort
         c. Quasi-intentional tort
      2. Contract Law
      3. Treaty Law
      4. Tax Law
      5. Other
II. Common Law
   A. Criminal Law
      1. Misdemeanor
      2. Felony
   B. Civil Law
      1. Tort Law
         a. Unintentional tort
         b. Intentional tort
         c. Quasi-intentional tort
      2. Contract Law
      3. Treaty Law
      4. Tax Law
      5. Other

Congress are called federal **statutes.** State-drafted laws are called state statutes. Individual cities and municipalities have legislative bodies that draft **ordinances,** codes, and regulations at their respective levels.

The laws that govern the profession of nursing are statutory laws. Most of these laws are written at the state level because licensure is a responsibility of the individual states. These laws include the nurse practice act, which establishes the state board of nursing, the scope of practice for nurses, individual licensure procedures, punitive actions for violation of the practice act, and the schedule of fees for nurse licensure in the state.

Common Law

Common law is different from statutory law in that it has evolved from the decisions of previous legal

cases that form a **precedent.** These laws represent the accumulated results of the judgments and decrees that have been handed down by courts of the United States and Great Britain through the years.

Common law often extends beyond the scope of statutory law. For example, no statutes require a person who is negligent and causes injury to another to compensate that person for the injury. However, court decisions that have addressed the same legal issues, such as negligence, over and over have repeatedly ruled that the injured person should receive compensation. The way in which each case is resolved creates a precedent, or pattern, for dealing with the same legal issue in the future. The common laws involving negligence or malpractice are most frequently encountered by the nurse.

Common law or case law is law that has developed over a long period. The principle of *stare decisis* requires a judge to make decisions similar to those that have been handed down in previous cases if the facts of the cases are identical. Common law decisions are published in bound legal reports. Generally speaking, common law deals with matters outside the scope of laws enacted by the legislature.

DIVISIONS OF LAW

In the U.S. legal system, there are many divisions in the law. A major example of such a division is the difference between criminal law and civil law, either of which may be statutory or common in origin.

Criminal Law

A System of Protection
Criminal laws are concerned with providing protection for all members of society. When someone is accused of violating a criminal law, the government at the county, city, state, or federal level imposes punishments appropriate to the type of **crime.** Criminal law involves a wide range of **malfeasance,** from minor traffic violations to murder.

Although most criminal law is created and regulated by the government through the enactment of statutes, a small portion falls under the common law. Statutes are developed and enacted by the legislature (state or federal) and approved by the executive branch, such as a governor or the president. Criminal law is further classified into two types of offenses: (1) **misdemeanors,** which are minor criminal offenses, and (2) **felonies,** which are major criminal offenses.

In the criminal law system, an individual accused of a crime is called the **defendant.** The prosecuting attorney represents the people of the city, county, state, or federal jurisdiction who are accusing the individual of a crime. A **criminal action** is rendered when the person charged with the crime is brought to trial and convicted. Penalties or sanctions are imposed on the violators of criminal law and are based on the scope of the crime. They can involve a range of punishment from community service work and fines to imprisonment and death.

> *The most common violation by nurses of the criminal law is through failure to renew nursing licenses. In this situation, the nurse is in effect practicing nursing without a license, which is a crime in all states.*

What Do You Think?

Do you know anyone who has filed a malpractice suit or a health-care provider who was the defendant in a malpractice suit? What was the situation that caused the case? How was it resolved? If you have never been involved with a malpractice suit or do not know anyone who has, how would you feel if a lawsuit were to be brought against you?

_____

_____

_____

_____

_____

_____

_____

_____

_____

_____

_____

The Nurse's Involvement

Nurses can become involved with the criminal system in their nursing practice in several ways. The most common violation by nurses of the criminal law is through failure to renew nursing licenses. In this situation, the nurse is in effect practicing nursing without a license, which is a crime in all states.

Nurses also become involved with the illegal diversion of drugs, particularly narcotics, from the hospital. This is a more serious crime, which may lead to imprisonment. Recent cases involving intentional or unintentional deaths of clients and assisted suicide cases have also led to criminal action against nurses.

Civil Law

Nurses are much more likely to become involved in civil lawsuits than in criminal violations. **Civil laws** generally deal with the violation of one individual's rights by another individual. The court provides the forum that enables these individuals to have their disputes resolved by an independent third party, such as a judge or a jury of the defendant's peers.

The individual who brings the dispute to the court is called the **plaintiff.** The formal written document that describes the dispute and the resolution sought is called the complaint. The individual against whom the complaint is filed is the defendant, who, in conjunction with his or her attorney, prepares the **answer** to the complaint. In civil cases, the **burden of proof** rests with the plaintiff.

Civil law has many branches, including contract law, treaty law, tax law, and tort law. It is under the tort law that most nurses become involved with the legal system.

Tort Law

A **tort** is generally defined as a wrongful act committed against a person or his or her property independent of a contract. A person who commits a tort is called the **tort-feasor** and is **liable** for **damages** to those who are affected by the person's actions. The word *tort,* derived from the Latin *tortus* (twisted), is a French word for injury or wrong. Torts can involve several different types of actions, including a direct violation of a person's legal rights or a violation of a standard of care that causes injury to a person. Torts are classified as unintentional, intentional, or quasi-intentional.

Unintentional Torts

Negligence

Negligence is the primary form of **unintentional tort.** **Negligence** is generally defined as the **omission** of an act that a reasonable and prudent person would perform in a similar situation or the commission of something a reasonable person would not do in that situation. **Nonfeasance** is a type of negligence that occurs when a person fails to perform a legally required duty.[1]

Malpractice

Malpractice is a type of negligence for which professionals can be sued (professional negligence). Because of their professional status, nurses are held to a higher standard of conduct than the ordinary layperson. The standard for nurses is what a reasonable and prudent nurse would do in the same situation: "A registered nurse is charged with utilizing the degree and skill and judgment commensurate with his or her education, experience, and position."[2]

> *Because of their professional status, nurses are held to a higher standard of conduct than the ordinary layperson.*

For instance, it is reasonable and prudent that the nurse put the side rails up on the bed of a client who has just received an injection of a narcotic pain medication, because the drug causes drowsiness and sometimes confusion. If the nurse gave an injection of a narcotic medication but forgot to put the side rails up, and the client fell out of bed and fractured his hip, the nurse could be sued for the negligent act of forgetting to put the side rail up.

Four elements are required for a person to make a claim of negligence:

1. A duty was owed to the client (professional relationship).
2. The professional violated the **duty** and failed to conform to the standard of care (breach of duty).
3. The failure to act by the professional was the **proximate cause** of the resulting injuries (causality).
4. Actual injuries resulted from the breach of duty (damages).

If any of these elements are missing from the case, the client will probably not be able to win the lawsuit (Box 9.2).

Case Study

Consider the following situation:

Mr. Fagin, a 78-year-old client, was admitted from a nursing home for the treatment of a fractured tibia after he fell out of bed. After the fracture was reduced, a fiberglass cast was applied, and Mr. Fagin was sent to the orthopedic unit for follow-up care. While making her 0400 rounds, the night charge nurse, a registered nurse (RN), discovered that Mr. Fagin's foot on the casted leg was cold to touch, looked bluish-purple, and was swollen approximately 1½ times normal size. The nurse noted these findings in the client's chart and relayed the information to the day-shift nurses during the 0630 shift report.

The charge nurse on the day shift promptly called and relayed the findings to Mr. Fagin's physician. The physician, however, did not seem to be concerned and only told the nurse to "Keep a close eye on him, and don't bother me again unless it is an absolute emergency." A short time later, Mr. Fagin became agitated, complained of severe pain in the affected foot, and eventually began yelling uncontrollably. The charge nurse called the emergency department (ED) physician to come to check on the client. The ED physician immediately removed the cast and noted an extensive circulatory impairment that would not respond to treatment. A few days later, Mr. Fagin's leg was amputated. His family filed a malpractice lawsuit against the hospital, the physician, and both the night and day charge nurses.

Are all the elements present in this case for a bona fide lawsuit? What could have been done to prevent this situation from happening? How should nurses deal with reluctant or hostile physicians?

Professional Misconduct

Malpractice is more serious than mere negligence because it indicates professional misconduct or unreasonable lack of skill in performing

Box 9.2

Malpractice Considerations

Nursing malpractice is based on the legal premise that a nurse can be held legally responsible for the personal injury of another individual if it can be proven that the injury was the result of negligence.[2] Nursing malpractice is based on four elements: (1) duty, (2) breach of duty, (3) causation (the "but for" test), and (4) damage or injury.

Inappropriate work assignment and inadequate supervision are a breach of duty and could be the basis for finding a nurse's actions to be negligent. Failure or breach of duty to delegate is established by proving that a reasonably prudent nurse would not have made a particular assignment or delegated a certain responsibility or that supervision was inadequate under the circumstances.

The act of improper delegation of tasks or inadequate supervision must be evaluated in light of the "but for" test related to the injury. If the person who performed the injurious act had not been assigned or delegated to perform the task, or had been adequately supervised, the injury could have been avoided. Consequently, the nurse is not being held liable for the negligent act of her subordinate, *but for the lack of competence in performing the independent duties of delegation and supervision.*

Off-Site Consideration

Registered nurses who practice in public health, community, or home care settings must rely frequently on written or telephone communication when delegating patient care duties to assistive personnel. The nurse who must supervise from off site has a particular duty to assess the knowledge, skills, and judgment of the assistive personnel before assignments are made. Regular supervisory visits and impeccable documentation will help the registered nurse ensure that care provided by assistive personnel is adequate.

Source: Aiken, TD: Legal, Ethical, and Political Issues in Nursing. FA Davis, Philadelphia, 1994, 66–69.

professional duties. Malpractice suggests the existence of a professional standard of care and a deviation from that standard of care. A professional **expert witness** is often asked to testify in a malpractice case to help establish the standard of care to which the professional should be held accountable.

A 1988 case in South Dakota presents an example of nursing malpractice. The nurse failed to question the physician's order to discharge a client when she discovered that the client had a fever. In this case, a supervisory nurse provided expert testimony and reported to the judge that the general standard of care for nurses is to report a significant change in a client's condition, such as an elevated temperature. It is the nurse's responsibility to question the physician's order as to appropriateness of discharge.

Issues in Practice

Nurse Malpractice in Client Fall

At a hospital in Washington State, a client with a recent leg amputation was still partially sedated after surgery. The nurse assigned to his care was called away from the room and failed to raise the bed rails. The client attempted to get out of bed, fell, and was injured.

The client sued the hospital for negligence. Using the hospital's own policies and procedures manual, the client's lawyer pointed out the requirement that satisfactory precautions be taken to restrain disabled or sedated clients.

The nurse's lawyer based the defense on the argument that the nurse was following the physician's standing orders to allow the client to ambulate postoperatively to hasten recovery and prevent complications.

The court agreed with the client and concluded that the nurse had an obligation, based on the hospital's policy and procedures, to assess the client's physical and mental condition. Nurses have an obligation to not leave clients unattended in an unsafe bed configuration.

All lawsuits alleging health-care provider negligence require expert witness testimony. Without expert witness testimony, courts will almost always dismiss a negligence case decided by a lay jury, even when it is as obvious as a fall from bed. In this case, the expert testimony not only supported the lawyer's contention that the hospital's policy and procedures upheld the suit, but emphasized the point that clients recently returned from surgery are disoriented from anesthesia and should never be left alone unless the bed rails are raised to their full upright position.

When the case was appealed, the court of appeals wrote the following ruling:

"A lawsuit against a hospital for negligence does not necessarily have to involve medical malpractice committed by a physician. A hospital's nurses have their own independent legal duties in assessing and caring for their patients.

"A hospital is not relieved of its own legal liability for negligence just because the hospital's staff nurses followed the physician's orders. That is, a hospital's nursing staff cannot necessarily rely on a physician's standing orders for a patient to be up and out of bed and leave the bed rails down.

"A patient freshly out of surgery who is taking pain and sedative medications must be evaluated continually by the staff. The patient's present physical and mental state is all that matters. The nurses may have to disregard the physician's standing orders and instead follow the hospital's policies and procedures for a restraint in the form of raised bed rails when necessary to insure the patient's safety."

Source: Greenberg v. Empire Health Services Inc., 2006 WL 1075574 Wash. App., April 25, 2006. Court of Appeals of Washington, April 25, 2006.

The records on this case indicated that the client's elevated temperature was charted after the physician had completed his rounds. The nurse did not notify the physician of the client's fever, and the client was subsequently discharged. The client was readmitted a short time after discharge and died in the hospital. The nurse was found negligent. The court held that negligence can be determined by failure to act as well as by the commission of an act.

Many other types of actions by nurses can produce malpractice lawsuits. Some of the more common actions include:

- Leaving foreign objects inside a client during surgery
- Failing to follow a hospital standard or protocol
- Not using equipment in accordance with the manufacturer's recommendations
- Failing to listen to and respond to client's complaints
- Not properly documenting phone conversations and orders from physicians
- Failing to question physician orders when indicated (e.g., too large medication dosages, inappropriate diets, etc.)
- Failing to clarify poorly written or illegible physician orders
- Failing to assess and observe a client as directed
- Failing to obtain a proper informed consent
- Failing to report a change in a client's condition, such as vital signs, circulatory status, and level of consciousness
- Failing to report another health-care provider's **incompetency** or negligence
- Failing to take actions to provide for a client's safety, such as not cleaning up a liquid spill on the floor that causes a client to fall
- Failing to provide a client with sufficient and appropriate education before discharge

If the Nurse Is Liable

If a nurse is found guilty of malpractice, several types of action may be taken. The nurse may be required to provide monetary compensation to the client for general damages that were a direct result of the injury, including pain, suffering, disability, and disfigurement. In addition, the nurse is often required to pay for special damages that resulted from the injury, such as all involved medical expenses, **out-of-pocket expenses,** and wages lost by the client while he or she was in the hospital.

Optional damages, including those for emotional distress, mental suffering, and counseling expenses that were an outgrowth of the initial injury, may be added to the total settlement. If the client is able to prove that the nurse acted with conscious disregard for the client's safety or acted in a malicious, willful, or wanton manner that produced injury, then an additional assessment of punitive or exemplary damages may be added to the award.

Intentional Torts

An **intentional tort** is generally defined as a willful act that violates another person's rights or property. Intentional torts can be distinguished from malpractice and acts of negligence by the following three requirements: (1) the nurse must intend to bring about the consequences of the act, (2) the nurse's act must be intended to interfere with the client or the client's property, and (3) the act must be a substantial factor in bringing about the injury or consequences.

The most frequently encountered intentional torts are assault, battery, false imprisonment, abandonment, and intentional infliction of emotional distress. With intentional torts, the injured person does not have to prove that an injury has occurred, nor is the opinion of an expert witness required for adjudication. Punitive damages are more likely to be assessed against the nurse in intentional tort cases, and some intentional torts may fall under the criminal law if there is gross violation of the standards of care.

Assault and Battery

Assault is the unjustifiable attempt to touch another person or the threat of doing so. **Battery** is actual harmful or unwarranted contact with another person without his or her consent. Battery is the most common intentional tort seen in the practice of nursing.

For a nurse to commit assault and battery, there must be an absence of consent on the part of the client. Before any procedure can be performed on a competent, alert, and normally oriented client, the client must agree or consent to the procedure being done. Negligence does not have to be proved for a person to be successful in a claim for assault and battery.

A common example of an assault and battery occurs when a nurse physically restrains a client against the client's will and administers an injection against the client's wishes.

False Imprisonment

False imprisonment occurs when a competent client is confined or restrained with intent to prevent him or her from leaving the hospital. The use of restraints alone does not constitute false imprisonment when they are used to maintain the safety of a confused, disoriented, or otherwise incompetent client. In general, mentally impaired clients can be detained against their will only if they are at risk for injuring themselves or others. The use of threats or medications that interfere with the client's ability to leave the facility can also be considered false imprisonment.

Intentional Infliction of Emotional Distress

Intentional infliction of emotional distress is another common intentional tort encountered by the nurse. To prove this intentional tort, the following three elements are necessary: (1) conduct exceeds what is usually accepted by society, (2) the health-care provider's conduct is intended to cause mental distress, and (3) the conduct actually does produce mental distress (causation). Any nurse who is charged with assault, battery, or false imprisonment is also at risk for being charged with infliction of emotional distress.

A 1975 case is an example of infliction of emotional distress. In *Johnson v. Women's Hospital,* a mother wished to view the body of her baby, who had died during birth. After she made the request, she was handed the baby's body floating in a gallon jar of formaldehyde.[1] The Johnson case demonstrates a clear lack of respect shown to the mother. If the mother in this delicate situation had been treated with dignity and respect, the situation would have been avoided.

Client Abandonment

Because of the ongoing nursing shortage, **abandonment** of clients has become an important legal and ethical issue for health-care providers. Abandonment occurs when there is a unilateral severance of the professional relationship with the client without adequate notice and while the requirement for care still exists. The nurse–client relationship continues until it is terminated by mutual consent of both parties.

From an ethical standpoint, the issue of abandonment falls under the umbrella of beneficence. From the legal view, client abandonment can be considered an intentional tort, breach of contract, or in some cases where injury occurs, malpractice. The key phrase to keep in mind when discussing client abandonment is "without adequate notice." If the client knows that the nurse's shift is scheduled to end at 7:00 p.m., then the client and the hospital both have adequate notice.

It is not uncommon for nurses in today's health-care system to be approached by nursing supervisors with the statement, "Everyone else called in, so you will have to work a double shift or you could be charged with client abandonment." In this case, the abandonment becomes the hospital's responsibility, not the nurse's. Nurses sometimes feel uncomfortable about going on strike because it seems to imply client abandonment; however, if there is adequate notice about the strike and if the facility has had time to make arrangements for care or discharge of clients, then there is no client abandonment. The growing practice of emergency client diversion that occurs when facilities can no longer safely care for emergency clients as the result of lack of space or staffing has the potential to fall under the legal definitions of abandonment.

Quasi-Intentional Torts

A **quasi-intentional tort** is a mixture of unintentional and intentional torts. It is defined as a voluntary act that directly causes injury or distress without intent to injure or to cause distress. A quasi-intentional tort does have the elements of volition and causation without the element of intent. Quasi-intentional torts usually involve situations of communication and often violate a person's reputation, personal privacy, or civil rights (Box 9.3).

Defamation of Character

Defamation of character, which is the most common of the quasi-intentional torts, is harmful to a person's reputation. Defamation injures a person's reputation by diminishing the esteem, respect, good will, or confidence that others have for the person. It can be especially damaging when false statements are made about a criminal act or an immoral act or when there are false allegations about a client's having a contagious disease. In *Schessler v. Keck* (1954), a nurse was found liable for defamation of character when she told a friend that a caterer for whom she was caring was being treated for syphilis. Even though the statement was false, when the

Box 9.3
Registered Nurse Licensure

The legislature of each state enacts laws that govern the practice of nursing. The purpose of licensing law is to ensure that the public is protected from unqualified practitioners by developing and enforcing regulations that define who may practice in the profession, the scope of that practice, and the level of education for the profession.

A fundamental premise of nursing practice is that a professional nurse is personally responsible for all acts or omissions undertaken within the scope of practice. The American Nurses Association defines delegation as "the transfer of responsibility for the performance of an activity from one person to another while retaining accountability for the outcome."[1] Additionally, the nurse is responsible for the adequate supervision of a task delegated to a subordinate. If the nurse fails to delegate appropriately or supervise adequately, any injuries resulting from the acts of the subordinate may result in licensure ramifications. The state licensing board may take disciplinary actions.

information became public, it destroyed his catering business.[1]

Defamation includes **slander,** which is spoken communication in which one person discusses another in terms that harm that person's reputation. **Libel** is a written communication in which a person makes statements or uses language that harms another person's reputation. To win a defamation lawsuit against the nurse, the client must prove that the nurse acted maliciously, abused the principle of **privileged communication,** and wrote or spoke a lie.

Medical record documentation is a primary source of defamation of character. Through the years, the client's chart has been the basis of many defamation lawsuits. Discussion about a client in the elevators, cafeteria, and other public areas can also lead to lawsuits for defamation if negative comments are overheard.

Invasion of Privacy

Invasion of privacy is a violation of a person's right to protection against unreasonable and unwarranted interference with one's personal life. To prove that invasion of privacy has occurred, the client must show that (1) the nurse intruded on the client's seclusion and privacy, (2) the intrusion is objectionable to a reasonable and prudent person, (3) the act committed intrudes on private or published facts or pictures of a private nature, and (4) public disclosure of private information was made.[3] Examples of invasion of privacy include using the client's name or picture for the sole advantage of the health-care provider, intruding into the client's private affairs without permission, giving out private client information over the telephone, and publishing information that misrepresents the client's condition. Because of the Health Insurance Portability and Accountability Act (HIPAA) of 1996, health-care providers have become more aware than ever of the issue of confidentiality in the health-care setting.

Breach of Confidentiality

Privileged Communication
Confidentiality of information concerning the client must be honored. A breach of confidentiality results when a client's trust and confidence are violated by public revelation of confidential or privileged communications without the client's consent. Privileged communication is protected by law and exists in certain well-defined professional relationships, for example physician–client, psychiatrist–client, priest–penitent, and lawyer–client.

Privileged communication ensures that the professional who obtains any information from the client cannot be forced to reveal that information, even in a court of law under oath. Nurses do not have privileged communication with clients. However, they can be bound, by extension, under the seal of privileged communication if they are in a room with a physician when the client reveals personal information.

Most breach of confidentiality cases involve a physician's revelation of privileged communications shared by a client. Nurses who overhear privileged communication or information, however, are held to the same standards as a physician with regard to that information.

Privileged client information can only be disclosed if it is authorized by the client. In accord with the HIPAA regulations, all health-care facilities must have specific guidelines dealing with client information disclosure. Disclosure of information to family members violates HIPAA regulations unless the client is under 18 years of age or gives permission for the disclosure. For instance, a client may not wish to disclose to a family member a specific diagnosis, such as cancer. If this is the case, the nurse should honor this request; otherwise, it is considered a violation of HIPAA regulations.

Electronic Pitfalls

Use of computerized documentation and telemedicine has led to several lawsuits based on breach of confidentiality and malpractice. (See Chapter 18 for examples.) The HIPAA regulations are the government's attempts to force the legal system to keep pace with the use of computers and electronic record keeping. Cases exist in which medical records have been lost because of computer failure.

Other issues, such as correction of errors in **charting,** are complicated by use of computers. On paper charts, health-care providers had to draw a line through the erroneous entry, initial the entry, and date it. Many new computerized charting systems have attempted to address the "delete button" issue by including programs that track any changes made in the charting and indicate both date and time of the change.

FACING A LAWSUIT

Because of the rapid proliferation of lawsuits since the 1990s, there is now a higher probability that a nurse, at some time in his or her career, will be involved either as a witness or as a party to a nursing malpractice action. Knowledge of the litigation process increases nurses' understanding of the way in which their conduct is evaluated before the courts.

> "Because of the rapid proliferation of lawsuits since the 1990s, there is now a higher probability that a nurse, at some time in his or her career, will be involved either as a witness or as a party to a nursing malpractice action."

The Statute of Limitations

A malpractice suit against a nurse for negligence must be filed within a specified time. This period, called the **statute of limitations,** generally begins at the time of the injury or when the injury is discovered and lasts until some specified future time. In most states, the limitation period lasts from 1 to 6 years, with the most common duration being 2 years. However, in cases involving children, the statute of limitations extends until the person reaches 21 years of age. If the client fails to file the suit within the prescribed time, the lawsuit will be barred.

The Complaint

Filing the suit (also called the complaint) with the court begins the litigation process. The written complaint describes the incident that initiated the claim of negligence against the nurse. Specific allegations, including the amount of money sought for damages, are also stated in the **legal complaint.** The plaintiff, who is usually a client or a family member of a client, is the alleged injured party, and the defendant (i.e., the nurse, physician, or hospital) is the person or entity being sued. The first notice of a lawsuit occurs when the defendant (nurse) is officially notified or served with the complaint. All defendants are accorded the right of **due process** under constitutional law.

The Answer

The defendant must respond to the allegations stated in the complaint within a specific time frame. This written response by the defendant is called the answer. If the nurse had liability insurance in force at the time of the negligent act, the insurer will assign a lawyer to represent the defendant nurse. In the answer, the nurse can outline specific defenses to the claims against him or her.

The Discovery

After the complaint and answer are filed with the court, the discovery phase of the litigation begins. The purpose of discovery is to uncover all information relevant to the malpractice suit and the incident in question. The nurse may be required to answer a series of questions that relate to the nurse's educational background and emotional state, the incident that led to the lawsuit, and any other information the plaintiff's lawyer deems important. These written questions are called **interrogatories.**

In addition, the plaintiff's lawyer may seek requests for production of documents. These are documents related to the lawsuit, including the plaintiff's medical records, **incident reports, card file,** the institution's policy and procedure manual concerning the specific situation, and the nurse's job description. The plaintiff is also required to disclose information as part of the discovery process that includes the plaintiff's past medical history.

The Deposition

The next step in the process is the taking of a deposition from each party to the lawsuit, as well as any potential witnesses, to assist the lawyers in the trial preparation. A **deposition** is a formal legal process that involves the taking of testimony under oath and is recorded by a court reporter. These are usually wide-ranging in scope and often include information not allowed in a trial, such as **hearsay** testimony. In some cases, videotaped depositions may be used. Nurses can prepare for a deposition by keeping some key points in mind (Box 9.4).

The deposition **testimony** is reduced to a written document called an **affidavit** for use at trial. If a witness during the trial changes testimony from that given at the deposition, the deposition can be used to contradict the testimony. This process is called impeaching the witness. Impeaching a witness on a specific issue can create doubt about that witness's credibility and can thus weaken other areas in the witness's testimony. In some situations, witnesses can later be charged with **perjury** if it is proved that they gave false testimony under oath.

The Trial

The **trial** often takes place years after the complaint was filed. Once **jurisdiction** is determined, the *voir dire* process, more commonly called jury selection, begins. After jury selection, each attorney presents opening statements. The plaintiff's side is presented first. Witnesses may be served with **subpoenas** that require them to appear and provide testimony.

Each witness or party is subject to direct examination, cross-examination, and redirect examination. Direct examination involves open-ended questions by the attorney. Cross-examination is performed by the opposing lawyer, and questions are asked in such a way as to elicit short, specific responses. The redirect examination consists of

Box 9.4

Giving a Deposition

1. Do not volunteer information.
2. Be familiar with the client's medical record and nurse's notes.
3. Remain calm throughout the process and do not be intimidated by the lawyers.
4. Clarify all questions before answering; ask the lawyer to explain the question(s) if you do not understand.
5. Do not make assumptions about the questions.
6. Do not exaggerate answers.
7. Wait at least 5 seconds after a question is asked before answering it to allow objections from other lawyers.
8. Tell the truth.
9. Do not speculate about answers.
10. Speak slowly and clearly, using professional language as much as possible.
11. Look the questioning lawyer in the eye as much as possible.
12. If unable to remember an answer, simply state "I don't remember" or "I don't know."
13. Think before answering any question.
14. Bring a resume or curriculum vitae to the deposition in case it is requested.
15. Request a break if you are tired or confused.
16. Avoid becoming angry with the lawyers or using sarcastic language.
17. Avoid using absolutes in the answers.
18. If a question is asked more than once, ask the court recorder to read the answer given previously.
19. Be sure to read over the deposition just before the trial.

Source: Aiken, TJ, and Catalano, JT: Legal, Ethical, and Political Issues in Nursing. FA Davis, Philadelphia, 1994, pp 87–88.

follow-up questions to address issues that were raised during the cross-examination.

After both parties have presented their case, the lawyers deliver their closing arguments. The case then goes to a jury or a judge for deliberation. If the facts are not in dispute, the judge may render a **summary judgment.** The decision or ruling made about the case can be appealed if either party is not satisfied. The party appealing the decision is called the **appellant.**

POSSIBLE DEFENSES TO A MALPRACTICE SUIT

Contributory Negligence

Damages awarded vary from one state to another and also with the types of injuries sustained. In a state with contributory negligence laws, clients are not allowed to receive money for injuries if they contributed to that injury in any manner. For example, a nurse forgot to raise the bed rail after administering an injection of a narcotic pain medication to a postoperative client but instructed the client to turn on the call light if he wanted to get out of bed. The client fell while attempting to go to the bathroom; because he did not use the call light, he contributed to his own injuries and thus could not receive compensation.

"I SUPPOSE THIS MEANS ANOTHER MALPRACTICE SUIT."

Comparative Negligence

In a state with comparative negligence laws, the awards are based on the determination of the percentage of fault by both parties. For example, in the aforementioned case, if $100,000 was awarded by the jury, it may be determined that the nurse was 75 percent at

fault and the client was 25 percent at fault. In that case, the client would receive $75,000. In general, if the client is 50 percent or more at fault, no award will be made. As can be seen, determination of these types of awards is highly subjective, and an **appeal** about the decision is often made to a higher court.

Case Study

Consider the following case:

Ms. Gouge, a 44-year-old client who weighs 307 lb, was admitted to a large university medical center ED with complaints of chest pain and disorientation and a blood pressure of 208/154 mm Hg. She also displayed aphasia, hemiplegia, and loss of sensation and movement on her right side.

After a magnetic resonance imaging (MRI) scan of the head, it was discovered that she had an inoperable cerebral aneurysm. In addition to appropriate medical treatment for blood pressure and circulation, her family physician told her that she had to lose a significant amount of weight. The nurse in the physician's office instituted a weight loss teaching plan for Ms. Gouge, planned out a calorie-restricted low-fat diet, and gave her a large amount of information about healthy diet and a DVD of low-impact aerobic exercises. At a follow-up visit 1 month later, Ms. Gouge weighed 315 lb.

Six months later, Ms. Gouge's aneurysm ruptured, leaving her in a vegetative state. Ms. Gouge's family filed a lawsuit against the physician and his office nurse, claiming that they had failed to institute proper and appropriate preventive measures and that they had failed to inform the client of the seriousness of her condition.

Did the nurse's decisions or actions contribute to the filing of this suit? Is there any contributory negligence? What is the nurse's role in defending against this suit? What might the nurse have done to prevent the suit in the first place?

Assumption of Risk

When the client signs the informed consent form for a particular treatment, procedure, or surgery, it is implied that he or she is aware of the possible complications of that treatment, procedure, or surgery. Under the assumption-of-risk defense, if one of those listed or named complications occurs, the client has no grounds to sue the health-care provider. For example, a common complication from hip replacement surgery is some loss of mobility and range of motion of the affected leg. Even if a client, after having a hip replaced, is able to walk only using a walker, he or she still does not have any grounds for a lawsuit.

Good Samaritan Act

Health-care providers are sometimes hesitant to provide care at the scene of accidents, in emergency situations, or during disasters because they fear lawsuits. The **Good Samaritan Act** is designed specifically to protect health-care providers in these situations. A health-care professional who provides care in an emergency situation cannot be sued for injuries that may be sustained by the client if that care was given according to established guidelines and was within the scope of the professional's education.

> " *Health-care providers are sometimes hesitant to provide care at the scene of accidents, in emergency situations, or during disasters because they fear lawsuits. The Good Samaritan Act is designed specifically to protect health-care providers in these situations.* "

For example, a nurse who finds a person in cardiac arrest administers cardiopulmonary resuscitation (CPR) to revive the person. In the process, she fractures several of the client's ribs. The client would not be able to sue the nurse for the fractured ribs if the CPR was administered according to established standards.

Good Samaritan laws do, however, have some limitations. They do not cover nurses for grossly negligent acts in the provision of care or for acts outside the nurse's level of education. For example, in the case of a person choking on a piece of meat, the nurse initially attempts the Heimlich maneuver but without success. As the person loses consciousness, the nurse decides to perform a tracheostomy. The client survives but can sue the nurse for injuries from the tracheostomy, because this is not a normal part of a nurse's education.

Unavoidable Accident

Sometimes accidents happen without any contributing causes from the nurse, hospital, or physician. For example, a client is walking in the hall and trips over her own bathrobe. She breaks an ankle. There were no puddles on the floor or obstacles in the hall, and the client was alert and oriented. Because no one is at fault, there are no grounds for a lawsuit.

Defense of the Fact

Defense of the fact is based on the claim that the actions of the nurse followed the standards of care, or that even if the actions were in violation of the standard of care, the actions themselves were not the direct cause of the injury. For example, a nurse wraps a dressing too tightly on a client's foot after surgery. Later, the client loses his eyesight and blames the loss of vision on the nurse's improper dressing of his foot.[4]

Going through the litigation process can produce high levels of anxiety. Placing every aspect of the nurse's conduct under scrutiny in a trial is very stressful. All aspects of the alleged negligent act will be examined and re-examined. Often events that happened years before can be brought in to establish a "pattern of behavior." Every word of the nurse's notes and the medical record will be closely analyzed and questioned. Nurses can survive the litigation process with the help of good attorneys and by being honest and demonstrating that they were acting in the best interests of the clients. From this viewpoint, it is easy to see the importance of carrying nursing liability insurance.

ALTERNATIVE DISPUTE FORUMS

Although most lawsuits against nurses are settled through the court system, there are other methods of settling them. Because of the large number of cases and the resultant overload of the judicial system, other methods of resolving disputes have become increasingly popular. These alternative forums of dispute resolution are being used for many types of conflicts and are seen more frequently in the area of torts, contracts, employment, and family law matters. Mediation and arbitration are the most commonly used alternatives to trial.

Mediation

Mediation is a process that allows each party to present his or her case before a mediator, who is an independent third party trained in dispute resolution. The mediator listens to each side individually. This one-sided session is called a caucus. The mediator's role is to find common ground between the parties and encourage resolution of the disputed matters by compromise and negotiation. The mediator aids the parties in arriving at a mutually acceptable outcome. The mediator does not act as a decision maker, but rather encourages the parties to come to a "meeting of the minds."

Arbitration

Arbitration, in contrast, allows a neutral third party to hear both parties' positions and then make a decision or ruling on the basis of the facts and evidence presented. Arbitration, by agreement or by statutory definition, can be binding or nonbinding. **Arbitrators** or mediators can be, and frequently are, retired judges who work on an hourly-fee basis or practicing attorneys. In the family law area, they are frequently social workers or specially trained mediators. Negligence and malpractice issues are frequently resolved through arbitration and mediation.

COMMON ISSUES IN HEALTH-CARE LITIGATION

Informed Consent

Informed consent is both a legal and an ethical issue. Informed consent is the voluntary permission by a client or by the client's designated proxy to carry out a procedure on the client. Clients' claims that they did not grant informed consent prior to a surgery or invasive procedure can and do form the basis of a small percentage of lawsuits.

Although these lawsuits are most often directed against physicians and hospitals, nurses can become involved when they provide the information but are not performing the procedure. The person who is performing the procedure has the responsibility to obtain the informed consent. However, some physicians have gotten into the habit of giving nurses the consent forms and saying, "Get the client to sign this." Informed consent can only be given by a client after the client receives sufficient information on:

- Treatment proposed
- Material risk involved (potential complications)
- Acceptable alternative treatments
- Outcome hoped for
- Consequences of not having treatment

The physician should provide most of this information. Nurses can reinforce the physician teaching and even supplement the information but should not be the primary or only source of information for the informed consent. It is often difficult to draw a clear distinction between where the physician's responsibility ends and that of the nurse begins.

What Do You Think?

Have you ever had a surgical procedure where you signed an informed consent form? Did it meet all five criteria listed? Which ones were missing?

Exceptions to Informed Consent

There are two exceptions to informed consent:

1. Emergency situations when the client is unconscious, incompetent, or otherwise unable to give consent.
2. Situations where the health-care provider feels that it may be medically contraindicated to disclose the risk and hazards because it may result in illness, severe emotional distress, serious psychological damage, or failure on the part of the client to receive lifesaving treatment.

Patient Self-Determination Act

The Patient Self-Determination Act of 1990, sponsored by Senator John Danforth, is a federal law that requires that all federally funded institutions inform clients of their right to prepare advance directives. The advance directives are meant to encourage people to discuss and document their wishes concerning the type of treatment and care that they want (i.e., life-sustaining treatment) in advance, so that it will ease the burden on their families and providers when it comes time to make such a decision.

> *Nurses can reinforce the physician teaching and even supplement the information but should not be the primary or only source of information for the informed consent. It is often difficult to draw a clear distinction between where the physician's responsibility ends and that of the nurse begins.*

There are two types of advance directives: the living will and the medical durable power of attorney (Box 9.5). The **living will** is a document stating what health care a client will accept or refuse after the client is no longer competent or able to make that decision. The medical durable power of attorney, or health-care proxy, designates another person to make health-care decisions for a person if the client becomes incompetent or unable to make such decisions.

Each state outlines its own requirements for executing and revoking the medical durable power of attorney and living wills.

Box 9.5

Common Questions About Advance Directives

Q. Which is better—a living will or a medical durable power of attorney for health care or health care proxy?

A. The documents are different and allow the nurse to do two different things. The living will states what health-care procedures a client will accept or refuse after the client is no longer competent or able to make that decision. The medical durable power of attorney or health-care proxy allows a client to designate another person to make health-care choices for him or her.

Q. If I change my mind and have a living will, can I cancel the living will or durable medical power of attorney?

A. Yes, each state has ways that your advance directives can be cancelled or negated. Most states require an oral or written statement, destruction of the document itself, or notification to certain individuals, such as the physician. Again, each state's statute should be checked for the specific details required.

Q. If I have a living will in one state, is it good in all states?

A. It may or may not be, depending on that state's requirements for the living will. It is important that you have your living will checked by an attorney to determine whether or not it may be effective in the states in which you are traveling or working.

Q. If I have a living will and have a medical durable power of attorney, who should get copies?

A. Copies should be given to your next of kin, your physician, and your attorney so that more than one person has a copy and knows what your intentions are. Some states will allow you to register your living will with certain state agencies such as the Secretary of State. There are also national groups that will allow you to register your living will with them so that there is access to it.

Nurses must also teach about advance directives and document all critical decisions, discussions with the client and client's family about such decisions, and the basis for the decision-making process.

Incompetent Client's Right to Self-Determination

The courts are protective of incompetent clients and require high standards of proof before allowing a physician to terminate any life-sustaining treatment for that client.

Nancy Cruzan was 30 years old and in a persistent vegetative state. She had a gastrostomy feeding and hydration tube inserted to assist with feedings, which her husband consented to. Her parents, however, petitioned the court for removal of the tube. In the Cruzan case, the court held that the state had the right to err on the side of life. The U.S. Supreme Court recognized that a living will would have been sufficient evidence of Cruzan's wishes to sustain or to remove her feeding tube.

> " *Because laws vary from state to state, it is important that nurses know the laws of the state in which they practice that pertain to advance directives, clients' rights, and the policies and procedures of the institution in which they work.* "

The issue before the U.S. Supreme Court was whether the state of Missouri could use its own standard of clear and convincing proof for removal of the tube or whether there was a 14th Amendment due process guarantee of a "right to die" that would override the state statute. It was decided that the constitutional right would not be extended and the state procedural requirement would be allowed, at which time the burden of proof was put on Cruzan's family to show that she would not have wanted to continue living in this manner.

Many aspects of the Terri Schiavo case in Florida parallel the Cruzan case. In the Schiavo case, after the feeding tube was removed by order of a Florida judge, the U.S. Congress became involved and passed a bill, signed by President George W. Bush, that required the case be heard by the U.S. Supreme Court. The goal was to have the tube reinserted until the high court could rule on the case. It is interesting to note that not much progress has been made in developing legal solutions for this type of case during the 20-plus years since the Cruzan case.

The Nurse's Role in Advance Directives

Because laws vary from state to state, it is important that nurses know the laws of the state in which they practice that pertain to advance directives, clients' rights, and the policies and procedures of the institution in which they work. Nurses must inform clients of their right to formulate advance directives and must realize that not all clients can make such decisions.

It is important for the nurse to establish trust and rapport with a client and the client's family so the nurse can assist them in making decisions that are in the client's best interests. Nurses must also teach about advance directives and document all critical decisions, discussions with the client and client's family about such decisions, and the basis for the decision-making process. Also, it is essential to prevent discrimination against clients and their families based on their decisions regarding their advance directives.

It is important that nurses determine whether or not clients have been coerced into making advance directive decisions against their will. Nurses need to become involved in ethics committees at hospitals or nursing specialty groups at local, state, or national levels to better help clients make decisions about advance directives.

Do-Not-Resuscitate Orders

Protection for the Nurse

Although a do-not-resuscitate (DNR) instruction may be included in an advance directive, DNR orders are legally separate from advance directives. For the health-care professional to be legally protected, there should be a written order for a "no code" or a DNR order in the client's chart.

Each hospital should have a policy and procedure that outlines what is required with regard to a client's condition for a DNR order. The DNR order should be reviewed, evaluated, and reordered. Different facilities have established different time periods for these reviews. Nurses must also know whether there is any law that regulates who should authorize a DNR order for an incompetent client who is no longer able to make this decision. Hospitals often have policies and procedures describing what must be done and which clients fit the requirements for a DNR order. The American Nurses Association (ANA) has published a position statement on nursing care and DNR decisions.

Nurses face many legal dilemmas when dealing with confusing or conflicting DNR orders. For example, it may be difficult to interpret a DNR order when it has been restricted: for instance, "do not resuscitate except for medications and defibrillation" or "no CPR or intubation." Often a lack of proper documentation in the medical records indicating how the DNR decision was reached can be an important and crucial issue if a medical malpractice case is involved and it is disputed whether or not the client or family actually gave consent for a DNR order.

Many facilities have developed DNR decision sheets. A DNR sheet may record information about DNR discussions or be dated and signed by the client and those family members who took part in the discussion. It then becomes a permanent part of the medical record.

Protection for the Client

It is very important that nurses not stigmatize clients by the use of indicators for DNR orders, such as dots on the wristband or over the bed. Health-care providers' attitudes often change because they feel that the client is "going to die anyway." This abandonment can jeopardize the care of a client designated with a DNR order. However, it is also important for the nurses and staff to know whether an order is to be honored, and what the policies and procedures are with regard to transfer clients and DNR orders that accompany the incoming client.

Information about the DNR status of a client should be obtained during shift reports. If there has not been a periodic review, is the order still in effect? If a client is transferred from one facility to another and has a DNR order that is time-limited and has not been reordered, what should a nurse do?

Standards of Care

A Measure of Action

Standards of care is the yardstick that the legal system uses to measure the actions of a nurse involved in a malpractice suit. The underlying principle used to establish standards of care are on the basis of the actions that would likely be taken by a reasonable person (nurse) placed in the same or similar circumstances.

The standard usually includes both objective factors (e.g., the actions to be performed) and subjective factors, including the nurse's emotional and mental state. Specifically, a nurse is judged against the standards that are established within the profession and specialty area of practice. The ANA and specialty groups within the nursing profession, such as the American Association of Critical-Care Nurses (AACN), publish standards of care that are updated continually as health-care technology and practices change.

External Standards. Both external and internal standards govern the conduct of nurses. External standards include nursing standards developed by the ANA, the state nurse practice act of each jurisdiction, criteria from accrediting agencies such as the Joint Commission on Accreditation of Healthcare Organizations, guidelines developed by various nursing specialty practice groups, and federal agency regulations. Nurses are encountering an increasing number of incidents where conflicts occur between institutional and professional standards, for example in staffing ratios. These conflicts are difficult to resolve and may require deliberation and decisions from institutional committees. As a general rule, when a conflict exists, it is safer legally to follow professional standards.

Internal Standards. Internal standards include nursing standards defined in specific hospital policy and procedure manuals that relate to the nurse in the particular institution. The nurse's job description and employment contract are examples of internal nursing standards that define the duty of the nurse.

> *Nurses are encountering an increasing number of incidents where conflicts occur between institutional and professional standards, for example in staffing ratios.*

Bibliography

Billings, DM: Seven steps for test-taking success. American Journal of Nursing 107(4):72, 2007.

Christiaens, G: Strategies for coping with test anxiety. Imprint 51(4):68–69, 2004.

Hickey, B: Help! I failed my first nursing exam! American Nursing Student, 8(6): 2, 2007.

King, N: How to prepare for the certification examination. Insight 29(2):26, 2004.

Ludwig, C: Preparing for certification: Test-taking strategies. Medical Surgical Nursing 13(2):127–128, 2004.

McDonald, M: NLN Assessment and Evaluation Division: Review Guide to RN Pre-Entrance Exam, ed. 2. Jones and Bartlett Publishers, Boston, 2004.

Rollant, PD: "How can I fail the NCLEX-RN with a 3.5 GPA?": Approaches to help this unexpected high-risk group. Annual Review of Nursing Education 14(5):259–273, 2007.

Smith, K: Lifelong learning, professional development, and informatics certification. Computer Informatics Nursing 22(3):172–178, 2004.

11

NCLEX: What You Need to Know

Joseph T. Catalano

Learning Objectives

After completing this chapter, the reader will be able to:

- Describe the NCLEX-RN, CAT test plan.
- Discuss the NCLEX-RN, CAT test format.
- Analyze and identify the different types of questions used on the NCLEX-RN, CAT.
- Select the most appropriate means for preparing for the NCLEX-RN, CAT.

I DON'T WANT TO TAKE THIS EXAM!

The primary purpose of licensure examinations is to protect the public from unsafe or uneducated practitioners of a profession. When you pass the National Council Licensure Examination (NCLEX), it indicates that you have the minimal level of knowledge or competency deemed necessary by the state to practice nursing without injury to clients. Licensure is a legal requirement for all professions that deal with public health, welfare, or safety.

Most people have varying levels of anxiety before taking an exam. The more important the examination, the higher the anxiety levels. Anxiety is sometimes defined as fear of the unknown. This chapter presents key information about the NCLEX test plan to better help you understand and anticipate what you will encounter when you take the exam. It also includes some suggestions for study for the NCLEX and do's and don'ts for the exam itself. This information should help lower your anxiety levels about the NCLEX. Sample practice questions throughout the chapter give you an idea of how the NCLEX asks about different types of nursing information. Try to answer these questions as you read. The answers and rationales are found at the end of the chapter.

NCLEX TEST PLAN

The NCLEX is a computerized, **criterion-referenced examination** that you take after you graduate from a school of nursing. Unlike a **norm-referenced examination,** which bases a passing score on the

Issues Now

Handling Your Anxiety

First, it is perfectly reasonable to be slightly anxious about taking the NCLEX. You have expended plenty of blood, sweat, and tears to come to this point. As one diploma grad told me, "I was in debt up to my ears and running out of money fast when I took the NCLEX. Passing was literally my meal ticket." Even if you're not in such dire financial straits, it's no small thing to be tested on years of accumulated knowledge. You would have to be comatose not to feel butterflies in your stomach at this point. Do not be anxious about being anxious.

Because you cannot go back and change answers, treat each question as an exam in itself; once you hit the enter key the second time, immediately turn your attention to the next question. Tell yourself not to be surprised by anything. You are at a psychological disadvantage if you expect the computer to turn off at a certain number and it doesn't. So if you can, avoid looking at the question number as you answer each question.

If you are distracted by the clicking of other people's computers or other such annoying sounds, you can ask for earplugs. The testing service provides them; they are disposable and not entirely unattractive.

Finally, there are going to be other people close to you or next to you who may sit down at the computer at the same time as you do. They may get up before you, but ignore them. The testing centers administer many different tests, so you can realistically tell yourself that the person next to you who finished in 45 minutes was not even taking the NCLEX. Even if they were taking the NCLEX, you do not need to think about it. A little denial in this situation can go a long way.

Source: Dunham, KS: How to Survive and Maybe Even Love Nursing School. FA Davis, Philadelphia, 2001, pp. 180–181, with permission.

scores of others who took the exam, criterion-referenced examinations compare your knowledge to a pre-established standard. If you meet or exceed the standard, you pass. The NCLEX measures nursing knowledge of a wide range of subject matter, but mostly measures your ability to think critically and make good sound judgments about nursing care. With computerized adaptive tests such as the NCLEX, the computer selects questions in accordance with the examination plan and how you answered the previous questions.

Changes in the Test Plan

Over the years since its institution, several substantive changes were made in the NCLEX Computerized Adaptive Testing for Registered Nurses (NCLEX-RN, CAT) test plan. The changes included reorganization of the test plan into three primary components: (1) client needs, (2) level of cognitive ability, and (3) integrated concepts and processes. The third component was expanded to include nursing process, caring, communication, cultural awareness, documentation, self-care, and teaching and learning.

Over the years since its introduction, additional changes have been made to the test format, the test vendor sites, and the percentages of questions in the various needs categories. Alternative format questions were added (discussed following), and the length of time allowed to complete the exam was increased from 5 hours to 6 hours. The number of pharmacology questions also increased (up to 19 percent), and the difficulty level was raised in 2007 (discussed below).

Client Health Needs

The NCLEX asks questions about four general groups of material called client health needs:

• Safe and effective care environment
• Physiological integrity
• Psychosocial integrity
• Health promotion and maintenance needs

Safe and Effective Care Environment (21–33 percent)

a. Management of care: 13 to 19 percent of NCLEX questions
b. Safety and infection control: 8 to 14 percent of NCLEX questions

The questions in this category make up between 21 and 33 percent of the total questions on the NCLEX. These questions deal with overt safety issues in client care, such as use of restraints, medication administration, safety measures to prevent injuries (such as putting up side rails), prevention of infections, isolation precautions, safety measures with pediatric clients, and special safety needs of clients with psychiatric problems.

This needs category also includes questions about laboratory tests, their results, and any special nursing measures associated with them; legal and ethical issues in nursing; a small amount of nursing management; and quality assurance issues. Questions on these issues are interspersed with other questions throughout the examination.

Physiological Integrity (43–67 percent)

a. Basic care and comfort: 6 to 12 percent of NCLEX questions
b. Pharmacological and parenteral therapies: 13 to 19 percent of NCLEX questions
c. Reduction of risk potential: 13 to 19 percent of NCLEX questions
d. Physiological adaptation: 11 to 17 percent of NCLEX questions

The physiological integrity needs are concerned with adult medical and surgical nursing care, pediatrics, and **gerontology.** This category comprises the largest groups of questions, with about 43 to 67 percent of the total number of questions on the NCLEX. The more common health-care problems, both acute and chronic conditions, that nurses deal with on a daily basis include:

• Diabetes
• Cardiovascular disorders
• Neurological disorders
• Renal diseases
• Respiratory diseases
• Traumatic injuries
• Immunological disorders
• Skin and infective diseases

There are also questions about nursing care of the pediatric client, including such topics as:

• Growth and development
• Congenital abnormalities
• Child abuse
• Burn injury

• Fractures and cast and traction care
• Common infective diseases in children
• Common childhood trauma such as eye injuries

Psychosocial Integrity (6–12 percent)

a. Coping and adaptation: 5 to 11 percent of NCLEX questions
b. Psychosocial adaptation: 5 to 11 percent of NCLEX questions

Psychosocial integrity needs are health-care issues that revolve around the client with psychiatric problems. This material also deals with coping mechanisms for high-stress situations such as acute illness and life-threatening diseases or trauma. These clients do not necessarily have any psychiatric disorders. This category constitutes at most 12 percent of the examination and includes questions about the care of clients with eating disorders, personality disorders, anxiety disorders, depression, schizophrenia, and organic mental disease. Also included in the psychosocial needs

> *Being able to remember and understand information is the most basic way of learning. Although this type of knowledge is important and underlies the other levels of knowledge, it is not sufficient to ensure safe nursing care.*

section are questions about therapeutic communication, crisis intervention, and substance abuse.

Health Promotion and Maintenance (6–12 percent)

a. Life span growth and development: 7 to 12 percent of NCLEX questions
b. Prevention and early detection of disease: 5 to 11 percent of NCLEX questions

Health promotion and maintenance needs deal with birth control measures, pregnancy, labor and delivery, the care of the newborn infant, growth and development, and contagious diseases, particularly sexually transmitted diseases. This section constitutes approximately 12 percent of the total examination. Teaching and counseling are important parts of the nurse's care during pregnancy, and knowledge of diet, signs and symptoms of complications, fetal development, and testing used during pregnancy is necessary.

Levels of Cognitive Ability

The level of cognitive ability is a component of the NCLEX that measures how information has been learned and how it can be used by the nurse. For the NCLEX, knowledge is tested at three different levels.

Level 1

Level 1 consists of knowledge and comprehension questions. Fewer than 10 percent of the questions are at this level; however, there is a good chance that you may not see any level 1 question. These questions involve recalling specific facts and the ability to understand those facts in relationship to a pathophysiological condition; they cover knowledge of specific anatomy and physiology, medication dosage and side effects, signs and symptoms of diseases, laboratory test results, and the elements of certain treatments and interventions.

Being able to remember and understand information is the most basic way of learning. Although this type of knowledge is important and underlies the other levels of knowledge, it is not

"These are my Health Promotion tutors."

sufficient to ensure safe nursing care. An example of a level 1 question is:

1. A client is admitted to the medical unit with respiratory failure. Identify the normal range for the Po_2.
   a. 10–30 mm Hg
   b. 35–55 mm Hg
   c. 10–20 cm H_2O
   d. 70–100 mm Hg

Level 2

Level 2 questions add an additional step to the answering process. These questions presume that you have the basic information memorized and then ask you to analyze, interpret, and apply information to specific situations. Analysis and application questions are more difficult to answer because they require you to do more than simply repeat the information you have read or heard in class. Analysis requires the ability to separate information into its basic parts, decide which of those parts are important, and then make a decision about what the information is telling you. Application requires that you be able to use that information in client care decisions.

Some examples of this type of question involve interpreting electrocardiographic (ECG) strips, interpreting blood gas values, making a nursing diagnosis based on a set of symptoms, or deciding on a treatment plan. These questions provide a better indication of your ability to safely care for clients. An example of a level 2 question is:

2. A client is becoming progressively short of breath. The results of his arterial blood gas (ABG) tests are pH, 7.13; Po_2, 48; Pco_2, 53; and Hco_3, 26. What do these values indicate?
   a. Metabolic acidosis
   b. Respiratory alkalosis
   c. Respiratory acidosis
   d. Metabolic alkalosis

Level 3

Level 3—synthesis, judgment, and evaluation—takes the process a step further. More than 90 percent of the questions on the NCLEX are at either level 2 or level 3. Questions at the synthesis and judgment level ask you to process information on more than one fact; apply rules, methods, principles, or theories to a situation; *and* make judgments and decisions about client care. The way you can identify these higher-level questions is by recognizing that they require you be able to

process two or more facts, concepts, theories, rules, or principles of care before you can answer the question.

One factor that adds to the difficulty of answering level 3–type questions is that there is often more than one correct answer. You may be asked to choose the best, or highest priority, answer from among several correct answers. Questions at this level often ask about the priority of care to be given, the priority of nursing diagnosis formulated, how to best evaluate the effectiveness of care you are giving, and the most appropriate nursing action to be taken. Your ability to make decisions about nursing care at these higher levels is the best indication of your critical thinking ability and best demonstrates the ability to provide safe nursing care. Three examples of level 3 questions are:

3. A client is becoming progressively short of breath. The results of his arterial blood gas (ABG) tests are pH, 7.13; Po_2, 48; Pco_2, 53; and Hco_3, 26. What action should the nurse take first?
   a. Call a code blue and begin cardiopulmonary resuscitation.
   b. Call the physician and report the condition.
   c. Make sure the client's airway is open and begin supplemental oxygen.
   d. Give the ordered dose of 200 mg aminophylline intravenous piggyback (IVPB) now.

4. After receiving shift report at 0645, identify the client the nurse should assess first.
   a. 65-year-old man with stable angina
   b. 37-year-old woman with possible GI bleeding; vital signs stable
   c. 56-year-old woman with COPD and an oxygen saturation of 89%
   d. 19-year-old man with type 1 diabetes and a fasting blood sugar of 55 mg/dL

5. The nurse assesses a 7-month-old hospitalized girl and finds that the infant has a positive tonic neck reflex. What intervention would be most important for the nurse to include in the child's nursing care plan?
   a. Daily head circumference measurements
   b. Measure intake and weigh all diapers
   c. Position the infant on her back for naps
   d. Assess neuro/developmental levels each shift

Integrated Concepts and Processes

The integrated concepts and processes component includes the following:

* Nursing process
* Concepts of caring

• Therapeutic communication
• Cultural awareness
• Documentation
• Self-care
• Teaching and learning

These concepts are integrated throughout the examination and are included as elements in the four needs categories.

Nursing Process

The nursing process has traditionally been a very important part of the NCLEX. The NCLEX-RN, CAT uses the five-step nursing process: assessment, analysis, planning, intervention and implementation, and evaluation. Each of the questions you will be asked on the NCLEX falls into one of these five categories.

It is important that you keep in mind the steps of the nursing process when answering questions. Often questions that ask, "What should the nurse do first?" are looking for an assessment-type answer because that is the first step in the nursing process. Questions on the nursing process are no longer equally divided on the examination. Recent analysis has shown a higher percentage of questions in the implementation phase of the nursing process.

ASSESSMENT. The **assessment** phase primarily establishes the database on which the rest of the nursing process is built. Some components of the assessment phase include both subjective and objective data about the client, significant history, history of the present illness, signs and symptoms, environmental elements, laboratory values, and vital signs. Often the examination will ask you to distinguish between appropriate and inappropriate assessment factors. An example of an assessment phase question is:

6. What would be the most important information for the nurse to obtain when a client is admitted for evaluation of recurrent episodes of Stokes-Adams syndrome?
   a. Ability to perform aerobic exercises for 15 minutes
   b. Bradycardia and increases in blood pressure
   c. Changes in level of consciousness
   d. Ability to discuss fat and sodium diet restrictions

ANALYSIS. The analysis phase of the nursing process involves developing and using nursing

diagnosis for the care of the client. The NCLEX uses the North American Nursing Diagnosis Association (NANDA) nursing diagnosis system. Questions concerning nursing diagnosis will often ask you to prioritize the diagnoses. (See Chapter 10 for information about prioritization). An example of an analysis phase question is:

7. A client is admitted to the unit with a diagnosis of bronchitis, congestive heart failure, and fever. The nurse assesses him as having a temperature of 101.8°F, peripheral edema, dyspnea, and rhonchi. The following nursing diagnoses are all appropriate, but which one has the highest priority?
   a. Anxiety related to fear of hospitalization
   b. Ineffective airway clearance related to retained secretions
   c. Fluid volume excess related to third spacing of fluid (edema)
   d. Ineffective thermoregulation related to fever

PLANNING. The **planning** phase of the nursing process primarily involves setting goals for the client. Included in the planning phase are such factors as determining expected outcomes, setting priorities for goals, and anticipating client needs based on the assessment. These questions may ask you to identify the most appropriate goal or may ask you to identify the highest-priority goal from several appropriate goals. You can prioritize goals the same way you did the nursing diagnosis. Remember that a good goal is measurable, client centered, time limited, and realistic. An example of a planning phase question is:

8. A client is found to be in respiratory failure and is placed on oxygen. Which goal has the highest priority for this client?
   a. Walk the length of the hall twice during a nurse's shift.
   b. Complete his bath and morning care before breakfast.
   c. Maintain an oxygen saturation of 90% throughout the shift.
   d. Keep the head of the bed elevated to promote proper ventilation.

INTERVENTION AND IMPLEMENTATION. The **intervention** and **implementation** phase of the nursing process involves identifying nursing actions that are required to meet the goals stated in the planning phase. Some of the material in the intervention and implementation phase includes:

- Provision of nursing care based on the client's goals
- Prevention of injury or spread of disease
- Therapy with medications and their administration
- Giving treatments
- Carrying out procedures
- Charting and record keeping
- Teaching about health care
- Monitoring changes in condition

An example of an intervention and implementation phase question is:

9. When the nurse ambulates a client who has been on bedrest for 3 days, he suddenly becomes very restless, displays extreme dyspnea, and complains of chest pain. Select the most appropriate nursing action.
   a. Call a code blue.
   b. Continue to help the client walk, but at a slower pace.
   c. Give the client an injection of his ordered pain medication.
   d. Return the client to bed and evaluate his vital signs and lung sounds.

> *Contrary to rumor, no graduates are randomly selected to take all 265 questions.*

EVALUATION. The **evaluation** phase of the nursing process determines whether or not the goals stated in the planning phase have been met through the interventions. The evaluation phase also ties the nursing process together and makes it cyclic. If the goals have been achieved, it is an indication that the plan and implementation were effective, and new goals need to be established. If the goals were not met, then you have to go back and find the difficulty. Were the assessment data inadequate? Were the goals defective? Was there a deficiency in the implementation?

Evaluation is a continual process. Material in the evaluation phase includes comparison of actual outcomes with expected outcomes, verification of assessment data, evaluation of nursing actions and client responses, and evaluation of the client's level of knowledge and understanding. Evaluation questions are often worded very similarly and are relatively easy to identify after you have

experienced a few of them. An example of an evaluation question is:

10. A client is being prepared for discharge. He is to take theophylline by mouth at home for his lung disease. Which statement by the client indicates to the nurse that her teaching concerning theophylline medications has been effective?
    a. "I can stop taking this medication when I feel better."
    b. "If I have difficulty swallowing the time-released capsules, I can crush them or chew them."
    c. "If I have a lot of nausea and vomiting or become restless and can't sleep, I need to call my physician."
    d. "I need to drink more coffee and cola while I am on these medications."

NCLEX FORMAT

You will take the NCLEX examination on a personal computer at a Pearson Professional Center (Fig. 11.1). The majority of the questions are in a multiple-choice format and are constructed similarly. They include a client situation, a question stem, and four answers, or distractors, like the sample questions you have seen so far in this chapter.

All the multiple-choice questions on the NCLEX stand alone, although a similar situation may be repeated. Occasionally a single question may be included without a case situation.

Choosing the Right Answer

For the multiple-choice questions, you are asked to select the one best answer from among the four possible choices. No partial credit is given for a "close" answer; there is only one correct answer for any particular question. The questions are totally integrated from the content areas that were previously discussed along with the approximate percentages that were identified. Each question carries an equal weight or value toward the final score.

When the question appears on the screen, read the question and answers using the process described in Chapter 10. When you decide what the correct answer is, place the cursor in the circle in

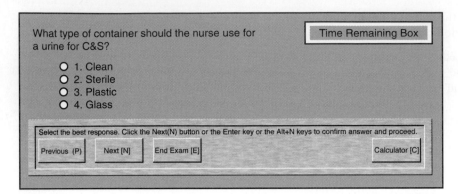

Figure 11.1 Sample multiple-choice question. Select the answer by placing the cursor in the circle and click or type in the answer. Change the answer by placing the cursor in a new circle and click. Move to the next question by clicking on the "Next (N)" button at the bottom of the screen.

front of the answer, and click (Fig. 11.1). This selects the answer. If you decide to change the answer (not a good idea; see Chapter 10), place the cursor on the answer you selected and click again. It will remove the indicator and you can move the cursor to another answer. When you are sure you have selected the correct answer, click the "N" next button on the button bar at the bottom of the screen. That question will disappear and a new one will appear. You cannot go back and change an answer after you click the "N" next button.

Alternative Format Questions

In 2004, alternative format questions were added to the exam. The latest information on these questions is that between 2 and 10 percent of the total number of questions will be alternative format and that each graduate will have at least two of them on the exam.

There are several types of these questions. They are scored like the multiple-choice questions in that they are either correct or incorrect (no partial credit). They are also given a difficulty rating based on the same criteria as the multiple-choice questions. If you want to practice these types of questions, go to www.ncsb.org/testing, where you will find several examples, or obtain one of several books that contain alternative format questions. Most of the NCLEX review books now have samples of these questions for students to practice.

Fill in the Blank

These alternative format questions may ask for a range of information. They may be calculation questions or ask for knowledge. After you read the questions, you need to type the answer in the box provided (Fig. 11.2). If it is a calculation question, you may use the pop-up calculator, accessible by

clicking the cursor on the "C" calculator button on the button bar (Fig. 11.3). After you have typed in your answer, you can go back and change it. Once you have decided that it is correct, click on the "N" next button and a new question will appear.

Multiple Answers

With the multiple-answer format questions, you are given a list of options or answers and must select all that are correct. You must get them all correct in order to get credit for the question. To select the options you think are correct, place the cursor in the circle or box before the option and click (Fig. 11.4). If you decide that one of the options is not really the one you want, you can click on the circle again and it will be removed. When you decide you have the options you want, click on the "N" next button and the next question will appear on the screen.

Sequencing Items

Sequencing format questions provide you with a question and then four or more options (items) that are related to the question. Your task with this type of question is to place them in the proper sequence (Fig. 11.5). You do this by selecting the circle or box in front of the option you think is number one and typing in "1." Then move to the option you believe is number two and type that number in, and so forth. You can change the numbering by clicking on the boxes to remove the numbers.

A variation on this type of question uses the "drag and drop" format. With drag and drop, you will be given a series of items in a box on the left side of the screen. You will be asked to sequence them by clicking on them one at a time and putting them in the proper order in a box on the right-hand side of the screen. When you have the options

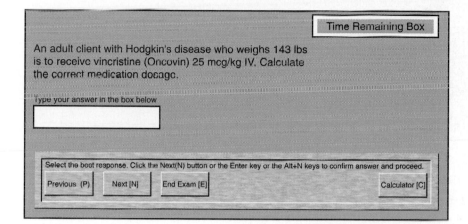

Figure 11.2 Alternative format question. Fill in the blank by clicking on the "Calculator (0)" button at the lower right corner of the bar.

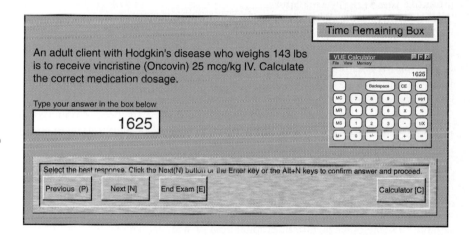

Figure 11.3 Alternative format question. Fill in the blank by using the calculator to click on number buttons. Then type in the answer box. Do *not* use spaces or commas in the answer. Close the calculator by clicking on the "X" button on the calculator screen.

Figure 11.4 Alternative format question—multiple answer.

> Time Remaining Box
>
> Identify the proper sequence for assessment of the abdomen starting with the number 1 for the first assessment. Type the number in the box before the statement.
>
> [3] Percussion
> [1] Inspection
> [4] Palpation
> [2] Auscultation
>
> Select the best response. Click the Next(N) button or the Enter key or the Alt+N keys to confirm answer and proceed.
>
> Previous (P)   Next [N]   End Exam [E]   Calculator [C]

Figure 11.5 Alternative format question—sequencing items.

sequenced the way you think they should be, click on the "N" next button on the button bar and a new question will appear on the screen.

Identify the Area (or Hot Spot)

These types of questions provide you with a picture or diagram and then ask you to identify an area or a structure on the picture (Fig. 11.6). You place the cursor on the area that you think is correct and click. An "X" will appear. If you decide that is not where you really want the "X" you can click on the "X" again to remove it and then place the cursor in a new spot and click again. Once you decide that you have it where you want it, click on the "N" next button and the next question will appear on the screen.

Chart/Exhibit Items

A chart or exhibit item will present you with a chart, graph, or some other picture or graphic item or with a series of charts, graphs, or other pictures. You will need to be able to read the chart, graph, or picture to obtain the information to answer the question. Then

you will be asked to select the correct answer from four or more options by using the information you gleaned from the chart, graph, or picture.

How Many Questions?

You may take between 75 and 265 questions, depending on how you answer. Of the first 75 questions, only 60 count. The other 15 are "trial" questions that will be used on future examinations, but you do not know which ones do not count, so you need to do the best you can on all of them. The National Council of State Boards of Nursing (NCSBN) is attempting to establish reliability and validity data on these questions.

If you seem to be getting a lot of questions in a particular category, for example pediatrics, it may mean one of two things. The NCSBN may be testing pediatric questions on your exam so you are receiving a lot of them, or it may mean that you are having some problems answering pediatric questions correctly. The computer will continue to give you questions in a particular content area until you meet

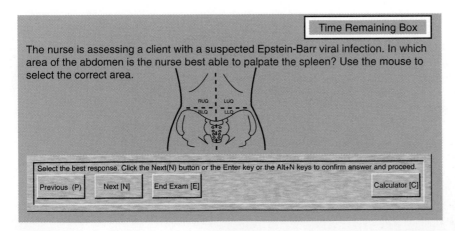

> Time Remaining Box
>
> The nurse is assessing a client with a suspected Epstein-Barr viral infection. In which area of the abdomen is the nurse best able to palpate the spleen? Use the mouse to select the correct area.
>
> RUQ   LUQ
> RLQ   LLQ
>
> Select the best response. Click the Next(N) button or the Enter key or the Alt+N keys to confirm answer and proceed.
>
> Previous (P)   Next [N]   End Exam [E]   Calculator [C]

Figure 11.6 Alternative format question—identify area. With this type of question, you are given a diagram or picture and asked to locate a structure or area. Place the cursor on the area you think is correct and click. An "X" will appear in that area. To deselect the answer, click on the "X" and move the cursor to the new area. When finished, click on "Next (N)."

the goals of the test plan. The computer randomly draws the questions you are seeing from a pool of more than 4000 questions.

The NCSBN, which is responsible for designing the test publicly, states that no graduates are randomly selected by the computer to take all 265 questions. You can pass or fail the test with either 75 or 265 questions or any number in between. The average number of questions taken over the past 5 years is 119, and the average time is just over 2 hours.

How Long It Takes

There is a maximum time limit of 6 hours for the entire examination, although there is no minimum time limit. There is a mandatory break where the computer "locks up" about $2\frac{1}{2}$ hours into the test. For 10 minutes, you will not be able to answer any questions. There is another optional break at about 4 hours into the test, although the computer will not lock up at this time. You can take breaks at any time during the exam if you need to use the restroom, but remember that you will lose this time off your total time for the exam.

The exam is not really timed except for the overall time limit. Theoretically you could sit at the computer for the full 6 hours with question number 1 on the screen. The computer does not make you take questions at any particular rate. Most people can answer a multiple-choice question in about 45 seconds. As a rule of thumb, if you are spending more than 2 minutes on any single question, put an answer down and move on to the next question.

If you calculate that you are going to take 265 questions in 6 hours, it comes out to about 80 seconds per question. Some of the alternative format questions may take a little longer to answer, although some may take less time than the multiple-choice questions. Take a watch along and keep an eye on the "Time Remaining" box at the top of the screen.

How It's Graded

The test is graded on a statistical model that compares your responses with a pre-established standard. If you can demonstrate a knowledge level consistently above the standard, you will pass the examination.

Because the NCLEX-RN examination is given by computerized adaptive testing (CAT), increases in the passing standard do not necessarily require the graduate to answer a higher number of items correctly. However, it does require that you answer questions correctly at a slightly higher difficulty level than last year's graduates. Questions are assigned a difficulty value on a seven-logit (unit) scale called the NCLEX-RN logistic scale, ranging from the easiest (−3), which all graduates should answer correctly, to the most difficult (3), which almost all graduates would be expected to miss (Box 11.1).

Level of Difficulty

The difficulty level of the questions is determined by the question writers and question reviewers and is based on factors such as when the material is usually presented in nursing programs (material presented earlier is considered less difficult) and the complexity of the material. To you, the test taker, difficulty level is somewhat relative. If you know the answer to a question, then it will seem relatively easy to you even if it is classified by the test writers as a higher difficulty-level question. Similarly, if you do not know the answer, then that question will be difficult for you even if it is determined to be at a relatively low difficulty level.

No Happy Questions. Keep in mind also that there are no "happy" questions on the NCLEX. There is always something wrong, and if there is a problem in the question, you need to worry about it. Also, as a general guiding principle, anything you know really well from your classes will NOT be on the NCLEX, so anticipate difficult questions.

Box 11.1

NCLEX-RN Logistic Scale

Logits	
3	Most difficult
2	
1	
0	Approximate pass level
−1	
−2	
−3	Least difficult

After you finish the mandatory tutorial on the use of the computer, the first real question you will see will be at a medium difficulty level, probably a little above or a little below the pass criteria. If you answer it correctly, the next question will be a little more difficult. If you answer that one correctly, the next question will also increase in difficulty and so forth until you start missing questions. Then the computer will give you slightly less difficult questions. The computer is trying to establish your "zone of knowledge." If that zone is above the pass standard, then you will pass the exam.

Your Zone of Knowledge. If you miss the first question, and many graduates do because of anxiety, the computer will give you a slightly easier question for number 2. If you answer that one correctly, then the next one will increase in difficulty level, and so forth until you start missing questions. If the computer can clearly determine your zone of knowledge within the first 75 questions, then it will stop the test and ask you to complete a short survey.

The reason many graduates take more than 75 questions is because the computer is having difficulty establishing a clear zone of knowledge above or below the pass standard. It will keep giving questions until a clear determination is made. Graduates who take all 265 questions have answered questions above and below the pass standard throughout the whole exam. If you do have to take all 265 questions, it does not necessarily mean you failed.

EXAMPLE: LOW DIFFICULTY LEVEL

11. What blood test does the nurse evaluate as the best measure of a client's long-term control of diabetes mellitus?
    a. Fasting blood sugar
    b. Arterial blood gases
    c. Glucose tolerance test (GTT)
    d. Glycosylated hemoglobin (Hgb A_1C)

EXAMPLE: MID-DIFFICULTY LEVEL (PASS CRITERIA)

12. While evaluating the results of a pulmonary function test, the nurse notes that an adult man who is short of breath has a vital capacity of 2800 mL, a tidal volume of 375 mL, and a residual volume of 2200 mL. Select the action the nurse should avoid implementing for this client.
    a. Position the client with the head of the bed elevated 45 degrees.
    b. Encourage fluid intake of 2 to 3 liters per 24 hours.
    c. Begin oxygen by nonrebreather mask.
    d. Encourage the client to cough and to breathe deeply every hour during the shift.

EXAMPLE: HIGH DIFFICULTY LEVEL

13. While monitoring a client with a pulmonary artery catheter, the nurse notes catheter fling artifact on the pressure tracing. Identify the nursing measure that best compensates for this problem.
    a. Record only mean pressures.
    b. Ask the physician to reposition the catheter.
    c. Irrigate the catheter forcefully with heparinized saline solution.
    d. Level and zero the transducer before taking readings.

> *Keep in mind that the NCLEX is designed so that no one can answer all the questions correctly. Even your most knowledgeable nursing instructor would not be able to answer some of the questions on the exam.*

Remember that it is probably a good sign that you are getting difficult questions. It means that you are answering questions above the pass standard. You do not want a lot of easy questions on the NCLEX. Also keep in mind that the NCLEX is designed so that no one can answer all the questions correctly. Even your most knowledgeable nursing instructor would not be able to answer some of the questions on the exam.

However, the NCLEX asks "entry-level" type questions that tend to be very "text-bookish." When you are answering NCLEX questions, look for the expected textbook-type knowledge. Don't look for exceptions. Each examination is different and unique to the person taking it because future questions depend on how you answered previous questions.

NCLEX BACKGROUND INFORMATION

Revisions in the Passing Standard

Passing standards are established by a nine-nurse panel of National Council members that includes diverse representation (i.e., regional, nursing specialty, minority, educator, new RNs). Their efforts combine with a survey of nursing professionals, such as nursing administrators of all types of facilities and directors of nursing. After consideration of all the data, including current trends in health care, the National Council Board of Directors may determine that safe entry-level practice for RNs requires a higher level of knowledge, skills, and abilities than was required in previous years.

The passing standard and test content are generally evaluated on a 3-year cycle, but revisions are not made every cycle. The National Council last revised the passing standard of the NCLEX-RN, CAT in 2007. Generally the national average pass rate drops by about 4 percent whenever there is an increase in the difficulty level.

Test Vendor and Logistics

The test vendor for the NCLEX is VUE, a subsidiary of NCS Pearson Professional Centers. The tests are given at Pearson Professional Centers. The test items and the format of the examination always stay the same, even if vendors change, because the exam is owned by the NCSBN, which contracts with vendors to administer the examination.

After you graduate from your nursing program, you must apply to the state board of nursing for permission to take the NCLEX. Once you have been approved by the State Board, that information is sent on to the NCSBN, which sends you an "authorization to test" card or document. You will receive your authorization document more quickly if you select the "e-mail" option on the application form for the examination.

You then call for an appointment at the center where you wish to take the test. Appointments are made on a first-come, first-served basis The centers are required to schedule the examination within 30 days from the time you apply. Each state establishes its own maximum time interval for the graduate to take the exam after graduation, usually 1 year.

There are both morning and afternoon sessions of 6-hour duration. Depending on the size of the center, between 8 and 15 graduates may be taking the test at the same time. There may be other people at the center taking examinations in other disciplines at the same time as the nursing graduates.

Testing by Computer

The computer skills required are minimal. The mouse is used for the majority of the examination, with minimal typing required. A digital picture is taken at the time you enter the examination room, and that picture, along with your information, appears on one of the computer screens in the room. A digital thumb print and signature are also obtained when you enter the exam center.

You sit at the computer with your picture on it and complete a tutorial on the use of the mouse and computer. You have two attempts at completing the tutorial successfully. If you are unable to do so after the second try, a person who is working at the testing center will come and help you. After the examination is completed, you will be asked to complete a short computerized personal data questionnaire and an evaluation of the examination site.

Questions appear one at a time on the computer screen, with a button bar on the bottom of the screen and a "time remaining" box in the upper corner. After you select an answer, the question is replaced with another question and answers. No question is ever repeated, nor are you able to change the answer once you have clicked on the "N" (Next) button.

An on-screen pop-up calculator is available for answering dosage and other questions that require calculations. Because of the increased emphasis on pharmacology and the concern about medication errors, it is probably safe to assume that the difficulty level of future calculation questions will increase markedly.

Security

Security is very tight at the examination sites. All exam sessions are videotaped and there is a proctor in the room monitoring all the test takers. Although cheating on the NCLEX is virtually impossible— every examination is different—it is important not to even look as if you are attempting to cheat. Do not talk to the person next to you. Keep your eyes on your own computer. Do not take out any papers or electronic devices during the exam. Magic slates are generally provided for use as "scrap paper," so you will not need any paper or pens during the exam. Lockers are provided and you must leave all your personal belongings at the door, so do not bring a lot of things with you to the examination site.

How the Test Is Graded

The NCLEX is graded on a pass–fail basis. If the graduate has failed, the entire examination must be taken again. The NCSBN requires a 45 day waiting period before repeating the examination, and first-time takers are given preference over those who are repeating the examination. A number of states have restricted the number of times the graduate can retake the test, usually to three. Check with your state board of nursing for the particular regulations.

When the computer shuts off, it knows if you passed or failed, but it will not give you that information at that time. At the end of the day, after the last testing session, results are downloaded electronically to NCSBN in Chicago. The next business day, NCSBN notifies the state board of nursing electronically and sends hard copy; then it is up to the state board of nursing to notify you.

The exam results may be sent to you by mail, usually within 7 to 10 days after the exam has been completed, although this time frame varies from state to state. Most states now offer online results within 72 hours after the exam. Check with your state board of nursing to make sure they offer this service and how to access the site. The NCSBN offers a service that allows you to obtain unofficial results by telephone 3 days after you take the examination. The telephone number is 900-225-6000; the cost for the call is $7.95. You can also access the NCSBN on the Web at www.nclex.com/store.asp. Not all states participate in the service, and your employment agency may or may not accept the results.

NCLEX STUDY STRATEGIES

There are several ways to prepare for examinations, including the NCLEX. To attempt to take the examination with an attitude of "If I don't know it by now, I never will" is to court failure. Carefully directed study and preparation will considerably increase the chances of passing the examination. Review Chapter 10 for general tips on how to study for and take exams. Below is some specific information for preparation for the NCLEX.

The NCSBN Web Site

You can access the NCBSN Web site at www.ncsbn.org. This Web site can provide significant help as you prepare to take the NCLEX. It provides the most recent information on any changes in the test, has a sample tutorial about the exam, and even has some sample questions. You can also access

sample examination questions at www.vue.com/nclex. The more you learn about the exam before you have to take it, the lower your anxiety and the better you will do.

Review Books

The material covered by review books is the key material found on the NCLEX. These books usually follow the NCLEX Test Plan very closely. A review book is, however, just that; it reviews the material that you should already know. Reviewing is important to reinforce learning and recall of information you may not have used in a year or more.

What Do You Think?

When was the last time you sat in on a group study session? List three of the problems you encountered at the session. How could they be solved?

_____

_____

_____

_____

_____

_____

_____

_____

_____

_____

_____

_____

Review books are not really designed to present any new information about key material. If you are totally unfamiliar with the material in a particular section of the review book, then reading a more comprehensive textbook on that particular subject area will be necessary.

Another important function of a review book is to point out areas of weakness. If you find a section that seems to contain "new" material, it is important to investigate that section in more detail. If you find most of the material familiar and easy to grasp, then you are probably well on your way to success on the NCLEX.

Group Study

Group study can be an effective method of preparation for an examination such as the NCLEX. To optimize the results of group study sessions, several rules should be followed.

Rule 1. *Be very selective when choosing the members of the study group.* They should have a similar frame of mind and orientation toward studying. They should be graduates who are also going to be taking the NCLEX. The ideal size for a study group is between four and six people. Groups larger than six become difficult to organize and handle. After the group has been formed and has begun its study sessions, it may be necessary to ask an individual to leave the group for not participating or for being disruptive to the study process or displaying negative attitudes about the examination.

Rule 2. *Have each individual prepare a particular section for each group study session.* Study groups generally meet once or twice a week. For example, if next week the group is going to study the endocrine system, assign group member 1 the anatomy and physiology of the system, member 2 the pathological conditions, member 3 the medications used for treatment, and member 4 the key elements of nursing care. When the group comes together, have each individual present his or her prepared section. This type of preparation prevents the "What are we going to study tonight?" syndrome that often plagues group study sessions.

Following this process organizes the study group and allows for more in-depth coverage of the topic. It also permits the members of the group to ask questions of the other members, thereby reinforcing the information being discussed.

Rule 3. *Limit the length of the study session.* No single study session should be longer than between 60 and 90 minutes. Sessions that go longer tend to get off the topic and foster a negative attitude about the examination. Try to avoid making group study sessions into party time. A few snacks and refreshments may be helpful to maintain the group's energy level, but a real party atmosphere will detract significantly from the effectiveness of the study session.

Rule 4. *Use role-playing to reinforce information.* The more senses you can involve in the learning process, the better the learning.

Rule 5. *Remain positive.* Although group study times should not be party times, relax and have some fun with the study.

Individual Study Tips

No matter what other study and preparation methods are used, individual preparation for the NCLEX is a necessity. This preparation can take several forms.

> *No matter what other study and preparation methods are used, individual preparation for the NCLEX is a necessity.*

> *Experts recommend that you take between 3000 and 5000 practice questions before you take the NCLEX. Obviously starting early in this process is important along with some planning and time management.*

Tip 1. As previously discussed, use of a review book is valuable to indicate areas of deficient knowledge. Reading and studying the appropriate textbooks and study guides can be helpful if it is approached correctly. It is important that the graduate mentally organize the information being read into a format similar to that found in the NCLEX. After reading each page of a textbook or study guide, the graduate should be able to ask three or four multiple-choice questions about that information. These questions can be asked silently or written out and should answer the question "How might the NCLEX test my knowledge of this material?"

Tip 2. Take practice exams on the computer. Practice answering questions similar to those found on the exam you are going to take or the NCLEX itself. Most of the review books come with a CD that has practice questions on it. It will help alleviate some of the unknowns, particularly if you have not had a lot of experience with computer-based exams.

Learning the Format. Experts recommend that you take between 3000 and 5000 practice questions before you take the NCLEX. Try to take at least 1000 questions using a computerized format. Obviously, starting early in this process is important, along with some planning and time management. When practice questions are answered, several important mental processes occur.

Getting Comfortable. First, you are becoming more familiar with and therefore more comfortable with the format of the examination. In research, this process is termed the practice effect; it must be accounted for when analyzing the results from pretest/post-test types of research projects. Individuals will have better results after a test, even without any type of intervention, because of having practiced answering questions on the pretest. Similarly, your score on the NCLEX may increase by as much as 10 percent through answering practice questions.

Reinforcing Information. A second result of answering practice questions is that it reinforces the information already studied. Although it is unlikely that a question on the NCLEX examination will be identical to a practice question, there are many similarities. Realistically, only a limited number of questions can be asked about any given subject. After a while, the questions will begin to sound very similar.

Identifying Weak Spots. A third advantage of answering practice questions is that it quickly reveals subject areas that you will need to study. It is relatively easy to say, "I understand the renal system pretty well." It is quite another to answer correctly 10 or 15 questions about that system. If you answer the questions correctly, then you can move on to the next topic. If you miss the majority of the questions, however, then further review is required.

In order to obtain the optimal benefit from working practice questions, it is probably best to spend 30 to 45 minutes each day working 20 to 100 questions rather than trying to do 1000 questions on one day during the weekend.

After you have answered the questions, you need to review them and compare your answers with the answers provided in the study book. You should also look at the rationales and the categories into which the questions fall. Try to understand why you missed the questions you did. Was it lack of knowledge? Didn't read the question carefully? Didn't use critical thinking?

Tip 3. Complete a 265-item test in one sitting in 6 hours. Many Web sites provide testing materials and sample examinations. One is http://passneclex.mcphu.eduwww.sjsu.edu/depts/itl/graphics/main.html.

Tip 4. Take the NCLEX as soon as possible after you graduate. The NCSBN has done some studies that show the following:

- The NCLEX taken less than 26 days after graduation has an 89 percent average pass rate.
- The NCLEX taken between 27 and 39 days after graduation has an 80 percent average pass rate.
- The NCLEX taken between 40 and 62 days after graduation has a 72 percent average pass rate.
- The NCLEX taken more than 62 days after graduation has a 45 percent average pass rate.

Formal NCLEX Reviews

The NCSBN does not endorse or sponsor any review courses for the NCLEX directly, but many companies offer reviews shortly after graduation. An online comprehensive review course for the NCLEX-RN examination on the NCSBN Web site is offered by an independent company (http://www.nclex.com). These review courses range from 2 to 5 days and basically cover the information found in review books. They are rather expensive, and the quality of NCLEX reviews varies. In general they are only as good as the people who are presenting the material. Also, look at the reported pass rate of the graduates after they take the review. Those with higher pass rates are probably better.

PREPARING FOR THE BIG DAY

Several Months to A Week Before the Exam

1. Get mentally and physically prepared. Eat a good healthy diet; emphasize foods with protein, vitamin K, and calcium. These foods have been shown to help control long-term stress.

Exercise regularly. Drink lots of water (64 ounces per day) to rid your body of accumulated toxins. Avoid alcohol, street drugs, and even over-the-counter medications like antihistamines that can affect your ability to concentrate and think. Ease off on the caffeine and stop smoking.

2. Practice doing NCLEX type questions—lots of them!
3. Avoid major life-altering activities, such as buying a car or planning a wedding, major vacation, or baby shower!

The Day Before the Exam

1. Don't work. Most employers understand that the NCLEX produces anxiety and are willing to let you have the day off. If your stress levels are high, it may be difficult for you to concentrate on your work, possibly compromising the health and well-being of your clients.
2. Do something fun and relaxing, but don't overdo it. Activities that involve some moderate exercise will help with anxiety levels.
3. Eat citrus fruits or drink liquids with vitamin C. Vitamin C has been shown to decrease short-term stress.
4. If you are unfamiliar with the area where the test center is located, drive to the test site. Note parking facilities and places where you can get a meal. This preparation will save you from getting lost the next day and help you be on time.

The Night Before the Exam

1. Make sure you have all the materials you will need for the exam, including two forms of picture ID, authorization to test card, and Social Security card.
2. Review formulas, common medications, information that can be summarized in tables, or on cards and lists. It is probably not a good time to pull out all your old textbooks and notes and try to read them. Concentrate on things that are visual and may have caused you some problems in the past, like the list of cranial nerves or the glands and hormones in the endocrine system. Don't try to study everything. The "If I don't know it now, I never will" attitude is a negative thought process. You can always learn something.
3. Avoid strange or exotic foods that you have never eaten before. This can be a real temptation if you have to travel away from home and stay in a hotel the night before the exam. Stick to your usual diet. New or unusual foods may cause some gastrointestinal consequences that can be very distracting during the exam.
4. Go to bed at a reasonable hour. It is probably best to stick to your normal schedule. Staying up all night trying to study is counterproductive. You will be nervous and may have some problems sleeping, but stay away from sleep aids. They will interfere with your decision-making ability on the exam. Even if you are not sound asleep, the fact that you are resting will be helpful.

The Day of the Exam

1. Stick to your regular schedule and routine as much as possible. Avoid drinking excessive amounts of caffeine or sugary beverages to try to stay awake. They will only make you nervous and may increase the amount of time you need to spend on breaks in the restroom.
2. Eat breakfast, especially if you are scheduled for the morning session. Eat something with some glucose for a quick start (bread with jelly) and something with protein to get you through the morning (cereal and milk; egg and bacon). Drink some cinnamon tea, eat some lemon drop candies, or chew some peppermint gum. These flavors have been reported to enhance learning and sharpen thought processes! If you are taking the exam in the afternoon, eat lunch, but avoid a large meal with a lot of greasy food. It will make you sleepy and sit in your stomach like a lump.
3. Don't let the security at the site fluster you. They will take a digital picture, thumbprint, and signature. They will make you leave all your belongings in lockers at the door. Someone will

be walking around the room during the exam. Just concentrate on your computer and answer the questions and you will do fine (see "Issues Now" box).

4. Wear comfortable clothes. You don't get extra points on the NCLEX for looking like a fashion model. Dress appropriately for the season, but keep in mind that some buildings are cool in the summer because of air conditioning and hot in the winter because of heating systems. Wear something you have worn before. Sweat clothes are a good choice, particularly because you can dress in layers. If you feel too warm, you can take a jacket off; if you feel cold, you can leave it on.

5. Think positive! If you truly believe you will do well, you will do well. If you go into the exam with an "I'm never going to pass this—I'm too dumb" attitude, you probably are not going to do as well.

Conclusion

Taking and passing the NCLEX-RN, CAT is a necessary step in the process of becoming a professional registered nurse. Like all licensure examinations, its purpose is to protect the public from undereducated or unsafe practitioners. The examination is comprehensive and includes material from all areas of the graduate's nursing education. Although most graduates have some anxiety about taking this examination, knowledge about its format and content and strategies for taking the examination can lower anxiety to an acceptable level.

Critical Thinking Exercises

- Obtain an NCLEX-RN, CAT review book. Analyze the questions in the practice examination for type, cognitive level, and level of difficulty.
- Identify three to five other students in your class with whom you would feel comfortable working in a study group. Organize a study group session before the next major course examination.
- When you get the results of your next course examination, identify why you missed the questions you missed and what strategies might have been used to answer those questions correctly.

Box 12.9

Symptoms of Burnout

- Extreme fatigue
- Exhaustion
- Frequent illness
- Overeating
- Headaches
- Sleeping problems
- Physical complaints
- Alcohol abuse
- Mood swings
- Emotional displays
- Anxiety
- Poor-quality work
- Anger
- Guilt
- Depression

elements are present in the nurse's work situation. It is possible to recognize nurses who are in the early stages of burnout by identifying some classic behaviors (Box 12.9).

How It Starts

One of the earliest indications of burnout is the attitude that work is something to be tolerated, rather than eagerly anticipated. Nurses in the early stages of burnout often are irritable, impatient, cynical, pessimistic, whiny, or callous toward coworkers and clients. These pre-burnout nurses take frequent sick days, are chronically late for their shifts, drink too much, eat too much, and often are not able to sleep.

Eventually, as their idealism erodes, their work suffers. They become careless in the performance of their duties, uncooperative with their colleagues, and unable to concentrate on what they are doing, and they display a general attitude of boredom and **apathy.** If allowed to continue, burnout may lead to feelings of helplessness, powerlessness, purposelessness, and guilt.[9]

Avoiding Burnout

Despite this bleak picture, nurses do not have to fall victim to the burnout syndrome. Many nurses practice their profession for many years, manage to deal with the stress, and find great personal satisfaction in what they do. These satisfied and

motivated nurses have developed ways to deal with the stress of their careers while maintaining their goals and purpose as nurses.

The first step in dealing with burnout is to be able to recognize its signs. Many nurses who are burning out use denial and rationalization to block recognition of burnout, because it is just too painful for them to think they put so much time, money, and effort into preparing for a career they no longer want or enjoy. It is important to realize that it is not the career that is producing the burnout, but rather the difficulty in coping with the stresses the career is producing. Although it may not be possible to change the requirements of the profession significantly, it is possible to learn how to cope more effectively with stress.

Manage Stress and Time

Although there are many schools of thought about stress- and time-management techniques, several common threads run through many of these theories. These views include setting personal goals, identifying problems, and using strategies for problem solving.

Set Personal Goals

Goals and goal setting are an important part of client care. Nursing students—and, by extension, practicing nurses—are highly proficient in the planning stage of the nursing process, in which goal setting is the primary task. They know that a good set of goals should be client centered, time oriented, and measurable and that they should write these goals with every care plan they prepare.

In their personal lives, however, these nurses may rush full tilt into one erratic day after another, subordinating their own needs to the needs of others and working long, hard hours, but without accomplishing very much and feeling frustrated about it. What is the problem here? Very simply, nurses can prepare realistic, beneficial goals for their clients, but they seem to be unable to do the same for themselves.

Long-Term Goals

Personal goals should include both long-term and short-term goals. Typically, personal long-term goals look into the future at least 10 years and include a statement about what the nurse wants to achieve during his or her lifetime. Some examples are going back to school to obtain an advanced degree, becoming a director of nursing, or even writing a book about nursing.

Practicing nurses who are caught up in the whirlwind of everyday life find it difficult to formulate statements about the future. One other important characteristic of long-term goals is that they need to be flexible. As life circumstances change, modifications are required.

Short-Term Goals

Short-term goals are those that the nurse expects to accomplish in 6 months to 2 years. These goals should be aimed primarily at making the nurse's professional or personal life more satisfying and fulfilling. Like long-term goals, they do not need to be related to work. Perhaps visiting a foreign country, going on a skiing trip in the mountains, and even learning how to paint a picture or play the piano may be achievable in a relatively short time. In the professional realm, joining a professional organization, becoming a head nurse, or changing an outdated hospital policy are goals that can be achieved in a short time. The fact that everyone ages over time cannot be altered, but that time can also be used to achieve personal satisfaction in life and increase knowledge and accomplishments.

An End Achieved

Although goal setting is an important first step in dealing with the stress that leads to burnout, any good nurse recognizes that a plan without implementation is useless. As difficult as goal setting may be for nurses, carrying it out may be even more difficult. Although goal achievement requires a degree of hard work and personal sacrifice, when people are working toward something they really want, the effort that it takes to achieve the end actually becomes enjoyable. At first glance, this process may seem like a lot of work (and it is), but it becomes an exciting adventure in its own right.

Identifying Problems

Another important step in dealing with burnout is to identify the problems that are producing the stress. Again, nurses are taught as students that they need to identify client problems so they can work toward solving them.

Self-Diagnosis

Formulation of a nursing diagnosis is nothing more than precisely stating a client's problem. One thing nurses realize early in the learning process is that what may appear to be an obvious problem may in reality not be a problem at all. Conversely, something that a client only mentions in passing may turn out to be the real source of the client's nursing needs. Perhaps nurses should look at their own lives and attempt to formulate nursing diagnoses that deal with their stress-related problems (setting the North American Nursing Diagnosis Association list aside).

What Do You Think?

List three tasks that you have put off today. Why did you avoid doing these? How can you get them done sooner?

_____

_____

_____

_____

_____

_____

_____

_____

_____

_____

_____

_____

_____

> " *It is important to realize that it is not the career that is producing the burnout, but rather the difficulty in coping with the stresses the career is producing.* "

For example, a new graduate has just completed a shift during which he was assigned to eight complete-care clients. He has had to supervise two badly prepared nurses' aides and has put in 55 minutes of overtime (for which he will not be paid) to complete the charting. This nurse is feeling tired, frustrated, and even a little bit guilty because of an inability to provide the type of care that he was taught in nursing school.

What is the problem? A possible nursing diagnosis might be: Alterations in personal satisfaction related to excessive workload, evidenced by sore feet, headache, shaky hands, feelings of guilt, frustration, and a small paycheck.

Goals and Interventions

Now that the problem has been identified, goals and interventions can be introduced to solve the problem. The goals may range from organizing time better to refusing to take care of so many complete-care clients. Interventions, depending on the goals, can include activities such as attending a time-management seminar, talking to the head nurse, or changing a policy in the policy and procedure book.

RESPONDING TO MAJOR STRESSFUL EVENTS

Crisis Intervention

Although nurses often learn how to deal with the stresses routinely found in their daily work, major traumatic events that produce overwhelming stress, such as the devastation of the World Trade Center Towers or Hurricane Katrina, may leave nurses with a sense of horror, helplessness, and powerlessness in addition to the normal stress responses of shock, disbelief, anger, and grief. Nurses do have a number of skills that help them deal with traumatic events in their workplace; however they are not super-people and should not expect that they can handle all stressful events without help. The end result may well be a complex of symptoms similar to burnout syndrome, including physical symptoms, depression, and chronic anxiety.

In response to major tragedies in recent years, the critical incident stress debriefing (CISD) process was developed to help health-care providers deal with major acts of violence and traumatic disasters. The American Red Cross has been instrumental in training and providing resources for local CISD teams. These are made up of mental health professionals specially trained in crisis intervention, stress management, and treating post-traumatic stress disorder (PTSD).

To be most effective, the CISD teams need to be on site within 2 to 3 days after serious events ranging from the death of coworkers to acts of terrorism and natural disasters, such as tornadoes.

The goal of the team is to encourage the participants to verbalize their feelings and thoughts, identify and develop their coping skills, and generally lower overall grief and anxiety levels. It is an intensive stress management course compressed into a few hours or few days.

Post-Traumatic Stress Disorder

One of the keys to working with nurses is to help them recognize that they are not expected to be able to handle all situations and can appropriately ask for help. Although nurses study the stress response and grieving process in school, it is sometimes hard for them to apply information about normal stress reactions to themselves. When nurses do not recognize their own problems in responding to traumatic stress, they increase their risk for developing long-term stress reactions. When they do not seek help, they can develop the symptoms of post-traumatic stress disorder (PTSD) anywhere from a few days to as long as 6 months after the event.

Warning signs of PTSD include:

1. Recurring nightmares and inability to sleep
2. Intrusive and vivid flashbacks
3. Prolonged depression
4. High levels of anxiety
5. Maladaptive coping behaviors, such as drug and alcohol abuse

The CISD session generally requires up to 3 hours. Sessions can be longer or shorter depending on the nature of the event and number of people affected. Besides having an opportunity to express emotions and feeling, the participants are educated in some ways about reducing anxiety and promoting mental and physical health. Advice includes:

1. Not watching televised replays of the event over and over
2. Staying with friends as much as possible
3. Avoiding unhealthy, high-fat diets
4. Engaging in regular aerobic exercise as much as possible
5. Avoiding excessive dependence on alcohol and drugs for sleep
6. Getting back to a comfortable routine as soon as possible
7. Feeling comfortable seeking professional help when it is needed

During the CISD sessions, nurses are asked for their input about the process. If the team feels it is necessary, additional referrals for long-term treatment may be recommended.

STRATEGIES FOR PROBLEM SOLVING

Nurses already know the nursing process as a client problem-solving technique. Why not apply the same knowledge and skills to personal problems? The stress level only increases if problems are left unsolved.

Although specific problems may require specific solutions, several widely accepted methods exist to deal with the general stresses produced by everyday work and personal life. Included in these methods are activities such as recognizing that nurses are only human, improving time-management skills, practicing what is preached, and decompression.

Time-Management Skills

In modern life there is often not enough time to do everything that needs to be done. The key to time management is setting priorities. In the world of nursing and client care, nurses are often required to do many tasks. Multitasking, the process of doing several tasks at the same time, tends to fragment the nurse's attention and concentration.

Nurses need to recognize that only some nursing activities are essential to the safety and well-being of clients. These include thorough assessment and ensuring that the clients get their medications on time, that their comfort needs are met, and that accidental injuries are prevented. Beyond these actions, nurses really have a great deal of discretion in what they can do when providing care to clients.

Make Room for Fulfillment

Burnout results mainly from personal and professional dissatisfaction. If nurses feel fulfilled in what they are doing, burnout is much less likely to occur. Activities that may increase nurses' satisfaction include spending time talking with clients, learning new skills, and decreasing the anxiety of families through teaching and listening. After such activities have been identified, time should be set aside for them during the shift. The real secret in using time management to prevent burnout is for the nurse to use the time left for those nursing activities that bring the most professional and personal satisfaction.

Several skills need to be developed to be able to allow time during a shift for these preferred activities. First, the nurse must learn to delegate by letting the licensed practical nurses (LPNs) or aides do those tasks they are supposed to be able to do. Many nurses graduate from nursing school with the attitude that if you want it done right, you need to do it yourself. After becoming familiar with the LPN's and nurse's aide job descriptions, nurses need to give others a chance to prove themselves.[10]

Overcome Procrastination

Another necessary skill is overcoming procrastination. Most people have a natural tendency toward procrastination, particularly when unpleasant or difficult tasks are involved. The primary reasons people postpone or delay doing something are that they either do not want to begin or do not know where to begin the task. More time and energy are expended in inventing excuses for putting off tasks than would be taken in doing the task.

The Most Distasteful Task. The best way to overcome procrastination is by starting the task, even if it is only a small step. An effective method is to select the most distasteful task to be done that day and to commit just 5 minutes to it. After 5 minutes are over, the task can be either set aside or continued. It is very likely that once the task is started and momentum builds, the task will be carried out to completion.

Tasks can be prioritized by listing them in three categories. Category A tasks (e.g., assessments, passing out medications, treatments, and dressing changes) are important and need to be completed on time. Category B tasks (e.g., baths, linen changes, lunch breaks, charting) are important, but can be postponed until later in the shift. Category C tasks (e.g., cleaning up, organizing the supply room) are tasks that can either be delegated or wait until the next day.

Problems Don't Solve Themselves. For daily tasks, both pleasant and unpleasant, the best time to do them is immediately. If achievement of the plan requires delegation, then it needs to be done at the beginning of the shift, not at the middle or end of the shift. Often nurses have a built-in fear of taking chances. As a result, they avoid doing things if there is a chance of failure, in the hope that somehow the problem will resolve itself.

Any time an important decision is made, there is a chance that someone will disagree or that the decision will be incorrect. These types of situations need to be viewed as a challenge or an opportunity rather than a life-altering risk to be avoided. Although mistakes in health care do have the potential to be fatal, learning from mistakes is one of the most fundamental ways of increasing knowledge.

Time management, like other skills, requires some practice. Once a nurse masters this skill, his or her life becomes more satisfying.

Practicing What You Preach

Because nursing is oriented toward keeping people healthy as well as curing illness, nurses spend a large amount of their time teaching clients about eating well; getting enough sleep; going for regular dental, eye, and physical examinations; avoiding too much drinking and smoking; and exercising regularly. It might make an interesting student research project to have nurses rank themselves on how well they have incorporated these health maintenance activities in their own lives. The results would probably indicate a low overall score on the "practice what you preach" scale.

Nurses know all about the food pyramid, but they do not translate that knowledge into feeding themselves properly. In reality, there are going to be some busy days when it is impossible to eat right, but it should be possible, on a regular basis, to follow a diet that will promote health and reduce the buildup of fat plaques in the arteries.

It is important to get enough sleep to avoid chronic fatigue. People can adjust to a state of fatigue, but it tends to decrease the enjoyment that they find in life, as well as make them irritable, careless, and inefficient. Most people need between 5 and 8 hours of good sleep each night. It also probably would not hurt for nurses to take a short nap during the afternoon on their days off.

The Right Kind of Exercise

Many nurses feel they get enough exercise during their busy shifts, and, in truth, the average staff nurse walks between 2 and 5 miles during each 8-hour shift. Unfortunately, this type of walking does not qualify as the type of aerobic exercise recommended for an improved cardiovascular condition. Exercise, in order to be beneficial, must be done consistently and must raise the heart rate above the normal range for an extended period. The short sprint-type walking involved in client care does not accomplish this goal.

> *Tension must be released or it will eventually cause a major explosion or (if turned inward) produce anxiety.*

Walking 1 to 2 miles a day outside of work is a beneficial, simple exercise that will improve health. Nurses can also use a wide variety of exercise equipment for those days when walking outside is undesirable. The important requirement is that the exercise be done consistently and frequently. Regular exercise not only improves the cardiovascular system but also helps improve stamina, raise self-image, and promote a general sense of well-being.

Decompression Time

The profession of nursing is stressful, even under ideal circumstances. Nurses are required to deal with other people constantly and to carry out numerous tasks that are potentially dangerous. At the end of any shift, even the most skilled and best-organized nurse has a sense of internal tension. This tension must be released or it will eventually cause a major explosion or (if turned inward) produce anxiety.

Establish a Daily Decompression Routine

It may take a little time to discover, through trial and error, what works to reduce the tension built up during the shift. Some effective techniques include setting aside approximately 30 minutes of private, quiet time to dream and reflect about the day's activities. Perhaps relaxing in a tub of hot soapy water or sitting in a favorite reclining chair might meet the need for decompression. Relaxation activities, such as swimming, shopping, or even going for a drive, can help reduce tension and act as a time for decompression. Of course, stress-management techniques learned at seminars (e.g., self-hypnosis or meditation) can be used by those who have developed these skills. Finally, meeting with a nurse support group can help the nurse vent feelings and make constructive plans for solving problems.

Conclusion

Although transition shock and burnout are realities of the nursing profession, they can be reduced or even avoided altogether. Nurses should be able to recognize the causes and early symptoms of transition shock and burnout to prevent them from developing into a problem. Therefore, nurses should use techniques to prevent these disorders from becoming insurmountable obstacles. In doing so, nurses will be able to practice their profession proficiently and gain the satisfaction that only nursing can provide.

Critical Thinking Exercises

- Make a list of the characteristics that would be found in the "perfect nurse." Make a second list of characteristics found in nurses observed in actual practice. Discuss how and why these lists differ.
- Outline a plan for implementing a preceptor clinical experience for the senior class of a nursing program. Make sure to include how many hours of practice are required, criteria for the selection of preceptors, student objectives from the experience, and methods of evaluation.
- Write at least three long-term and five short-term personal or professional goals. Develop a realistic plan and time frame for achieving these goals. Make sure to include what is required to achieve these goals.
- Complete this statement, using as many examples as possible: "I feel most satisfied when I am done with my shift in knowing that..." Analyze these answers and discuss how they can be implemented in everyday practice.
- Think of at least three situations in which you were asked to do something that you really did not want to do. How did you handle these situations? How could they be handled in a more assertive manner?

References

1. Mennick, F, and Kennedy, MS: In the news: Good news, bad news on the nursing shortage: Nursing school enrollment continues to rise, but who will teach them? American Journal of Nursing 107(4):22, 2007.

2. National survey: RNs struggle to balance work and home life. Nursing 36(12):33, 2006.

3. Buerhaus, PI: Impact of the nurse shortage on hospital patient care: Comparative perspectives. Health Affairs 26(3): 853–862, 2007.

4. Bruce, TJ: Online tutors as a solution to the shortage of nurse practitioner educators. Nurse Educator 32(3): 122–125, 2007.

5. Cockerell, P: Applicant's secrets are few in internet age. Daily Oklahoman 115: 6D–7D, November 27, 2006.

6. Jones, JM: ePortfolios in nursing education: Not your mother's resume. Annual Review of Nursing Education 13(50): 245–258, 2007.

7. Cockerell, P: Business cards out: Icons, thlogs are in. Daily Oklahoman 115: 1A, 6A, November 27, 2006.

8. Vinje, HF: Job engagement's paradoxical role in nurse burnout. Nursing & Health Sciences 9(2): 107–111, 2007.

9. Browning, L: Nursing specialty and burnout, Health and Medicine 12(2): 248–254, 2007.

10. Cohen-Katz, J: The effects of mindfulness-based stress reduction on nurse stress and burnout: A quantitative and qualitative study. Holistic Nursing Practice 18(6): 302–308, 2004.

Bibliography

Bartram, T: Factors affecting the job stress and job satisfaction of Australian nurses: Implications for recruitment and retention. Contemporary Nurse 17(3):293–304, 2004.

Chatterjee, M: Nursing staff shortages are putting patients in danger. Nursing Times 100(45): 4, 2004.

Corcoran, J: Learning portfolios: Evidence of learning: An examination of students' perspectives. Nursing in Critical Care 9(5): 230–237, 2004.

Endacott, R: Using portfolios in the assessment of learning and competence: The impact of four models. Nurse Educational Practices 4(4): 250–257, 2004.

Jenkins, R: Stressors, burnout and social support: Nurses in acute mental health settings. Journal of Advanced Nursing 48(6): 622–631, 2004.

Leichtling, B: Leadership & management: Preventive medicine for "compassion [sic] fatigue." Caring 23(10): 90–91, 2004.

Lemin-Stone, K: Careers: Learn to manage your stress levels. Nursing Times 100(46): 74–75, 2004.

Lipley, N: How many staff is enough? Emergency Nurse 12(7): 5, 2004.

Lupoli, J: The impact of technology on the "older" nurse. Home Health Nurse 22(10): 668–670, 2004.

O'Dowd, A: Global nurse shortages are "staggering." Nursing Times 100(46): 5, 2004.

Raiger, J: Applying a cultural lens to the concept of burnout. Journal of Transcultural Nursing 16(1): 71–76, 2005.

Sanner, T: Using telehealth to address the nursing shortage. Home Health Nurse 22(10): 695–702, 2004.

Santucci, J: Facilitating the transition into nursing practice: Concepts and strategies for mentoring new graduates. Journal of Nurses Staff Development 20(6): 274–284, 2004.

Schaffer, M, et al.: Using portfolios to evaluate achievement of population-based public health nursing competencies in baccalaureate nursing students. Nursing Education Perspectives 26(2): 104–112, 2005.

3

Leading and Managing

13

Principles of Leadership and Management

Joseph T. Catalano

Learning Objectives

After completing this chapter, the reader will be able to:

- Identify and discuss the three major theories used to explain leadership.
- Define and distinguish between the three styles of leadership.
- Discuss the relationship of transformational and situational theories to leadership style.
- Identify the key behaviors and qualities of effective leaders.
- Distinguish the differences between management and leadership.
- Identify and discuss the two major theories of management.

In today's health-care system, even new graduates who have an "RN" after their name will be placed quickly in positions of leadership and management.

LEADERSHIP

The old saying that "leaders are born, not made" implies that at birth a person either is a leader or is forever relegated to the rank of follower. Not many agree with this statement. Although some people may have an easier time filling the leadership role than others, most experts believe that almost everyone can develop leadership skills.

Many definitions of leadership refer to the ability of an individual to influence the behavior of others. When nurses exert leadership, they inspire other health-care workers to work toward one or more of several goals that include providing high-quality client care, maintaining a safe working environment, developing new policies and procedures, and increasing the power of the profession.

Some leadership theories try to explain why some people are leaders and others are not, but as yet none covers all the possibilities. That may be because leadership requirements differ according to the situation. In the intensive care unit (ICU), for example, where quick decisions are a matter of life and death, the leader is the nurse with highly developed critical thinking and analytical skills and the confidence to make decisions under pressure. In quality management, where the problems are often long term and complicated, the leader tends to be well organized and can methodically sift through a mountain of information and statistics to develop a policy that covers the widest range of possibilities. Several of the better-known leadership theories are discussed here.

Trait Theory

The trait theory identifies qualities that are common to effective leaders (Box 13.1). Trait theory by itself is limited, because it focuses only on the traits of the individual and does not take into account how

Box 13.1
Leadership Traits

- High level of intelligence and skill
- Self-motivation and initiative
- Ability to communicate well
- Self-confidence and assertiveness
- Creativity
- Persistence
- Stress tolerance
- Willingness to take risks
- Ability to accept criticism

the person acts in specific situations. The question left unanswered is why everyone who has these traits does not become a leader.[1]

Leadership-Style Theory

One of the best-known theories of leadership looks at three leadership styles:

1. Laissez-faire
2. Democratic
3. Authoritarian

Although these theories are discussed separately, they are a continuum of leadership style ranging from a mostly passive approach to a highly controlling one (Table 13.1).

> *The old saying that 'leaders are born, not made' implies that at birth a person either is a leader or is forever relegated to the rank of follower.*

The Laissez-Faire Style

The **laissez-faire** (French for "leave it alone") leadership style is also described as permissive, nondirective, or passive. The laissez-faire style leader allows the group he or she is leading to determine their own goals and the methods to achieve them. There is little planning, minimal decision making, and a lack of involvement by the leader. This style works well in only a few settings, for example, in a research laboratory that is staffed by self-motivated scientists who know what they want to achieve and are familiar with the means of achieving it.

The laissez-faire style works best when the members of the group have the same level of education as the leader and the leader performs the same tasks as the group members. In most situations, however, the laissez-faire leadership style can leave people feeling lost and frustrated because of the lack of direction by the leader. When they do try to achieve some goal, often the only input from the leader is that they are doing it incorrectly. When faced with a difficult decision, laissez-faire leaders usually avoid making a decision in the hopes that the problem will resolve itself.

The Democratic Style

In the **democratic** (also called supportive or participative) leadership style, all aspects of the process of achieving a goal, from planning and goal setting to implementing and taking credit for the success of the project, are shared by the group.

Table 13.1 Comparison of Authoritarian, Democratic, and Laissez-Faire Theories

	Authoritarian	Democratic	Laissez-faire
Degree of freedom	Little freedom	Moderate freedom	Much freedom
Degree of control	High control	Moderate control	Little control
Decision making	By the leader only	Leader and group	Group or no one
Leader activity level	High	High	Minimal
Responsibility	Leader	Leader and group	Abdicated
Quality of output	High quality	High quality/creative	Variable
Efficiency	Very efficient	Moderately efficient	Variable

Source: Tappen, RM, et al.: Essentials of Nursing Leadership and Management, ed. 2. F.A. Davis, Philadelphia, 2001, p 6

The democratic leadership style is based on four beliefs.

1. Every member of the group needs to participate in all decision making.
2. Within the limits established by the group, freedom of expression is allowed to maximize creativity.
3. Individuals in the group accept responsibility for themselves and for the welfare of the whole group.
4. Each member must respect all the other members of the group as unique and valuable contributors.[2]

The leader using the democratic style provides guidance to the group, and all members share control. This style works best with groups whose members have a relatively equal status and who know each other well because they have worked together for an extended period. In its purist form, democratic leadership can be time consuming and inefficient in some situations, particularly when group members disagree strongly, but in the end, when a goal is achieved or a decision made, there is a strong sense of ownership and achievement by the whole group. Many leaders are uncomfortable with this style of leadership because of the minimal control they have over the group. Participative leadership allows the leader more control over the final decision. After considering all the opinions of the group, the leader makes the final decision based on what is best to achieve the goal.

The Authoritarian Style

The leader with an **authoritarian** (also called controlling, directive, or autocratic) style

maintains strong control over all aspects of the group and its activities. Authoritarian leaders provide direction by giving orders that the group is expected to carry out without question. The final decision-making authority rests with the leader alone, although input from the group may be considered.

The Dictator. A leader using a dictatorial authoritarian style has no regard for the feelings and needs of the group members. Achieving the goal is the only thing that matters, and the leader will use any means, including harsh criticism, to do so. A military mission to destroy a terrorist group by a SEAL (sea air land) assault team is an example of this type of leadership.

What Do You Think?

Have you ever had to be a leader in a group? What type of leadership style did you use? How successful was the outcome of the group work?

_____

_____

_____

_____

_____

_____

_____

_____

_____

_____

_____

The Benevolent Leader. The benevolent authoritarian leader uses a more paternalistic approach to achieving the goal. That leader attempts to include the group's feelings and concerns in the final decision, but ultimately the leader makes the decision. Some group members may feel that the benevolent leader is condescending and patronizing.

The authoritarian leadership style works best in emergency situations, where clear directions are required to save a life or prevent injury, or in situations where it is necessary to organize a large group of individuals. Although highly efficient in achieving goals and completing tasks, authoritarian leadership suppresses the creativity of the group members and may reduce the long-term effectiveness of the group. Authoritarian leadership also reduces the motivation levels of the group and may lead to passive–aggressive behavior by the members that will further reduce the effectiveness of the group. Although some people can accept the need for the total control exerted by an authoritarian leader, most people in a long-term work relationship with this type of leader will become frustrated and even rebellious at some point.

In reality, few leaders use only one style. Most leaders use multiple leadership styles that depend on the situation. Many factors may influence what type of leadership style is used at any given time, including external regulations and requirements, the ability of the group members, the work setting, and the problem being solved. For example, a nurse manager on a hospital unit may use a highly democratic style in most of the routine activities of the unit, but when a client goes into cardiac arrest, she may revert to a highly authoritarian style while directing the staff through a code.

Relationship–Task Orientation

High Relationship–Low Task

Another commonly used theory of leadership rates leaders on whether they are oriented more toward establishing relationships or achieving assigned tasks and resolving problems. Leaders with high relationship–low task orientations are usually well liked by their groups because of their acceptance of the group members as individuals, consideration of their feelings, encouragement, and promotion of good feelings among all the group members.

However, this kind of leader often sacrifices the achievement of the task or resolution of a problem when it conflicts with the feelings or good will of the group. This leader often allows the group to make its own decisions without regard to the task at hand and ultimately may not achieve the goals the group was organized for in the first place.

What Do You Think?

Think of the best leader you have ever worked with. What traits did that person have? Now think of the worst leader you ever worked with. What traits did that person have?

_____

The authoritarian leadership style works best in emergency situations, where clear directions are required to save a life or prevent injury, or in situations where it is necessary to organize a large group of individuals.

The situational theory recognizes that no one approach works in all situations. A leader needs to acknowledge this and adjust the leadership style and behavior to the situation, considering the many variables that may be involved. Good leaders seem to do this instinctively.

High Task–Low Relationship

The opposite extreme is the leader with a low relationship–high task orientation. This form of leadership is similar to the authoritarian style, where the leader does all the planning with little regard to the input or feelings of the group, gives orders, and expects them to be carried out without question. Various forms of punishment are used by this leader, ranging from verbal put-downs to poor performance evaluations that are used to determine pay raises.

Both Extremes

The worst leader is the person with a low relationship–low task orientation. This leadership style simulates the laissez-faire style, where the leader is uninvolved, does no planning, has little concern for the group members' feelings, and accomplishes little. On the other hand, the best leader is the one with a high relationship–high task orientation. This leader combines the best of both worlds: he or she is open to input and actively communicates with the group members, provides constructive direction, quickly resolves conflicts, and ultimately achieves creative and effective solutions to problems.

Certainly, perfect leaders are difficult to find. Most use a combination of styles and adjust them to the circumstances surrounding the problem. Again, think of the nurse manager who uses a high relationship–high task orientation for managing the unit in most day-to-day operations. In the cardiac arrest situation, this nurse manager may quickly change her or his orientation to one of low relationship–high task until the crisis is resolved.

RECENT THEORIES OF LEADERSHIP

Although the behavior and trait theories remain popular, researchers have come to the conclusion that leadership is really a more complex process. The situational theory recognizes that no one approach works in all situations. A leader needs to acknowledge this and adjust the leadership style and behavior to the situation, considering the many variables that may be involved. Good leaders seem to do this instinctively. One of the key factors is the type of organization in which the group is located. The environment is always important in exercising leadership.

The transformational theory takes the situational theory one step further. This theory recognizes that multiple intangibles exist whenever people interact. Factors such as sense of meaning, creativity, inspiration, and vision all are involved in creating a sense of mission that exceeds good interpersonal relationships and rewards. Although this is true in most work settings, health care and nursing, where care of human beings is the primary goal, require that nurses do something positive. In

many health-care facilities, nursing leaders are expected to inspire excitement and commitment in nurses, who often must provide care to very ill clients in less than ideal circumstances.

KEY LEADERSHIP BEHAVIORS

Traits are characteristics that an individual possesses. Traits may or may not lead to the actions or behaviors that are required for successful leadership. It is also possible to lack leadership traits, yet be able to carry out successful leadership behaviors.

Critical Thinking. The ability to think critically is a multistep process similar to the nursing process. Critical thinkers must be able to analyze data, organize and plan, and use creativity in the resolution of problems (see Chapter 6). Leaders must often make important decisions on the basis of incomplete data.

Problem Solving. Being able to use the problem-solving process effectively is essential to effective leadership. Leaders in the health-care setting face problems that arise from many sources, including staffing and personnel, scheduling, and administrative, budget, and client demands.

Acknowledgment and Respect for Individual Differences. Personality is the sum total of people's experiences. Because no two people have identical experiences, each one has different needs, feelings, and orientations. The effective leader recognizes these differences and is able to direct people to their highest level of achievement given their varying orientations.

Active Listening. To be effective, leaders must be able to not only hear the words that the person is saying but also to observe the body language and its underlying emotions and meaning. The experts tell us that only 7 percent of communication is verbal; 93 percent is all the other nonverbal content. Leaders often fail in their leadership roles when they do not listen to the full message of the individuals they are attempting to lead.

Skillful Communication. Communication is a complex process that involves an exchange of information and feedback (see Chapter 14). Mistakes happen on both sides when the information being shared is incomplete or confusing. Providing frequent and positive feedback is one of the best methods for leaders to determine how well they are communicating and how open the communication channels remain. It also can boost morale and improve the working environment. Effective leaders should also be able to give and use negative feedback to improve performance. If negative feedback is given in a nonthreatening and encouraging manner, the person receiving it will often appreciate the chance to improve his or her skills.

Establishment of Clear Goals and Outcomes.

The old question, "How do you know when you've arrived if you don't know where you are going?" is a truism that all leaders must address at some point by establishing clear goals and outcomes for the group. Groups who lack clear goals often feel frustrated and lost. Initially, leaders must clearly identify their goals. Then they must identify the goals shared by the group and use them to motivate the group. Successful outcome is often a thoughtful melding of the vision of the leader and that of the group.

Continued Personal and Professional Development.

One of the most valuable lessons that nursing students can learn while in school is that education does not end when they graduate—it just begins. One of the primary goals of the nursing education process should be to teach the student how to learn. Lifelong learning is a goal that effective leaders seek not only for themselves but also for those whom they are leading. Leaders can function as teachers in certain settings, but a more effective means of encouraging others to continue to learn is to set a good example. It is important to recognize that learning takes place not only in a formal school-like setting, but in all those encounters and situations that affect attitudes, beliefs, and behavior.

KEY LEADERSHIP QUALITIES

No matter what style a leader favors, successful leaders have common qualities (Box 13.2).

Integrity. For many years, nursing has been ranked number one as the most trusted and respected profession in the annual Gallup Poll. One of the keys to this trust and respect is the integrity of the profession as it is perceived by clients and their families. The public expects nurses, as a group, to be honest, trustworthy, ethical, moral, and professional. The American Nurses Association (ANA) Code of Ethics for Nurses

> *One of the most valuable lessons that nursing students can learn while in nursing school is that education does not end when they graduate—it just begins.*

(see Chapter 7) is directed toward promoting and maintaining the integrity of the profession. If a group observes less than complete integrity in their leader, that person's ability to lead is markedly diminished.

Courage. Although all leaders must have the courage to maintain their convictions in the face of adversity, certain leadership positions may require a higher degree of courage. Nurses in middle management positions, such as unit managers, house supervisors, or quality control coordinators, often find themselves caught in a no-man's land between two opposing worlds.[3] For example, higher management may be attempting to implement a plan or procedure that the staff nurses strongly object to, or the staff nurses may be complaining about some issue, such as staffing, that the middle manager has little control over. The leader

---

Box 13.2

Keys to Leadership

Key Qualities
- Integrity
- Courage
- Initiative
- Energy
- Optimism
- Perseverance
- Well-roundedness
- Coping skills
- Self-knowledge

Key Behaviors
- Critical thinking
- Problem solving
- Acknowledgment of and respect for individual differences
- Active listening
- Skillful communication
- Establishment of clear goals and outcomes
- Continued personal and professional development

Source: Adapted from Tappen, RM, et al.: Essentials of Nursing Leadership and Management, ed. 2. F.A. Davis, Philadelphia, 2001, p 8.

in this situation may need to risk offending one or the other of the groups to resolve a difficult problem.

Initiative. Effective leadership demands that the leader be a "self-starter" and have the ability to start projects without pressure from above. Often the group relies on the leader to begin the process of completing a task or resolving a problem.

Energy. Energy refers not only to the ability to do work but also to the display of that energy in the form of enthusiasm for the work. Energy and enthusiasm are contagious. Charismatic leaders are the ones who are the most energetic and enthusiastic. The group needs to see that the leader is willing to work as hard as they are being asked to work. However, energy has to be rationed carefully to maintain the optimum levels. It is easy for a leader to burn out, particularly when the expenditure of energy seems to produce little or no tangible result.

Optimism. A positive attitude is also contagious. Conversely, so is a negative attitude, which often leads to discouragement and failure (Table 13.2). A leader who has an overall positive attitude and views new problems as opportunities for success will be much more successful than the leader who constantly complains about each new crisis.

Perseverance. Leaders need to be able to continue to work through difficult problems in difficult circumstances, even when others feel like quitting. Again, if the leader sets the example for the group with a "there's more than one way to skin a cat"

Table 13.2 Winner or Whiner—Which One Are You?

A Winner Says . . .	A Whiner Says . . .
We have a real challenge here.	This is a big problem.
I'll do my best.	Do I have to do this?
That's great!	That's nice, I guess.
We can do it.	It can't be done, it's impossible.
Yes.	Maybe, when I have some time.

Source: Tappen, RM, et al.: Essentials of Nursing Leadership and Management, ed. 2. F.A. Davis, Philadelphia, 2001, p 8.

attitude, the group will be encouraged to find new and creative solutions.

Well-Roundedness. Leaders, as well as those they are leading, live multifaceted lives. It is important to develop and foster nonwork relationships with friends and family. The time at work should be balanced with recreational, spiritual, social, and cultural activities that complete the person and round out the personality. Time must also be invested in maintaining good health through proper nutrition and regular exercise, which will also help prevent burnout (see Chapter 12).

Coping Skills. All jobs have some degree of stress, although people in leadership positions often experience higher levels. Stress can be handled in two ways: unconsciously, through defense mechanisms, or consciously, by bringing learned coping skills into play. A more productive way to deal with stress is to use coping skills developed in dealing with past stressors to promote a positive and healthy resolution to the stress. Some people learn how to use the stress they experience to motivate them and to tap into the energy it generates to achieve at a higher level of functioning.

Self-Knowledge. Leaders who do not know and understand themselves are less able to understand those who are working for them. Self-awareness is the beginning of self-acceptance as a thinking, feeling person who interacts with other thinking, feeling persons. Unless leaders understand and accept their motivations, biases, and perceptions, they will not be able to understand why they feel and react in certain ways to certain individuals and situations.

Important aspects of modular nursing include relying on unlicensed assistive personnel (UAP), also called unit service assistants, for the provision of direct care, grouping clients with similar needs, developing relative intensity measures, and emphasizing team concepts in small groups that remain constant.

Strong, Explicit Leadership

Cross-training of personnel is another important aspect of modular nursing. For example, using this system, respiratory therapists do not just provide respiratory treatments but also help clients to the bathroom and turn bedridden clients. Nurse managers in this system are responsible for providing explicit job descriptions, maintaining the work group's cohesiveness, carefully monitoring each staff person's abilities, delegating tasks as appropriate, and evaluating the effectiveness of care.

The role of UAPs is one area of the client-focused care model that needs more definition, particularly in relation to the registered nurse's accountability and responsibilities in supervising these workers. State boards of nursing across the country are considering possible changes in nurse practice acts necessitated by the use of UAPs.

> *Leadership can be exerted either formally or informally. Often the most effective leaders in a group are not the ones who are officially designated as the leaders.*

Benefits of this care delivery model include decreased staffing cost and greater autonomy of cross-trained personnel. The nurse manager must be a strong leader for this model of care delivery to succeed. Consistent collaboration between the nurse manager and physician is of utmost importance in planning client care.

LEADERSHIP VERSUS MANAGEMENT

Several questions arise when people speak about leadership and management.

Are They the Same Thing?

Leadership can be exerted either formally or informally. Often the most effective leaders in a group are not the ones who are officially designated as the leaders. On the other hand, managers are given the title by some higher authority and have formally designated authority to supervise a group of employees in the achievement of a task. Similarly, managers can be held formally responsible for the quality, quantity, and cost of the work that the supervised employees produce.

Do Managers Need Good Leadership Skills?

The most effective managers will have highly developed leadership skills. However, by virtue of their title and position, even managers with poor leadership skills are still the official authority, although their effectiveness is reduced. Often, in groups where the manager is not a good leader, unofficial leaders emerge and exert either a strong positive or a negative influence on the group. If the unofficial leader is generally supportive of the manager's and administration's goals, then the work group can be highly productive and the organization's goals will be achieved. Conversely, if the unofficial leader's goals are opposed to those of the manager and administration, productivity may decrease to a point where higher-level management asks the manager to leave the position.

Are Leaders Always Good Managers?

A person who has leadership ability may not have good management skills. This phenomenon is often seen in the nursing profession when a highly effective and skilled staff nurse who functions as the unofficial unit leader is taken out of that role and promoted to an official management position. Some do well; others may require additional training in management principles and skills. Some never quite master the skills needed for management.

Management and leadership skills complement each other. As with all skills, they can be learned and require practice and experience to be developed fully. Even new graduate nurses can be effective leaders within their new nursing roles. As they gain experience and develop new skills, their ability and opportunities to provide leadership will also increase. Learning and improving skills in one area will increase the ability in the other.

FUNCTIONS OF THE NURSE MANAGER

Nurse managers often find themselves located on the organizational chart between employees and upper-level management. The functions and duties of nurse managers depend to a great degree on how the institution defines the role. One of the first activities of a new nurse manager is to make sure he or she understands the job description, responsibilities, and level of authority the position has in the institution where he or she is employed. Some of the tasks that have been identified as being a regular part of a nurse manager's position are listed in Box 13.4.

In today's health-care system, nurse managers continue to follow the trend of moving away from close supervision of the staff nurses' work to helping them complete their work safely and effectively. As this role continues to evolve, the emphasis will shift from traditional management functions to highly supportive functions, such as are seen in the leadership role.

Box 13.4

Common Tasks for Nurse Managers

- Conduct orientation of new staff
- Evaluate staff
- Terminate employees with unsatisfactory work performance
- Develop time schedules that cover the unit safely
- Make team and staff assignments
- Develop a realistic budget for the unit
- Justify the number of nursing hours used by the unit
- Call in nurses on their days off when staffing falls short
- Attend nursing management meetings
- Hold regular meetings with unit staff to resolve problems and implement new policies and procedures
- Set unit goals for staff
- Contribute to facility goals
- Communicate regularly with physicians about unit problems
- Conduct quality assurance studies
- Provide rewards for high-quality care

Conclusion

Over the years, there has been one constant in the changing health-care system: the registered nurse is still expected to provide leadership and management skills to direct and ensure the high quality of the health care given to clients. Both leadership and management require sets of skills that can be learned. Nurses who learn these skills will become successful managers and the leaders of the health-care system in the future.

Successful leaders and managers understand and often combine the best aspects of the many theories that deal with leadership and management. Knowledge of one's strengths and weakness provides the basis for successful management. Developing effective leadership and management skills is a lifelong, ongoing process. Learning from books and articles, as well as from other successful nurse managers, presents an opportunity for professional and personal growth.

Issues in Practice

Jill, a registered nurse, was recently appointed as the evening charge nurse on a busy postsurgical unit. She has been an active participant in the hospital's quality assurance committee for the past 2 years since her graduation. One of the issues the committee identified as a problem was the higher-than-average surgical wound infection rate on Jill's unit. After some research, Jill determined that a major component of the high infection rate was the procedures that were used when changing postoperative dressings.

After obtaining permission from the unit manager and hospital education director, Jill developed a new procedure for dressing changes, incorporating the most current research. She presented the changes in a short in-service program to the unit personnel, several times to each of the three shifts to make sure that all the nurses and staff on the unit were familiar with the new changes. The expectation was that there would be a 25 percent reduction in wound infections after the new procedures had been used for 1 month.

At the end of the first month of using the new dressing change procedures, the postoperative wound infection rate showed no improvement over the previous month's rate. At the monthly staff meeting, Jill discovered that the licensed practical nurses (LPNs) on the unit were refusing to use the new procedures because they "took too much time" and had reverted to the procedures they had always used before.

Answers to Case Study Questions

Issues Now: Leadership/Management Case Study

1. A nurse manager who uses the authoritarian system would maintain her position that the proposed plan was unworkable. Relying on her position of authority, she would insist that the nurses continue to use the established system of assignment. Any staff nurse who felt she or he could not work under this system could seek reassignment to another unit.

2. A nurse manager using the laissez-faire system would allow the nurses to try out the proposed system as they wanted. If any problems resulted from it, they would have to figure out how to resolve the problems themselves.

3. A nurse manager using the participative system would recognize that there is always some common ground between herself and the staff nurses. It is important to identify the common points and then work toward resolving the areas of disagreement. For example, the nurse manager could work with the staff nurses to develop a set of criteria for assignments that would be agreeable to all parties and ensure the quality of client care. The nurse manager would then retain the ability to assign clients, but would be using criteria that were developed by the staff. In the end, staff cooperation and morale would increase, as would the continuity and quality of care being provided by the unit.

4. The initial mistake the nurse manager made was meeting with the staff nurses as a group. The staff nurses would have done better to select one or two representatives to bring their issues to the nurse manager. Using this approach eliminates the "mob mentality" that sometimes develops with large groups. It also forces the staff nurses to identify the specific issues they want to resolve.

(Adapted from Tappen, RM: Essentials of Nursing Leadership and Management, ed 4. F.A. Davis, Philadelphia, 2006.)

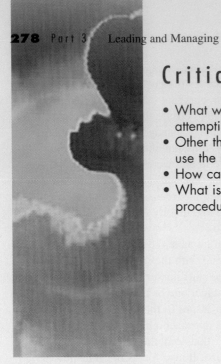

Critical Thinking Questions

- What was the style of leadership and management that Jill used when attempting to initiate the dressing procedure change?
- Other than the stated reason, why do you think the LPNs did not want to use the new procedures?
- How can Jill increase the level of compliance by the LPNs on the unit?
- What is the role of the unit manager in initiating the new dressing change procedures?

References

1. Grossman, SC, and Valiga, TM: The New Leadership Challenge: Creating the Future of Nursing, ed. 2. F.A. Davis, Philadelphia, 2005.
2. Hertzberg, F, et al.: The motivation to work. Wiley, New York, 1959.
3. Patronis Jones, RA: Nursing Leadership and Management. F.A. Davis, Philadelphia, 2007.
4. Pearce, C: Leadership resource. Ten steps to managing change. Nursing Management 13(10):25, 2007.
5. Simons, J, et al.: Psychology - The search for understanding. West Publishing Company, New York, 1987.
6. Tappen, RM: Essentials of Nursing Leadership and Management, ed. 4. F.A. Davis, Philadelphia, 2006.

Bibliography

Bliss, J: Effective team management by district nurses. British Journal of Community Nursing 9(12):524–526, 2004.

Bradley, E: Translating research into clinical practice: Making change happen. Journal of the American Geriatric Society 52(11):1875–1882, 2004.

Isaacson, J: Nursing students in an expanded charge nurse role: A real clinical management experience. Nursing Education Perspectives 25(6):292–296, 2004.

Jeong, S: Innovative leadership and management in a nursing home. Journal of Nursing Management 12(6):443–431, 2004.

Kuzmits, F: 360-feedback in health care management: A field study. Health Care Manager 23(4):321–328, 2004.

Leichtling, B: Leadership & management. Preventive medicine for "compassion [sic] fatigue." Caring 23(10). 90–91, 2004.

Owens, J, and Patton, J: Take a chance on nursing mentorships: Enhance leadership with this win–win strategy. Nursing Education Perspectives 24(4):198–204, 2005.

Patterson, P: A few simple rules for managing block time in the operating room. Operating Room Manager 20(11):1, 9–12, 2004.

Robotham, M: How to handle complaints. Nursing Times 97(30): 5–28, 2001.

Sanford, K: Become competent in confrontation. Nursing Management 35(7):14, 2004.

Tracy, B: What makes a good leader. The Oklahoman Jan 9, 2005, 1H.

Vestal, K: Lessons learned: Making time for leadership. Nurse Leader 2(6):8–9, 2004.

West, B. Evaluation of a clinical leadership initiative. Nursing Standard 19(5):33–41, 2004.

14

Communicating Successfully

Joseph T. Catalano

Learning Objectives

After completing this chapter, the reader will be able to:

- Explain the importance of understanding human behaviors.
- Describe conflict resolution and relationship tools.
- Identify communication styles.
- Analyze and apply problem-solving and conflict-resolution tools.
- Discuss the use of the nursing process in conflict resolution.
- Formulate coping strategies to handle difficult people.

THE NURSE AS COMMUNICATOR

Good communication skills are often advertised as the answer to many of the problems encountered in everyday life. Television personalities, instructors, and psychologists promote improved communication skills as the answer to parental, marital, financial, and work-related problems. The nursing profession recognizes communication as one of the cornerstones of its practice. Nurses must be able to communicate with clients, family members, physicians, peers, and associates in an effective and constructive manner to achieve their goals of high-quality care. Good communication is essential for good leadership and management.

In today's rapidly evolving health-care system, registered nurses (RNs) are called on to supervise a growing number of assistive and unlicensed personnel. One of the keys to good supervision is the ability to communicate to people what they must do to provide the required care and, often, how the care should be given. It is not always easy. Many of the people whom nurses supervise have limited training, lack the theoretical and technical knowledge base of the nurse, and may display attitudes that make them resistant to direction. However, nurse supervisors can be and often are held legally responsible for the actions of those individuals who work under their direction.

"Change can produce many emotions, ranging from excitement and anticipation to stress, fear, and anxiety. At minimum, change makes most people feel uncomfortable."

FACTORS THAT AFFECT COMMUNICATION

Change

Change is one of the few absolute certainties in today's health-care system. Change can produce many emotions, ranging from excitement and anticipation to stress, fear, and anxiety. How people deal with change can affect how they respond to the environment and communicate with others.

At minimum, change makes most people feel uncomfortable. Any change can be simultaneously positive and negative. During the process of learning new skills, treatments, or techniques, most people feel a sense of accomplishment at the same time that they feel afraid of making mistakes, being judged by others, or being labeled as "slow learners."

Fear of the Unknown

Imagine a new graduate nurse starting his or her first day at work, very excited about the new experience and the potential for career development. However, at the same time the nurse is worried about being accepted into the group, being able to practice what was learned in nursing school, and being able to learn the new skills required by the unit. Almost everyone has a sense of dread when moving away from activities with which they have become comfortable. Setting realistic personal goals and time lines for learning new information helps reduce fear and stress when making major changes.

Change affects communication in various ways. People may be afraid to ask questions about new procedures or policies because they fear that they might appear "stupid" in front of their colleagues. Fear of being criticized closes individuals off to positive suggestions and new ideas. Others may hesitate in sharing ideas because they are afraid of being labeled as confrontational.

For example, a nurse is reassigned from the medical/surgical unit to the intensive care unit (ICU). This nurse will initially be somewhat fearful in the new environment with the highly trained and assertive expert unit nurses who always seem to be in control. A more positive approach would be for the new nurse to take advantage of the unit nurses' expertise and learn from their examples. The new nurse needs to remember that everyone on that unit was a novice at one time. In the current health-care system, almost everyone is fearful much of the time of making mistakes and of falling short of the high standards of the profession.

> *People may be afraid to ask questions about new procedures or policies because they fear that they might appear 'stupid' in front of their colleagues.*

The Need to Take Risks

Change can have both positive and negative effects. Often when a staff is initially resistant to a change and fights to prevent it, once they have gone through the process, would never go back to the old way of doing things. All change involves some risk taking, and some people are better at risk taking than are others. Consider the following case study:

After analyzing the needs of the clients and the nursing workload of a busy medical unit, the unit manager decided to change the work shift times. In addition to the standard 7 a.m. to 3 p.m., 3 p.m. to 11 p.m., and 11 p.m. to 7 a.m. shifts, she decided to add a 5 a.m. to 1 p.m. shift to increase coverage during the busiest period of the shift. The RN assigned to the new shift recognized the benefits to the unit and clients; thus, she accepted and supported the change with few objections. Also, the change in shift times allowed her to alter her personal schedule so that she could take extra courses toward her master's degree at a local college. For the RN, the change in shifts was a positive experience.

However, the licensed practical nurse (LPN) assigned to this new shift was upset with the change. She was a "late sleeper" and did not want to come in so early. She liked the shifts the way they were and did not see any advantages to changing things needlessly.

After the new shift was initiated, the LPN was usually 15 to 30 minutes late, called in sick frequently, and was "grumpy" and hard to talk to when she did come in to work. For this LPN, the change was negative and unacceptable.

Grief Stages

Nurses need to keep in mind that the communication abilities of clients who are experiencing change will be affected in very much the same way as nurses who are experiencing change. As a result of disease, trauma, or surgery, many clients face sudden and major alterations in their bodies, as well as changes in their ability to function and carry out daily self-care activities. For example, a client with a new colostomy must adapt to major physiological, psychological, and emotional changes.

Most clients who have surgical procedures that result in major body function alterations go through the stages of the grief process: denial, anger, guilt, depression, and resolution. Communication with a client in the anger stage, who is hostile, critical of his care, and verbally abusive, will be very different than communication with a client in the depression stage, who is withdrawn, reticent, and sleeps most of the time. Recognition of the communication behaviors of each of the grief stages is essential in understanding why clients are acting in a particular way. A decision must then be made regarding the most effective communication technique to use when providing care.

Stress

Stress is produced by many factors and always affects an individual's ability to communicate. Some common causes of stress for health-care workers include institutional restructuring, group interaction and dynamics, unilateral management decisions, or personal issues and experiences. Regardless of the source, stress usually decreases people's ability to interact and communicate and increases the demands on their coping mechanisms.

A Destructive Circle

When people are unable to cope with a stressful situation successfully, they may experience an increased state of tension or anxiety. They may develop physiological symptoms, such as nausea, stomach cramps, diarrhea, or palpitations; in extreme cases, they may even become paranoid or psychotic. Uncontrolled high levels of stress on a nursing unit

may lead to competition among the nurses that affects their teamwork, productivity, and the quality of the care given.

Physicians who are stressed by worry about a severely ill client, or threats to their autonomy, practice, and income from changes in reimbursement policies, may become tense and highly critical of or even verbally abusive toward nurses. The hospital management may also experience increased stress owing to the escalating responsibility of maintaining high-quality services with ever-shrinking revenues. Management often deals with its stress by becoming more autocratic, making increased demands on the nursing staff while reducing the control that nurses have over their practice and becoming closed off to input from nurses and physicians.

> *At some point, one group's stress always affects another group's stress level, whose stress in turn increases another group's stress. The process becomes a destructive circle of cause-and-effect responses that increases the stress levels for everyone in the facility.*

At some point, one group's stress always affects another group's stress level, which in turn increases another group's stress. The process becomes a destructive circle of cause-and-effect responses that increases the stress levels for everyone in the facility.

Issues in Practice

Managing Change

The busy nonacute outpatient unit at a large hospital had become disorganized. It consistently received evaluations of "poor" when clients were asked about the care being provided. They often complained about the long waits to be evaluated and treated. The staff also recognized the problems with the care they were providing but didn't have any solutions.

In an attempt to improve the evaluations, the administration replaced the current director with a new director from an even larger facility across town. She was charged with the task of improving client care and was promised that she would have whatever resources she needed.

Within 6 months, the new director completely reorganized the staffing patterns and modernized all the information systems using the latest software. She replaced old equipment with new models and bought additional equipment that the unit had never used before. She also managed to expand and brighten up the unit by remodeling extensively and by securing unused space from the radiology department, which occupied adjacent rooms. She increased the salaries of the nursing staff, hired new nurses, and expanded the hours of service. She implemented a "management by objectives" model for evaluation that allowed the staff nurses increased input into their working conditions and evaluations.

Client surveys indicated an increase in overall satisfaction with the care being provided; the wait time had been decreased to a point where there were hardly any complaints. However, approximately half the experienced nurses on the unit resigned, and the rest of the nurses began the process of organizing into a collective bargaining unit for the first time in the history of the nonacute outpatient unit.

QUESTIONS FOR THOUGHT

1. What was the underlying issue that led to the nurses' responses to the changes?
2. What could the director have done to increase the staff's acceptance of change?

   (Answers are found at the end of the chapter.)

List four factors or situations that have produced high levels of stress for you in the hospital or health-care setting. Why did these incidents produce stress? How did you deal with the stress?

_____

_____

_____

_____

_____

_____

_____

_____

_____

_____

_____

Clients Under Stress

Stress in the health-care environment is not just experienced by health-care providers. Stress for clients starts when they first come into contact with the health-care system, peaks when they have to undergo physical examinations, surgery, or invasive treatments, and continues throughout the recovery period. The fear that a nurse may not respond to clients' needs increases clients' stress levels, and they sometimes become more demanding of care, which in turn increases the nurse's stress levels. If the nursing staff is experiencing high stress levels, clients often sense this subconsciously, and as a result, clients' stress levels also will increase.

Several techniques can be used to reduce clients' stress levels so they can better communicate and become more receptive to teaching. Stress reduction techniques range from very simple measures that everyone can use, such as distraction with music or simple activities, exercise, or reduction in stimuli, to more advanced techniques such as meditation, **biofeedback,** and even antianxiety medications.

Eliminate the Situation

Nurses need to be able to identify situations that produce stress, recognize the symptoms shown by

someone in a stressful situation, know how to reduce stress, and be able to use appropriate communication techniques with someone under stress. Of course, if possible, the best way to reduce stress is to eliminate the stressful situation. Consider the following case:

> The hospital management has just sent a memo to all the hospital units that a new client assessment form they have developed is to be implemented next week. This new form is in addition to the ones that the nurses already fill out each day. The new form is to be completed by RNs only and must be done each shift on every client and then sent to the house supervisor so that management can track acuity. Because of recent facility restructuring and changes in staffing patterns, often there is only one RN on the 3 p.m. to 11 p.m. and 11 p.m. to 7 a.m. shifts to cover a 42-bed unit. This extra, time-consuming, and seemingly redundant paperwork increases the stress of the staff RNs to an unacceptable level.
>
> They meet as a group with management and propose that the assessment forms they are already using be modified to include the data that management wants on the new forms. Photocopies of the revised form could then be made by the unit clerk for each shift and given to the supervisors, thus eliminating the new form. Management notes the high stress levels of the RNs, recognizes that increased stress lowers the quality of care, and decides to follow the RNs' proposal, thus eliminating the primary source of the RNs' stress.

Although all sources of stress cannot be eliminated completely, in most situations they can be reduced to a manageable level. However, high stress levels should never be used as an excuse for destructive anger and behaviors, failure of communication, or abuse of individuals.

Anger

In addition to being one of the stages of the grief process, anger can be a symptom of personal frustration, lack of control, fear of change, or feelings of hopelessness. Anger is one of the strong primitive natural emotions that help individuals protect themselves against a variety of external threats. Although everyone experiences anger, how it is expressed often depends on a person's family and ethnic background, life experiences, and personal values. In some cultures, loud and physically expressive outbursts are the norm for the expression of anger, whereas in other cultures, anger is internalized and expressed only as a "controlled rage."

Positive or Negative Expression

As with most of the other factors that affect communication, anger can be either positive or negative. When anger is used in a positive, productive manner, it can promote change and release tension. Anger can be used positively to increase others' attention, initiate communication, problem solve, and energize the change process. Sensitivity to internal anger can warn individuals that something is wrong either within themselves or with someone or something in the external environment.

Many individuals have difficulty expressing and using their anger in a positive manner. Anger that is used negatively is very destructive. It hinders communication, makes coworkers fearful, and erodes relationships with others. Anger expressed by abusive behaviors, such as pounding on nursing station counters, throwing charts or surgical instruments, verbal outbursts, or even violent physical contact, is never acceptable and may lead to civil or criminal action against the perpetrator.

The negative expression of anger may cause the person who is the object of the anger to retaliate or seek revenge, but probably the most destructive form that negative anger can take is when it is internalized and suppressed. Long-term, suppressed anger has been associated with a number of physiological and psychological problems ranging from gastric ulcers and hypertension to myocardial infarctions, strokes, and even psychotic rage episodes.

What Sets People Off

Nurses who understand what makes both themselves and others angry are better able to either avoid anger-producing situations or cope effectively with their own anger or with that of others. For example, even new graduate nurses soon learn that some situations will almost always evoke an angry response from hospitalized clients. These include serving meals that are cold or poorly cooked, not answering call lights in a timely manner, waking up soundly sleeping clients at midnight to give them a sleeping pill, or taking 10 attempts to start an intravenous (IV) line.

Similarly, unit managers and hospital administrators quickly learn that some of the things they do will almost always produce angry responses from the staff. These actions include unilateral changes in the work schedule, additional paperwork, reduction in staffing levels, or refusal for requests for vacation or time off.

It is important that nurses understand that anger is a normal human emotion. Once it is recognized, it should be dealt with and then let go. Sometimes situations are not going to change, no matter how angry the person becomes, and sometimes no amount of anger will prevent changes from occurring.

GROUP DYNAMICS

The power of the group over an individual's behavior should never be underestimated. Groups establish and exert their power through a set of unique behaviors or norms that their members are expected to follow. These norms may be formal or informal, written or unwritten, promulgated or merely understood. Unfortunately, in most nursing units the norms are often not clearly expressed, yet they may be used as judgment tools or standards for evaluating work behaviors. When new nurses begin work on a particular unit, they must quickly learn the unwritten unit norms and identify the informal leaders to function effectively.

Unwritten Rules

As with most elements in communication, group dynamics may be positive or negative. Nurses who do not learn and fail to display the expected group behaviors may be ostracized from the group, thus making the work environment psychologically uncomfortable and perhaps even physically difficult. For example, nonconforming nurses may find that there is no one around when they need help ambulating an unsteady client. A particular nursing unit staff may have a strong team approach. If the new nurse is highly independent and prefers to work alone, he or she may not "fit in" and may experience hostility or sarcasm from the other nurses on the unit.

Going Against the Group

Consider the following scenario demonstrating group dynamics:

The ICU has the responsibility for on-call coverage for the recovery room for unscheduled postoperative clients on the evening shifts, night shifts, and all of the weekend shifts. There is no formal written policy, but coverage has traditionally been handled on a voluntary, rotating basis.

Because it is "voluntary," one of the ICU nurses has decided that he does not want to take call any more. He is the only member of the ICU staff who does not take call. Soon after he announces his decision, he begins to sense anger and experience alienation from his peers. He is very knowledgeable, has highly developed nursing skills, and provides consistently high-quality care to assigned clients on his regular shifts. However, on his semiannual peer evaluation, he receives low ratings from his coworkers on the basis of the informal call coverage standard and expectations. The unit nurses feel that he is no longer a team player.

The nurse becomes angry because he feels that the use of unclear, unwritten standards is an unfair way to evaluate his ability as a nurse. He soon finds that the other ICU nurses accidentally "forget" to invite him to group functions. He also seems to be assigned the most difficult and largest number of clients during any given shift, seemingly to compensate for not taking call.

Group dynamics involves many factors, including methods of communication, professional behaviors, professional growth, flexibility, problem solving, participation, and competition. The ability to understand and use the elements of group dynamics has a direct relationship to the behaviors, cooperation, and effectiveness of the team. Often, when a team labels an individual member as "difficult," it most likely means that the individual is not following one or more of the informal, unwritten group norms.

> *The ability to understand and use the elements of group dynamics has a direct relationship on the behaviors, cooperation, and effectiveness of the team.*

COMPETITION

Competition can be a very powerful element in group dynamics and communication. Depending on how it is channeled, expressed, and used, competition can be a positive or negative force within the group. The various forms of competition can be individual, team, or unit focused.

Peer Evaluation. A common expression of competition in the group setting is peer evaluations. For peer evaluations to be a positive form of competition, the unit must decide ahead of time on the norms and expectations that they value and then design an objective measurement tool to evaluate whether the individual is meeting the norms. Each individual being evaluated must be aware of the criteria before the evaluation is conducted. The evaluation team must be educated on evaluation techniques and must be as objective and professional as possible.

In the health-care setting, it is important for all professionals, unit groups, and management to promote competition in a positive, progressive, and supportive environment. When competition is channeled positively, it leads to new and creative ideas, better programs, increased growth, more productive interactions, and higher-quality client care. When the competition is negative, it often produces failures, depression, sabotage, unit turf conflicts, decreased productivity, and lower-quality care. Consider the following case:

The competition on a nursing unit turned negative: the nurses on the 7 a.m. to 3 p.m. shift began competing with the nurses on the 3 p.m. to 11 p.m. shift in order to appear more knowledgeable about client care to the nurse manager. To "look better," the nurses on the 7 a.m. to 3 p.m. shift intentionally withheld selected client laboratory test results during shift report.

As a result of this action, several tests scheduled for the 3 p.m. to 11 p.m. shift were not done, angering the physicians, potentially threatening the safety of the clients, and making the nurses on the 3 p.m. to 11 p.m. shift appear incompetent. In addition, the nurses on that shift had to complete several incident reports on the errors that occurred on their shift.

One informal component the unit manager uses to evaluate the staff nurses' performance is the number of incident reports that a nurse must file. The more incident reports, the poorer will be the nurse's performance evaluation. To the unit manager, the nurses on the 7 a.m. to 3 p.m. shift appear to be more competent because of the seemingly poor care, indicated by a large number of incident reports, that is being given on the 3 p.m. to 11 p.m. shift. However, when the nurses on the 3 p.m. to 11 p.m. shift discovered what had really happened, they devised several ways to "get even" with the nurses on the 7 a.m. to 3 p.m. shift.

WORKING ENVIRONMENT

The delivery of health care is currently in a rapid transition from a fee-for-service to a managed care environment. Health care is shifting from acute, inpatient care to long-term outpatient care and from being illness based to a prevention and wellness focus. The changes produced by this transition are creating a high degree of stress at all levels of the health-care system. As discussed earlier, both change and stress are major barriers to effective communication.

Active Involvement in Change

One measure that can be taken to both alleviate some of the stress caused by the current changes in health care and improve unit communication is to encourage all members of the health-care team to participate in the renovation of their work environment. Through active participation, workers have an opportunity to have an impact on and direct the changes that are being made. Some people mistakenly believe that if they do not become involved, the changes will not happen. Unfortunately, when people are not actively involved in the restructuring process, others who are probably less qualified will make the changes anyway.

Increased fear, high stress levels, angry outbursts, and feelings of insecurity all are potential results of a work environment where the workers do not participate in the change process. Difficult behaviors resulting in unclear communication become more evident during times of change and stress. Ugly rumors, feelings of resentment, and increased insecurity often result when intergroup communications are not clear. An open, interactive work environment increases the probability of successful communication and adaptation to change.

Coping With Difficult Behavior

Understanding what motivates a person's behavior permits the individual to design a plan or develop coping mechanisms for communication based on sound interpersonal techniques. When individuals are able to separate themselves from the difficult situation, they are less likely to take things personally and more likely to begin to focus on the underlying issues causing the problems than on the other person's difficult behavior. The interaction becomes less judgmental and threatening to the other person. However, understanding the other person's motives never excuses unacceptable behaviors such as sarcasm, angry outbursts, and abusive language. Rather, it allows for direct confrontation of the behavior in a more controlled and less emotional way.

What Do You Think?

Have you ever been in a situation where others have intentionally sabotaged your work? What was the situation? How did you feel? How did you deal with it? Did you try to retaliate?

All professional nurses need to develop coping mechanisms to deal with difficult people. The very nature of the profession exposes nurses to a large number of people who are experiencing change, are under stress, and have a wide range of backgrounds and values as well as varying expectations. By understanding communication, using **behavior modification,** developing **assertiveness,** avoiding submissive and aggressive behaviors, and appreciating diversity, the nurse can develop the coping skills required for problem solving, handling conflict in the work setting, and confronting the unacceptable behaviors of difficult people.

UNDERSTANDING COMMUNICATION

Encoding and Decoding

Communication is an interactive sharing of information. It requires a sender, a message, and a receiver. After the sender sends the message, the receiver has a responsibility to listen to, process, and understand (encode) the information and then to respond to the sender by giving feedback (decoding). The encoding process occurs when the receiver thinks about the information, understands it, and forms an idea on the basis of the message.

> *Through active participation, workers have an opportunity to have an impact on and direct the changes that are being made. Some people mistakenly believe that if they do not become involved, the changes will not happen.*

Several factors can interfere with the encoding process. On the sender's side, these can be factors such as unclear speech, monotone voice, poor sentence structure, inappropriate use of terminology or jargon, or lack of knowledge about the topic. On the receiver's side, factors that may interfere with encoding include lack of attention, prejudice and bias, preoccupation with another problem, or even physical factors such as pain, drowsiness, or impairment of the senses.

For example, a staff nurse is in a mandatory meeting where the unit manager is discussing a new policy that will be starting the next month. However, the nurse is thinking about an important heart medication that her client is to receive in 5 minutes. The nurse's primary concern is to get out of the meeting in time to give the medication. After the meeting, the nurse has only a minimal recollection of what was said because she did not encode the information well. The following month, when the new policy is started, the staff nurse is confused about what she should do and makes several errors in relation to the policy.

> *Effective communication requires understanding that the perceptions, emotions, and participation of both parties are interactive and have an effect on the transmission of the message.*

Verbal or Nonverbal?

There are two primary methods of communication: verbal and nonverbal. **Verbal** communication is either written or spoken and constitutes only about 7 percent of the communicated message. **Nonverbal** communication, which makes up the other 93 percent of communication, is everything else, including body language, facial expressions, gestures, physical appearance, touch, vocal cues (tone, pauses), and spatial territory (personal space).

When the verbal and nonverbal messages are congruent, then the message is more easily encoded and clearly understood. If the verbal and nonverbal messages are conflicting, the nonverbal message is probably the most reliable. It is relatively easy for people to lie with words, but nonverbal communication tends to be unconscious and more difficult to control.

For example, the nurse suspects that the mother of a newborn infant may be experiencing postpartum depression. The nurse asks the mother how she feels about her new baby. The mother responds in a low-volume, very slow monotone, "I'm so happy I have this baby," while looking down at her feet in a slouched-over posture. The message from the mother is conflicting. The words are saying she is happy, but all the nonverbal signs indicate that she is depressed. The observant nurse concludes that more assessment for depression is required.

Effective communication requires understanding that the perceptions, emotions, and participation of both parties are interactive and have an effect on the transmission of the message. Nurses often encounter situations that require clarification of the information for accuracy and encoding. The following is an example of client teaching requiring a return demonstration:

A nurse gave a teaching session to a client who was being sent home with a T-tube after surgical removal of gallstones from the

Box 14.1

Barriers to Clear Communication	Benefits of Clear Communication
• Unclear/unexpressed • Confusion • Retaliation • Desire for power • Control of others • Negative reputation • Manipulation • Low self-esteem • Biased perceptions • Inattention • Mistrust • Anger • Fear/anxiety • Stress • Insecurity • Prejudice • Interruptions • Preoccupation	• Clear expectations • Understanding • Forgiveness • Recognized leadership • Companionship • Respect • Independence • Realistic self-image • Acceptance • Clear direction • Trusting relations • Self-control • Comfort • Motivation/energy • Security • Increased tolerance • Increased knowledge • Concentration

common bile duct. After the nurse finished, she asked the client whether he understood how to empty the drainage bottle and measure the drainage. The client looked very confused, but mumbled "yes," while shaking his head back and forth. The nurse recognized that although the verbal response was positive, the nonverbal responses indicated that he really did not understand. The nurse surmised that further explanation or demonstration was required for this client to encode the message properly.

Nurses should recognize the many barriers to clear communication as well as the benefits of clear communication. Once the barriers to communication are identified, they can be overcome and the benefits of clear communication will follow. These barriers and the benefits that result when they are overcome are outlined in Box 14.1.

COMMUNICATION STYLES

There are two predominant styles of communication: assertive and nonassertive. Nonassertive communication can be either submissive or aggressive. Individuals develop their communication styles over the course of their lives in response to many personal factors. Although most people have one predominant style of communication, they can and often do switch or combine styles depending on the situation in which they find themselves. For example, a unit manager who uses an assertive communication style when supervising the staff on her unit may revert to a submissive style when called into the nursing director's office for her annual evaluation. Recognizing which communication style a person is using at any given time, as well as a person's own style, is important in making communication clear and effective.

Assertive Communication

Assertive communication involves interpersonal behaviors that permit people to defend and maintain their legitimate rights in a respectful manner that does not violate the rights of others. Assertive communication is honest and direct and accurately expresses the person's feelings, beliefs, ideas, and opinions. Respect for self and others constitutes both the basis for and the result of assertive communication. It encourages trust and teamwork by communicating to others that they have the right to and are encouraged to express their opinions in an open and respectful atmosphere. Disagreement and discussion are considered to be a healthy part of the communication process, and negotiation is the positive mechanism for problem solving, learning, and personal growth.

Assertive communication always implies that the individual has the choice to voice an opinion, sometimes forcefully, as well as to not say anything at all. One of the keys to assertive communication is that the individual is in control of the communication and is not merely reacting to another's emotions.

What Do You Think?

Consider the health-care providers whom you have worked with in the recent past. What were their communication styles? How did it affect the way you communicated with them?

_____
_____
_____
_____
_____
_____
_____
_____
_____
_____
_____
_____

Assessing Self-Assertiveness

Answer the following questions to assess your self-assertiveness:

- Who am I and what do I want?
- Do I believe I have the right to want it?
- How do I get it?
- Do I believe I can get it?
- Have I tried to be assertive with a person I am having difficulty communicating with?
- Am I letting my fears and perceptions cloud my interactions?

- What is the worst that can happen if we communicate?
- Can I live with the worst?
- Will communications have a long-term effect?
- How does it feel to be in constant fear of alienation or rejection?

Rules for Assertiveness

Anyone can learn to use an assertive communication style and develop assertiveness. When first developing this skill, people often feel frightened and overwhelmed. However, once individuals become comfortable with assertiveness, it helps reinforce their self-concepts and becomes an effective tool for communication. There are a few rules to keep in mind while developing assertiveness along with an assertive communication style:

- It is a learned skill.
- It takes practice.
- It requires a desire and motivation to change.
- It requires a willingness to take risks.
- It requires a willingness to make mistakes and try again.
- It requires an understanding that not every outcome sought will be obtained.
- It requires strong self-esteem.
- Self-reward for change and a positive outcome is essential.
- Listening to self is necessary for identifying needs.
- Constant re-examination of outcomes helps assess progress.
- Role-playing with a friend prior to the interaction builds skill and confidence.
- Goals for assertiveness growth need to be established beforehand.
- Assertiveness requires recognition that change is a gradual process.
- Others should be allowed to make mistakes.

Personal Risks of Assertive Communication

There are always personal risks involved in learning any new skills or in attempting to change behavior. Learning assertive communication is no exception. People often fear that they may not choose the "perfect" assertive response. However, even seasoned assertive communicators may err from time to time because every encounter is unique, involving different people and situations. The person who is new to assertive communication needs to recognize that it is a skill that takes practice.

"You really need to work on your verbal skills."

I Win, You Win

Assertiveness does not mean that a person will always get his or her way in every situation, and it is likely the individual will handle some situations better than others. Remember that the goal of assertive communication is not to have an "I win, you lose" situation, but rather an "I win, you win" outcome. A win-win goal is achieved when both parties have the ability and willingness to negotiate even though they do not get all they want. However, there may be situations when personal goals are not achieved. Some questions to consider when this occurs are:

> *Assertiveness does not mean that a person will always get his or her way in every situation, and it is likely the individual will handle some situations better than others. Remember that the goal of assertive communication is not to have an "I win, you lose" situation, but rather an "I win, you win" outcome.*

- How do I feel about losing?
- Did I express my opinion clearly? Why not? How could I make it more clear?
- Did I do the best I could do? How could I have done better?
- Was I in control when responding to the situation? When did I lose control? What should I have done to regain control?
- Did I stay focused on the issues? What side issues distracted me? How could I have avoided distractions?

- Did I allow the situation to get personal? Did the other person initiate the personal attack? How could I have redirected it away from the personal?
- Was what I asked for under my control? If not, why did I ask for it? What would have been more realistic?

Reviewing these questions and analyzing the answers will help when you attempt to be assertive in future communications. For example, if the answer to the second-to-last question was yes, then during the next communication, a special effort can be focused on avoiding personal attacks during the encounter. Learning to communicate assertively is a process of continual improvement.

Familiar Barriers to Change

Another risk factor that quickly becomes evident when changing to an assertive communication style is the impact that it has on those who know the person best. Sometimes family, friends, peers, and coworkers become barriers to change. As was mentioned earlier, change always produces some degree of stress. Those individuals who are closest to the person trying to initiate changes may feel uncomfortable because they have become accustomed to the old communication styles and behaviors over a long time. They can no longer anticipate and depend on the person's responding and reacting in the usual way. In addition, they will have to develop new communication patterns of their own to match the changes caused by assertive communication.

Sometimes family, friends, peers, and coworkers become so uncomfortable that they may try to sabotage the person's attempts at assertive communication. It is important to recognize why and when these sabotage efforts occur and also to remember that assertiveness is an internal, personal process. Everyone has a right to change, and it must be respectfully communicated to others that their support for these changes is important.

Box 14.2

Rights and Responsibilities of Assertiveness

- To act in a way that promotes your dignity and self-respect
- To be treated with respect
- To experience and express your thoughts and feelings
- To slow down and make conscious decisions before you act
- To ask for what you want
- To say "No"
- To change your mind
- To make mistakes
- To not be perfect
- To feel important and good about yourself
- To be treated as an individual with special values, skills, and needs
- To be unique
- To have your own feelings and opinions
- To say "I don't know"
- To feel angry, hurt, and frustrated
- To make decisions regarding your life
- To recognize that your needs are as important as others'

It is also important to know and periodically review the rights and responsibilities of assertiveness to help reinforce the assertive communication process. The rights and responsibilities of assertiveness are listed in Box 14.2.

Practice and reinforcement of assertiveness skills may be required, especially when preparing for an anticipated conflict negotiation or a confrontational meeting with another. Although a confrontational situation always produces anxiety, rather than being feared, it should be recognized as having the potential to be highly productive. Box 14.3 lists several behaviors that, if practiced and used, will help increase confidence and assertiveness skills during anticipated confrontational meetings.

You can use the checklist in Box 14.4 to determine your own degree of assertiveness.

Box 14.3

Conflict Resolution Tips

In nursing practice, good communication and conflict management skills are essential. The following tips may help resolve communication problems:

Improve Your Conflict Management Skills
- Seminars
- Books
- Mentors

Change Your Paradigm
- Focus on the positive, not the negative.
- Realize that appropriately confronting is a risk-taking activity for:

Better communication
- Improved relationships
- Improved teamwork
- Mentoring

Understand Your Values
- Focus on a win–win.
- Be willing to negotiate and compromise.
- Be direct and honest.
- Focus on the issues.
- Do not attack the person.
- Do not make judgments.
- Do not become the third person; encourage peers to go direct.
- Do not spread rumors.

Set Personal Guidelines
- Confront in private, never in front of anyone else.
- Confront the individual; do not report him or her to the supervisor first.
- Do not confront when you are angry.
- Start with an "I" message.
- Express your feelings and opinions.
- Allow the other person to talk without interruptions.
- Listen attentively.
- Set goals and future plans of action.
- Let it go.
- Keep it private and confidential.

Box 14.4

Assertiveness Self-Assessment

Evaluation

Statement   *Communication Behavior*

1. I didn't say what I really wanted to say at
   the last staff meeting.   _____

2. I always express my opinion because it is
   better than everyone else's.   _____

3. I have the courage to speak up almost all
   the time.   _____

4. I wish someone else would speak up at the
   meetings besides me.   _____

5. I am not intimidated by the high-pressure
   tactics of supervisors, physicians, and/or
   teachers.   _____

6. I have trouble stating my true feelings to
   those in authority.   _____

7. I really put that know-it-all aide in her place
   last shift.   _____

8. After the last meeting with my unit director I
   felt hopeless, resentful, and angry.   _____

9. I speak up in meetings without feeling
   defensive.   _____

10. When I need to confront someone, I avoid
    the problem because it will usually resolve
    itself.   _____

11. When I need to confront someone, I
    address them directly.   _____

12. When I confront someone, I let them know
    in no uncertain terms that they are wrong
    and need to change their behavior.   _____

13. When I'm reprimanded, I keep silent even
    though I'm seething inside.   _____

14. The last time I was asked to stay over for
    another shift, I said "no" and didn't feel
    guilty.   _____

Nonassertive Communication

Two types of interpersonal behaviors are considered to
be nonassertive: submissive and aggressive behaviors.

Submissive Communication

When people display submissive behavior or use a
submissive communication style, they allow their
rights to be violated by others. When people use
submissive behavior and submissive

communication, they surrender to the requests and
demands of others without regard to their own
feelings and needs. Many experts believe that
submissive behavior and communication patterns
are a protective mechanism that helps insecure
persons maintain their self-esteem by avoiding
negative criticism and disagreement from others. In
other situations, it may be a means of manipulation
through a type of passive–aggressive behavior.

Recall a recent exchange with someone (i.e., friend, instructor, parent, physician, etc.) where you felt you "lost" the exchange. How did you feel? How did you respond? How could using an assertive communication style have helped?

_____

_____

_____

_____

_____

_____

_____

_____

_____

_____

_____

Because of their great fear of displeasing others, personal rejection, or future retaliation, submissive communicators dismiss their own feelings as being unimportant. However, at a deeper level, submissive behavior and communication merely reinforce negative feelings of powerlessness, helplessness, and decreased self-worth. Rather than being in control of the communication or relationship, the person is trading his or her ability to choose what is best for the avoidance of conflict. Every communication by a submissive person becomes an "I lose, you win" situation. However, subconsciously it is more of "You may think you win, but I really am winning because I'm getting what I want or need."

> " *Rather than being divisive, diversity, when recognized and used correctly, can promote teamwork, improve communication, and increase productivity.* "

Aggressive Communication

Sometimes there is only a very fine line separating assertiveness from aggressive behavior and communication. Whereas assertive communication permits individuals to honestly express their ideas and opinions while respecting the rights, ideas, and opinions of others, aggressive communication strongly asserts the person's legitimate rights and opinions with little regard or respect for the rights and opinions of others.

Aggressive communication—used to humiliate, dominate, control, or embarrass the other person or lower that person's self-esteem—creates an "I win, you lose" situation. The other person may perceive aggressive behavior or communication as a personal attack. Aggressive behavior and communication are viewed by some psychologists as a protective mechanism that compensates for a person's own insecurities. By demeaning someone else, aggressive behavior allows the person to feel superior and helps inflate his or her self-esteem.

Aggressive communication can take several different forms, including screaming, sarcasm, rudeness, belittling jokes, and even direct personal insults. It is an expression of the negative feelings of power, domination, and low self-esteem. Although aggressive persons may seem outwardly to be in control, in reality they are merely reacting to the situation to protect their self-esteem.

DIVERSITY

Diversity is a multifaceted issue that involves many areas of people's lives, including culture, values, life experiences, instinctual responses, learned behaviors, personal strengths and weaknesses, and native abilities or skills. Each time two people interact, they bring the sum total of all these elements into their communication. To communicate effectively, both parties need to first recognize that the other person is different, then understand how these differences affect the communication, and finally accept and build on these differences.

Building on Differences

Rather than being divisive, diversity, when recognized and used correctly, can promote teamwork, improve communication, and increase productivity. Recognizing diversity helps people better understand each other as well as themselves. The ultimate goal of diversity recognition is to use each individual's strengths, rather than emphasizing the weaknesses, to build a stronger, more self-confident, and productive environment. For example, consider the following scenario:

> Anne B., RN, is a nurse in your unit who has a reputation for being a "nitpicker." She is constantly judging her peers and criticizing their actions on the basis of her own personal standards. Her judgments of others are not well accepted by her coworkers, who try to avoid her as much as possible.
> Betty A., RN, another nurse on the unit, always seems to be coming up with ideas for changing things in the unit, but then avoids joining the committees that are formed to put the ideas into practice. When she does join a committee, she quickly gets bored and does not follow through on her responsibilities. The other committee members become angry and frustrated by Betty's behavior. They feel that because it was her idea in the first place, she should work as hard as everyone else to make the change.
> You have been selected as the chairperson for a committee that has been formed to design a new client care documentation tool. Both Anne and Betty are on the committee. The other committee members are upset because Anne and Betty are on the committee. Everyone knows about Anne's and Betty's personality quirks. As chairperson of the team, you need to draw on everyone's strengths while recognizing their diversities to develop a new, comprehensive, yet easy-to-use form. If you perform well in your chairmanship role, each team member's self-esteem should be enhanced, and the morale of the group should improve.

At first glance, these may not seem like diversity issues. However, Anne is a detail-oriented person, whereas Betty is a visionary. Although their interests and abilities are very diverse, neither one is right or wrong. Persons who are preoccupied with details are left-brain dominant; creative, visionary individuals are usually right-brain dominant.

Two primary tasks are required to complete the project.

Task 1. Conduct brainstorming sessions with staff members, physicians, and ancillary personnel to develop a general concept of what the documentation should include and how the form should look.

Task 2. Work with the print shop to design the specific layout and content of the final form.

Plan

Task 1. It would be most appropriate to include Betty in the group that directs the brainstorming efforts and collects different ideas. She probably has no preconceived form in mind before starting the process and will feel comfortable investigating and researching a variety of different possibilities. Anne would have difficulty with this task. The lack of structure of the brainstorming process would make her feel out of control and would probably frustrate her urge to consider all the details of the project. Anne would most likely already have a good idea of the form she wanted.

Task 2. Anne would be much better at this task because of her orientation to structure and detail. Working with the print shop, she could focus her attention on each item on the form, decide where it should be placed, how much room it should be given, and how it flows in the document. She would make sure the form met all the standards and regulatory requirements of the Joint Commission as well as ensuring it was error free. Betty, on the other hand, would very quickly become bored with this aspect of the project. To her, all the attention given to the details would seem like a waste of time, and she would probably start recommending changes in other unit forms.

Placing people in the working environments that correspond with their strengths will ensure success for the project. The project will be a successful experience for the nurses and will promote positive changes in peer relationships.

A Focus on Strength

For many people, working with diversity can be difficult, especially when individuals feel insecure about their skills or abilities. When people feel insecure, they may revert to submissive or aggressive behavior or communication styles to hide their weaknesses or differences.

Because assertive persons recognize that everyone, including themselves, has both strengths and weaknesses, they feel comfortable with diversity and are more likely to accept and support others by recognizing and using their strengths. Focusing on people's strengths provides them with positive feedback and helps them grow personally and professionally. Focusing on weaknesses and differences tears down an individual's self-esteem, creates an uncomfortable work atmosphere, and makes people defensive and sometimes hostile.

PROBLEM SOLVING

Problem solving is a process that everyone uses all the time. For example, on the way to work, a tire goes flat on a person's car. That is a problem. How the person solves the problem depends partially on critical thinking skills, partially on past experiences, and partially on physical abilities. If the person with the flat tire is a 250-lb, 33-year-old male construction worker in good health, he most likely has changed tires before and will probably be physically able to remove the flat tire and put on the spare without difficulty. However, if the person with the flat tire is a 90-lb, 67-year-old female church organist who is unable to distinguish a lug nut from a tire valve, her solution to the problem will likely be different. She will probably call the automobile association and have someone come and change the flat for her.

One of the primary activities for nurses in the work setting is problem solving using the nursing process. It really does not matter whether the problem is client centered, management oriented, or an interpersonal issue; the nursing process is an excellent framework for problem resolution. It focuses on the goals of mutual interaction and communication to establish trust and respect. Using the process of assessment, analysis, planning, implementation, and evaluation helps the nurse organize and structure interpersonal interactions in a way that will produce an "I win, you win" situation.

Everyone experiences conflict at one time or another as a part of daily life. Often people feel more comfortable addressing the conflict that arises in their personal lives than the professional conflicts that arise in the job setting.

The basic problem-solving steps of the nursing process form the framework for successful conflict management. Nurses who are good problem solvers using the nursing process also tend to be good at conflict resolution, and nurses who are good at conflict resolution tend to be excellent problem solvers. Rather than being avoided in the work setting, conflict should be considered an opportunity to practice and grow in the use of problem-solving skills.

CONFLICT MANAGEMENT

Many people experience less anxiety when practicing personal problem solving than when they are involved in conflict management. Problem solving is often perceived as less emotional and more structured, whereas conflict management is considered to be more emotionally charged, with the potential to produce hostility. However, the steps of conflict management are almost identical to those of the nursing process. The one additional element that must be included in conflict resolution is the ability to use assertive behaviors and communication when discussing the issues.

Conflict on the Job

Everyone experiences conflict at one time or another as a part of daily life. Often people feel more comfortable addressing the conflict that arises in their personal lives than the professional conflicts that arise in the job setting.

A common situation that causes conflict is the nurse's feeling of being overworked or overwhelmed by assignments. The overloaded nurse might say something like "I have such a heavy load today, why isn't anyone helping me?" rather than asking a particular individual for help. When the person who is expected to help fails to comply with the implied request, the overworked nurse becomes angry and resentful. The other person may not understand where this anger is coming from and often avoids addressing the angry person for fear of making him or her angrier. This type of poor communication and lack of direct, respectful conflict management produces tension among workers, deterioration of working relationships, decreased efficiency, and, ultimately, poor client care.

Individuals are uncomfortable handling or addressing conflict for many reasons, including:

- Fear of retaliation
- Fear of ridicule
- Fear of alienating others
- Mistaken belief that they are unable to handle the conflict situation
- Feeling that they do not have the right to speak up
- Past negative experiences with conflict situations
- Family background and experiences
- Lack of education and skills in conflict resolution

Conflict Resolution

Several different strategies can be used to resolve workplace conflicts. Depending on a person's communication style and personality traits, different outcomes may occur.

Strategy 1: Ignore the Conflict

- Submissive personality: Person avoids bringing the issue to the other through fear of retaliation or ridicule if he or she confronts and expresses honest feelings or opinions.
- Aggressive personality: Person has decided not to pursue the conflict because the other person is "too stupid to understand" or it would just be a "waste of my time."

Strategy 2: Confront the Conflict

- Submissive personality: Person does not handle the situation directly but refers the problem to a supervisor or to another person for resolution.
- Assertive personality: Person sets up a time and place for a one-on-one meeting. At the meeting, the two parties focus on the issues that caused the conflict and negotiate to define goals and problem solve.
- Aggressive personality: Person confronts the other loudly, in front of an audience, and attacks the other's personality rather than the issue. Person either walks away before the other can speak or keeps talking without stopping and does not allow

the other person to respond. The communication is strictly one-sided and very negative.

Strategy 3: Postpone the Conflict

- Submissive person: Person keeps track of the issues until they reach a critical point, then dumps all the issues at one time on the offender in a highly aggressive manner. The other person generally has no idea why he or she is being attacked and may respond with anger or submission.
- Aggressive personality: Person waits until he or she can either use the incident as a threat or blackmail or express the conflict in front of an audience.

Professional nurses need to be assertive and feel comfortable when handling conflict situations and confronting others. The conflict situations that nurses may encounter range from uncooperative clients and lazy coworkers to hostile, insecure, but influential physicians and administrators. Practicing assertiveness skills during confrontational situations helps increase the nurse's confidence in handling daily work-related conflicts and allows the honest but respectful expression of opinion and ideas. Keep in mind that unresolved conflicts never really go away. Ignoring a conflict situation may postpone it, sometimes for a long time, but it will not resolve the issue. Unresolved conflicts often fester until they either reach the boiling point or are manifested in negative behaviors or feelings. Some of the feelings and behaviors that are symptoms of unresolved conflicts include:

> *Keep in mind that unresolved conflicts never really go away. Ignoring a conflict situation may postpone it, sometimes for a long time, but it will not resolve the issue.*

- Tension and anxiety manifested as sudden angry outbursts
- Generalized distrust among the staff members
- Gossiping and rumor spreading
- Intentional work sabotage
- Backstabbing and lack of cooperation
- Isolation of certain staff members
- Division and polarization of the staff
- Low-rated peer evaluation reports

Improved Communication Skills

Often, when conflict is handled appropriately, it produces much less anxiety than was initially anticipated. An individual who prepares for a say without interruption before responding creates an atmosphere where honest and open communication can occur. In some situations, merely allowing a person to ventilate emotions by using active listening reduces the levels of anger and animosity and sometimes even solves the conflict situation. Also, when intelligent people are allowed to speak openly and freely, they may be able to develop a new solution to the problem that they had not considered previously.

Before responding to a person, it is important to ask clarifying questions that validate the person's concerns, feelings, and perceptions. Validating will help ensure that the responses address the real issues. Also, avoid reflex-type reactions to hostile or aggressive statements. It is a human instinct to become defensive when attacked and to attack back. However, this behavior only escalates the anger and tension and blocks effective communication.

> *It is a very human tendency to become preoccupied with trivial and unimportant issues. If people spend large portions of their energy dealing with trivia, they will have little energy left to deal with major issues when they come along.*

Ignore Trivia

A third strategy that is useful in developing communication coping skills is to always make a conscious decision about the importance of the issue that needs to be discussed. When individuals can identify the issues that really matter and focus their efforts on them, they gain credibility among their peers and develop a reputation for caring and realism. Again, it is a very human tendency to become preoccupied with trivial and unimportant issues. If people spend large portions of their energy dealing with trivia, they will have little energy left to deal with major issues when they come along. By establishing and analyzing the outcomes to be attained and by being open to negotiations and compromise, both parties will leave the confrontation with a sense of accomplishment and fair resolution even if they did not get everything they wanted.

Setting the Stage

After a decision is made to deal with a difficult issue or person, it is important to set the stage for a positive experience. The location for the exchange should be private. The format of the meeting needs to be established ahead of time, including an explanation to the other person that both parties will take turns expressing their opinions and feelings without interruption.

Establishing Trust

An important issue in conflict negotiations is the establishment of trust. Trust can be established by a show of respect for the other person's opinions and ideas, and by talking first and directly to the person about the problem rather than to everyone else on the unit. Being talked about behind one's back makes people resentful and defensive.

You can reinforce trust by making it known that all you want is to resolve the issue and then move on. When the threat of retaliation is removed, people are more likely to express themselves honestly, as well as becoming more open to the other side's ideas. Once two people begin to trust each other, even if they disagree about some of the issues, they are much more likely to come to a satisfactory resolution of the problem.

The Exchange

When the exchange takes place, it is important to avoid "I" language and be direct by focusing on the facts and issues. Remember that active listening is a two-way street. A person's body language, tone of voice, and eye contact can say much more than the words spoken. Showing the other person that his or her opinion is respected, even if not agreed with, helps develop that important sense of trust between the two parties (Box 14.6).

After both people have had a chance to express themselves and validate the communication, they begin to address the issues and develop a solution for the problem. Sometimes there is a need to set goals for, or at least agree on, how the issues are to be approached and settled. It is fairly common that some issues will remain unresolved after the first meeting. A decision about when and where the second meeting will take place needs to be made before leaving the first meeting. Also, before leaving

Box 14.6

Seven Principles of Communication

1. Information giving is not communication.
2. The sender is responsible for clarity.
3. Use simple and exact language.
4. Feedback should be encouraged.
5. The sender must have credibility.
6. Acknowledgment of others is essential.
7. Direct channels of communication are best.

Source: Adapted from Tappen, RM: Nursing Leadership and Management Concept and Practice, ed. 3. F.A. Davis, Philadelphia, 1995, with permission.

the first meeting, both parties should summarize what they agreed to and how they felt about the exchange. This summarization will help clarify any miscommunications and give each party one last chance to introduce any issues that remain unresolved.

Dealing with difficult people and conflict resolution are never pleasant undertakings. However, like most skills, the more they are practiced, the more comfortable you will become using the communication techniques discussed. The importance of handling problematic situations in a timely, honest, and caring manner is self-evident. The anxiety and fear provoked by confrontation are part of the price that nurses must pay to do their jobs well and provide high-quality client care.

Conclusion

A person's professional and personal life is influenced by communication styles and behavioral patterns. The ability to analyze personal strengths, weaknesses, and communication behaviors is particularly important in dealing with difficult people.

Certain specific communication qualities and skills are essential for interacting with difficult people. First, it is important to develop the skill of assertive communication, which allows people to express themselves openly and honestly while respecting other people's opinions and ideas. Being able to identify submissive and aggressive behavior is also essential in trying to resolve problems, as well as recognizing issues of diversity, which underlie many problems in communication. Difficult situations are ultimately resolved through the practice of conflict management. Because it is an outgrowth and extension of the problem-solving method, nurses should be able to quickly grasp its structure and master its use.

Issues in Practice

Julie H, RN, has been working the 7 p.m. to 7 a.m. shift in a busy, 32-bed surgical unit of a large university hospital since her graduation from a small bachelor of science in nursing (BSN) program 6 months ago. Although Julie was told by the unit director when she was hired that she would have at least a full year of training before she had to work as charge nurse, tonight the other two RNs who usually work the shift called in sick, and Julie was left in charge. The 7 p.m. to 7 a.m. shift is always busy because the unit has to discharge clients who are ready to go home after surgery, as well as admit clients who are coming in for surgery the next day. Hospital policy requires that the RN make and sign both the discharge and admission assessments.

Although Julie is nervous about this new role as charge nurse, she feels that she can handle the responsibility if she has some additional help. Normal staffing for the unit on this shift is three registered nurses (RNs), three licensed practical nurses (LPNs), and three unlicensed assistive personnel (UAPs). Julie calls the house supervisor to see if she can get some help. The only place in the hospital that is not busy that night is the obstetrics (OB) unit, so the supervisor sends two of the OB unit's UAPs to the surgical unit to help Julie.

It was not the help Julie really wanted, but she feels that she can handle the responsibility. However, when Julie begins to make assignments, the older of the OB unit UAPs, Hanna J, informs Julie that she, for the past 15 years, had worked only in the newborn nursery and does not know anything about the care of adult clients who had surgery. In addition, Hanna states that she has a bad back and cannot lift or turn adult clients and is afraid that she might catch some disease from the adults that she would take back to the babies. Julie asks Hanna, "What do you feel you are qualified to do on the surgical unit?" In response, Hanna crosses her legs, folds her arms across her chest, puts her head down, and mumbles under her breath, "A lot more than a new know-it-all RN like you."

Answers to Case Study Questions

Issues in Practice: Managing Change

1. The underlying problem was that there was too much change too quickly. Even though the staff recognized that change was needed, there is always a built-in resistance to change. Sudden, unpredictable change creates the most anxiety and therefore the most resistance. It also can produce a great deal of cohesion among those being asked to change when it is viewed as a threat. This last point is borne out by the nurses seeking to organize into a collective bargaining unit.

2. The director of the unit could have decreased resistance by having the staff "buy into" the changes, allowing them to participate in decision making from the beginning. Also, the whole process of change could have been slowed down–perhaps spread over 1 year to 18 months. A slower process would have given the nurses a chance to adjust to one change before another was implemented.

Sources: Tappen, RM: Essentials of Nursing Leadership and Management. ed 4. F.A. Davis, Philadelphia, 2006.

Pearce, C: Leadership resource: Ten steps to managing change. Nursing Management 13(10): 25, 2007.

Critical Thinking Exercises

- What messages, both verbal and nonverbal, are being communicated? How should Julie respond to this comment? What should she do to rectify the situation?
- Using what you learned in this chapter, identify the personality type of each of the persons involved in the situation.
- How can the RN best communicate with this UAP? What were some of the communication mistakes the RN made?
- What background, cultural, and diversity factors played a part in this situation? Develop a strategy for resolution of this conflict.
- Make a list of your values and where they came from. Describe how each value affects your work ethic and life.
- List your communication strengths and weaknesses. Rank them on a scale of 1 to 10 (10 being the highest). Determine which weaknesses you want to change and create an improvement plan.
- Identify your primary communication style and character type.
- Complete this statement, using as many situations or statements as possible: "In a conflict situation, I have difficulty saying _____." Analyze reasons that prevent you from saying it. What would have been the worst thing that could have happened to you if you had said it? Create a phrase that you feel comfortable with that you could use the next time you want to say something difficult to the members of your team.
- Identify the communication and behavior characteristics of your work group or team. List areas of diversity for each member, including yourself. Identify their strengths and weaknesses. Identify methods for using the team members' diversity to enhance the team.

Bibliography

Banks, C: Careers: Improving your communication skills. Nursing Times 101(3):48–49, 2005.

Callister, L: Toward evidence-based practice: How delivery ward staff exercise power over women in communication. MCN 30(1): 70, 2005.

Cole, A: Reaping the benefits of teamwork. Nursing Times 101(1): 59, 2005.

Dunham, K, and Smith, S: How to survive and maybe even love your life as a nurse. F.A. Davis, Philadelphia, 2005.

Grossman, SC, and Valiga, TM, The New Leadership Challenge: Creating the Future of Nursing, ed. 2. F.A. Davis, Philadelphia, 2005.

McGrath, JM: The influence of electronic medical record usage on nonverbal communication in the medical interview. Health Informatics Journal 13(2): 105–118, 2007.

McHarg, L: Starting out: Good communication skills can have a magical effect. Nursing Times 103 (22). 13, 2007.

Patronis Jones, RA: Nursing Leadership and Management. F.A. Davis, Philadelphia, 2007.

Pearce, C: Leadership resource. Ten steps to managing change. Nursing Management 13(10): 25, 2007.

Raiger, J: Applying a cultural lens to the concept of burnout. Journal of Transcultural Nursing 16(1): 71–76, 2005.

Stone, JH: Communication between physicians and patients in the era of e-medicine. New England Journal of Medicine 14; 356(24): 2451–2454, 2007.

Tappen, RM: Essentials of Nursing Leadership and Management, ed. 4. F.A. Davis, Philadelphia, 2006.

Windsor, K: Managing conflict: Get rid of the baggage. Advance for Nurses 15–16, 2006.

15

Delegation and Supervision in Nursing

Joseph T. Catalano

Learning Objectives

After completing this chapter, the reader will be able to:

- Apply the principles of delegation to nursing practice.
- Analyze and identify situations where delegation is used improperly.
- Discuss the legal implications of delegation in the current health-care setting.
- Distinguish between delegation and supervision.

AN ESSENTIAL SKILL

In today's health-care system, delegation has become an essential component of client care and management of nursing units. It allows health-care managers to maximize the use of caregivers who are educated at multiple levels in a variety of programs. Delegation, if performed properly, permits nurses to meet the requirements of quality care for all clients and has become a basic skill that registered nurses (RNs) must learn. The goal of delegation is to meet the cost restraints of limited health-care budgets by using less-expensive personnel to maximize the use of time by RNs and to promote team building.

DELEGATION OR SUPERVISION?

Although delegation and supervision are closely related concepts, they are different. **Delegation** is recognized as assigning or designating a competent individual the responsibility of carrying out a specific group of nursing tasks in the provision of care for certain clients. Delegation includes the understanding that the authorized person is acting in the place of the RN and may be carrying out tasks that generally fall under the RN's scope of practice. **Supervision,** on the other hand, is the initial direction and periodic evaluation of a person performing an assigned task to ensure that he or she is meeting the standards of care. Although delegation almost always requires supervision, it is possible to have supervision without delegation.

When nurses delegate nursing tasks to non-nurses, the RNs are always legally responsible for supervising those people to ensure that the care given meets the standards of care. However, if the facility, the state board of nursing, or some other official body has a predesignated list of tasks that non-nursing personnel may undertake in the care of clients, then the RN is responsible only for supervising them to make sure the tasks are carried out safely.

Legally, the power to delegate is restricted to professionals who are licensed and governed by a statutory practice act. RNs are considered professionals, with state-sanctioned licenses governed by a nurse practice act, and therefore are authorized to delegate independent nursing functions to other personnel.

NURSING RESPONSIBILITIES WHEN DELEGATING

Look to All These Things

The concept of delegation has been a part of health care since the time of Florence Nightingale, when she instructed the nurses she educated ". . . to look to all these things yourself does not mean to do them yourself."[1] In more recent times, the American Nurses Association (ANA) initially addressed and defined delegation in 1991 when it was beginning to become a more widespread practice in health care. They further refined the definition in 1997.

The ANA defines delegation as "the transfer of responsibility for the performance of an activity from one individual to another while retaining accountability for the outcome."[2] The ANA stresses the belief that even though the leader or manager delegates a task to another employee, he or she remains responsible and accountable for the care that is provided.

> *When nurses delegate nursing tasks to non-nurses, the RNs are always legally responsible for supervising those people to ensure that the care given meets the standards of care.*

The Nurse's Responsibilities

Assess the Client. Prior to delegating any task, RNs should give careful consideration to the condition of the client and the client's health-care needs. Assessing clients is a designated **responsibility** of RNs. Without a thorough assessment, it is likely that critical needs will remain unidentified by less-trained personnel, leading to potential errors in care. Clients who are relatively stable and not likely to experience drastic changes in health-care status are the most suitable for delegation. Also, the tasks being

delegated must be relatively uncomplicated and routine, must be performed without variation from policy or procedure, and should not require the use of nursing judgment while being performed.

What Do You Think?

Is delegation used in the facility where you have clinical rotations? Who does the delegation on the unit? Does it work well?

_____

_____

_____

_____

_____

_____

_____

_____

_____

_____

_____

_____

_____

Know Staff Availability. The delegating nurse needs to know the availability of staff, the education, and competency levels of the personnel to be assigned. These factors must be matched with the level of care required by the client. Key information to obtain is how often the delegatee has performed the required tasks or cared for this type of client, what units the delegatee has worked on and feels comfortable in, and his or her organizational abilities.

Know the Job Description. One large group of health-care workers to whom RNs delegate is generally called unlicensed assistive personnel (UAP). This group includes individuals who have been through some type of training program ranging from a few hours up to several months (Box 15.1). They may receive a certificate of completion, but they do not have any type of licensure and therefore do not have legal status.

Box 15.1

Other Names for Unlicensed Assistive Personnel

Certified Nurse Assistant (CNA)
Nurse's Aide
Home Health Aide
Registered Nurse Assistant (RNA)
Nurse Technician (NT)
Medication Technician (MT)
Nursing Assistant
Patient Care Assistant (PCA)
Orderly
Patient Attendant
Psychiatric Attendant

The RN needs to know the institution's official position description for the unlicensed assistive personnel (UAP) as well as the individual UAP's abilities. For example, the position description may state that the UAP can care for postoperative clients who have multiple wound drains. However, when the RN assigns a specific UAP to such a postoperative client, the nurse discovers that the UAP has worked only in the newborn nursery for the past 5 years and has no knowledge of how to care for adult postoperative clients. If the RN assigns this UAP anyway and a major complication develops as a result of the UAP's lack of competence (even though the position description states that this is an appropriate function for the UAP), the RN will be held legally responsible for the poor outcome. When the RN determines that the client's needs match the skills and abilities of the UAP or licensed practical nurse (LPN), only then should that person be assigned.

Educate the Staff Member. RNs who delegate are also responsible for educating the UAP about the task to be done. If the UAP is unfamiliar with the task, the RN is required to demonstrate how the task or procedure is performed and then document the training. Education also includes telling the UAP what is expected in the completion of the task and what complications to watch for and report to the RN. The ANA suggests that the RN watch the UAP perform the designated task at least initially, then make periodic observations throughout

> *It is important to remember that when nurses delegate nursing tasks, they are not delegating nursing.*

the shift to ensure safe and competent care for the client.[3] Furthermore, the RN must always be available to answer questions and help the UAP whenever assistance is required. Consider the following situation:

Elsie Humber, RN, is the evening charge nurse on a busy oncology unit of the county hospital. On one particularly busy evening, she discovers during shift report that one of the scheduled LPNs has called in sick and no other LPNs are available to take her place. Ms. Humber assigns the LPN's duties and clients, including a heat lamp treatment for a decubitus ulcer, to a UAP who has worked on the unit for several months. The UAP protests the assignment, but Ms. Humber rebukes her, saying, "I have no one else. If you don't care for these clients, they won't get any care this shift." In setting up the heat lamp treatment, the UAP knocks the lamp over and burns the client. Because of his suppressed immune system from chemotherapy and generally debilitated condition, the burn does not heal and develops into an infection. The client later sues the hospital for malpractice. The hospital in turn attempts to shift the legal responsibility for the burn to Ms. Humber. Who is legally responsible for the incident? Does the client have grounds for a successful case?

(text continues on page 311)

Issues in Practice

Leadership/Management Case Study

Poor Staff Performance

Angela is the Emergency Department Nurse Manager in a small rural hospital. Hiring qualified RNs for her staff had become more of a challenge as the nursing shortage worsened. For eight months, a full-time evening RN position had gone unfilled. During this time, the position was filled by cross-training nurses from other departments, paying bonus shifts and overtime, contracting with agencies, and hiring available nurses from other hospitals. These nurses were excellent, but the continuity of regular staffing was lacking in the ED. Angela believed the lack of continuity was negatively affecting morale and efficiency in the department.

At this hospital, the Vice President of Nursing Services (VPNS) made all the final decisions about hiring new staff after consulting with the nurse managers. The VPNS suggested an employee who was interested in the position but did not have the experience of the nurses usually hired for the ED. Ted, who had been an LPN in a long-term care facility, had gone back to nursing school and received his BS in nursing 6 months earlier. His most recent experience after graduating was working in a physician's office. Although his combined health-care experience was more than 10 years, he had never worked in an acute care setting.

When Angela interviewed Ted, he appeared highly motivated, intelligent, a self-starter, and well groomed. Because of the nursing shortage, it had become fairly common practice to let new graduates work in specialty areas, such as EDs or ICUs, without the traditional mandatory year of medical–surgical experience. Angela believed that Ted could, over time, learn the ED routines. He would have an experienced RN working with him for at least a year. Also, at this hospital, 90 percent of ED visits were nonurgent, office-type visits. Ted's experience of coordinating and moving clients through a busy office practice would be an asset.

Angela started by giving Ted a thorough and extended orientation to the ED. She consulted with each nurse he would be working with and asked for support in mentoring him. She encouraged the nurses to begin by letting Ted care for the more routine cases and then gradually allow him to care for clients with more acute conditions. During the orientation, Ted seemed to master the assessment and documentation aspects of the job well. Ted was also studying for ACLS certification. Obviously, he was unfamiliar with many of the medications routinely used in the ED. Angela encouraged him to ask questions and use the unit's medication reference books.

However, despite all the efforts at orientation, Ted made four serious medication errors during his first 2 months in the ED. Fortunately they were discovered early enough so that no serious harm came to the clients. Ted was counseled by the hospital's Nurse Educator, who worked with him on a medication review. He completed the course of study successfully and passed the medication exam.

Angela began receiving feedback from the other ED staff members who had been working with Ted. They expressed insecurity about the quality of the care he was giving, and some believed he was not "carrying his load" during busy

(continued)

Issues Now (continued)

times. He would manipulate client assignments and shift work to other nurses. A personality conflict had also arisen between him and some of the nurses. They had begun watching his every move and documenting what he was doing or not doing. Some observed that he would leave the ED for unscheduled long breaks without notifying anyone. Others remarked that he was not monitoring clients with cardiac problems as closely as they thought he should. Angela noted that Ted seemed to have lost the support of his coworkers and that the overall morale of the unit was deteriorating.

Angela met with Ted and suggested that he attend a Certified Emergency-Room Nurse review course to improve his knowledge and skills in emergency nursing. He did attend the course. Angela also met with him several times to develop plans for improving his work. Each time he would complete the requirements of the plan, and the situation would improve for a while. After a week or two, however, he would slip back into his previous behaviors.

As the morale of the unit continued to decline, Angela began feeling depressed and under stress. She sensed that she was losing the credibility and respect of her staff. One day she overheard one of the staff nurses say, "At this hospital, any warm body can have a job!," implying that the standards and quality of care were poor. On the other hand, Angela felt responsible for placing Ted in a situation in which he could not succeed.

QUESTIONS FOR THOUGHT

1. Identify the erroneous assumptions used in the initial hiring of Ted.
2. What other measures could Angela have taken to help Ted in his adjustment to the ED?
3. What can Angela do now about the situation?

(Answers are found at the end of the chapter.)

Predictable and Uncomplicated

When a nurse delegates tasks, the outcomes of tasks should be expected and predictable. For example, when a UAP is assigned the task of feeding a client who has suffered a stroke and has hemiplegia, the predicted outcome will be that the client will eat and not choke on the food. The task should not require excessive supervision, complex decision making, or detailed assessment during its performance. If any of these elements are required, then it needs to be reassigned to an RN.

It is important to remember that when nurses delegate nursing tasks, they are *not* delegating nursing. Professional nursing practice is both a science, based on a unique body of knowledge, and an art, guided by the nursing process. It is not merely a collection of tasks. Of all health-care workers, professional nurses are the most qualified to provide holistic care of the client by promoting health and treating disease. Nurses' education and experience provide them with the skills and knowledge to coordinate and supervise nursing care and to delegate specific tasks to others.

Although mastering delegation skills can seem like a daunting task, a nurse can take several common-sense steps to attain this skill (Box 15.2). Nursing students often have tasks delegated to them by the RNs on the units where they are having clinical rotations. It is easy to identify the RNs who have developed good delegation skills and those who still need to work on those skills.

DEVELOPING DELEGATION SKILLS

Clear Communication

In the process of developing delegation skills, students should try to emulate the good delegators. Develop good communication and interpersonal relationship skills. Make eye contact with the other person, be pleasant, and ask for suggestions. However, avoid allowing the person to whom the tasks are being delegated to control the exchange by intimidation or resistance.

After a nurse delegates a task, it's a good idea to make a written list of the responsibilities that are expected from the person, if one does not already exist. The list will help clarify what is expected and head off possible misunderstandings. It is also important to be flexible. Clients' conditions change, new clients may be admitted, and other clients may be

---

B o x   1 5 . 2

Five Rights of Delegation

- Right task
  Do the tasks delegated follow written policy guidelines?
- Right person
  Does the person have the proper qualifications for the tasks?
- Right direction or communication
  Are the instructions and outcomes clearly stated? When should the person report changes?
- Right supervision or feedback
  How can the delegation process be improved? Are the client goals for care being achieved?
- Right circumstances
  Are the tasks that are being delegated free from requiring independent nursing judgments?

Sources: Fisher, M: Do you have delegation savvy? Nursing 2000(9):58–59, 2000.
Tappen, RM: Nursing Leadership and Management, ed. 4. F.A. Davis, Philadelphia, 2001.
Wheeler, J: How to delegate your way to a better working life. Nursing Times 97(36):34–35, 2001.

---

discharged. The original assignments may have to be modified in response to changes in the environment.

Careful Monitoring

Effective delegation includes monitoring the delegatees while they are giving care. Are they doing what they should be doing? Do they understand the responsibilities involved in the client's care? Help them if they need help. Effective delegation also presumes that the delegator will teach the delegatees who demonstrate a lack of knowledge. Most important, at the end of the shift, say, "Thank you. I appreciate the hard work (good job) you've done today."

Certain delegation situations may place the RN at an increased risk for liability (Boxes 15.3, 15.4). When delegating, try to avoid the following:

- Assigning tasks that are highly invasive or have the potential to cause significant physical harm to clients
- Assigning tasks that are designated under the scope of practice or standards of care as belonging

Box 15.3

Barriers to Effective Delegation

A. Internal barriers (person delegating):
1. Lack of experience delegating
2. Lack of confidence in others
3. Personal insecurity
4. Demanding perfectionism
5. Poor organizational skills
6. Indecision
7. Poor communication skills
8. Lack of confidence in self
9. Fear of not being liked by everyone
10. Micromanaging management style
B. External barriers (circumstances or person being delegated to):
1. Unclear policies about delegation
2. Policies that do not tolerate mistakes
3. Management-by-crisis model for facility
4. Unclear delineation of authority and responsibilities
5. Poor staffing
6. Lack of competence
7. Overdependence on the person delegating
8. Unwillingness to accept responsibility for one's own practice
9. Immersion in trivia and gossip
10. Work overload

Source: Tappen, RM, et al.: Essentials of Nursing Leadership and Management. F.A. Davis, Philadelphia, 2001.

Box 15.4

Delegation Decision Tree

1. Are there laws and rules in place supporting the rules of delegation?
2. Is the task within the scope of practice of the UAP, LPN/LVN, RN, or new graduate?
3. Has there been an assessment of the client's needs?
4. Is the UAP, LPN/LVN, RN, or new graduate competent to accept the delegation?
5. Does the ability of the caregiver match the care needs of the client?
6. Can the task be completed without requiring nursing judgments?
7. Is the result of the task somewhat predictable?
8. Can the task be safely performed according to directions?
9. Can the task be performed without repeated assessment?
10. Is appropriate supervision available?

Source: Tappen, RM: Nursing Leadership and Management, ed. 4. F.A. Davis, Philadelphia, 2001.

What Do You Think?

What qualities have you observed in good delegators? What qualities made the poor delegators ineffective?

exclusively to the RN (admission assessments, care plan development)
• Assigning tasks that the person is not trained for or lacks the knowledge to safely complete
• Assigning tasks when there is inadequate time to safely monitor or evaluate the practice of the person performing the tasks[4]

The long-term effect of the growing trend to delegation on the quality of client care remains to be seen. However, the knowledge and judgment of the professional nurse will remain essential elements in any health-care system reforms, including clinical integration, case management, outsourcing practices, **total quality management (TQM),** and **continuous quality improvement (CQI).**

LEGAL ISSUES IN DELEGATION

One area of fallout from the movement to managed care is the increase in nurses' liability for lawsuits in the area of supervision and delegation. In the search for cost-effective client care, current managed-care strategies attempt to make optimal use of relatively expensive RNs by replacing them with less-costly and less-educated personnel. As more and more health-care facilities move toward restructuring, the use of UAPs who have minimal education and experience will continue to increase. Although RNs have always been responsible for the delegation of some tasks and the supervision of less-qualified health-care providers, it is now one of the primary functions of RNs in today's health-care system.

Delegation does have some advantages. It is an RN extender in that it allows more care to be given to more clients than can be given by one RN. Delegation can free the RN from lower-level, time-consuming tasks so that more time can be spent planning for care and performing those skills that less prepared individuals would be unable to perform. For those to whom tasks are delegated, it can serve as an incentive to learn additional skills, increase knowledge, develop a sense of initiative, and perhaps seek further formal education. Delegation, if performed properly, maintains accountability and decision making where they belong—with the RN.

"Why don't I get someone else to remove Mrs. Lemke's sutures?"

WHO CAN DELEGATE—LEGALLY?

An Ethical Obligation

Most state practice acts do *not* give delegatory authority to **dependent practitioners** such as licensed practical nurses and licensed vocational nurses (LPNs/LVNs) or UAPs. In addition, professionals who delegate specific tasks retain accountability for the proper and safe completion of those tasks, as well as responsibility for determining whether the assigned personnel are competent to carry out the task. One exception

occurs when the person who is assigned a task also has a license and the tasks fall under that person's scope of practice.[5] Then again, the RN is responsible only for supervision of the other licensed person. These situations are often seen when LPNs or LVNs are assigned to client care.

The delegation and supervision responsibilities of RNs have been and continue to be a major concern for the nursing profession, both ethically and legally. The ANA Code of Ethics for Nurses states, "The nurse is responsible and accountable for individual nursing practice and determines the appropriate delegation of tasks consistent with the nurse's obligation to provide optimum patient care" (statement 4).[6] From the ethical viewpoint, RNs have an obligation to refuse assignments that they are not competent to carry out and to refuse to delegate particular nursing tasks to individuals who they believe are unable or unprepared to perform them (Fig. 15.1).

> " *From the ethical view, RNs have an obligation to refuse assignments that they are not competent to carry out and to refuse to delegate particular nursing tasks to individuals who they believe are unable or unprepared to perform them.* "

Direct and Indirect Delegation

The legal side of the delegation issue has also been addressed by the ANA in the *ANA Basic*

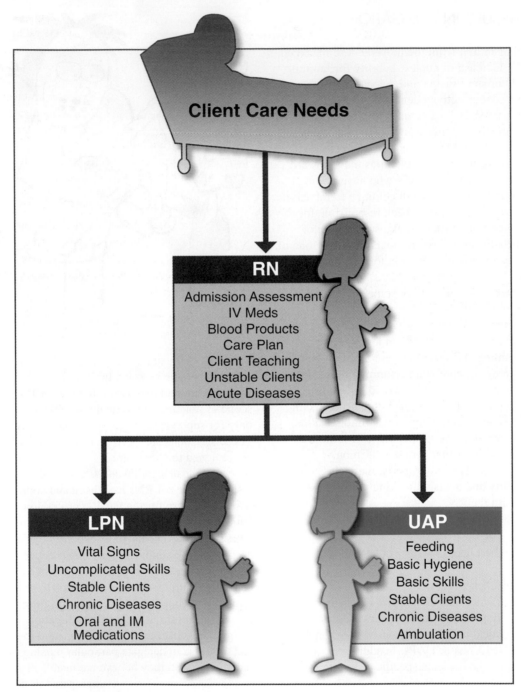

Client Care Needs

RN
Admission Assessment
IV Meds
Blood Products
Care Plan
Client Teaching
Unstable Clients
Acute Diseases

LPN
Vital Signs
Uncomplicated Skills
Stable Clients
Chronic Diseases
Oral and IM
Medications

UAP
Feeding
Basic Hygiene
Basic Skills
Stable Clients
Chronic Diseases
Ambulation

Figure 15.1 Delegation of responsibilities.

Guide to Safe Delegation. This document makes a distinction between direct delegation, which is a specific decision made by the RN about who can perform what tasks, and indirect delegation, which is a list of tasks that certain health-care personnel can perform that is produced by the health-care facility.[3]

The **consensus** among many experts is that indirect delegation is really a form of covert institutional licensure. Lists of activities from the facility allowing non-nursing personnel, who do not have the education of the RN, to carry out professional nursing functions is a de facto permission to practice nursing without a license. Indirect delegation places RNs in a precarious legal position.

Basically, indirect delegation takes away much of the authority of the RN to assign personnel tasks, yet the RN remains accountable for the safe completion of the tasks under the doctrines of **respondeat superior** and **vicarious liability.** Although some states are beginning to address the UAP and delegation issues in their nurse practice acts, many states either have no official standards for UAP delegation or include UAP standards under the medical practice act.

Delegation and the NCLEX

Because delegation is such an important issue in today's health-care system, and because decisions

> *Most state practice acts do not give delegatory authority to dependent practitioners like licensed practical nurses/licensed vocational nurses (LPNs/LVNs) or UAPs.*

about delegation require considerable critical thinking skill, the number of questions about delegation on the NCLEX has been increasing steadily. It is not unusual for 10 percent to 25 percent of questions to deal with delegation issues. One problem graduates may encounter with these questions is that the NCLEX uses strict parameters for determining delegation. In the real world of health care, LPNs, LVNs, and UAPs often perform functions beyond their legal scope of practice. The following lists may be helpful in answering NCLEX questions about delegation:

Although LPNs and LVNs can do most skills, for the NCLEX they:

- **Cannot** do admission assessments
- **Cannot** give IV push medications
- **Cannot** write nursing diagnoses
- **Cannot** do most teaching
- **Cannot** do complex skills
- **Cannot** take care of clients with acute conditions
- **Cannot** take care of unstable clients

For questions concerning UAPs, CNAs, and aides on the NCLEX:

- Look for the **lowest level of skill** required for the task.
- Look for the **least complicated** task.
- Look for the **most stable** client.
- Look for the client with the **chronic illness**.

Conclusion

With the increased use of less-educated and unlicensed personnel in today's health-care system, it is essential that the nurse develop effective delegation and supervision skills. The nurse needs to be mindful that the tasks that can be delegated can change on the basis of work setting, client needs, position descriptions, institutional training of personnel, and the ever-changing requirements of nurse practice acts and professional standards. Nurses also need to know when delegation is inappropriate.

Critical Thinking Exercises

- Obtain a copy of your state's nurse practice act. Review the section that deals with delegation. Apply those criteria to the case study at the beginning of this chapter.
- As a student, you have had tasks delegated to you. Identify how delegation has changed in regard to your learning and level of skills as you have progressed through your program.
- Obtain a copy of the policy on delegation from at least two of the clinical sites where you have practiced. How do these policies differ? How are they similar? What are the reasons for the similarities and differences?

Answers to Case Study Questions

Issues in Practice:
Leadership/Management Case Study

1. The first erroneous assumption was that a nurse with no acute care hospital experience could be taught to provide safe care in a specialty area with only minimal orientation. The second assumption was that the other nurses would be enthusiastic about spending extra time and effort in orienting and teaching a new nurse. This group seemed to resent the imposition. The third assumption was that, because most of the care in the ED was "routine," a person with only limited experience could work there.

2. When Angela first discovered that Ted was having problems adjusting, she could have suggested that he work on a medical–surgical unit and cross-train for the ED. This approach would have given him a range of learning experiences that he could later apply to his work in the ED. After Ted had received 6 to 8 months of medical–surgical experience and cross-training, Angela and the other unit managers would have been able to better evaluate his skills and knowledge.

3. Because of the declining morale and the loss of trust in Angela by the staff, Ted needs to be removed from the ED. If his performance so indicates, he may be terminated. However, in this age of nursing shortages, a better option would be to place him on another unit and evaluate him there. Not everyone is destined to be an ED nurse, and Ted may find another unit with a more relaxed pace to be more suited to his personality and skills.

References

1. Nightingale, F: Notes on Nursing. What It Is and What It Is Not. Harrison and Sons, London, 1859, p 17.
2. American Nurses Association: Position Statement: Registered Nurse Utilization of Unlicensed Assistive Personnel. American Nurses Association, Washington, DC, 1997
3. American Nurses Association: Registered Professional Nurses and Unlicensed Assistive Personnel, ed. 2. American Nurses Association, Washington, DC, 1996.
4. Hudspeth, R: Understanding delegation is a critical competency for nurses in the new millennium. Nursing Administration Quarterly 31(2):183–184, 2007.
5. Guitard, V: Ask a practice advisor. Assigning vs delegating: Is there a difference in nursing care? Informatics Nursing 38(1): 12, 21, 2007.
6. ANA Code of Ethics for Nurses 2001. Available at: www.ana.org.

Bibliography

American Nurses Association: Policy Series: Regulation of Unlicensed Assistive Personnel. American Nurses Association, Washington, DC, 1996.
Creighton, H: Law Every Nurse Should Know, ed. 5. WB Saunders, Philadelphia, 1986.
Curtis, E: Delegation: A key function of nursing. Nurse Manager 11(4):26–31, 2004.
Garvis, M: Advice of counsel: When it's OK for an RN to delegate. RN 66(12):70–71, 2003.
Henderson, L: Nursing delegation. Pulse 41(2):1, 4, 2004.
Khaliullah, K: Professional misconduct: Nurse who compromised patient care through delegating a task. British Journal of Nursing 13(11): 668, 2004.
Pearce, C: Careers: Honing the art of effective delegation. Nursing Times 100(29):46–47, 2004.
Tappen, RM: Nursing Leadership and Management, ed. 4. F.A. Davis, Philadelphia, 2001.
Tappen, RM, et al.: Essentials of Nursing Leadership and Management, ed. 2. F.A. Davis, Philadelphia, 2001.
Teasdale, K: Tips for the top: Better delegation. Professional Nursing 19(12):56, 2004.
Williams, J: Navigating the difficulties of delegation. Nursing 34(9):32, 2004.

by collective bargaining units, such as strikes or work slowdowns. There is a feeling among many health-care providers that these types of actions constitute abandonment of their clients and therefore violate the code of ethics.

Those who support collective bargaining stress that poor working conditions, such as lack of qualified staff, are as much a threat to clients' health and well-being as the work actions taken to correct these conditions. The ability of nurses simply to threaten to strike, even though the strike may never materialize, is often powerful enough to bring about change.[8]

Law requires that a 10-day notice must be given before a strike takes place. This gives the hospital a chance to prepare for the strike and to make changes to ensure client safety, such as transferring critical-care clients to another hospital, eliminating elective surgeries, and refusing to admit new clients. If the hospital fails to take appropriate measures when they have received adequate notice, then the issue of client abandonment becomes their responsibility, not that of the nurses who have gone on strike.

In the few times when nurses have gone on strike, client safety and well-being have not been affected. The institutions involved were always given enough lead time to discharge or transfer the majority of the clients. The few remaining clients were cared for by management personnel, who are not covered by unions.

Is It Divisive?

Nurse Against Nurse

Does the process of collective bargaining set nurse against nurse? Collective bargaining is adversarial by nature. It sets two groups, management and employees, against each other. Although this relationship can result in conflict, it allows the staff nurses to be heard and to initiate changes that affect the practice of nursing. Nurses have been attempting for years to improve working conditions in the health-care setting and to achieve **comparable worth.** Administrators pay little attention to an

> *The collective bargaining unit establishes a grievance procedure by means of which the employee can bring a complaint against management without fear of reprisals. These grievance procedures also provide a mechanism for the employee to follow up on the complaint to a satisfactory conclusion.*

individual nurse or to a small group of concerned nurses. When a collective bargaining unit speaks for all of the nurses, however, administration will listen.[1]

The chief executive officer (CEO) of a large home health-care agency in a southwestern resort area called a general staff meeting. She reported that the agency had grown rapidly and was now the largest in the area.

"Much of our success is due to the professionalism and commitment of our staff members," she said. "With growth come some problems, however. The most serious problem is the fluctuation in client census. Our census peaks in the winter months when seasonal visitors are here and troughs in the summer. In the past, when we were a small agency, we all took our vacations during the slow season. This made it possible to continue to pay everyone his or her full salary all year. However, with the pressures to reduce costs and the large number of staff members we now have, we cannot continue to do this. We are very concerned about maintaining the high quality of client care currently provided, but we have calculated that we need to reduce staff by 30 percent over the summer to survive financially."

The CEO then invited comments from the staff members. The majority of the nurses said they wanted and needed to work full-time all year. Most supported families and had to have a steady income all year around. "My rent does not go down in the summer," said one. "Neither does my mortgage or the grocery bill," said another. A small number said that they would be happy to work part-time in the summer if they could be guaranteed full-time employment from October through May. "We have friends who would love this work schedule," they added.

"That's not fair," protested the nurses who needed to work full-time all year. "You can't replace us with part-time staff." The discussion grew louder and the participants more agitated. The meeting ended without a solution to the problem. Although the CEO promised to consider all points of view before making a decision, the nurses left the meeting feeling very confused and concerned about the security of their future income. Some grumbled that they probably would begin looking for new positions "before the ax falls."

> " *Collective bargaining does not have to be adversarial, and in facilities where the administration is open to change and the collective bargaining unit is realistic in its requests, the process can be very smooth and amicable.* "

The next day, the CEO received a telephone call from the nurses' union representative. "If what I heard about the meeting yesterday is correct," said the representative, "your plan is in violation of our collective bargaining contract." The CEO reviewed the contract and found that the representative was correct. A new solution to the financial problems caused by the seasonal fluctuation in client census would have to be found.

Source: Tappen, RM, et al.: Essentials of Nursing Leadership and Management, ed. 2. F.A. Davis, Philadelphia, 2001, pp 106–107, with permission.)

Closed or Open Shop?

Different collective bargaining units have different requirements for membership, which are often included in the negotiations. Many unions negotiate a *closed shop* or *agency shop* clause in the contract. A closed shop institution requires that all the employees pay membership dues whether they belong to the union or not. The rationale behind the closed shop approach is that because all the employees benefit from the union's negotiations, they should all pay for it. It also encourages employees to join the union because they are already paying the dues.

However, many states have *right to work* laws that make closed shop contracts illegal. In these states, the *open shop* collective bargaining model is used, and only those employees who desire to be members join the union and pay dues. There is more chance for nurse-to-nurse conflicts in open shop institutions because of the divisions between those who belong to the union and those who do not.

Collective bargaining does not have to be adversarial, and in facilities where the administration is open to change and the collective bargaining unit is realistic in its requests, the process can be very smooth and amicable.

Is There a Threat to Job Security?

Although the main goals of collective bargaining are improvement of working conditions and protection from unfair labor practices, it can itself pose a threat to job security. In some cases, employees who are active in the collective bargaining process become well known to management and may become the targets of reprisals, particularly if the collective bargaining fails. Facilities sometimes suggest that granting RNs higher wages and benefits will cause bankruptcy and closure of the facility or that the higher RN wages will at least drain the organization's resources so much that it has to cut back the number of other employees.

In reality, recent changes in contract law have resulted in some job losses. Nurses can be replaced during strikes, and even if a settlement is reached, they are hired back only after new employees leave or openings occur. If no settlement is reached, striking nurses may never be hired back.

Taking action always carries risk. Nurses involved in collective bargaining have to consider the risk-to-benefit ratio before they take action. Are the working conditions so poor and the pay so inadequate that they overshadow the risk of possible job loss? The first attempts at organizing a collective bargaining unit are usually the most dangerous in terms of job security.

Initial attempts at organizing nurses are usually made outside the hospital between representatives of the SNA and the union. This type of activity may prevent individuals from becoming targets of management's anger and makes reprisals from management more difficult for a short time. However, it is virtually impossible to keep knowledge of collective bargaining activities secret. Hospital information and rumor "grapevines" are very well developed, and at times it seems the administration hears of the activities almost before they start.

Some legal protections exist for nurses who organize collective bargaining. Grievance procedures against vengeful administrators can be initiated under the unfair labor practices rules, which vary somewhat from state to state. However, even if successful, nurses may pay a heavy toll in both financial and emotional terms in the process of proving they were in the right.

THE CONTRACT

Negotiation

After a collective bargaining unit has been selected, the next important step is to develop or negotiate a contract between the nurses and the hospital. The contract is a legal document that is binding for both management and the union.[2] Contracts can be very specific and include just a few items or very broad and include many. Contracts often contain requirements for union membership by the employees and set the cost of dues for that membership.

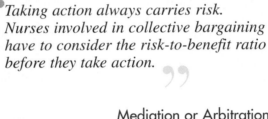

> *Taking action always carries risk. Nurses involved in collective bargaining have to consider the risk-to-benefit ratio before they take action.*

Representation. Negotiating teams are selected by both management and employee groups. One member of each of these teams is designated as the spokesperson who will be the main representative for the group. Before negotiations start, each team meets separately to decide on its position on various issues and on what they are willing to compromise. A list of demands is exchanged by the two sides; it should include everything each might possibly want.

Power and Benefits. Generally, management is reluctant to give up power or relinquish money. The employees' group tries to gain some of management's power and gain benefits for its members. Often many meetings between the two groups are required before they discover the key issues and determine where compromise is possible. Posturing and showmanship play a big part in the initial negotiations. Later, when serious issues are discussed and dealt with, final agreements may be reached behind closed doors.

Good-Faith Bargaining. The law requires that each side bargain in good faith. Good-faith bargaining requires that both parties must agree to meet at reasonable times, to send individuals to the negotiations who can make binding decisions, and to be willing to bargain with the other side.[2] A lack of willingness to negotiate is not bargaining in good faith.

Mediation or Arbitration?

Working With a Mediator

When the sides are unable to reach a settlement, a stalemate occurs. Stalemates are sometimes resolved through mediation, in which a neutral third party provided by the Federal Mediation and Conciliation Service meets with each side. After determining the nature of the conflict, the mediator brings the two sides together to attempt to work out a settlement. Both sides must work with the mediator, but they are not required to accept the mediator's recommendations.

If mediation fails, the Federal Mediation and Conciliation Service may appoint a fact-finding panel to investigate the conflict and to make recommendations. The panel's report is made public and can exert pressure on both sides to accept the recommendations of the mediator.

Binding Arbitration

In some situations, an arbitrator with binding power may be appointed. This person is a neutral third party who, like the mediator, investigates the conflict, meets with both sides, and makes a recommendation for settlement. However, the arbitrator's recommendation, unlike that of the mediator, must be accepted by both sides. Both labor and management try to avoid binding arbitration because it limits their negotiating powers and they may lose something gained during previous negotiations.

The Prospect of a Strike

When all else fails, the final step in the contract negotiation process is work slowdowns or stoppages (strikes). Although strikes are usually the tool used by employees to gain power, management can use a form of enforced strike called a lockout, whereby employees are not permitted to enter the work facility.

> " *Nurses should also be concerned about the public image of the collective bargaining unit they select to represent them. Some nurses' groups have been represented by a machinists' union, a teamsters' union, or even a meat cutters' union.* "

The prospect of a strike is usually accompanied by more intense negotiations that may lead to a last-minute settlement. Strikes are detrimental to both sides. Employees lose pay and benefits during a strike, and management loses income. In addition, the overall public image of strikes is negative, and they have little support. Some collective bargaining units have developed alternative ways of achieving their goals without a strike. Methods such as disruption of services on a random basis or boycott of an organization can achieve the same effects as a full-blown strike without damaging the image of the union.

What Do You Think?

Did you ever sign a contract for employment? Did you read the contract? Were all the elements of a good contract present?

Ratifying the Contract

After a settlement has been reached, the contract must be ratified. The collective bargaining unit takes the contract back to the employees, who must approve it (Box 16.2). Once it is approved by a majority of the employees, the contract becomes legally binding for both management and the employees.

CONCERNS

Representation

One of the most difficult decisions that nurses have to make is who will represent them as a collective bargaining unit. It is reasonable to conclude that only a professional organization, such as the state nurses' association, which understands the complex and varied needs of the

Box 16.2
Elements of a Good Contract

- A statement outlining the objectives of both management and the employees
- A description of the official collective bargaining group
- A description of the benefits included in the contract, such as wages and salary, overtime pay, holiday pay, shift differentials, differentials for advanced education or certifications
- A description of other benefits, such as health insurance, life insurance, retirement, and legal benefits, among others
- A description of acceptable in-house labor practices, such as transfers, promotions, seniority, layoffs, **grievance** procedures, and work schedules
- A description of the procedure to be used when employees have disciplinary problems or when there is a **breach of contract**
- A description of the grievance procedures and the due process to be followed
- A description of what is expected of the professional, including standards of care and codes of ethics

profession, will be able to represent that profession in a collective bargaining situation.

Over the years, SNAs have developed into skilled representatives able to negotiate contracts with considerable success. However, nonprofessional unions have years of experience with negotiations and large sums of money to spend on developing skilled individuals whose only job is negotiating contracts. The union must be able to convince the group of nurses that it is able to represent their interests more effectively than the SNA.

Union groups that attempt to represent nurses soon find that nurses have difficulties forming a consensus concerning problems and issues. Individuals outside the nursing profession have difficulty understanding issues such as quality and standards of care, ethical dilemmas, or even the different levels of nursing education.

Nurses should also be concerned about the public image of the collective bargaining unit they select to represent them. Some nurses' groups have been represented by a machinists' union, a teamsters' union, or even a meat cutters' union. Although these unions are highly proficient at negotiating contracts to gain benefits for their members, some feel the image of nursing is tarnished in the process.

Nursing Supervisors: Employees or Management?

Everyone is familiar with the idea of the traditional nursing supervisor. This is the older, more experienced nurse who guides the less experienced nurses. Nursing supervisors make sure staffing is adequate for their assigned shifts, resolve problems that are beyond the skills of the staff nurse, act as mediators between physicians and nurses, and use their higher skill levels to assist the staff nurses with code blues or complicated procedures. The term *nursing supervisor* also includes nurse educators, directors of nursing, head nurses, unit supervisors, assistant head nurses, and sometimes even charge nurses on the 3 p.m. to 11 p.m. or 11 p.m. to 7 a.m. work shift.

Redefining the Supervisor

Under the amendments to the Taft-Hartley Act of 1974, a supervisor was defined as any individual with authority to hire, transfer, suspend, lay off, promote, assign, reward, or discipline another employee.[2] From this legal viewpoint, nursing supervisors were no longer employees but really members of

management. Management cannot be involved in collective bargaining activities and is therefore prevented from joining unions. A careful reading of the definition of a supervisor as presented in the Taft-Hartley Act makes the category of supervisor open to interpretation. Anybody who assigns a task to another nurse could be considered a supervisor.

Management has sometimes used this provision in the Taft-Hartley Act in an attempt to control the organization and function of collective bargaining units. Management, if so inclined, can use this distinction to induce tension between nursing staff and supervisors, thus reducing the cohesion of the group. Supervisors often serve on important hospital committees to develop standards of care, foster professional recognition, and support nurse advancement. When contracts are negotiated, the supervisors are on the opposite side of the table from the staff nurses. Often, in the heat of negotiation, things are said that foster negative feelings. After the negotiations have ended, it is difficult to re-establish that sense of unity that contributes to high-quality client care.

Some health-care institutions have attempted to categorize all of their RNs and licensed practical nurses (LPNs) as supervisors, thus preventing any of them from organizing into a collective bargaining unit.

A Supreme Court Decision

In 1994 in a 5 to 4 vote, the Supreme Court of the United States supported the decision that LPNs at the Heartland Nursing Home in Urbana, Ohio, should be considered supervisors because they directed the work of nurses' aides "in the interest of the employer." Under this ruling, these LPNs were not protected under the NLRA. This ruling has been of great concern to all nurses, but particularly to the ANA's Department of Labor Relations and Workplace Advocacy committee.

The implications of this decision are far-reaching and pose a direct threat to the ability of RNs to pursue collective bargaining. Employers have already begun to use this ruling to fight nurses in collective bargaining units from Alaska to Washington, DC.

The ANA has been working toward developing language that would follow the description of a supervisor as found in the NLRA and the Taft-Hartley Act (see earlier discussion). Since the passage of the NLRA, nurses who provide client care have been considered to be acting within the

Issues in Practice

2006 Case Reinforces Supreme Court Decision

In the *Extended Health Services Inc versus N.L.R.B.* case, Extended Health Services, Inc. (EHSI), a privately owned nursing home, refused to negotiate with the union that represented RNs, LPNs, and CNAs who worked at the facility. EHSI claimed that nursing home RNs and LPNs are classified as supervisors, not rank-and-file employees, and were therefore not covered by the union contract.

The nurses complained to the U.S. National Labor Relations Board (NRLB). The Board ordered EHSI to negotiate with the union or be found guilty of unfair labor practices. The initial finding was for the union and the nurses. However, on appeal to the Sixth Circuit Court of the U.S. Court of Appeals, the decision was reversed. The Appeals Court ruled that the union's claim was invalid and that the RNs and LPNs at EHSI were not covered by the union contract.

The Appeals Court's decision was based on the principle that only employees, and not supervisors, have the right to union representation. The court defined a supervisor as "someone who uses his or her own independent judgment in exercising authority over others in the workplace." The court upheld EHSI's claim that RNs and LPNs in the nursing home setting use their independent judgment to assess and plan care for nursing home clients, as well as directing CNAs in the provision of care. They must use their own independent nursing judgment in making decisions about meeting clients' needs and providing daily care.

The decision that RNs and LPNs are supervisors and not employees was based on a second element: the determination of disciplinary actions for CNAs who make errors in the work setting. Because the disciplinary actions can range from verbal warnings to written complaints to recommendations for termination, the court believed that nurses were exercising their independent supervisory judgment.

The EHSI decision is in line with a 2006 decision in a Michigan case, in which the NLRB defined a supervisor as an employee who gives assignments to other workers, is held responsible for the performance of those assignments, and exercises independent judgments. The board determined that to be classified as a "supervisor," the nurse must be involved in supervisory activities during 10 percent to 15 percent of working hours. All nurses can still join unions, but those designated as supervisors would not be protected by the contract from firing or disciplinary actions.

Sources: *Extended Health Services Inc v N.L.R.B.* 2006 WL 1307474 (6th Cir., May 9, 2006). Roman, LM: Professional update: NLRB finally rules on nurses' supervisory status. RN 69(11): 12, 2006.

professional nature of nursing and not in the interests of the employer (as a supervisor would primarily be).

Under the ANA's proposed revisions, the scope of the definition of supervisor would be narrowed to include only employees of health-care institutions. This change would allow the NLRB to continue to determine, on a case-by-case basis, whether nurses were supervisors or professional or technical employees. This legislation, introduced to Congress in 1996, was initially tabled. Although it was never officially acted on, recent court rulings have supported the position that not all RNs are supervisors, with resulting successful work actions and strikes nationwide.[4]

GOVERNANCE

The term *governance* has a variety of meanings in different contexts. In general, the term describes the arrangement of the hierarchy of power within an organization and how that power flows through the organization.

A System of Control

In relationship to nursing, governance has been defined as "the establishment and maintenance of social, political, and economic arrangements by which nurses maintain control over their practice, their self-discipline, their working conditions, and their professional affairs."[9] The traditional structure of authority in the health-care industry has been based on the triad of the board of directors, the administrator, and the medical staff.

Authority is a type of power that has its origins in the position that an individual holds within an organization.[2] This individual has this power only because others are willing to accept the decisions made by the person in that position. This allows relatively few people in the organization's hierarchy to control large numbers of employees, as well as the directions and functions of the rest of the organization.

The Board of Directors. At the top of the governance hierarchy is the board of directors, also called the trustees or governors. The board of directors is usually composed of influential business people who are considered community leaders.

> *Some health-care institutions have attempted to categorize all of their RNs and licensed practical nurses (LPNs) as supervisors, thus preventing any of them from organizing into a collective bargaining unit.*

Although they retain the ultimate legal and ethical responsibility for the operation of the organization, generally the day-to-day operation is delegated to the administrator. The board's main function is to set general policies and to plan for the long-range development of the organization. Most boards become directly involved in the facility's operations only when there is a crisis, such as a financial shortfall or a major lawsuit.

The Administrator. The administrator is usually the highest-ranking member of the hierarchy to be involved in the daily operation of the facility. The administrator has the education and knowledge required to direct the highly complex and technologically advanced elements that are an essential part of today's health-care system.

The Medical Staff. In most health-care facilities, the medical staff exerts a great deal of control over the governance structure. The medical staff also has its own internal governance structure with higher- and lower-level members. Traditionally, the physicians in a facility had a great deal of influence in the facility because they were neither employed nor controlled by the facility. However, the advent and spread of managed care have markedly altered the traditional physician–institution relationship in many facilities. In a managed-care setting, physicians are hired and salaried employees just like nurses, housekeepers, administrators, and security personnel. Their practice and productivity are monitored and evaluated, and they can be terminated from the facility for poor performance.

Nurses' Role in Governance

In the recent past, nurses had little say in the governance of their facility or agency. Because of their traditional ideology of professionalism, nurses were more oriented toward loyalty and respect than autonomy of practice and independent decision-making about the quality of care.[1] Nurses often accepted the work hours assigned to them without question, withstood disrespect and abuse from physicians and administrators as part of the work environment, and were satisfied with the meager salaries paid to them because theirs was a profession of caring and dedication. This situation has, however, changed drastically since the 1970s.

The AMA Example

Self-governance is a concept that is important to all professions. The most powerful professional groups are those that maintain a strong sense of self-governance for their members. The American Medical Association (AMA) is a classic example of the power that an organized group can exert. Much of the physicians' power to affect institutional governance, and even broader issues such as managed care, comes from the AMA.

Membership in a powerful organization can be an alternative to unions. Up to this time, the ANA has split its activities and focus between self-governance and collective bargaining. It has been successful in most of its efforts at collective bargaining but somewhat limited in its success at self-governance.

> *Self-governance is a concept that is important to all professions. The most powerful professional groups are those that maintain a strong sense of self-governance for their members.*

Autonomy for the Nurse

As nursing responsibilities increased with advancing technology and changes in the health-care system, nurses began to recognize that their responsibilities far exceeded their authority to influence their practice. They started to view professional autonomy, authority, and accountability as essential elements in high-quality client care. One approach to gaining these elements was to change the organizational structure of the health-care facilities where they were employed.

Nurses have challenged the traditional governance structure at a number of levels with varying amounts of success. Nursing service administrators are the leaders of the largest single group of health-care professionals in most health-care organizations—generally about 50 percent of all the employees.[2] Because of their education and

> *Nurses have gained greater control over their practice by fostering change in the organizational structures of health-care facilities and agencies. The changes include decentralization of authority, identification of professional nurses as peers, agreement on the philosophy and goals of nursing care, and increased responsibility for directing and planning the care given to clients while they are in the facility.*

experience, many nursing administrators have moved into positions of power in the health-care system and are no longer willing to accept the traditional role to which nurses were once relegated.

As middle managers, nursing administrators are often caught in the middle of conflicting expectations. For example, the chief administrator may want to cut the budget by reducing staffing, whereas the nurses on the units recognize that they can no longer provide high-quality nursing care because the staffing levels are already too low.

Positional Authority

Staff RNs often view themselves as located at the bottom of the hierarchy with very little power. This is rarely the case. Depending on the organization of the facility, RNs have positional authority over LPNs, nursing assistants, and individuals from the laboratory and radiology department.

Nurses have gained greater control over their practice by fostering change in the organizational structures of health-care facilities and agencies. The changes include decentralization of authority, identification of professional nurses as peers, agreement on the philosophy and goals of nursing care, and increased responsibility for directing and planning the care given to clients while they are in the facility.[10]

Alternative Models for Governance

In an attempt to redistribute power and authority within health-care organizations, several alternative forms of governance have been developed. Some of these work better than others, depending on the facility and the willingness of the individuals involved to cooperate.

Board of Nursing

In this model of governance, the nursing staff structure is similar to the medical staff structure.

There is a general board of trustees at the top and immediately below, at the same level, a medical board of directors, a nursing board of directors, a board of directors representing other professionals, and the hospital administration itself.[2] The nursing board of directors deals with such matters as credentials and standards of care and promotes cooperation between nurses and the other professionals of the facility.

Although this type of structure places nurses on an equal administrative footing with the physicians, administration, and other professionals in the facility, it does have the tendency to create a large number of administrative personnel. A tendency for conflicts to arise between the different board members does exist.

Contracting for Nursing Services

The **fee-for-service** model proposes that clients be billed for nursing care as a separate item, much the same way that they are billed for medical care by the physicians. Currently, when a client receives a hospital bill, the care provided by nurses is included in the overall room charge. To make this model work, nurses select individual clients for whom they wish to care and then accept responsibility for providing that care. Some type of scale would need to be developed so that the nurse could charge a higher rate for taking care of more seriously ill clients with more complex health-care needs. Nurses would take responsibility for scheduling and for self-management. As with physicians, there would have to be a **peer review** mechanism to monitor the quality of health care provided.

Although this model supports primary care and the expansion of the nurse's role and responsibility, it would be very difficult to implement. Some of the problems include establishing acceptable pay scales, ensuring adequate staffing, and paying ancillary help, such as orderlies and nursing assistants. Probably the most significant single factor that affects the implementation of this model is the hospital administration's loss of control over the nursing staff. If the nurses' pay were to come directly from the client, rather than the hospital, nurses would tend to place the client's needs before the needs of the facility. This model is still unacceptable to most facilities.

Shared Governance

In the shared governance model, power and authority are transferred to the nursing staff rather than being seated primarily in nursing administration. The key to shared governance is decentralization of the nursing administration structure. Its goal is to involve professional nurses in the decision-making process at all levels to ensure that their knowledge and expertise are used to deliver the highest quality care possible.[1]

Shared governance gives the nurse autonomy in decisions about nursing practice, working conditions, staffing levels, standards of care, and other areas. It gives professional nurses the chance to be held accountable and responsible for their clinical judgment and the care they give to clients. It allows their peers a chance to recognize their knowledge and competence as true health-care professionals.

In general, shared governance locates the source of power in clinical areas rather than in **administrative** areas. Several different types of shared governance exist.

> *Shared governance is a model that the staff is willing to undertake, rather than being forced into it by the administration. Unfortunately, many facilities that profess a shared governance structure really are using a traditional hierarchy structure with somewhat more open lines of communication.*

Congressional Model.

In the congressional shared governance model, a group of professional nurses is organized into a congress. This congress develops bylaws, elects representatives, and forms committees to govern the activities of the nursing staff.[9] Composed entirely of professional nurses, the committees oversee professional practice, evaluate quality of care, provide continuing education, plan for staffing, conduct research, and discipline errant nurses. Although this is a highly effective method to provide nursing care and to increase the autonomy of nurses, it does require a tremendous initial expenditure of time, effort, and money. Many institutions are not willing to make that commitment.

Unit-Based Model. In the unit-based model, the shared governance is on a smaller scale. Groups of nurses on each unit form councils for professional practice that perform many of the functions that the professional congresses perform. To make this model succeed, there must be a real transfer of decision-making power from the head nurse or unit supervisor to the staff nurses.

Shared governance is a model that the staff is willing to undertake, rather than being forced into it by the administration. Unfortunately, many facilities that profess a shared governance structure really are using a traditional hierarchy structure with somewhat more open lines of communication. The test of a true shared governance model quickly becomes evident when difficult decisions have to be made. For example, if the staff nurses decide that more staffing is needed for their unit, but the administration refuses to make money available for new nurses, then the structure is not a true shared governance model.

> *In the shared governance model, power and authority are transferred to the nursing staff rather than being seated primarily in nursing administration. The key to shared governance is decentralization of the nursing administration structure.*

Governance and Collective Bargaining

Forms of governance directly affect which issues are likely to be involved in nurses' collective bargaining. Although salary and benefits are important considerations in professional nursing, issues of autonomy, accountability, and control of practice are gaining importance for many nurses.

In a health-care facility with a form of governance that allows nurses to have a relatively large degree of control over their practice, the issues discussed at the bargaining table are more likely to revolve around a professional agenda. In facilities with rigidly structured hierarchies of authority that give nurses little autonomy, accountability, or control over their practice, collective bargaining is more likely to center on control and power issues.

Nurses are highly educated professionals. They recognize that they can practice autonomously and can make sound decisions about client care. They also recognize that an increased understanding of the governance process requires many of the same skills used in collective bargaining. Key elements in both processes are an understanding of negotiation, compromise, and consensus building to attain one's goals. Changes in methods of governance also will require major changes in the health-care system. Professional nurses have the power to produce those changes and the ability to deal with the future of health care successfully.

Conclusion

Although few issues elicit such strong emotions among nurses as collective bargaining, it is a reality in today's health-care system. Nurses are beginning to realize that they are not in a strictly altruistic profession, but rather one in which they use their knowledge and skills to provide high-quality services to clients. The knowledge and skills used in client care are gained at the cost of years of expensive education in schools of nursing and dedication to an often underappreciated profession. Nurses no longer need to apologize or feel guilty about seeking payment for their work on a level commensurate with their knowledge and skills.

Negotiation is the process of give and take between groups with the goal of reaching an agreement acceptable to both sides. Negotiations may be formal or informal, hostile or friendly. A cooperative atmosphere fostered by both sides that recognizes the similarity of each side's demands will be the most productive in reaching a satisfactory contract.

Although not a new concept for nursing, collective bargaining is an issue that is still hotly debated among professional nurses. Collective bargaining is viewed by some as unprofessional, unethical, divisive, and a fundamental threat to job security. However, the goals of collective bargaining, including improvement of economic benefits, better staffing and scheduling, fair treatment for all nurses, and improved quality of care for clients, are common to all health-care providers.

Nurses must decide at some point in their careers whether joining a collective bargaining unit will best help them to achieve these goals. This is not an easy decision to make, and each nurse should gather as much information as possible about the situation before making a decision.

Nurses need to recognize that the time has arrived to elevate the profession to a new level. Change in forms of governance is one method that nurses can use to change the health-care system. Nursing as a profession now has the opportunity to gain tremendous power and take its rightful place as an indispensable force in the health-care system. All that is required is for nurses to become educated in the issues involved and to take an aggressive stance in shaping the future.

Issues in Practice

Deciding to Go on Strike

Sharon S., RN, was completing her charting on another busy 3 p.m. to 11 p.m. shift. While she was walking down the hall toward the time clock, she wondered who would be taking her place for the rest of the week. Like most of the other nurses at the medical center, she had decided to go on strike starting with the 7 a.m. to 3 p.m. shift the next day. The decision to strike had not been an easy one and had been reached only after many hours of meetings and conferences with the hospital negotiators and animated discussion among the nurses' negotiating team.

Sharon could see both positive and negative sides to a strike. On the positive side, increased salaries, better fringe benefits, and improvements in working conditions and staffing would be a plus for all the nurses and clients at the medical center. Sharon herself had felt increasingly stressed during the past year because of the hospital's measures to reorganize. From what Sharon was able to see, reorganization meant saving money by cutting professional staff and partially replacing them with less-trained, unlicensed individuals. This pattern of restaffing had led to longer hours, increased responsibilities for the RNs, and fewer support services. She also felt that the overall quality of care had decreased noticeably.

On the negative side, Sharon was experiencing a real ethical and emotional dilemma about going on strike. The quality of care was sure to deteriorate even further because of the reduced services caused by the strike. Was it really fair to decrease the services and care for clients who had nothing to do with the issues that brought on the strike? Of course, during the past 3 days, the clients who were well enough had been sent home early in anticipation of the

Issues in Practice (continued)

strike. Some whose conditions were too complicated for them to be cared for at home were sent to other facilities. The hospital had severely restricted admissions, reducing the census to an all-time low.

Yet there were several clients who were too ill to transfer or send home. Mrs. Anderson, a 78-year-old client with renal failure, congestive heart failure, and a recent colostomy for a bowel obstruction, came to mind. Mrs. Anderson and a number of other clients like her, who had no family nearby and few resources, were highly dependent on the nursing staff to meet their needs of care. Mrs. Anderson was just beginning to be taught how to care for her colostomy. Even if she was discharged to a nursing home, there was no way to ensure that she could receive the teaching needed for her eventual self-care. Although there was to be a skeleton crew of nurses left in the facility, they would be stretched very thin in trying to care for the remaining clients.

Sharon also thought about the ANA Code of Ethics for Nurses she had been taught in nursing school, particularly the passage that stated, "the nurse participates in the profession's effort to establish and maintain conditions of employment conducive to high-quality nursing care." The reason for the strike was to bring about improved working conditions that would benefit future clients in the hospital, but should these measures be carried out when nursing services were already operating at a reduced level of care and at a minimal level of safety? Didn't that somehow contradict the first statement in the code, that "the nurse provides services with respect for human dignity"? When Mrs. Anderson had been admitted to the hospital 4 days before, she came with the expectation of the best possible care under any circumstances. The code seemed to have a split personality on strikes. While calling for service to the profession to maintain high standards and quality of care, the code also insisted that the health, welfare, and safety of the clients should be the nurse's first consideration.

What should Sharon do? Does the overall welfare of the profession ever supersede the obligation to provide client care? If Sharon does go on strike, will she be "abandoning" her patients in the legal or ethical sense of the term?

Critical Thinking Exercises

- Develop a position paper either supporting or opposing collective bargaining.
- A nurse on your unit states one day, "Membership in the state nurses' association is a waste of time and money. They can't help you make a better living!" How would you respond to this nurse?
- Develop an ideal contract for nurses. Which elements would receive the highest priority?
- Develop a plan for shared governance in a facility you are familiar with. How would the organizational process take place? What are some of the major difficulties in developing this plan?

References

1. Gordon, S: Collective thinking. Nurse Manager 11(2):8, 2004.
2. Tappen, RM: Essentials of Nursing Leadership and Management, ed. 4. F.A. Davis, Philadelphia, 2006.
3. Adler, J: The past as prologue? A brief history of the labor movement in the United States. Public Personnel Management 5(4):311–329, 2006.
4. Radebe, E: Can nursing be unionized? Nursing Update 31(1): 24–25, 2007.
5. Budd, K: Traditional and non-traditional collective bargaining: Strategies to improve the patient care environment. Online Journal Issues in Nursing 9(1):1–6, 2004.
6. Snow, T: Biggest private NHS providers do not negotiate with unions. Nursing Standard 21(19):7, 2007.
7. New plan for bargaining: Union adapts to changed IR system. Lamp 64(1):29, 2007.
8. ANA rejects NLRB decision to block nurses' freedom to unionize. Nursing News 31(1):11, 2007.
9. McKeown, C, and Thompson, J: Clinical governance: Implementing clinical supervision. Nursing Management 8(6):10–13, 2001.
10. Roman, LM: Professional update: NLRB finally rules on nurses' supervisory status. RN 69(11):12, 2006.

Bibliography

Briles, J: Zapping conflict in the health care workplace. The Oklahoma Nurse 49(2):23, 2004.

Cross, LL: Protected whistle-blowing or a legal firing? The Oklahoma Nurse 47(1):14–16, 2002.

Curtin, L: Ethics in management. case study: A showdown over overtime. Journal of Clinical Systems Management 6(5–6):14, 2004.

DeMass-Martin, S: Striking nurses win from coast to coast. American Nurse 34(2):8–10, 2002.

Green, A: Common denominators: Shared governance and work place advocacy—strategies for nurses to gain control over their practice. Online Journal Issues in Nursing 9(1):1–7, 2004.

Kennedy, MS, et al.: To supervise or unionize? That is the question: A Supreme Court ruling may limit nurses' ability to form unions. American Journal of Nursing 101(8):21, 2001.

Oregon nurses strike for pay, health care. American Nurse 34(1): 7, 2002.

Rigiero, D: Empowering nurses to raise their voices in unity. Massachusetts Nurse 75(3):1, 3, 2004.

Sanford, K: Become competent in confrontation. Nursing Management 35(7):14, 2004.

Trossman, S: Illinois nurse loses job for helping Sept. 11 victims. American Nurse 34(1):1–2, 2002.

17

Health-Care Delivery Systems

Nicole Harder

Learning Objectives

After completing this chapter, the reader will be able to:

- Analyze the evolution of the health-care delivery system in the United States.
- Analyze the evolution of the health-care delivery system in Canada.
- Evaluate the factors that influence the evolution of the health-care delivery system.
- Synthesize the concerns surrounding the uninsured in this country.
- Analyze industry efforts to manage health-care costs.
- Evaluate the efforts being made to ensure high-quality cost-effective health care.
- Describe and list the levels and types of health-care delivery.

THE NEW FACE OF HEALTH CARE

Traditionally, the primary purpose of health care was to provide services to those who were ill or injured. These services were typically delivered in a hospital or clinic-like setting. Currently, an awareness of and interest in maintaining optimal health are resulting in a movement toward preventive and primary care as a means of promoting health. This focus has produced substantial changes to the ways in which health-care services are delivered and health-care professionals interact with these systems. As professionals, nurses need to understand health-care delivery systems. Nursing practice is influenced by political, societal, and cultural realities and needs to adapt to the changing world that affects everyday practice. Today's health-care institutions are heavily affected by the costs of delivery, access to services, and health-care professionals.

The 2007 movie *Sicko*, directed and produced by controversial Oscar winner Michael Moore, identified many inequities and failings of the health-care delivery system in the United States. Moore's movie made the point that, although individual health-care services in the United States. are among the best in the world, the overall health-care delivery system is at best mediocre. In many key health-care indicators, such as infant mortality and chronic diseases, the United States is well behind other countries, ranking 37th out of 50.

The number of U.S. citizens who were not covered by any type of health-care insurance in 2007 was over 47 million, about 25 percent of the population. Of the top 25 industrialized counties, the United States is the only one that does not have any type of universal health-care coverage for its citizens. Moore calls for a system that will offer all residents of the United States the same type of health care enjoyed by members of the U.S. Congress. He challenges politicians to forego their current health coverage until all the people are covered by a similar system.

Although this approach may seem radical to some, it certainly opened up a dialogue on the subject. As one of the primary groups of health-care providers, nurses need to be involved in this dialogue. Nurses see, on a daily basis, the effect of lack of health care among the most vulnerable population, infants and children.

DEMOGRAPHICS AFFECTING HEALTH-CARE DELIVERY

Age

Between now and the year 2050, the number of persons 65 years of age or older is expected to double. By 2050, one in five people living in Canada or the United States will be elderly, and their numbers will reach an estimated 80 million.[1] Of this number, many will eventually become more dependent on the health-care delivery system as a result of chronic health problems.

Although an aging population constitutes a sizable number of persons who will potentially require expensive long-term health care, their community activism and powerful influence at the ballot box may provide them with better access to health care than other less vocal and politically savvy groups. Additional at-risk groups consist of persons residing in urban areas with limited incomes and individuals living in remote rural areas where access to care is limited.

> *Between now and the year 2050, the number of persons 65 years of age or older is expected to double. By 2050, one in five people living in Canada or the United States will be elderly, and their numbers will reach an estimated 80 million.*

Chronicity

Another factor influencing the climate of health-care delivery is the long-term and expensive nature of many health problems. Although significant strides have been made in the treatment of some acute infectious diseases, many challenges still exist in the management of health concerns, such as cancer, heart disease, Alzheimer's disease, diabetes, chronic obstructive pulmonary disease, and human immunodeficiency virus (HIV). Additional concerns include environmental and occupational safety, drug abuse, and mother and child health care.

HEALTH CARE AS AN INDUSTRY

In most developed countries, health care is one of the largest industries. According to a report produced by the Kaiser Foundation, total expenditures on health accounted for 9.9 percent of the gross domestic product in Canada and 16 percent in the United States in 2005 (last year of available statistics).[1] Total expenditure was more than $2 *trillion* dollars and is expected to reach $4 trillion dollars by 2015. These numbers alone indicate the significance of health care and health-care spending to the people of these two countries.

In the United States, with the introduction of managed care, the organizations that pay for health care have the capacity to dramatically influence who provides care, how the care is furnished, and who receives compensation.[2] The significance to the economy, along with other factors, is evident.

Health Care in the Global Context

Understanding the approach to health care in comparison with other countries is important in assessing the challenges to and potential of health-care delivery. How and why health-care systems differ is a function of multiple influences. These may include societal values and beliefs, sociocultural climate, the state of the economy, political ideologies, geographic density, international influences, historical realities, established practices and programs, and other factors. For health-care systems to develop, several factors must come into play at different points. This development is similar for health-care systems throughout the world, as can be seen by examining the contexts in which various health-care systems were developed.

One way to think about system differences is to consider that Western countries provide for health care in several ways, all of which involve variable combinations of private or public funding of services and private or public delivery of services.[3] Table 17.1 shows the degree of public involvement in financing health services and the essential role envisioned for the health-care system.[4]

Table 17.1 Types of Health-Care Systems in the Western World

Type I	Type II	Type III	Type IV
Private health insurance	National health insurance	National health service	Socialized health system
Primary goal: preserve autonomy	Primary goal: egalitarian	Primary goal: egalitarian	Primary goal: essential service
Secondary effect: acceptance of social differences	Secondary effect: preserve autonomy	Secondary effect; public management	Secondary effect: physicians as state employees

Source: Najman, J, and Western, J: A comparative analysis of Australian health policy in the 1970s. Social Science and Medicine 18(1): 949–958, 1984, with permission.

Type I Systems

In the type I health-care system, private approaches to health services predominate. Physicians, other caregivers (such as midwives), and clients have maximum autonomy. In this plan, individuals who can afford private health insurance, or who simply can pay for their health care, chose their care providers and receive health services. Those who cannot pay do not have choice or benefit.

In the pure form of the type 1 system, there would be no option other than to pay for service. In reality, most countries have adopted a mixture of system types. For example, although the United States has a mainly private payment system of health care, some publicly funded programs assist elderly and poor people. Even with these programs, it is estimated that 45 percent of Americans have no health insurance and therefore are limited in their ability to access health care.

Type IV Systems

On the opposite end of the spectrum from type 1 is type IV. This type of health-care system focuses on keeping the general public healthy so they can continue to contribute to society and the economy. Health care is considered an essential service or even a right, not necessarily involving compassionate motives, and the goal is to keep the population healthy so that national productivity will remain high. Physicians are considered agents of the state who work to keep others working efficiently.

In Canada, the type IV structure is seen in such organizations as the military, hockey teams, and other sports teams. Physicians are hired by these organizations to ensure the players stay healthy and can do their part to achieve the goals of the group.

Type III Systems

Between the extremes of type I and type IV health-care systems are two less extreme types. The type III system is funded and operated by the government, as was seen in Great Britain some years ago. With this system, the state-operated and state-funded health services were based on an egalitarian value. Public management of each service was considered key to efficient and effective operation.

Type II Systems

The type II system is a hybrid of type I and type III systems. Egalitarian values are given high priority, but so are practitioner and client autonomy. The type II system uses tax dollars to pay for health services through health insurance available from a nonprofit agency (e.g., government).

Each health service is operated more or less autonomously by others including municipalities, citizen groups, physicians, nurse practitioners, and physiotherapists in private offices, group practices, and other groups. All services rendered to clients are then paid from the central pool of health insurance funds created through taxation. This type of system is used in Canada and embodies the collective sharing of burdens and benefits while allowing a degree of autonomy in delivery.[5]

Third World Alternatives

It is important to note that the four systems described above exclude a group of third world countries that cannot afford the type of health care enjoyed in most developed countries. Yet many third world countries have managed to develop primary care systems that are not as institution dependent as the systems found in Canada and the United States. In their systems, primary care includes preventive health care, first point of contact, and continuing care. However, in some countries, the primary and preventive systems have been undermined by the influence of Western countries promoting high technology and institutionalization.

What Do Taxes Cover?

Even in countries that finance health insurance through tax dollars, there are variations in services provided. For example, some fund home care but others do not; some provide coverage for prescription drugs and others do not. Regardless of the type of system, it is important to reflect on the influences that have created it and continue to maintain it.

What Do You Think?

What type of health-care system was used the last time you accessed health care? Did you use the health-care system for preventive care or illness care?

_____

_____

_____

_____

_____

_____

_____

_____

_____

_____

_____

ADMINISTRATION AND FUNDING OF HEALTH-CARE SYSTEMS

Financing and administering health-care systems can be an overwhelming responsibility. The Canadian government spends $3048 on health care per year for each of its citizens. For the year 2007, the Department of Health and Human Services calculates that in the United States, expenditure will be $7498 per citizen per year.[5] With these staggering numbers, it is easy to see how this trillion-dollar industry can be difficult to manage.

Health Care in Canada

In Canada, health-care services are provided under the Canada Health Act. The Canadian federal government collects funds through taxes and gives the responsibility of administering health-care services to the provinces. As in the United States, the cost of financing health-care services has risen tremendously since the first Medical Care Act was introduced in 1967–1968. In Canada, medical insurance premiums became an increasing burden for the federal government as a result of the improved services promised to all Canadians.

Federal Transfer Payments

In an attempt to control the costs to be paid to all provinces, the Canadian government proposed a system of block funding. In 1977 the Federal–Provincial Arrangements and Established Programs Financing Act were established after lengthy negotiations with all provinces. The formula for federal transfer payments consisted of four components:

1. Per capita payments were made, on the basis of previous expenditures and adjusted regularly in relation to the gross national product.
2. Tax points were transferred by the federal government, allowing provinces to reduce their tax contribution to the federal government and at the same time increase the portion of tax collected at the provincial level.
3. Equalization of tax points was distributed among poorer provinces.
4. Additional per capita payments were indexed to help pay for nursing home, residential, home, and ambulatory.

Issues in Practice

National Coalition on Health-Care Findings

A recent survey by the National Coalition on Health-Care Findings developed some interesting information:

- The primary reason given by people in a survey of why they are uninsured is because of the lack of health insurance coverage.
- As health-care costs rise, the number of insured decreases.
- Almost half the American public surveyed indicated that they are very worried about how they will meet the increased premiums for health insurance and 42% are worried that they may not be able to afford health insurance at all.
- Twenty-five percent of Americans identified paying for health insurance as a problem during the past year.
- Medical debt was a leading reason (50%) for people to file for bankruptcy, with the average medical debt being $12,000 per person.
- Elderly couples who retire today will need between $200,000 and $300,000 just to pay for medical coverage.

Source: Catlin, A, et al.: National health spending in 2006. Health Care Affairs 26(1):142–153, 2006.

This new act changed the funding formulae from a 50–50 cost sharing arrangement to one that gave taxation points to the provinces in exchange for lower cash transfer payments. The provinces were initially very receptive, as this meant they had more taxation power in an economy that was very healthy. However, with rising costs of health care, owing in part to an aging population and increased technology, some physicians and provinces struggled with health-care coverage. With extra billing or balance billing becoming prevalent, there was a heated public debate, and the new Canada Health Act was passed in 1984.

The Canada Health Act

Although the Canadian federal government has a limited constitutional basis for making health-care decisions, it has considerable economic clout to develop and shape a national health-care plan. To support their positions on health care, the federal government enacted the Canada Health Act (CHA). The purpose of the CHA is to "establish criteria and conditions in respect of insured health services and extended health-care services provided under provincial law that must be met before a full cash contribution may be made."[6]

The insured health services defined by the CHA include all medically necessary hospital services and medically required physician services, as well as medically or dentally required surgical–dental services that needed to be performed in a hospital for safety. New criteria, conditions, and provisions were formulated to eliminate extra-billing and user charges.

For the provinces to qualify for full cash refunds from the federal government under the Canada Health and Social Transfer agreement (CHST), they must meet five basic criteria and conditions. These criteria and conditions must be met for each fiscal year and include:

1. Public Administration: The health-care insurance plan must be administered and operated on a nonprofit basis by a public authority, responsible to the provincial government and subject to audit of its accounts and financial transactions.
2. Comprehensiveness: The plan must ensure all insured health services provided by hospitals, medical practitioners, and dentists and, where permitted, services rendered by other health-care practitioners.
3. Universality: One hundred percent of the insured population of a province must be entitled to the

insured health services provided for by the plan on uniform terms and conditions.

4. Portability: Residents moving to another province must continue to be covered for insured health services by the home province during any minimum waiting period imposed by the new province of residence not to exceed 3 months. For insured persons, insured health services must be made available while they are temporarily absent from their own provinces on the following basis:

- Insured services received out of province, but still in Canada, are to be paid for by the home province at host province rates unless another arrangement for the payment of costs exists between the provinces. Prior approval may be required for elective services.

- Out-of-country services received are to be paid, as a minimum, on the basis of the amount that would have been paid by the home province for similar services rendered in the province. Prior approval may be required for elective services.

5. Accessibility: The health-care insurance plan of a province must provide for:

- Insured health services on uniform terms and conditions and reasonable access by insured persons to insured health services not precluded and unimpeded, either directly or indirectly, by charges or other means

- Reasonable compensation to physicians and dentists for all insured health services rendered

- Payments to hospitals in respect to the cost of insured health services

Although discussion and debate continue surrounding the federal and provincial responsibilities for health-care funding and the escalating costs associated with health care, the Canada Health Act of 1984 continues to be the model that the Canadian health-care system operates under.

Health-Care Systems in The United States

The United States has a far different method of funding and administering health-care services.

> *According to the World Health Organization, the United States spends more per person on health care than any other country, yet in overall quality its care ranks 37th in the world.*

According to the World Health Organization, the United States spends more per person on health care than any other country, yet in overall quality its care ranks 37th in the world. This disparity is attributed in large part to the cost of health-care services, not the quality of the services available.

In the attempt to contain some of these costs, professional standards review organizations (PSROs) were introduced to review the quality, quantity, and cost of hospital care through Medicare. The primary goal of PSROs was to review the care provided by physicians to determine whether the best diagnostic and treatment approaches were being used. Another measure was the introduction of utilization review committees, requiring Medicare-qualified facilities to review admission, diagnostic testing, and treatments with the goal of eliminating overuse or misuse of services.

What Do You Think?

Review the bill from your last hospitalization or the bill of a family member. What do you think about the charges listed? Does the bill seem excessive?

_____

_____

_____

_____

_____

_____

_____

_____

_____

_____

_____

_____

Prospective Payment Systems

Although these measures have assisted with cost containment to some degree, one of the most significant factors that have influenced cost control was the prospective payment system (PPS) that was established by the U.S. Congress in 1983. This system required facilities providing services to Medicare clients to be reimbursed using a fixed-rate system and included monetary incentives to reduce the length of hospital stays. Medicare clients are classified using a diagnosis-related group (DRG), and the facilities are reimbursed a predetermined amount. Clients may be classified into one of 468 DRGs, and reimbursement occurs regardless of the length of stay.

If the client is discharged sooner than anticipated, the facility keeps the difference. If the client requires a lengthier hospital stay, the hospital pays the extra cost. Under the PPS, the emphasis is on the efficient delivery of services in the most cost-effective manner.

Capitated Payment Systems

Capitation, or a capitated payment system, is a health-care payment structure that was introduced to encourage cost effectiveness in a growing health-care system. In a capitated payment system, participants pay a flat rate, usually through their employer, to belong to a managed care organization (MCO) for a specified period of time. The health-care providers who serve the participants receive a fixed amount for each participant in the health-care plan.[7]

Controlled Access

The goal of capitation is to have a payment plan for selected diseases or surgical procedures that provides the highest quality of care, including essential diagnostic and treatment procedures, at the lowest cost possible. Any expenses that are in excess of the capitated rate are the responsibility of the MCO. If the MCO spends less on the care of a client than it is given for delivery costs, it can keep the excess as profit, providing it with a strong incentive to reduce the cost of services.

Another goal of managed care is to enhance the efficiency and effective use of health-care services. A key underlying concept of managed care is to maintain administrative control over access and provision of primary

health-care services for the members of the plan. The MCO controls all aspects of care including delivery, financing, and the purchase of health-care services for clients who are enrolled in the program. Clients are allowed to use only the services of primary care physicians who are approved by the organization. Any referrals to other medical specialists must be approved by the MCO. The MCO contract determines what treatments or procedures will be reimbursed.

A Spending Increase

The effectiveness of the MCO plan rests on the theory that health-care costs can be reduced by decreasing the number of hospitalizations, shortening the length of inpatient stays, providing less-expensive home care services, and keeping people healthy through health promotion and illness prevention services. It is logical to conclude that if people stay healthy, the cost of health-care services should decline.

Although much debate surrounds managed care and its advantages and disadvantages, the reality is that managed care has *not* reduced health-care costs nationally. Increases in spending are attributed to rising health-care wages, legislation that increased Medicare spending, increasing insurance premiums, technology, and consumer demands for less restrictive plans.

QUALITY ASSURANCE

Continuous Quality Improvement

Quality assurance initiatives are essential when efforts are being made to cut costs and, at the same time, maintain high standards of care. To ensure high-quality care, the health-care industry borrowed the philosophy of **continuous quality improvement (CQI)** from the business world. The **Joint Commission on Accreditation of Healthcare Organizations (JCAHO)** was so impressed with its potential to improve health-care delivery that in 1994 it began requiring hospitals to implement CQI strategies.

Exceeding Expectations

Continuous quality improvement, also known as **total quality management (TQM)**, is

> *The effectiveness of the MCO plan rests on the theory that health-care costs can be reduced by decreasing the number of hospitalizations, shortening the length of inpatient stays, providing less-expensive home care services, and keeping people healthy through health promotion and illness prevention services.*

based on the belief that the organization with the higher quality service will capture a greater share of the market than competitors with lower-quality services. Emphasis is placed on not only meeting the expectations of the customer (in this case, the health-care consumer) but exceeding those expectations.

According to the CQI philosophy, there are internal customers and external customers. The external customers are clients and their families; internal customers are individuals working within the health-care setting. Delivering high-quality services is valued above all else, and the ideal goal is that every constituent be completely satisfied with the services provided.

A Proactive Approach

Continuous quality improvement requires that the process used to deliver services receive close and constant scrutiny, and everyone is encouraged to generate ideas for improving quality. Although change on the basis of systematically documented evidence is encouraged, standardization of the process is also valued so that efficiency is maximized. CQI is proactively oriented so that emphasis is placed on anticipating and preventing problems rather than reacting to them after the fact.

Nurses are in an excellent position to implement CQI strategies. On a daily basis, they assess the functioning of the health-care delivery system and the effectiveness of specific treatment approaches. For example, on the basis of evidence that inexpensive saline is as effective as heparin in keeping intermittent intravenous catheters patent, nurses at one hospital implemented a new protocol and saved $70,000 within 1 year.[8]

Case Management Protocols

There is another mechanism for monitoring cost-effective, high-quality care: outcomes-based case management protocols, also known as **clinical pathways.** The development of clinical pathways grew out of a need to assess, implement, and monitor cost-effective, high-quality client care in a systematic manner.

Clinical pathways were an outgrowth of nursing care plans but have the advantages of streamlining the charting process, encouraging documentation across multidisciplinary team members, and systematically monitoring variances from prescribed plans of care. The ability to identify how client care and progress vary from a predetermined plan enables more accurate assessment of client care costs and maintenance of quality control measures. Integration of clinical pathways into practical usage has been enhanced by computerization of client records and online bedside documentation.

Overview of Health-Care Plans

See Boxes 17.1 through 17.5 to compare the principal features of different health-care models.

Box 17.1

Managed Care Organizations (MCOs)

Definition: Provide comprehensive, preventive, and treatment services to a specific group of voluntarily enrolled persons.

Managed Care Structures

Staff model: physicians are salaried employees of the MCO

Group model: MCO contracts with single group practice

Network model: MCO contracts with multiple group practices and/or integrated organizations

Independent practice association (IPA): MCO contracts with physicians who usually are not members of groups and whose practices include fee-for-service and capitated clients.

Characteristics: Focus on health maintenance and primary care. All care provided by a primary care physician. Referral needed for access to specialists and hospitalization.

Medicare MCO

Definition: Program same as MCO but designated to cover health-care costs of senior citizens

Characteristics: Premium generally less than supplemental plans

References

1. Health care spending in the United States and OECD countries. www.kff.org/insurance/snapshot/chcmo1o307oth.cfm, 2007.
2. Health insurance costs: National Coalition on Health Care. www.nchc.org/facts/cost.shtml, 2007.
3. Health Canada: Canada's health care system. 2007. www.hc-sc.gc.ca/datapcb/iad/hcsystem-e.htm.
4. Jeffs, L: Creating reporting and learning cultures in health-care organizations. Canadian Nurse 103(3):16–17, 27–28, 2007.
5. Department of Health and Services center of Medicare and Medicaid Expenditures. National Health Expenditures Projections 2006–2016. www.cms.hhs.gov/NationaHealthExpendData/downloads.
6. Lynn, J: Academia and clinic. The ethics of using quality improvement methods in health care. Annals of Internal Medicine 146 (9):666–673, 2007.
7. Gray, V: The political management of managed care: Explaining variations in state health maintenance organization regulations. Journal of Health Politics, Policy and Law 32(3): 457–495, 2007.
8. Haselkorn, A: New technology planning and approval: Critical factors for success. American Journal of Medical Quality 22(3): 164–169, 2007.
9. National Health Information Center, U. S. Department of Health and Human Services: Income Poverty, and Health Insurance Coverage in the United States: 2007. Washington, DC, 2007.

Bibliography

Bradford, N: Commissioning Ideas: Canadian National Policy Innovation in Comparative Perspective. Oxford University Press, Toronto, 1998.

Brittain, B: Who is being accountable for the well-being of the patient? Hospital Quarterly 1(2):56–58, 1998.

Dwivedi, O, and Gow, J: From Bureaucracy To Public Management: The Administrative Culture of the Government of Canada. Broadview Press, Toronto, 1999.

Evans, R: Going for the gold: The redistributive agenda behind market-based health reform. Journal of Health, Politics, and Policy Law 22(2):426–465, 1999.

Kernaghan, K, and Langford, W: The Responsible Public Servant. Institute for Research on Public Policy, Montreal, 1999.

Singer, P, and Mapa, J: Ethics resource allocation: Dimensions for healthcare executives. Hospital Quarterly 1(4):29–31, 1998.

18

Nursing Informatics

Kathleen Mary Young

Learning Objectives

After completing this chapter, the reader will be able to:

- Discuss the impact of the information revolution on society in general and on health care specifically.
- Define nursing informatics.
- Explain the importance of nursing informatics to nursing practice.
- Analyze the availability of resources and references in the practice site.
- Evaluate the importance of human factors engineering on equipment design.
- Compare the electronic health record to the paper record system.

INFORMATION CHANGES EVERYTHING

The information revolution continues to expand exponentially, pushing the systems of modern culture to the breaking point. The information revolution is changing both the way teachers teach and the way learners learn. It is changing the way people work, communicate, and play. Teaching in public schools, and even in colleges, now demands fast-moving, entertaining lessons that capture the students' attention, because classroom teachers must compete with television and the computer games with which this generation has been raised.

School children and college students no longer read as extensively as they once did. Technology has accustomed them to 30-second "sound bites" of information. Libraries are evolving from

> *Not only does technology change the way in which people communicate and work, but it also creates a new decision-making process that affects all aspects of industry and commerce, including health care.*

repositories of hardbound volumes and journals to providers of Internet access to online journals and books. Many people spend 8 to 10 hours a day in front of a computer. People who have lost traditional jobs in manufacturing and service industries are finding that to become marketable in today's workplace, they must have computer skills.

TECHNOLOGY AND COMMUNICATION

The information revolution has changed both the form and the format of communication. Before the advent of the telephone, people communicated through the written word. Letter writing was an art. Before television and the computer were invented, people gathered together in neighborhoods and developed a sense of community.

Today the whole world is the community and every corner can be reached from a home computer. Senior citizens use their computers not only to chat but also to organize get-togethers and other social activities. Teenagers use their cell phones and text-messaging to meet friends and stay connected, even when they are in the bathroom with their pajamas on.[1]

Asymmetrical Information

Not only does technology change the way in which people communicate and work, but it also creates new decision-making processes that affect all aspects of industry and commerce, including health care. Informed decisions produce better outcomes. When people are able to sift through and use the vast amount of information available to them, it gives them a decided advantage in conducting business.

The use of multiple sources of data in economics and business is called asymmetrical information. Many businesses currently are characterized by asymmetric information: individuals on one side of the transaction may have much better information than those on the other. Borrowers know more than lenders about their repayment prospects, managers and boards know more than shareholders about the firm's profitability, and prospective clients know more than insurance companies about their accident risk.[2] The fact that the person with more information has an advantage seems like common sense, but a grasp of the impact of asymmetric information will lead to a better understanding of day-to-day economic activity.

Competitive Health Care

Competition has become a driving force in the pricing and marketing of health care. Payment methods that promote competition are encouraged by Medicare and Medicaid prospective payment systems (PPSs), health maintenance organizations (HMOs), preferred provider organizations (PPOs), and managed care. For an organization to offer competitive and high-quality services, information must be available to make decisions. More information is available to decision makers with information technology.

Technologically driven organizations have a competitive edge through the collection of large amounts of information and its application to decision making in health care. To stay competitive in national and international health care, the health-care delivery system—specifically nursing—must open itself to new information and ideas.

The health-care information revolution is progressing at the speed of light. Computers are involved in almost every area of client care today including the assessment of the quality of care, decision making, management, planning, and medical research.[3]

DEFINING INFORMATICS

Two definitions of informatics are commonly used in health care. The term *medical informatics* was coined in the mid-1970s. Borrowed from the French expression *informatique medicale,* it included all the informational technologies that deal with the medical care of the client, medical resources, and the decision-making process.[4]

Health informatics is a more comprehensive term that is defined as the use of information technology with information management concepts and methods to support the delivery of health care. Health informatics includes the medical, but also encompasses nursing, dental, and pharmacy informatics as well as all other health-care disciplines. The definition of health informatics focuses attention on the recipient of care rather than on the discipline of the caregiver.

Models for Nursing Informatics

The nursing community has been working toward developing a discipline of informatics that is specific to the delivery of nursing care based on the science of nursing. Nursing has distinct and discrete information needs. The content and application of nursing information are substantively different from those of other disciplines. Data gathered by the nursing profession present unique problems for the use of information in the delivery of nursing care on the basis of critical thinking.[5]

Three Basic Elements

An early model for nursing informatics can be traced back to 1989. Although somewhat simplistic, it viewed nursing informatics primarily as combining computer science, information science, and nursing science in a manner that would help the nurse in the planning and delivery of care to clients. These technologies aid in the collection and analysis of data so that the nurse can make informed and accurate decisions about the type of care required by clients.[6]

In this early definition of nursing informatics, computer science was seen primarily as the computer and the institution-wide system to which it was connected. Information science refers to the computer software, including how data or tasks are processed, how problems are solved, and where products are produced. Nursing science is all the research data from nursing and other associated disciplines that relate to and support nursing practice.[7]

More Complex Elements

In newer models of nursing informatics, a fourth element, cognitive science, has been added. Cognitive science combines psychology, linguistics, computer science, philosophy, and neuroscience in a way that is useful for the delivery of client care. Cognitive science is also concerned with perception, thinking, understanding, and remembering. This model unites information science, computer science, and cognitive science into a framework of nursing science.[8]

It is also believed that wisdom should be added as a component of nursing informatics in addition to data, information, and knowledge. With wisdom, the nurse is able to know how and when to use the available information in managing clients' problems and meeting their needs.[9]

Data, Information, and Knowledge

In most theories of nursing informatics, *data* are defined as raw and unstructured facts. For example, the numbers 102 and 104 are raw data: by themselves, these numbers have little meaning because they lack interpretation. *Information* consists of data that have been given form and have been interpreted. If the number 102 is given additional data so that it becomes a 102°F oral temperature of a 25-year-old man taken at 9 a.m., it becomes information that has meaning to the nurse.

Knowledge takes the process one step further because it is a synthesis of data and information. Knowing that an oral temperature of 102°F is higher than normal for a 25-year-old man, and combining that information with an understanding of human physiology and pharmacology, the nurse is able to decide what treatment should be given.

> " *The nursing community, however, has been working toward developing a discipline of informatics that is specific to the delivery of nursing care based on the science of nursing. Nursing has distinct and discrete information needs.* "

What Do You Think?

Have you used computerized health-care records? Describe your experience.

This process relies on critical thinking and decision making and can be used in research to create new knowledge.

The data-to-information-to-knowledge model of informatics is linear in design, but the process of synthesizing data into information to create knowledge is circular. New knowledge creates new questions and areas of research, which in turn lead to more new knowledge. To answer any research question, new data are required that must be processed into information to create more knowledge. The goal of this process is to provide the most accurate and current information so that nurses can make informed decisions in their daily practice.

Areas of Focus in Informatics

Over the years, the specialty of nursing informatics has evolved through three levels of special interest: technology, concepts of nursing theory, and function.

Technology. The earliest attempts to define nursing informatics focused solely on the use of technology. A commonly used early definition of nursing informatics stated that it existed whenever the nurse used any type of information technology in delivering nursing care or in the process of educating nursing students.10 Some of the key points in the use of technology or computer systems to store, process, display, retrieve, and communicate health-care information quickly in the health-care setting include:

• Administering nursing services and resources
• Managing the delivery of client and nursing care
• Linking research resources and findings to nursing practice
• Applying educational resources to nursing education

Nursing Theory. As nursing informatics has evolved, it began to combine nursing theory and informatics. Without a well-articulated theoretical basis to guide the gathering of data, nurses soon become overwhelmed with meaningless data and information. Obviously, there is a need for common definitions, a standardized nursing language, and criteria for organization of the data.

Function. An additional step in the evolution of nursing informatics is the inclusion of the concept of function. The function of nursing informatics is to manage and process data to help nurses enter, organize, and retrieve needed information. Technology is then developed to achieve specific purposes related to client care needs. Although technology forms the foundation of informatics, the nurse's ability to use that technology and make it function to meet clients' needs is the real test of the system's effectiveness.

In reality, nursing informatics includes all three of these areas—technology, nursing theory, and function. However, the field of informatics has become so large that it is difficult for any one person to be an expert in all three areas.

INFORMATICS AS A SPECIALTY

A Broader Definition

A broader definition of nursing informatics is provided by the American Nurses Association (ANA). It defines nursing informatics as

A specialty that integrates nursing science, computer science, and information science in identifying, collecting, processing, and managing data and information to support nursing practice, administration, education and research; and to expand nursing knowledge. The purpose of nursing informatics is to analyze information requirements; design, implement and evaluate information systems and data structures that support nursing; and identify and apply computer technologies for nursing.[11]

Nursing informatics is now recognized as a nursing specialty for which a registered nurse (RN) can receive certification. The catalogue of the American Nurses Credentialing Center (ANCC) states that the nursing informatics practice

. . . encompasses the full range of activities that focus on the methods and technologies of information handling in nursing. It includes the development, support, and evaluation of applications, tools, processes, and structures that assist the practice of nurses with the management of data in direct care of patients/clients. The work of an informatics nurse can involve any and all aspects of information systems, including theory formulation, design, development, marketing, selection, testing, implementation, training, maintenance, evaluation, and enhancement.[12]

Nursing informatics supports all areas of nursing, including practice, education, administration, and research. It facilitates and guides the management of data.

Articulation

Informatics is no longer just an elective subject. In today's competitive and rapidly changing health-care delivery system, mastery of informatics is a basic requirement. The importance of the role of informatics is apparent in the need for the articulation of nursing practice. Articulation is an important way for

> *Although technology forms the foundation of informatics, the nurse's ability to use the that technology and make it function to meet clients' needs is the real test of the system's effectiveness.*

> *Informatics is no longer just an elective subject. In today's competitive and rapidly changing health-care delivery system, mastery of informatics is a basic requirement.*

nursing to demonstrate its accountability and credibility so that it can remain an essential element of the health-care system.

The Need for a Standard

Historically, the nursing profession has had difficulty in locating relevant nursing information quickly because there was no universally accepted nomenclature and taxonomy for either nursing clinical information or management data. In the past, this lack of access to information has presented several seemingly insurmountable challenges for nurse executives, including being able to identify what the nursing staff actually does, determining the impact nurses have on outcomes, and establishing appropriate reimbursement for nursing activities.[13]

For example, how does a nurse interpret the term *weak grasp* when it is seen in the chart of a client? The meaning of "weak grasp" differs widely depending on the client. If the client is a premature infant, the term has an entirely different meaning than if it were applied to a 25-year-old professional football player with a head injury or even a 60-year-old with a stroke. Imagine the difficulty that a researcher will have when investigating the phenomenon of weak grasp because of the lack of a standardized definition among the nursing community. Because of the need to standardize nursing language to name

What Do You Think?

Think of four terms, not defined actions, carried out by nurses that have multiple meanings. How could these terms be clarified?

_____

_____

_____

_____

_____

_____

_____

_____

_____

_____

_____

_____

and communicate what nurses do, nursing classification schemes, taxonomies, and vocabularies have come to the forefront with the evolution of nursing informatics.

Unified Nursing Language System

The American Nurses Association Database Steering Committee was formed in 1991 to develop a common nursing language called the Unified Nursing Language System (UNLS). UNLS maps concepts by identifying common terms from different vocabularies and acknowledging them as synonyms of the same concept.

Twelve classification systems are recognized by the ANA as uniquely developed to documenting nursing care. They are designed to record and track the clinical care process for an entire episode of care for clients in the acute, home, or ambulatory setting or any combination of these. Standards and scoring guidelines for nursing languages can be found in Box 18.1.

Nursing Minimum Data Set

Standardization of the data in a client's record is the first step toward unifying information to make it

Box 18.1

Standards and Scoring Guidelines for Nursing Languages

1. Terms in data dictionaries and tables are appropriate to the domain of nursing.
2. Terms from ANA-recognized languages for nursing are used as a core for the nursing vocabulary.
3. The system allows for the development and addition of new terms as needed, without duplicating existing terms or disrupting the integrity of existing languages.
4. In "local" languages, terms are mapped to appropriate ANA-recognized nursing languages, which may include reference terminologies

The system accommodates the use of reference terminologies to map nursing languages to other existing standardized data sets, classification systems, or nomenclatures.

usable to the bedside nurse. The second step is the development of criteria to determine the necessary elements that must be included in every client record or encounter. The Nursing Minimum Data Set (NMDS), developed in 1985 and accepted by the ANA in 1998, is a list of the data elements necessary in any computerized client record system or national database. The NMDS is considered to be the umbrella for other nursing process schemes. The purpose of the NMDS is to

1. Describe the nursing care of clients and their families in various settings, both institutional and noninstitutional.
2. Establish comparability of nursing data across clinical populations, settings, geographical areas, and time.
3. Demonstrate or project trends regarding nursing care provided and allocation of nursing resources to clients according to their health problems or nursing diagnoses.
4. Stimulate **nursing research** through linkages of detailed data existing in nursing information systems and in other health-care information systems.
5. Provide data about nursing care to influence health policy and decision making.[14]

The NMDS has 16 elements divided into 3 main categories: nursing care (e.g., nursing diagnosis, intervention, outcome, and degree of nursing care), client demographics (e.g., the client's personal identification, date of birth, sex), and service elements (e.g., the unique service agency number, the admission and discharge dates, client's condition, and expected payer).

Accountability

Intuitively, the nursing profession has long known that the presence of RNs improves the quality of care and client outcomes while decreasing the cost of health care. According to the Congressional Office of Technology Assessment, better use of nurse practitioners could result in savings for clients, employers, and society owing to the cost-effectiveness of both their training and their services. Nurses

affect client outcomes positively and contribute measurably to the goals of a competitive health-care delivery system. However, nurses traditionally have not been very good at documenting their worth and effectiveness.[15]

To measure effectiveness with accurate information about client care and outcomes, nurses must use standardized language in both practice and documentation. The ability to measure the resources used and the client outcome achieved will help distinguish one health-care provider from another. This process forms the basis for evidence-based practice (EBP).

As nursing practice becomes more efficient and can demonstrate improved client outcomes, the quality of care will increase and health-care organizations will become more financially stable.

Credibility

The credibility of the nursing profession rests on its ability to document how nursing care improves clients' health and saves money for health-care institutions. Nurses must be able to measure their effectiveness with accurate information about both the care given and the client outcomes achieved. Having control over the process of care as well as the information and assessments of the quality of care is an important element in achieving this goal.

Improvements in quality do not occur in isolation. They result from a continual process of assessing care and measuring outcomes that produces improvements in treatments, changes in care procedures, and an increased number of support services.[16]

A standardized language will facilitate the nursing profession's ability to delineate the costs and benefits of nursing care from the costs and benefits of other health-care providers. If the nursing profession cannot articulate and measure the unique contributions that nurses make to the client's health and well-being, then the profession will continue to have difficulty justifying its higher costs over less-educated and less-qualified health-care providers.

> *If the nursing profession cannot articulate and measure the unique contributions that nurses make to the client's health and well-being, then the profession will continue to have difficulty justifying its higher costs over less-educated and less-qualified health-care providers.*

Accessing Information

An Information Explosion

Health-care journals and textbooks form a key element in the information explosion. The amount of health-care information contained in scientific journals has grown to a point where no individual is able to read all of the material. With just a nightly perusal of the latest journals, even the most conscientious practitioners will have difficulty keeping up with all the current research and new developments in their specialty field.

Coping with the volume of biomedical and nursing literature is an enormous task. In 2005, 34,000 references from 4000 journals were added each month to the National Library of Medicine Medline database from among the more than 100,000 scientific journals published.[17] In the past 20 years, the number of articles indexed annually in the Medline database has nearly doubled, the number of clinical trials in cardiology has increased five times, and the number of clinical trials in health services has increased 10 times. One new article is added to the medical literature every 26 seconds.

Conflicting Paradigms

Although a large amount of new information is available, only a small portion is read by and incorporated into the practice of many health-care professionals. The traditional paradigm that still seems to guide the decision-making process for many nurses is to:

- Refer back to the knowledge learned in school
- Confer with a colleague
- Look up the problem in any textbook or reference book available in the work setting
- Use previous experiences and "gut" instincts

Although this process is useful and has some merit, it is questionable whether it is adequate for the delivery of high-quality care in today's complex health-care system. For the information age, EBP is more appropriate.[18] This process includes:

- Accessing current literature concerning the latest diagnostic techniques and treatment modalities
- Conferring with a knowledgeable colleague
- Evaluating the effectiveness of previous experiences

Research on the Job

Ironically, even though EBP produces higher-quality care, the nursing profession has only recently embraced its use. However, with increasing client care responsibilities, nurses rarely have time to go to the library to research solutions to client care problems. Furthermore, nurses still are not being rewarded for taking the initiative to use EBP

One development encouraging the use of EBP is that nurses no longer have to leave the practice setting to access relevant information. Literature can be searched from the nurses' station or even the client's bedside using available information systems. Nurses find that having access to literature about clinical issues increases their confidence levels in dealing with clients and other health professionals. It also allows them to contribute more fully to the multidisciplinary health-care team.[19]

Nurses must continue to make time for information searches that promote improved client care (Box 18.2). The creation of workplaces in which nurses can easily access client information, including research information, is essential to high-quality nursing practice.

THE HUMAN FACTOR

Is the System Friendly?

When information tools, machines, and systems are developed, they must include recognition of human factors, including knowledge about human

Box 18.2

Principles for Access to Library and Information Services

1. All nurses should have access to a free library service funded by their employer that contains appropriate literature and multimedia resources.
2. Library services should have flexible opening hours and be staffed by qualified librarians.
3. Nurses should have equal rights, similar to those of other health-care professionals, to paid study time to update their practice.
4. Every nurse should have access to training on the Internet and appropriate databases.
5. Every nurse should be educated in electronic systems and services to support evidence-based practice.

Source: Urquhart, C, and Davis, R: The impact of information. Nursing Standard 12(8):23–31, 1997.

capabilities, human limitations, and characteristics that may affect the use of the system. The terms *human factors, human engineering, usability engineering,* and *ergonomics* are often used interchangeably.

The study of human factors examines how to make the interaction of people and equipment safe, comfortable, and effective. Cognitive science, one of the components of informatics discussed earlier, forms part of the foundation for the study of human factors. Cognitive science includes the human acts of perception, thinking, understanding, and remembering.

In order to manage and process information, especially with an automated system, the individual must be able to understand and remember a great deal of data. The more logically this information is arranged, the easier it is to use the system. "User-friendly" systems are intuitive, self-evident, and logical, even if they are complicated.

Does the System Make Sense?

Every day in their client care, nurses use complex machinery, including many types of monitors, ventilators, intravenous (IV) pumps, feeding pumps, suction devices, electronic beds and scales, lift equipment, and assistive devices. The directions for using many of these machines are not self-evident and may be highly complicated. Although hospital equipment producers are becoming better at incorporating the human factor in the design and use of this complicated equipment, consulting with practicing nurses or "field testing" equipment in the workplace prior to its mass production would make it more user friendly.

Confusing Technology

New computer systems present many learning challenges for health-care providers. Many computer systems are not as user friendly as they might be. Computer system designers are notorious for supplying computers with numerous advanced but obscure functions. These systems often seem to make relatively simple daily tasks much more complicated. Millions of dollars have been wasted on computer systems that are not used or are underused because the user's needs were not considered before the systems were designed.

Individuals encountering complicated computer systems for the first time commonly feel that they are stupid, incompetent, or too old to learn because they cannot quickly master the new technology. However, the fault often lies not with the individual but with the design of the technology.

Nurses, through their education and philosophical orientation, are generally more in tune with the human factor than computer designers, particularly as it relates to client care. Nurses can use their human factor orientation in the process of evaluating new technology before it is purchased. Also, nurses may be able to make suggestions to medical equipment producers to help improve the equipment after it has been used for some time.

> *The creation of workplaces in which nurses can easily access client information, including research information, is essential to high-quality nursing practice.*

Is the System Well Designed?

There has been an ongoing concern in the United States about the problem of health-care error and the large number of client deaths attributed to it. Estimates of how many people die annually in the

United States as a result of medical error range from 44,000 to almost 100,000. On the basis of these numbers, medical error ranks as the eighth leading cause of death in the United States.[20]

Medical Error

The most common type of health-care error was related to medications, followed by wound infections; technical complications were ranked in third place. The proliferation of new medications and the increasing complexity of medication therapy have dramatically increased the risk of medication errors and adverse drug events both inside and outside hospitals.

Also, the increased use of "fast tracking" medications through the testing process has led to withdrawal of several medications from the market because of long-term complications not seen in the initial shortened testing phase. Well-designed computerized physician-order entry systems can reduce serious prescribing errors by more than 50%.[21]

Poor Design

Poor user design is responsible for thousands of health-care "accidents" each year. Complex medical devices are often used under extremely stressful conditions in which the user's cognitive abilities are not as focused as they might be in a less stressful situation. Often the users are not considered during the design phase, because the designers believe they know what is needed.

Errors Increase

The inevitable result of poor design in all types of equipment, ranging from laboratory forms to life-support devices, is an increased error rate.[22] Cognitive science studies have shown that the average person's memory can retain only six to eight pieces of information at a time. A well-designed system takes these elements into account (Box 18.3) and should reduce the number of errors. However, a poorly designed system can just as easily increase the number of errors rather than reduce them.

Training Doesn't Compensate

Employees are commonly trained to use an information system to reduce errors. Although

> " *Estimates of how many people die annually in the United States as a result of medical error range from 44,000 to almost 100,000. Based on these numbers, medical error ranks as the eighth leading cause of death in the United States.* "

Box 18.3

Elements of a Good Technology Design

- Can be operated intuitively with minimal reliance on complicated manuals
- Easy-to-read displays that are logically arranged
- Controls that are easy to use and reach
- Positive and safe electrical and mechanical connections
- Alarms that sound only when there is a real problem so that they are not turned off because of annoyance
- Long-life reliability with few malfunctions
- Easy, quick repair and maintainance

---

training is important, by itself it may not be adequate. In one study, there was no reduction in the number of errors even with an increase in training time. However, well-designed computer-based reminder systems did help clinicians reduce errors significantly. Even after the clinicians received additional training, errors returned to the previous level when the computerized reminder system was removed.[23]

When automated and computer systems are made user friendly by incorporating engineering techniques based on human needs, they can make a valuable contribution to monitoring and preventing error in clinical practice. As nursing professionals, it is important to understand that human performance is not perfect and cannot be perfected through education and training. Professionals must look for well-designed systems that can reduce and even eliminate errors.

THE ELECTRONIC HEALTH RECORD

A health record serves multiple purposes. It is used primarily to document client care. It also provides communication among health-care team members.

It acts as a financial and legal record and is used for research and continuous quality improvement (CQI). Although the health record can take many forms, the most common forms are either paper or electronic. Both forms have advantages and disadvantages (Box 18.4).

Advantages

Electronic health records (EHRs) have many advantages. Multiple care providers can access them simultaneously from remote sites. They can provide reminders about completing information or carrying out protocols as well as providing warnings about incompatibilities of medications or variances from normal standards.

Redundancy is reduced with the EHR. Rather than every health-care worker asking a client for his or her health history, allergies, and current medications, the information is captured once and then transmitted to every record requiring the information. EHRs require less storage space, are more difficult to lose, and are much easier to research. Improved communication, increased completeness of documentation, and reduction in error are the most important advantages of the EHR.

Disadvantages

Electronic health records have some obvious disadvantages. There is a high front-end cost in buying an electronic system and converting from a paper system. Employees may have problems adapting to the new system because of the steep learning curve involved. EHR systems are becoming more portable with the advent of the wireless network; however, they are also subject to all the glitches of electronic systems.

Decisions must be made about who can enter data into the system and when the entries should be made. The Health Insurance Portability and Accountability Act (HIPAA) regulations currently creating so many headaches for health-care providers were written specifically to address the many legal and ethical issues involving privacy and access to client information (see Chapter 9). Some issues still remain to be resolved.

The Ideal Record

The ideal EHR would be a lifelong continuous record of all the care that the client has received, rather than the episodic, piecemeal data that it now provides. This one record would reflect an individual's current health status and lifetime medical history. It would be unique to the person and not to the institution. This record would reside in multiple data sites and would accept multiple data types (e.g., graphs, pictures, x-rays, text) and be accessible worldwide.

Several Places at Once

The information on the EHR does not physically have to reside in one place, like a paper record. When viewed from a computer workstation, the EHR only appears to be in one place. In reality, the individual records are retrieved from many information systems, such as laboratory, radiology, document imaging, anatomic pathology, anesthesiology, bedside, and accounting.

With proper authorization, this record could be accessed from anywhere in the world, at any time. Many people around the world could look at the same record simultaneously. If an individual became

---

Box 18.4
Advantages and Disadvantages of the Paper Record

Advantages
- People know how to use it.
- It is fast for current practice.
- It is portable.
- It is nonbreakable.
- It accepts multiple data types, such as graphs, photographs, drawings, and text.
- Legal issues and costs are understood.

Disadvantages
- It can be lost.
- It is often illegible and incomplete.
- It has no remote access.
- It can be accessed by only one person at a time.
- It is often disorganized.
- Information is duplicated.
- It is hard to store.
- It is difficult to research, and CQI is laborious.
- Same client has separate records at each facility (physician's office, hospital, home care).
- Records are shared only through hard copy.

critically ill on a cruise ship or in a foreign country, the local health-care provider would be able to access the medical record to facilitate the client's diagnosis and treatment.

New Forms of Access

Health-care providers and technology designers are still working to resolve the many barriers to implementation of the ideal EHR. The issues of maintaining confidentiality and security are now closer to resolution. The high cost of starting up the system is still a barrier.

Access to the system would probably require a universal ID code or a unique client identifier.[24] Many organizations may resist a universal ID because they now use either their own client numbering system or social security numbers to identify individual records. Neither of these systems is adequate for the global access of the future. Fingerprinting, iris and retinal imaging, face prints, and voiceprints all are identification methods under investigation for use as the universal ID.

Bedside or Point of Care?

Bedside System. Some currently used systems allow nurses to enter information through bedside systems. A bedside system, as the name implies, is a computer terminal installed in each client's room or next to each bed.

Point-of-Care System. A point-of-care system has a broader meaning and includes not only the bedside but also many other points of care in the health-care environment and community, including the laboratory, radiology department, outpatient clinics, and even the client's home for home health-care providers. Many facilities currently have a unit system that can be accessed at only one terminal in the client care area (e.g., the nurses' station).

A Process Redesigned

Taking a paper record and typing it into a computer does not, in itself, constitute a modern electronic record. Automating the paper record in its present form only automates inefficient practices based on outdated requirements. Modern systems go beyond merely computerizing paper records. These new systems gain control over the generation of information and develop new techniques for using it creatively.

One of the most important characteristics of a bedside or point-of-care system is that client information can be input directly from the terminal. Then the nurse is freed from having to keep notes or chart from memory at the end of the shift. Documenting at the time of care is an important change in workflow for most health-care workers, who are accustomed to documenting at the end of a shift in a workroom with other professionals.

The re-engineering and streamlining of departmental workflow is accomplished by the automatic and continual routing of electronic documents and medical images from one person or department to another throughout the shift. With this system, traditional manual tasks are now automated, increasing the efficiency of management decisions and improving the distribution and evaluation of complex client records and electronic documents by authorized staff. This redesign of the old manual processes provides the real return on investment for implementing the electronic health record.

> *One of the most important characteristics of a bedside or point-of-care system is that client information can be input directly from the terminal rather than the nurse having to keep notes or chart from memory at the end of the shift.*

ETHICS, SECURITY, AND CONFIDENTIALITY

Information for Sale

Most people assume that all doctor–client communications are strictly confidential. However, in the new electronic world, confidential information has become a commodity that is bought and sold in the electronic marketplace. Although the HIPAA laws have tried to deal with this issue (see Chapter 9), people who use the Internet or e-mail quickly realize that their personal information is no longer so personal.

Examples of violations of client confidentiality abound. In 1996, a convicted child rapist working as a technician in a Boston hospital rifled through 1000 computerized records looking for potential victims. He was caught when the father of a

9-year-old girl used caller ID to trace a call back to the hospital.

A banker on Maryland's State Health Commission pulled up a list of cancer clients from the state's records, cross-checked it against the names of his bank's customers, and revoked the loans of those clients diagnosed with cancer. At least a third of all Fortune 500 companies regularly review health information before making hiring decisions. More than 200 subjects in a case study published in *Science and Engineering Ethics* reported that they had been discriminated against as a result of genetic testing.

A Question of Ownership

One of the key ethical questions is "Who owns the client's health-care data?" Does the individual's health-care information belong exclusively to the individual? Does it belong to the organization (e.g., insurance company, PPO) that paid for the care or should it belong to the physician who directed and ordered the care? What about the facility in which the care occurred—can they claim some ownership to the information, particularly if it is stored there? Do all these groups and individuals own a part of the information?

Should Society Benefit?

Those who argue the "individual rights" end of the ethical spectrum believe that each individual should have total and exclusive control over the information concerning his or her health and the care rendered. Those on the utilitarian, or "social good," end of the ethical spectrum believe that society as a whole benefits from shared information about disease occurrence and treatment. Therefore, the information should be available to all interested parties. As with most ethical dilemmas, a single definitive answer has not been proposed regarding who owns the data.

However, public policy debates have increased concerning the collection of health-care information for use as aggregate databases to underpin health-care planning. Many consumers are concerned about the status of future physician–client

relationships. Driving the development of data collection policy is the public's fear about the damage that may result from excessive and uncontrolled disclosures through automated health-care information systems.[25]

The Implications of Consent

When clients enter the health-care system, they are generally asked to sign consent forms so that other organizations can obtain information about their health status and the care that they received (particularly insurance companies so that bills can be paid). They are usually unaware that this information can be supplied to many other organizations or institutions.

For example, reports to the trauma registry are made about injuries resulting from accidents. The tumor registry collects information about benign and malignant tumors, and infectious disease reports are made to the Public Health Department. Currently, health-care information is shared to develop payment systems, examine access to care, identify cost differences of treatment modalities, research disease trends and epidemiological implications, and expand consumer information.

The Evolution of HIPAA

The HIPAA policies covering the collection, development, and use of client data are based on issues of confidentiality and security. In 1996, the federal government started to develop the guidelines that have become HIPAA. The primary objectives of HIPAA include:

- Ensuring health insurance portability
- Reducing health-care fraud and abuse
- Guaranteeing security and privacy of health information
- Enforcing standards for health information

In 2000, rules governing the exchange of electronic administrative health-care information were developed and added to HIPAA. The object of these rules was to simplify and standardize the electronic forms required for claims for services rendered. Every organization must now use the same form.

> *... most health-care institutions have policies prohibiting unauthorized access to confidential information. Individuals can lose their jobs because of unauthorized access or sharing of client information and, under recently enacted HIPAA laws, may be convicted of a crime.*

Rules for Disclosure

In 2001, HIPAA was modified by the addition of rules that address the use and disclosure of individually identifiable health information in any form, electronic or paper. Health-care providers and facilities must obtain client consent before using or disclosing client information for treatment, payment, or health-care operations. The full HIPAA was enacted in 2004.

What Do You Think?

Who do you think owns health-care information? How does your decision affect health-care policy in the future?

_____
_____
_____
_____
_____
_____
_____
_____
_____
_____
_____
_____
_____
_____
_____

Even with HIPAA regulations, confidential client information can be legally used for such purposes as quality assurance, institutional licensing and accreditation, biomedical research, third-party reimbursement, credentialing, litigation, regional and national databases, court-ordered release of information, and managed care comparisons. Although automated information systems did not cause these information uses, automation does make acquiring this information much easier.

Threats to Security

Unauthorized Access

Unauthorized sharing of health-care information is generally unethical and, now, always illegal. The code of ethics for most health-care professionals prohibits unauthorized or unnecessary access to client information. In addition, most health-care

institutions have policies prohibiting unauthorized access to confidential information. Individuals can lose their jobs because of unauthorized access or sharing of client information and, under recently enacted HIPAA laws, may be convicted of a crime.

A new wrinkle has been added to unauthorized access to health-care information. Under the policies of the current administration's Patriot Act, some national governmental agencies, such as the Federal Bureau of Investigation (FBI) and National Security Administration (NSA), now have the authority to wiretap or access, without court approval, any electronic information they believe may be associated with a terrorist threat. This information includes physicians' and nurses' records, laboratory information such as DNA profiles and blood type, and financial information. Although some believe this unrestricted access is necessary to prevent future attacks against the United States, others believe that it is a major violation of American citizens' right to privacy. It certainly seems to violate the regulations set forth in HIPAA.[26]

Unauthorized access or sharing of information is not a new problem associated only with the electronic age. It is just as easy to gain unauthorized access to a paper record as it is to the automated electronic record. The professional codes of ethics that stress client confidentiality have always

Do the policies of the Homeland Security Act that allow unrestricted governmental access to all electronic information violate HIPAA? How would you feel if your electronic medical records were accessed by the FBI?

_____

_____

_____

_____

_____

_____

_____

_____

_____

_____

_____

been the primary protector of client information. Still, access to the paper record is available to anyone who picks up the chart.

In some ways, the automated electronic record provides greater privacy. Access to the automated record is generally restricted to employees who have been issued a password. Also, most organizations have periodic **audits** that can track each person who has accessed a record, and some systems can even detect unauthorized access at the time of entry into the system.

Accidents

Threats to the security of information can be either accidental or intentional and affect both paper and electronic systems. Accidental threats involve naturally occurring events such as floods, fires, earthquakes, electrical surges, and power outages.

The paper record has little security against natural events. Typically, paper records are secured in a locked file cabinet or medical records room. Although current safety regulations require fire detection and suppression systems in these areas, even a small fire can destroy a large number of paper

records very quickly. There is little that can be done to protect paper records against major flooding. Once the charts are destroyed, they cannot be reproduced.

Facilities with automated systems usually have well-developed natural disaster plans built into the system design. These plans include the automatic production and storage of a backup tape of the data at a protected location some distance from the health-care facility. The frequency of data backup varies with the organization's requirements. Most systems automatically save all the data in the system every 24 hours, although this time interval can be shortened or increased to meet the facility's needs.

Although these measures provide a high degree of protection from major natural events such as floods and fires, power surges and outages create problems for electronic systems but leave paper systems unaffected. Anyone who works with computerized equipment recognizes the major disruptions in service and work that occur when the system goes down. Again, some safeguards can be built into the system so that not all the most recent information is lost when the power goes out. Power surges can be controlled with surge protection devices.

Intentional Acts

Intentional threats to the security of information involve the actions of an individual or individuals who wish to damage, destroy, or alter the records. In most cases, it is difficult to protect paper records from intentional tampering. It is a rather simple task for a determined individual to gain access to paper records and erase, add to, or rewrite sections of the chart. These changes are often very difficult to detect. In addition, a person could simply remove the chart and destroy it so that there would be no record left at all. Although automated electronic records are vulnerable to several kinds of intentional threats, they are, overall, more secure than the paper record. All current automated systems have computer virus-checking programs that protect the automated record from both intentional and accidental introduction of destructive computer viruses into the system.

Once data have been entered into the automated system, they are difficult to alter. Modern

> *Although automated electronic records are vulnerable to several kinds of intentional threats, they are, over all, more secure than the paper record.*

automated systems are designed with "write once, read many" (WORM) programs. If a legitimate change in the electronic record needs to be made, it must be an addendum. Any changes made in the electronic record are logged by the time and the person who made them and can always be tracked to the point of origin.

Although it is true that a determined and gifted hacker can still obtain access to almost any electronic database, electronic security systems are becoming more and more difficult to breach. However, terrorist acts, ranging from detonation of bombs in key locations to development of "superviruses" to destroy electronic records, are difficult to defend against and present an ever-increasing threat.

USES OF THE INTERNET

For nursing professionals, the Internet has become a valuable resource for communicating with colleagues and professional organizations, researching clinical information, and educating consumers about health resources and information. Because of the lack of standardization and regulation, it is important that the nurse evaluate each site for accuracy of information, authority, objectivity, currency or timeliness, and coverage.[27]

A Resource for Professionals
Most professional organizations maintain a Web site containing information about the organization. Many include policy statements and lists of publications. **Continuing education units (CEUs)** can be obtained via the World Wide Web to help nurses remain current and retain licensure. The Nursing Network (www.nursingnetwork.com), for example, is a site that lists education courses, position vacancies, conferences, and other pertinent information. News groups, such as those listed at www.nursingworld.org, provide professional information and access to experts in specific areas of interest.

Disease-specific Web sites publish clinical information for both the consumer and the professional. OncoLink is an example of a resource for information about cancer. Often the most recent information about a disease is found on the Internet. Publishing is quicker and easier on the World Wide Web than in a peer-reviewed journal. Web-based support groups disseminate information on both technical and consumer levels. Protocols and policies are shared through Web sites and news groups.

A Guide for Consumers
Today, consumers are more knowledgeable about health care through use of the Internet. Clients are better informed than they were in the past, because they now have easy access to a wide range of health-care information. Preventive and wellness services are available electronically through articles, chat groups, and health risk assessment surveys posted on consumer Web sites. Clients can now purchase medications over the Web, often at a much lower cost than they can get from their local pharmacies.

Healthfinder is a consumer health and human services information Web site created and maintained by the federal government. The site links the user with online government publications, clearinghouses, databases, Web sites, and support and self-help groups, as well as the government agencies and not-for-profit organizations that produce reliable information for the public. The goal of this information source is to help consumers make better choices about their health and human services needs for both themselves and their families.

TELEHEALTH

Health Care at a Distance
From its fledgling beginnings almost 40 years ago, clinicians, health services researchers, and others have been investigating the use of telecommunications and information technology to improve health care. Physicians examine and treat clients from distant sites with video cameras, thus saving money by exchanging office visits for online appointments.

The terms *telehealth* and *telemedicine* are often used interchangeably.[28] As defined here, telehealth is the use of electronic information and communications technologies to provide and support health care when distance separates the physician and the client. Telehealth includes a wide range of services and technologies, from "plain old telephone service" (POTS) to highly sophisticated digitized cameras, telemetry, voice systems, and even interactive robots.[29] Telemedicine is just one of the services provided by the overall telehealth system that primarily involves consultation with a physician.

Issues Now

Tomorrow's Technology Today

Almost any health-care provider with even a passing familiarity with the *Star Trek* movies or television shows has been envious of the tricorder used by fictional medical personnel to diagnose and treat a variety of ills by just waving the device over the client in distress. Although present technology is not quite to that point, it certainly is a lot closer than even a few years ago.

Wearable computers, initially developed for use in the military as a type of flak jacket/telemetry vest, are currently being tested. The Massachusetts Institute of Technology has improved on the technology by developing a heart brooch that sends heart sounds back to the health-care provider. It looks like an elegant piece of jewelry that anyone can wear. The Japanese are beginning production of "smart" toilets that can collect, process, and transmit data based on their contents.

A technology company called BodyMedia has developed an integrated program that combines principles of wellness with technology. People who wish to join the program are fitted with a BodyMedia SenseWear Armband, a personal body-monitoring apparatus. It is a little smaller than an arm radio, weighs about 3 ounces, and is worn on the back of the right triceps. The brain of the unit is a computer, memory chip, and sensors that continuously monitor body motion, skin temperature, heart rate, evaporation heat loss, and the amount of heat being dissipated by the body. The device, when programmed with the wearer's sex, age, height, and weight, provides data on the expenditure of energy during various activities. The armband can be used to treat clients with congestive heart failure, improve client compliance, and alter lifestyle habits.

Nurses will soon be exposed to these smart devices. They will provide more data for integration into the health-care record; allow comparison of clients' progress not only from day to day, but from hour to hour or even minute to minute; and provide highly accurate and detailed information.

Another technology that nurses will be experiencing sooner rather than later is voice-activated information systems. We are used to seeing sportscasters, singers, and others in the media with the headset–microphone devices. Nurses will soon be wearing something very similar, a voice-activated headset that will allow them to dictate their documentation as they go about

Issues Now (continued)

their daily tasks. Nurses have long realized that most of their work is highly activity directed and performed on the run. Sitting behind a computer, or even standing in a room at a computer console, is not the reality of nursing. This technology will allow for more timely documentation and free up some time now devoted to paperwork.

These are just two areas of many that are around the corner in health care. One important element in any developing health-care technology is input from the people who are going to use it. Too often new technology is developed by people who are experts in computers but have very little experience with health care. Unless a technology is user friendly, it is not going to be effective. Nurses need to play an active role in designing and testing new systems.

Telehealth is being used in emergency departments across the United States. The University of Pittsburgh offers neurological consults to physicians at seven linked hospitals. In Baltimore, providers are using cellular telephone technology to transmit live video and client data back to home base.

Some uses of telehealth, such as emergency calls to 911, are so common that they are often overlooked as part of telehealth systems. Other applications, such as telesurgery, involve advanced technologies and procedures that are being used on a limited basis and are still considered experimental.

Serving Remote Populations

Historically, consumer concerns about access to health care have been the driving force behind the development of many clinical telehealth systems. Early applications focused on remote populations scattered across mountainous areas, islands, open plains, and arctic regions where medical specialists, and sometimes even primary care practitioners, were not available.

Many telehealth projects from the 1960s through the early 1980s failed because they were expensive, awkward to use, and often not guided by the strategic plans of the facilities using them. However, as the technology has become more common, the costs of many systems have decreased dramatically. With the development of cellular technology, many of the newer systems are tapping into the systems already in place for telephone service.

Renewed interest in telehealth has been spurred by managed care initiatives seeking to reduce health-care costs while maintaining or increasing the

quality of and access to care. Overall costs have decreased for many of the information and communications technologies used by telehealth systems. In addition, the ever-developing National Information Infrastructure is making these technologies more accessible and user friendly. Medicare reimburses some types of telehealth care, although other third-party payers have been slow to include reimbursement for telehealth services.

Telehealth in an Emergency

Telehealth offers many advantages that will affect the cost of and access to the health-care system of the future. The telehealth system allows access to centralized specialists who can support primary care providers in outlying areas. Outlying areas can be either rural or urban areas that lack access to the full range of health-care services. Outlying clinics staffed only with nurse practitioners or physician assistants have immediate access to physician referrals through the telehealth system.

University medical centers can offer specialist consulting services to primary care physicians at distant locations, thus reducing unnecessary travel and increased cost to clients. Here is an example of how the telehealth system functions in an emergency situation:

In 1996, a 72-year-old man with a collapsed lung walked into the emergency department (ED) in a small town in North Dakota. The general practitioner who usually saw routine emergency cases immediately called the trauma II medical center in Bismarck and arranged a teleconsult with an ED physician and a thoracic surgeon. The man would have died without a thoracotomy. Following the surgeon's instructions, the physician was able to insert the chest tubes needed to safely transport the client by helicopter to Bismarck.

Telehealth services often save lives and prevent permanent disability, especially when time is a factor in treatment. For example, health-care providers know that if thrombolytic medications are given within 3 hours after the onset of symptoms of a stroke, the likelihood of death or permanent disability is reduced by 50 percent. Using telehealth technology, neurology specialists can evaluate a client's condition while he or she is still in the ambulance en route to the hospital, thus saving valuable time in making the decision about using lifesaving medications. The ED is prepared to administer the medications as soon as the client enters the department rather than having to wait several hours for all the routine evaluations and consults to be completed.

Nurses who practice in rural and underserved urban areas will have more autonomy and provide higher-quality care when linked electronically with the support services of a large medical center.

Telehealth services often save lives and prevent permanent disability, especially when time is a factor in treatment.

Issues for the Future

A Boost for Home Care
In the future, home care may benefit the most from telehealth. By investing in telehealth technologies, home care providers should be able to balance cost reductions with increased quality of care.

Clients can be monitored at home using a combination of telephone calls, home visits, video visits, and in-home monitoring via the telehealth system. In-home monitoring devices for conditions ranging from congestive heart failure and diabetes to cancer and cardiac conditions can send information from the client's home to a central base for assessment by professionals.

Future Challenges

System Design. Many of the older systems are poorly designed and may be totally incompatible with the systems used in modern health-care facilities. The human factor design and user assessments must be carefully considered in developing any new technologies.

Expense. Although the overall costs of electronic systems continue to gradually decrease, initial expenditures are still a barrier to implementation, especially in smaller facilities. Lack of **third-party payment** for telehealth systems also limits their development and use.

Legal Issues. Several legal issues still need to be resolved, including health-care provider licensure when consults are given across state lines and the liability incurred by providers who examine a client by television rather than in a face-to-face, hands-on encounter. Federal and state policies protecting privacy and confidentiality need to be developed with specific provisions for telehealth systems.

Effects on Nursing Practice. The telehealth system also affects nursing practice. Nurses are the primary users of telephone triage systems that rely on computerized decision-making trees to suggest appropriate actions when given a set of client symptoms. Nurses who practice in rural and underserved urban areas will have more autonomy and provide higher-quality care when linked electronically with the support services of a large medical center. The use of remote monitoring devices provides nurses with immediate information about changes in their clients' conditions, improves outcomes, reduces complications, and lowers the number of readmissions to the hospital.

Education and Conferencing. The same types of technology used for telehealth can be used for distance and **nontraditional education** applications. Widespread use of **continuing education** is achieved through distance technology. Courses are video conferenced with two-way interaction. Continuing education credits can be earned through courses on the Internet. Even college credits can be earned via Internet access. Grand rounds are conducted at multiple sites with video conferencing equipment, and in-services are beamed to multiple locations.

Conclusion

The information revolution affects every aspect of health care, not only in the United States but also throughout the world. Advanced communications technology and its increased availability worldwide promotes ties between people and nations, bridging the gap between isolated rural communities and major metropolitan areas.

The nursing profession needs to be actively involved in developing clinical information systems and the electronic health record, establishing care standards, safeguarding client privacy, using the Internet, and researching better ways of improving access and the quality of care through technology. The nursing profession is transformed, enhanced, and enriched as nurses become active participants in the information revolution.

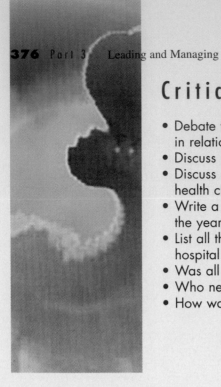

Critical Thinking Exercises

- Debate the ethical issues of personal privacy and the greater social good in relation to availability of health-care information.
- Discuss how the design of equipment increases or decreases error rates.
- Discuss uses of telehealth for patient teaching and monitoring of home health clients.
- Write a vision paper describing your view of technology in health care in the year 2030.
- List all the pieces of data you had to give at your last visit to the doctor or hospital.
- Was all of the information necessary for your care?
- Who needed the information?
- How was the information recorded or transmitted?

References

1. Bittner, LA: My journey as a student in informatics. Delaware Nurses Association Reporter 32(2): 3, 2007.
2. Lin, J: An exploration of nursing informatics competency and satisfaction related to network education. Journal of Nursing Research 15(1): 54–66, 2007.
3. Lang, M: Nursing informatics: The integration of nursing science, computer science and information science. Delaware Nurses Association Reporter 32 (2): 1, 2007.
4. Hunt, E: The Alliance for Nursing Informatics (ANI) achieving the strategic vision. Computers, Informatics, Nursing 25 (2): 118–119, 2007.
5. Lin, J: An exploration of nursing informatics competency and satisfaction related to network education. Journal of Nursing Research 15 (1): 54–66, 2007.
6. Featherly, K: News & trends. Nursing informatics: Nurses champion clinical technologies. Healthcare Information 21(8):10–12, 2004.
7. Thede, LQ, Craig, GP: How to implement a laptop computer requirement: Lessons learned. Computers, Informatics, Nursing 25 (1): 11–15, 2007.
8. Nelson, R, and Joos, I: On language in nursing: From data to wisdom. PLN Visions, Fall 1989, pp. 6–7.
9. Fischetti, L: A framework for strategic action: The report from HHS's Secretarial Summit on Health Information Technology, cornerstones for electronic health care. Caring Newsline 3rd Quarter 19(3): 1, 3–4, 2004.
10. American Nurses Association: Scope and Standards of Nursing Informatics Practice. American Nurses Publishing, Washington, DC, 2001.
11. American Nurses Credentialing Center Catalog. American Nurses Publishing, Washington, DC, 2001.
12. Currell, R: Nursing record systems: Effects on nursing practice and health care outcomes. The Cochrane Library, 2005, n. 1.
13. Oermann, MH: Hit the Web to help guide your practice. Nursing Management 38(2): 20–21, 2007.
14. i-NMDS Project Portal 2007 www.nmds.org.
15. Goldenberg, G: Pediatric nurse practitioners: All the possibilities. Academic Nurse 24 (1): 19–35, 2007.
16. Brokel, J: Technology. Creating sustainability of clinical information systems: The chief nurse officer and nurse informatics specialist roles. Journal of Nursing Administration 37(1): 10–13, 2007.
17. Humphries, BL: Building better connections to the National Library of Medicine and public health. Journal of Medical Library Association 9(3): 293–300, 2007.
18. Britt Pipe, T: Optimizing nursing care by integrating theory-driven evidence-based practice. Journal of Nursing Care Quality 22(3): 234–238, 2007.
19. Kresse, MR: An evidence-based template for implementation of multidisciplinary evidence-based practices in a tertiary hospital setting. American Journal of Medical Quality 22(3): 148–163, 2007.
20. McCormick, KA: Guideposts to the future—an agenda for nursing informatics. Journal of the American Medical Informatics Association 14 (1): 19–24, 2007.
21. Eslami, S: Evaluation of outpatient computerized physician medication order entry systems: a systematic review. Journal of the American Medical Informatics Association 14(4): 400–406, 2007.
22. Focus on five. Reducing the risk of laboratory errors. Joint Commission Perspectives on Patient Safety 6(10): 11, 2006.
23. Gardner, R: Using computer technology to detect, measure, and prevent adverse drug events. Journal of the American Medical Information Association 11(6): 535–536, 2004.
24. Macy, D: Using electronic wristbands and a triage protocol to protect mental health patients in the emergency department. Journal of Nursing Care Quality 22(2): 180–184, 2007.
25. Collmann, J: Breaching the security of the Kaiser Permanente internet patient portal: The organizational foundations of information security. Journal of the American Medical Informatics Association 14(2): 239–243, 2007.
26. Kluge, E: Ehealth, the USA Patriot Act and other hurdles: The black lining on the silver cloud. British Journal of Healthcare Computing & Information Management 23(9): 16–23, 2006.
27. Cosby, H: Using the Internet for nursing. Web wows and wonders. Gastroenterology Nursing 30(2): 146, 2007.
28. Winters, JM: Videoconferencing and telehealth technologies can provide a reliable approach to remote assessment and teaching without compromising quality. Journal of Cardiovascular Nursing 22(1): 51–57, 2007.
29. Ratner, T: Robots lend a helping hand. Nursing Spectrum 15(2): 10–11, 2006.

Bibliography

American Nurses Association: Scope and Standards of Nursing Informatics Practice. American Nurses Publishing, Washington, DC, 2001.

Bartholomew, K: High-tech, high-touch: Why wait? Nurse Manager 35(9): 48, 50–54, 2004.

Curran, C: The informatics nurse: Helping to build the knowledge infrastructure for nursing. Nurse Leader 2(3): 26–29, 2004.

Englebardt, S, and Nelson, R (eds): Health Care Informatics: An Interdisciplinary Approach. Mosby, St. Louis, 2002.

Nicoll, LH: Nurses' Guide to the Internet, ed. 3. Lippincott, Philadelphia, 2001.

Puskar, K: Implementing information technology in a behavioral health setting. Issues in Mental Health Nursing 25(5): 439–450, 2004.

Roscoe, T: An assessment tool for medical informatics skills. Health Information Journal 10(2): 155–159, 2004.

Shifman, M: Exploring the portability of informatics capabilities from a clinical application to a bioscience application. Journal of American Medical Information Association 11(4): 294–299, 2004.

Young, KM: Informatics for Healthcare Professionals. F.A. Davis, Philadelphia, 2000.

4

Issues in Delivering
Care

19

The Politically Active Nurse

Donna Gentile O'Donnell

Learning Objectives

After completing this chapter, the reader will be able to:

- Explain why it is important for nurses to understand and become involved in the political process.
- Discuss how a bill becomes a law.
- Identify the major committees at the federal level that influence health policy.
- Identify four points at which nurses can influence a bill.
- Give examples of how nurses may become politically involved.
- List and describe four methods of lobbying.

A NUTS-AND-BOLTS APPROACH

The word *politics* conjures up various images—some positive and some negative. There are images of great statesmanship, like the inaugural speech of John F. Kennedy, who exhorted the nation, "Ask not what your country can do for you, but what you can do for your country." There are also images of ignoble moments, like the national tragedy of Watergate, the resignation of Richard Nixon, the impeachment proceedings against Bill Clinton, the dubious election practices that put George W. Bush in office, or the numerous negative campaign commercials vilifying political opponents. Politics touches people's lives at all levels, crossing national boundaries, affecting individual states, and permeating local governments.

This chapter will provide a foundation for understanding the political basics by using a nuts-and-bolts approach and will motivate nurses to become active in the political world. Politics is examined both within the profession of nursing and within society at large. In addition, this chapter discusses the forces that drive politics and the three concepts it comprises: partisanship, self-interest, and ideology.

Almost everyone, ranging from political candidates, academicians, and members of the press to regular citizens, has something to say about politics. People define politics in many ways. One of the most cynical definitions of politics is offered by Ambrose Bierce in *The Devil's Dictionary*, where it is described as "A strife of interests masquerading as a contest of principles. The conduct of public affairs for private advantage." Other, more widely accepted definitions include "the art or science of government," "the art or science concerned with guiding or influencing government policy," or "the total complex of relations between [people] in society."[1]

THE NURSING SHORTAGE

The nursing shortage is a good example of where nurses' concerns intersect with the political process. In many areas of the United States, the nursing shortage has reached crisis levels, and there do not appear to be any permanent cures on the near horizon. Different areas of the country are attempting to deal with the shortage in the short term with quick, stopgap political measures that may have an adverse effect on the nursing profession in the long term.

Foreign Recruitment

One quick and easy solution some hospitals are initiating is recruitment of nurses from outside the country. Hospitals in various parts of the country have started programs to bring nurses from countries such as the Philippines. These foreign nurses generally receive the same pay and benefits as the American registered nurses (RNs). They also often receive permanent resident visas and housing if they desire it. Currently, foreign-born RNs comprise 14 percent of the nursing workforce, a significant increase from less than 9 percent in 1994.[2] These foreign nurse recruitment plans do not address obtaining U.S. licensure, an issue that affects the state boards of nursing and nurse practice acts.

Institutional Licensure

In regard to foreign nurses, the issue American nurses should be concerned with is legislative, namely institutional licensure (see Chapters 3 and 12). The practice of institutional licensure has been universally rejected by every major nursing organization; however, health-care facilities continue to attempt "back-door" institutional licensure. When foreign nurses are allowed to practice in specific institutions without taking the American licensure examinations, de facto institutional licensure exists even if it is not called by that name.

What's so bad about institutional licensure? The primary problem is the lack of external standards to determine the level of competency. Obviously, when the representatives of hospitals planning to hire foreign nurses interview candidates, they are looking for certain characteristics or qualities. What are these qualities? Ability to speak English? Not having a family? Knowledge in critical care, obstetrics, or pediatrics? The hospital establishes the criteria and no one outside the administration really knows how the finalists are selected.

Without external standards, the designations of RN or LPN/LVN (licensed practical nurse/licensed vocational nurse) become relatively meaningless. In addition, without an American nursing license, these foreign nurses would not be under the control of the state board of nursing. What if the foreign nurse was practicing unethically or made grievous negligent errors that caused harm to the client? Who would be responsible? Who would discipline the nurse? Most health-care facilities now require criminal background searches for all employees. How do they obtain these from countries that do not keep records of arrests or convictions for crimes?

> *Politics touches people's lives at all levels, crossing national boundaries, affecting individual states, and permeating local governments.*

Nurses practicing in states where the importation of foreign nurses is being planned or actually practiced need to contact their state board of nursing. It is highly probable that the practice violates a standard in the nurse practice act, and the facilities conducting the practice should be investigated.

Luxury Health Care

Guest Suites for Gourmets

Some nurses are attempting to deal with the consequences of the nursing shortage—such as understaffing, mandatory overtime, supervision of undertrained personnel, and erosion of the quality of care—by seeking employment in what have become known as "luxury health-care centers."

Luxury health-care centers are for-profit facilities that specialize in specific, high-revenue health care. They offer high-end perks for the clients, such as gourmet meals; well-decorated, "resort-like," comfortable rooms that are sometimes called "guest suites"; and one-room stays rather than a move from the intensive care unit (ICU) to a medical–surgical unit. These facilities attract nurses who are tired of the working conditions in traditional hospitals.

Profitable Procedures

The luxury health-care centers focus on providing specific services for particular procedures that generate high profits. Heart and orthopedic hospitals, cancer centers, and freestanding surgery facilities currently are the most common focus for this type of health care. The heart hospitals offer the services usually found in a general hospital, such as angioplasty, pacemaker insertion, and bypass surgery, but with a much higher level of care. These hospitals use the client-focused care model, in which a client spends the entire stay in one room and is cared for by the same nurses until discharge.

These facilities generate revenue by offering only certain high-end medical procedures that have a large profit margin and are covered by insurance. The luxury facilities save money by having a minimal number of administrators and allowing the nurses more input into the policy decisions and day-to-day provision of care.

In many of these facilities, up to 60 percent of the nursing staff is involved in direct client care, whereas the average in general hospitals is about 40 percent. Nurses are also cross-trained so they can function in multiple roles. In addition, the facilities reduce costs by shortening the length of client stays. Several limited research studies have shown that in luxury facilities where the client-centered model is used, client stays are routinely reduced by 25 to 50 percent.

What Attracts the Nurse?

Nurses find a luxury health-care environment attractive for several reasons. They feel that they can provide a higher level of continuity of care because the same nurse admits the client, cares for the client during the stay, and then handles the discharge when the client goes home.

Nurses feel that the quality of care is much higher in luxury facilities. They work primarily with adequate numbers of well-trained professionals. Cross-training allows nurses to practice in several different settings, reducing the monotony of practice sometimes experienced in general hospitals. Also, because they have a bigger say in the work environment, policies, and care they

> 66 *Nurses employed at magnet hospitals have a high degree of job satisfaction and a much lower than average turnover rate compared to nurses in other hospitals of similar size.* 99

provide, one of the primary elements of burnout—lack of control—is significantly reduced.

Finally, nurses in luxury care facilities earn on average $5.00 to $7.00 more per hour than nurses in traditional hospitals. Retirement and health insurance plans are often better, and some even offer stock options as part of the benefit package.

The Downside

Revenue Siphoning

What is the downside to luxury hospitals? One significant problem is the siphoning off of the highest-revenue procedures from the general hospitals. Most general, not-for-profit hospitals do a continual financial juggling act in an attempt to balance services that lose money or make little money (trauma centers, burn units, obstetric units) with areas that have a high income (cardiac centers, orthopedic centers, one-day surgery). Some analysts believe that the competition from luxury hospitals will force general hospitals to improve the quality of their care so they can draw in more clients, but the reality is that if the general hospitals run at a deficit for too long, they will be forced to close.

Increased Shortages

Another concern is that the most experienced and most qualified nurses are being lured away from general hospitals. The nursing shortage has made it an employees' market. Luxury hospitals, because of their higher pay, can pick and choose from the best of the best. Heart hospitals are particularly interested in hiring ICU and critical care unit (CCU) nurses, as well as nurses with surgical and recovery room experience. This group represents some of the best-educated and most skilled nurses in any facility. As a result, the staffing shortages in the general hospitals will increase, and the quality of care will suffer more from the loss of experienced nurses.

Magnet Hospitals

Another, more positive, approach to the nursing shortage is the establishment of "magnet hospital" status for hospitals that retain a high percentage of the nurses they hire. In 1980, the American Academy of Nurses conducted a study to identify those elements that were present in hospitals that attracted and retained nurses. Several key factors were identified in hospitals that seemed to fulfill the magnet status, including a participative management style, allowing the nurses a relatively high degree of autonomy in practice and decision making, high-quality leadership at the unit level, a horizontal organizational structure, allowing nurses to practice as full professionals, opportunities for career development, and high-quality client care. Nurses employed at magnet hospitals have a high degree of job satisfaction and a much lower than average turnover rate than nurses in other hospitals of similar size.

The magnet hospital program has grown markedly since the original study. The ANA has established rather rigorous standards for hospitals to meet to obtain the magnet designation. Most hospitals have found achieving magnet status to be very challenging and only a small percentage are able to achieve it on the first try. However, hospitals that do obtain magnet status have achieved a well-deserved level of prestige among their peers. Nurses working at these hospitals have more control over their practice, and the end result is that higher-quality care is provided to the clients.

Late-Entry Nurses

A recent trend being studied indicates that, whereas the number of "traditional" early-twenties college students entering nursing has declined, more students in their late twenties and early thirties are seeking admission to nursing schools. These are often students who have gotten an associate degree and come back after several years to complete their baccalaureate degree. Almost as many did not attend any institution of higher education after high school, working at entry level–pay jobs or staying at home to raise families.

One factor that may be attracting this cohort of "twenty somethings" into nursing is the well-publicized nursing shortage and the promise of a well-paying career with lots of job security. Older students are generally looking for a new start, whereas younger students are often looking for jobs in one of the few fields they believe are open to them. Although the exact effect that this trend will have on the nursing shortage is still unclear, any increase in the supply of nurses will most likely help to relieve the impending nursing shortage.[2]

A Long-Term Solution

None of the above-mentioned measures really address the underlying problem of the nursing shortage. The long-term solution is to increase the supply of nurses by encouraging more young men and women to enter schools of nursing, and providing the schools with sufficient funds to educate those who apply.

National trends in nursing school enrollments have shown a gradual increase in enrollment over the past few years, offering some hope for a long-range cure. However, because of an acute shortage of nursing faculty, many nursing schools are turning away qualified students. In 2006, more than 147,000 qualified applicants were turned away from entry into nursing schools because of the shortage of nursing faculty, clinical sites, and classroom facilities.[3] For those who do choose to enter the nursing profession and manage to get into nursing school, the future looks bright. There are many opportunities, and health-care facilities are beginning to appreciate and reward nurses at the level they deserve.

Legislating Nurse-to-Client Ratios

One attempt to legislate a fix to the nursing shortage occurred in California in 1999. The California state legislature made the precedent-setting move to establish minimum nurse-to-client ratios by enacting legislation. The regulations were phased in over several years and took full effect in 2003.

After several years of implementation, the evaluation of the results remains mixed. Nurses' unions and consumer advocacy groups, such as the American Association of Retired Persons (AARP), point to the increase in client safety, the reduction in medical errors, and the increased nurse retention rates as indications that the program has been a success. Groups opposed to this type of legislation, such as state hospital associations and state medical associations, believe that mandated staffing ratios have failed, citing decreases in physician and hospital income and reduction in the total number of clients seen. Several other states implemented similar staffing ratio measures, with results similar to those of California. However, few states currently seem interested in mandating staffing ratios. An unintended result of mandated staffing ratios is that, to avoid legislative action, many health-care facilities have moved to self-regulate their ratios. The increased interest in the magnet program may be an offshoot of legislated staffing ratios.

The nursing shortage and the various attempts to resolve it are health-care issues that have become political. They have the potential to significantly affect the profession of nursing, and nurses need to get out in front of the issues if they want to have a say in what is decided about their future.[4]

GOVERNMENT AND POLITICS

Keep in mind that *government* is a very broad term that refers to almost any type of hierarchical structure that functions to organize and direct an organization. From this context, the governance structure of any health-care facility can be considered a type of government that has its own politics. At this level, nurses have the potential to have a considerable amount of political influence.

Relevance to Nursing
Historically, most nurses have avoided becoming engaged in government, perhaps because they agree with definitions similar to the one presented by Bierce. However, nurses, both as individual citizens and as a professional group, need to recognize that their personal lives and professional practice are affected by the political world. Some recent trends in health care, particularly the nursing shortage, managed care, and cost containment, have made nurses increasingly susceptible to the "bottom line."

Issues Now

The Need for Organization at the State Level

Why do nurses need to organize at the state level? A debate is just starting in nursing about the political activity of the ANA at the federal level. The ANA over the past several years has successfully raised money through telemarketing in every state in the country. Many nurses do not realize that the ANA Political Action Committee (PAC) is now the second-largest federal PAC in Washington. In the last election cycle, they raised $1.2 million, which was spent on political activities exclusively at the federal level. However, it is important to realize that many of the political battles nurses have to fight are at the state level.

There is an ongoing discussion between the federal and state governments about what constitutes a legitimate course of action for the federal government and what constitutes the same for the state government. The 10th Amendment to the Constitution says essentially that any powers not expressly articulated to be part of the federal government mandate go to the states. This amendment underlies the current debate about Medicaid and Medicare and whether or not the states should be responsible for their administration.

The Role of State Nursing Organizations

The concept of unfunded mandates has come to the forefront in the past few years as a result of the states' rights push. There is an ongoing discussion among members of the National Governors' Association demanding that the federal government give governors more latitude in governing their states. They are saying, "Don't give us mandates. Give us the opportunity to set our own standards, our own regulatory actions, and our own legislative and governmental agenda." The nation is moving toward greater state control governmentally. It would be ideal if nurses could organize and just concentrate on issues at the federal level Washington, but because most nursing issues are at the state level, this strategy would probably not work.

For nursing organizations to be effective, there has to be organized political action among nurses and by nurses in every state in this country. In states where nurses are not active and organized politically, there is going to be trouble, and the nurses in them will fare badly. Nurses need to realize that the trend is toward state nursing organizations becoming more active politically and determining their own fate. Consequently, nurses need to organize politically at the state level to increase their political power.

Another thing to keep in mind is that nurses' licensure, as well as the certification and regulation of hospitals, is a function of the state. Again, it does not make sense to concentrate all the resources of nursing at the national level. Of course, there are some issues and programs, particularly with respect to funding, in which federal action is necessary. However, most of the issues nurses will be dealing with occur at the state level, and that is where attention needs to be focused. The reality is that the states have the capacity to define and regulate objective standards for both nurses and hospitals. The mandate for nursing is to define how those standards are established and then develop an achievable agenda for political action by nurses at the state level.

In addition, because of politics, nurses are confronting major changes in health care on a daily basis. They have experienced the erosion of the profession through their replacement with less-educated personnel and have seen the quality of client care deteriorate. Nurses, if they decide to act, are not powerless against such trends.

The Sleeping Giant

As a large group of voters, nurses have the power, influence, and skill to take an active role in the political process. Senator Daniel Inouye of Hawaii referred to nurses as the "sleeping giant in health care." Nurses can gain much by using the tools of political action, and now more than ever their professional survival depends on it.

Individual nurses can take attainable, deliberate actions that can create a powerful political force. However, before nurses can realize their full potential, a basic knowledge and understanding of the political system is necessary. Henry Adams stated long ago that "knowledge of human nature is the beginning and end of a political education." If he is correct, it is logical to conclude that nurses, who are among the most astute observers of human nature, are in many ways ideally suited to the art and science of politics.

WHY SHOULD NURSES BE INVOLVED?

Every Aspect of Life

A widely accepted definition of politics is the process of influencing *public policy,* including all forms and levels of governmental regulations. The effects of politics are pervasive and related to almost every aspect of life.

On a personal level, politics influences where children go to school, the quality of food, the water that flows from your kitchen tap, what medications are prescribed, and the speed limit on roadways. On a professional level, politics influences where nurses work, what they do and how they do it, the ability to organize professionally, and even the nurse's professional status through licensure and certification. The effects of politics on a person's life seem to have no limits.

Is Acceptance Necessary?

Nurses experience the effects of governmental regulations both directly and indirectly. Examples of directly experienced government regulations include some recent reforms that many states have initiated. Some state legislatures have enacted nurse-to-client ratios. All states now have granted advanced practice nurses prescriptive privileges, although the regulations governing their implementation vary widely from state to state.

During the 2008 election cycle, national health-care reform again became a central issue. Many Americans do not have any type of health-care coverage, and this situation is inflicting hidden costs on the health-care system. These realities have pushed politicians to consider new legislation. Many nurses respond to these proposed changes with stoic resignation and believe that they can do nothing to influence the direction of the legislation.

Saul Alinsky provides useful pointers regarding tactics that nurses can use. Box 19.1 summarizes and gives examples of Alinsky's Rules for Radicals.[3]

POLITICS AND POLITICAL ACTION

Politics

As a dynamic process, politics plays a key role in all forms and levels of government, including federal, state, and local government. It can be seen as the complex interaction between public policy and various public and constituent interests.

Politics is directly and indirectly influenced by the self-interest of political officials, both elected and appointed. The mass media also have both a direct and indirect impact on the political process through numerous political commentators, political commercials, and investigations into the backgrounds of selected political figures.

Political Action

Political action is a set of activities, methods, tactics, and behaviors that affect or have the potential to affect governmental and legislative processes and outcomes.[6] Examples of political action include grassroots efforts to change policies, the activities of lobbyists to change elected officials' opinions or votes, the give and take of political compromise within legislative bodies, and even the power of veto by the chief executive of a governmental structure.

Box 19.1

Alinsky's Rules for Radicals (with O'Donnell's Comments)

- Power is not only what you have but what the enemy thinks you have.
  This concept is widely used in political organizing. Fundraising reports are a classic example. Candidates work very hard to get their financial commitments before filing their candidacy, to inform people of their ammunition.

- Never go outside the experience of your own people.
  This is the fundamental mistake that has been made in some efforts to organize nurses. The American Nurses Association (ANA) and the state associations too often reflect an elite group not connected to the real world. Their leadership tends not to be nurses from the bedside or those intimately connected with frontline nursing. Their concerns, although legitimate, do not reflect the experience of the nurses entrenched in patient care issues.

- Wherever possible, go outside the experience of your enemy. Pick your battlefields.
  During a press conference around the March on Washington in 1996, nurses talked about their experiences that were foreign territory to the press. They presented a compelling picture. Most of the press were not accustomed to listening to nurses talk about high-tech procedures and gained a new level of respect for what nurses do. To the extent to which you can impress people with your knowledge and go outside their experience, it forces them to compete.

- Make them live up to their own book of rules.
  An example of this rule happened many years ago. Bob O'Donnell, former speaker of the Pennsylvania House, tells a story about when he was first breaking into the political world. There was a party machine that was not interested in supporting the common interests of the neighborhoods. Undaunted, O'Donnell learned the rules by which the next ward leader and committee person election would be held.
  Ward leaders and committee people are the smallest unit of the partisan political system. Usually committee people are responsible for districts. The districts add up to the ward. The ward leader oversees the committee people who manage those districts and register people to vote.
    Standing within the system is necessary to be successful in a political system. The way to do that in the ward structure is to either be ward leader or have significant influence over the ward leader. Over a period of several years, O'Donnell assisted his allies in obtaining committee positions. When there was an election for the ward leader, the committee people elected O'Donnell to the position. The party machinery refused to seat the ward leader. O'Donnell used their own rule book to bring the issue to federal court and forced them to seat him as the new ward leader. He beat them at their own game.

- Ridicule is man's and woman's most potent weapon.
  This is also known as the Dan Quayle phenomenon. Dan Quayle has been repeatedly characterized as a political buffoon. Dan Quayle is not as unintelligent as people assume him to be. Unfortunately for him, Vice President Quayle did some uninformed things while he happened to be standing in front of a magnifying glass with the national press behind it. More recently, Bill Clinton became the focus of many a political joke because of his involvement with Monica Lewinsky. His Republican enemies seized on the incident to the point where they made it an issue of impeachment.

- A good tactic is one that your people enjoy.
  The 1996 March on Washington is a wonderful example. Nurses enjoyed the national forum that permitted a massive demonstration for their voices to finally be heard.

- A tactic that drags on too long becomes a drag; use the concepts of reward and momentum.
  This is the most dangerous pitfall for nurses attempting political organizing. The process is difficult and takes time to reach a successful conclusion. Nurses can become discouraged by the slow pace of the

change process in the political arena. Rather than focusing only on long-range goals, it is important to concentrate on smaller objectives such as achieving a significant role in a city council race.

- Keep the pressure on. Become the constant by which all other variables are defined.

    Currently, the ANA defines issues and concepts at the national level. The ANA has raised money in every state and has translated that money into a political power base in Washington. When a senator or congressman who has been a beneficiary of the ANA's largess takes a position, it is with the ANA in mind. Nurses need to become the standard by which all related variables are measured in their states. State legislators need to consider nurses' opinions the same way they do now with the teachers' association.

- The threat is usually more terrifying than the thing itself. Threat is multiplied by the unknown and the imagination of someone under attack.

    This principle can be used very effectively over time. Imagine if someone opposed pro-nursing legislation and nurses threatened to demonstrate. The public image of thousands of nurses donning their uniforms would be a very powerful image for legislators to contend with.

- The major premise for tactics is the development of operations that will maintain a constant pressure on the opposition. The pressure must be sustainable over time.

    This is the concept of "if what, then what." In a tactical plan, you have to be able to look beyond and determine what happens after you reach the end of this tactic.

- Pick the target. Freeze it. Personalize it. Polarize it. And use a focused and strategic attack.

    Essentially, nurses need to be focused in their political activities. For example, imagine that nurses have considerable support from various legislative groups for objective standards and want to pass a law. A solid bill has been drafted, but a Democrat or Republican will not introduce your bill.

    The strategy is to target the one person who is slowing it down, whether it is the speaker, the senate pro tem president, or the majority leader. Pick the target. Freeze it. Go after it with a vengeance. Personalize the attack and look at the person's constituencies. If he or she has a large senior citizen constituency, proclaim to the media that the prevention of the passage of your legislation is putting senior citizens in your legislative district in danger. The legislator will have to respond. Remember the one cardinal tenet of legislative action: never hurt "Mom," "Pop," or the "little guy." That is a focused and strategic attack.

Source: Alinsky, S: Rules for Radicals: A Practical Primer for Realistic Radicals. Random House, New York, 1971, with permission.

A Series of Processes

Government is often thought of as a series of processes used to maintain society. As both an element of and a result of politics, government is also influenced by the forces that drive politics and the three concepts that constitute it:

- Partisanship
- Self-interest
- Ideology

Partisanship

Partisanship refers to membership in a political party. Because of the limited nature of this chapter, it focuses on Democrats, Republicans, and to a lesser extent, Independents.

Self-Interest

Self-interest is almost always the most important factor in politics. It dictates the kind of issues that legislators become involved in and present to their constituencies as the key issues. For instance, a congressman who resides in a blue-collar industrialized district that has a majority who support unionization will most likely be pro-union. The legislative structure in the United States was designed so that elected officials represent the people in their districts rather than having the whole population of the country trying to make policy decisions. If a candidate does not represent the beliefs of the district, it is unlikely that he or she will succeed in that district.

In the larger world of electoral politics, the principle of self-interest often means that an elected official will not make legislative or political decisions that could lead to professional damage, namely loss of an election. Occasionally, there are exceptions to this rule. There have been a few cases in which elected officials were so ideologically committed to an issue that they defied conventional wisdom and made decisions that went against their self-interest. Generally, to be effective in politics, a person needs to understand and accept the self-interest of his or her constituents and use it as the driving force in political decision making.

Ideology

Ideology is a broad concept that embodies the beliefs and principles of an individual or group. Conservatives, liberals, populists, Libertarians, and radicals represent five examples of ideologies.

Conservatives

Traditionally, conservatives support fewer governmental regulations, less involvement in everyday life, lower taxes, and smaller social programs. The general characterization of the conservative belief system is "less government equals better government." Applied to the current range of issues, conservatives tend to be anti-abortion, anti–gun control, anti–stem cell research, anti–universal health care, pro–death penalty, pro–choice on education, and supportive of the big business interests. Conservatives have also wrapped themselves in the mantle of "antiterrorism," suggesting that they are the best qualified to protect the country from terrorist attacks.

However, in recent years, conservative politicians have moved away from some of their core values. Under a self-proclaimed conservative president and congress, national spending and debt have reached all-time record highs, with huge deficits that will take generations to pay off. The power of the executive branch has been greatly expanded. Government has inserted itself more and more into citizens' daily lives. Examples include government intervention in the right-to-die case of Terri Schiavo, the use of warrantless wiretapping, and the use of government appropriations to fund religious schools.

Liberals

In recent years the term "liberal" has taken on a negative connotation falsely associated with the idea that anything goes. However, traditional liberals believe that government has a moral responsibility to do good for society and that government intervention is necessary for the greater good of the citizens. They believe that only government can do certain things because of its size and funding ability. This ideology traditionally translates into larger government structures, taxes at a level to maintain programs without deficit, and more spending for a wide range of social programs. Liberals are traditionally pro–environment, pro-choice on abortion, pro–gun control, pro–universal health care, anti–choice on education, and supportive of women and minority groups.

Populists

Populists are probably the most dominant political force in the United States at a grassroots level. Although populists in general do not like paying high taxes, ideologically they may represent a variety of positions on any particular issue. For instance, one group of populists may be anti-abortion, whereas another may be pro-choice.

The common bond among all populists is that they have a sense of being burdened by a large, oppressive government structure. Populists constitute the middle ground between liberals and conservatives and are often considered the group that has the most influence in deciding national elections.

Libertarians

Libertarianism is both a political party and an ideology. As a political partisan group, Libertarians represent an electoral fringe element. Ideologically, they differ from populists because they do not have the underlying middle-class anger that often drives the populists to take political action. Although they do believe in fiscal conservatism and dislike paying high taxes, Libertarians tend to be "laid back" in their approach to politics. Typically, they avoid ideological battles and choices on gun control, health care, schools, or abortion.

Radicals

Radicals exist at both ends of the ideological spectrum in both of the major parties. It is important to recognize that, although most voters tend toward the middle of the political spectrum between conservatism and liberalism, radicals attempt to force their parties to the extreme ends of the spectrum.

For instance, Republicans are challenged by the radical right, which consists of the anti–big government and pro-life forces that make conspicuous demands on the party. To counteract the rhetoric of the radicals, the Republican party tries to find candidates who are ideologically near the middle of the spectrum because they know that most Republican voters have similar opinions.

UNDERSTANDING THE PLAYING FIELD

Structure
The three branches of the government are the executive, judicial, and legislative branches. These branches exist simultaneously at the federal, state, and local government levels.

The Executive Branch
At the federal level, the executive branch consists of the president, vice president, cabinet, and various executive administrative bodies. The executive of a state is the governor. Boards and commissions can also be construed as part of the executive branch because they are appointees of the chief executive. In county government, one or more county commissioners function as executives. Larger cities usually have a mayor. Smaller cities and townships sometimes also elect mayors (Fig. 19.1; Box 19.2).

The Judicial Branch
The judicial branch is the court system. It is important to note the distinction between state court and federal court; appeals and supreme courts are found at both levels. At the state level, there are supreme courts, appeals courts, and the lower courts. At the federal level, there is the Supreme Court, federal courts of appeal, and district or circuit courts. Additionally, many cities and counties have a local court system.

The judicial branch of government should not be discounted as unimportant to nurses. Over the years, courts have decided several important issues that have an effect on the practice of nursing. These include the Supreme Court's decision regarding the right of nurses to organize into collective bargaining units (see Chapter 16), the requirement of health-care providers to report potentially violent clients to the police, the obligation of nurses to refuse to carry out physician orders they deem dangerous, and criteria permitting nurses to withdraw life support measures.

New test cases that are continually being brought before the Supreme Court have the potential to dramatically change the way nurses are perceived and what they are permitted to do in the workplace.

The Legislative Branch
At the federal level, the legislative branch of government consists of the House of Representatives and the Senate. Each state also has a legislative branch of government, and, except for Nebraska, all states have a bicameral legislature with both a house of representatives and a senate. The primary function of the legislative branch of government is the formation of policy by the making of laws.

Key Players in the Legislative Process
Members of the legislative branch of government have a wide range of ability and influence. It is important to remember that legislators are human and respond to the same forces that all people respond to, including interpersonal dynamics, peer pressure, and both internal and external factors.

The Majority Leader
The majority leader in the House of Representatives is the person who generally supervises and directs the activities on the House floor. Some consider it to be the most powerful job in politics. The majority leader has control over the legislative calendar, which ultimately determines when many of the House session activities take place and even when bills are introduced for consideration. The majority leader is also the central figure in crafting the budget, which is the most important activity the legislature performs on an annual basis.

The Majority Whip
The majority whip is responsible for collecting votes when legislators may be leaning toward voting against their party. At the same time the majority leader is supporting a bill, the whip is negotiating on the House floor for the votes necessary to successfully pass the bill. The whip is responsible for collecting support and votes for various issues both during the legislative session and when it is in recess.

The Minority Leader
The minority leader represents the party that does not have a numerical majority in the House and helps organize support against bills introduced by the

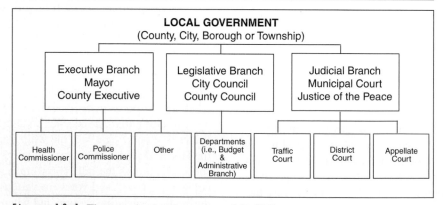

Figure 19.1 The organizational structure of the U.S. government.

Box 19.2

Know the Structure to Play the Game

One of the keys to creating power is understanding the organizational structure of the government. The Constitution of the United States establishes three separate branches of the federal government: legislative, judicial, and executive. The Constitution also ascribes certain auxiliary powers to the individual states. It is the role of the state governments to serve their citizens within these parameters and to delegate discrete areas of activity to local governments.

Beneath the federal and state level of government in the United States, there exist five layers of local government identified by the U.S. Census Bureau: county, municipal, township, school district, and special district governments (which include various utility, construction, and facility authorities). The qualifications for the classification of these local government structures are generally determined by the parent state governments. State governments are defined by their individual state constitutions and in turn delineate responsibility for the local governments.

It is important for nurses to understand that there are three levels in each governmental sector: federal, state, and local. These distinctions are important and are the most common source of confusion for nurses.

most legislators will support it even if they must vote against their party.

The Conference Committee

The conference committee attempts to reconcile differences in bills from the House and the Senate. The rules governing the structure, composition, and function of the conference committee vary from state to state. Generally, they consist of an equal number of appointed members from both the House and the Senate. Often a specified combination of votes, such as two votes from the House and two votes from the Senate, is necessary to approve a compromise bill and move it out of committee.

What Do You Think?

Who do you know in the legislature of your state government? Who is your representative or congressperson? Make a list of the things you would want that person to do for health care.

_____

_____

_____

_____

_____

_____

_____

_____

_____

_____

_____

_____

_____

majority leader. The minority leader presents an alternative point of view. There is an expression in the legislature: "The majority will have their way, and the minority will have their say."

In most cases, the majority party has the capacity to pass almost any bill they support over the objections of the minority. The minority leader usually only has the capacity to speak against it. However, there are some issues that legislators will almost never vote against: "mom," "pop," and the "little guy." When these issues are included in a bill,

Caucuses

Caucuses are formed when the legislature divides into groups consisting of people with mutual interests. These groups operate as a unit, trading on their capacity to bring a block of votes for or against an issue or bill, rather than an individual vote. Examples are the Black Caucus, the Women's Caucus, the Hispanic Caucus, and the Business Community Caucus.

Although caucuses may be bipartisan, many are partisan. For example, the largest caucus groups are the Democratic Caucus and the Republican

Caucus. Each caucus develops its own internal governance structure and leadership, including a speaker who leads the caucus and speaks for the group. After a group member achieves a leadership role, he or she must try to balance the wishes of the group against his or her own political survival in the caucus and the political pressures exerted by the larger world.

> *The media have become a tangible power in government, often driving and shaping public opinion that eventually evolves into a legislative agenda.*

THE POWER OF THE MEDIA

When Is It News?
The media and the voters are external forces that influence policy makers. The media have become a tangible power in government, often driving and shaping public opinion that eventually evolves into a legislative agenda. The public often perceives media personalities as the people who know, write, and speak about important public issues and matters of substance.

Although they claim to be objective, the major news organizations decide what is and what is not news. For many years, conservatives have accused the major news media outlets of a "liberal bias." To act as a counterbalance to this perceived bias, other networks have purposely taken a conservative spin.

In recent years, the Internet has become a force in politics with which politicians must reckon. Politicians well versed in electronic media have learned to use them as a tool to get their message out. Younger voters no longer rely on the national networks' nightly newscasts to get their information about politics and most all other issues, but use the Internet and the short "sound bites" through which it conveys ideas. Some politicians have learned that the Internet is a practically free and unrestricted way to publicize their positions and slant their information. However, politicians are now dealing with new issues related to the Internet. Often, fringe radical groups will put rather sophisticated and professional-looking political advertisements on the Internet attacking the other candidate in a personal way or falsely attributing a radical viewpoint to their own candidate. These ads are picked up by the mainstream media

and then the candidate has to spend time and money letting the voting public know that the ad was not from them and that they do not support the position.

Election by Media
Before media campaigns became the norm, with millions of dollars being spent on television and radio advertising, the printed news media used to publish what the candidate said and often printed whole speeches. This approach allowed the public to read the speeches and make up their minds about which issues the candidate supported. Today, the trend is to give a 30-second sound bite of a speech, then have 10 minutes of political analysis by a well-known commentator who tells the public what the candidate is saying.

Some of the printed media have adopted a similar approach to political issues. In newspapers, it is not unusual to see a lengthy editorial comment positioned next to a statement made by a candidate. Elected officials have a great respect for the power of the media to influence public opinion. Those who learn to use the media to their advantage get elected.

Legislator Beware
Legislators, while recognizing and using the power of the media, have also become wary of it. They know that although they can use the media to proclaim their message, the media also pose a risk to their political survival, depending on the vulnerability of their position. Some legislators have a false sense of invulnerability because of the nature of their constituency.

A Story with Legs
For example, a legislator may have a large population of senior citizens in his district who have supported him for many years. The legislator publicly supports senior citizen issues and believes that the senior citizen support will always be there. However, during an election campaign, a political opponent's investigation uncovers information that the legislator voted against several bills that would have increased senior citizens' benefits. In addition, the opponent discovers that the legislator is having an affair with his married secretary.

In recent years, stories involving sexual misconduct seem to trump all other issues, even those as serious as violations of the U.S. Constitution, such as the erosion of separation of powers and misuse of executive power. It would seem that everyone understands sex but many people have difficulty understanding the more serious and complicated issues that will have long-term effects on their lives.

The opponent leaks this information to the media, which immediately put it on television and report it in the newspapers. If the story develops "legs," meaning it takes on a life of its own and continues to grow without further information from the opponent, it will be on television news programs and in the newspapers every day. The major networks will do investigative reporting on the issues. Eventually the talk show and television tabloid programs will become interested and begin interviewing people who know or have heard more "dirty little secrets" about the legislator.

The Internet has contributed to the "legs" phenomenon. Today, almost everything a person in a public position has ever said or done is recorded on tape somewhere, and political Web sites show these recorded clips. If they are entertaining enough, they are often picked up by the mainstream media and shown over and over again, giving the information a much wider audience than it might otherwise have had. Internet-savvy people are proficient at "data mining" and can obtain private records and information on individuals running for office. This information can become a potent tool in the hands of a political rival.

At this point, the legislator who is the subject of that story is in political jeopardy. There is little that a politician fears more than being the subject of this type of negative story.

THE POLITICAL PROCESS

Who Introduces Legislation?

Where Laws Begin

Laws serve to maintain order in a complicated society and regulate the interactions of its citizens. As society becomes more complex, more laws are needed to ensure the survival and smooth functioning of the population.

For example, although computers and electronic communications have increased the quantity of information individuals can process and the speed at which it is transmitted, they have also added to the complexity of the world. Just a few years ago, there were no laws that dealt with hacking, computer fraud, computer theft of bank funds, or online pornography. Today, there is an ever-growing body of law that deals with computers, and whole sections of police agencies, such as the Federal Bureau of Investigation's Computer Crime Unit, are dedicated to enforcing these laws. Where do ideas for laws and policies come from, and how do these ideas become laws?

Elected Officials

Any elected official, including governors, mayors, county commissioners, and city council members, can propose a program or initiative that requires passage by the legislature. This initiative is called a *bill*. The elected official will go to the legislative leadership in the parties and ask them either to submit the bill or to help move the bill through the legislative process.

Lobbyists, constituency groups, and advocates are a major source of proposed legislation. They represent various interests ranging from public interest groups to corporate lobbyists. Lobbyists frequently craft legislation and then pass it on to a friendly legislator. Consumer groups are often visible at the legislature through demonstrations and lobbying.

Constituency groups can best be described by example, such as the AARP. These groups are made up of individuals interested in advancing an agenda that promotes a range of issues based on self-interest. Advocates, in contrast, are groups that have a single issue or point of view that they are trying to advance, such as housing or abortion rights.

Government Agencies

Legislation is also generated from government agencies. When agencies are seeking fee increases or another type of policy reform, they can introduce legislation. For example, policy reforms in the Internal Revenue Service are a type of agency-initiated legislation. Frequently the employees of the agency draft the legislation and then direct it toward a supportive legislator.

What Drives Legislation?

Funding. Because almost all government agencies depend on legislative funding to sustain their operations, they become actively engaged, overtly or covertly, in seeking the passage of a budget that will sustain their survival.

Public Demand. Legislators are very careful to listen to the demand of their voters and avoid voting against an issue to which the public is emotionally attached. A classic example of this process was seen in New Jersey, where a child was sexually molested and murdered by a known convicted sex offender who moved into the child's neighborhood. The tragedy prompted a public outcry: How could this happen? Something needs to be done! Ultimately, the outcry produced the now famous Megan's Law, which requires public disclosure of a known sex offender's residence.

Program Issues. These issues recur periodically and require legislative attention. Requests for increases in television cable rates constitute an example of a programmatic issue. The cable industry will be very interested in the outcome of legislation that may affect what they can charge for their services. Both cable and consumer group lobbyists actively seek the ear of key legislators at these times.

Constituent-Specific Issues. Groups of voters may have specific interests that can lead to introduction of a bill. For example, in legislative districts where a large population of senior citizens resides, the escalating cost of prescriptions may be an important issue. Legislation specific to that constituency will be introduced at a greater rate than in areas with fewer senior citizens.

How Bills Become Law

The Tracking Number

Any legislator can introduce a bill from any source. Additional legislators can sign on as the bill's cosponsors. A bill is considered to be strong if it has strong sponsorship, including a number of powerful cosponsors, a high degree of bipartisanship, and the interest of powerful individuals, both political and nonpolitical. After the bill is introduced, it is taken to the chief clerk, who assigns it a number that permits it to be tracked throughout the process.

What Do You Think?

Contact your state legislature's Web site and identify two bills that deal with health care. How do you feel about these bills? How should your representative vote on this issue?

The Committee

After the bill is assigned a number, it is referred to a **committee.** The house and senate leaders decide which committee considers the bill. This decision, greatly influenced by politics, is critical to the survival and ultimate passage of a bill.

It is no coincidence that most bills die in committee. Invariably, the leadership discusses their expectation for the bill with the committee chairs. If the leadership wants a bill to fail, it is referred to a committee that will never vote on it or pass it on to the House.

Full Committee Hearing

At the federal level, bills are referred to a full committee and, generally, because of the enormous number of bills being introduced, to a subcommittee. Most of the work of Congress takes place within the committee structures. Committee action is perhaps the most important phase of the congressional process; this is where the most intensive consideration is given to proposed measures and where people are provided with an opportunity to be heard.

Subcommittee Hearing

The subcommittee studies the issue carefully, holds hearings, and reports the bill back to the full committee with recommendations. There are numerous standing committees in the House and Senate. In addition, there are several select committees and several standing joint committees. Each committee has jurisdiction over certain subjects and often has two or more subcommittees.

In the U.S. Congress, the committees with greatest jurisdiction over health matters and their subcommittees are:

- **House Ways and Means Committee:** Social Security and Medicare (health-care subcommittees).
- **House Commerce Committee:** Health legislation including Medicaid (Subcommittee on Health and the Environment).
- **Senate Finance Committee:** Medicare and Medicaid (health subcommittees).
- **Senate Labor and Human Resources Committee:** Health legislation in general; also works cooperatively with the Senate Finance Committee in considering issues involving Medicare and Medicaid.
- **House and Senate Appropriations Committee:** Authorizes all money necessary to implement action proposed in a bill (subcommittees for labor, education, and health and human services).

The Next Step

As a result of full committee hearings, several things may happen to a bill. It may be:

- Reported out of committee favorably and be scheduled for debate by the full House or Senate.
- Reported out favorably, but with amendments.
- Reported out unfavorably.
- Killed outright.

For example, a bill reforming the way judges are elected ideally would go to the judiciary committee. However, there is no legal requirement that the speaker or the Senate pro tem president send the bill to any particular committee. For political reasons, the speaker may refer the bill to the committee on intergovernmental affairs, where it will languish and die.

Can the Bill Survive?

For a bill to survive, the bill's sponsor must have the knowledge and the political standing to move the bill out of committee. If sponsors are truly committed, they will trade on their political capital. *Political*

capital generally refers to some type of favor or action that a politician can exchange for something he or she wants. It is an extremely important element in the legislative process and consists of, but is not limited to, votes, amendments to bills, appointments, and support from constituency groups. Political capital often consists of an "If you vote for my bill, I'll vote for your bill" type of exchange.

A Scheduled Debate

After a bill has been reported out of a House committee (with the exception of ways and means or appropriations committees), it goes to the Rules Committee, which schedules bills and determines how much time will be spent on debate and whether or not amendments will be allowed. In the Senate, bills go on the Senate calendar, after which the majority leadership determines when a bill will be debated.

After a bill is debated, possibly amended, and passed by one chamber, it is sent to the other chamber, where it goes through the same procedure. If the bill passes both the House and the Senate without any changes, it is sent to the president for signature.

Opposing Versions

If the House and Senate pass different versions of a bill, however, the two bills are sent to a conference committee, which consists of members appointed by both the House and the Senate. This committee seeks to resolve the differences between the two bills; if the differences cannot be resolved, the bill dies in committee. When the conference committee reaches agreement on a bill, it goes back to the House and Senate for passage. At this juncture, the bill must be voted up or down, because no further amendments are accepted.

Passage or Veto?

If the bill is approved in both houses, it then goes to the chief executive—at the federal level, the president, or at the state level, the governor—who makes determinations about the bill. Governors can do one of two things: sign the bill into law or actively **veto** it. At the federal level, the president has the same options, with the addition of the pocket veto. Pocket vetoes, found only at the federal level, occur when the president, rather than actively vetoing a bill, simply does not sign it so that it does not become law. If vetoed, it is sent back to the House and Senate. To override the veto, a two-thirds vote by both chambers is required.

The Fiscal Note

Clearly, the passage of a law can be a long and difficult process. This is often quite frustrating for action-oriented nurses who are used to seeing immediate outcomes—forming plans and making things happen quickly.

All bills that are passed need a fiscal note attached to them. Therefore, the appropriations committee is operationally very powerful. A piece of legislation that is passed without a fiscal note attached will never become a law. Over the years, many pieces of legislation have been passed by the legislature but have been starved to death financially. These are called unfunded mandates.

Housekeeping Bills

Major regulatory change occurs in laws in the form of housekeeping bills. Legislators can use this tactic to move a piece of legislation through the process, especially when the bill is more significant than the leadership acknowledges it to be. Although regulatory reform and change may seem tedious, they are important to the legislative process and have the capacity to do enormous public good or harm.

Executive Orders

Executive orders provide the chief executive, the governor or the president, with a means for moving an agenda item forward. Executive orders are in many cases a convenient way to formulate policy with minimal involvement of the legislature. They also allow the executive to make a statement about an issue that can be entered on the public record.

The legislature can leave executive orders uncontested or challenge them by characterizing them as beyond the scope of the executive branch. This may involve turning to the third branch of government, the judiciary.

Regulatory Agencies

Regulatory agencies are also arenas where policies are made and amended. For instance, the role of the Intergovernmental Regulatory Reform Commission is to examine regulatory issues across the state.

HOW TO BE POLITICALLY ACTIVE

Why Be Active?

The first step in becoming politically active is to identify the specific goals that nurses, as a group, want to accomplish. Nurses recognize many important issues in today's health-care system, including:

- Increasingly acute conditions of hospitalized clients, who require higher levels of care and more complex levels of support than ever before
- Increasing responsibilities for nurses in supervision of rising numbers of unlicensed health-care personnel
- Loss of control of the work environment caused by managed care organizations
- Ever-shortening hospitalizations resulting in clients being sent home "quicker and sicker"

Any one of these issues can become a focal point at which nurses aim their considerable political power.

For example, most nurses are concerned that RNs, who have traditionally been at clients' edsides, are being replaced by individuals who are less prepared and less able to deal with high-acuity clients. Nurses believe that when they are replaced in large numbers by unlicensed assistive personnel, including nursing assistants, as well as with personnel who provide specific services, such as technicians who sit in front of cardiac monitors, the quality of client care decreases. Nurses know that these technicians often take on responsibilities for which they have had little training. Rarely are there established national standards that require these assistive personnel to demonstrate their ability to provide a specific level of care, or even standards that protect the public safety.

Feeling Powerless

Nurses are usually employees at will and can be fired for any reason. Although some efforts have been made in this direction, whistle-blower protection is generally not available to protect nurses who wish to speak out against unsafe staffing levels or employment practices. Nurses are, at times, torn between their obligations to maintain high standards of safe, ethical care and their obligations to their families.

Although nurses often feel powerless against a monolithic health-care bureaucracy, in reality they have the potential to be a potent political force. Nationally, with almost 3 million nurses licensed to practice, the nursing profession constitutes the largest single body of health-care providers in the country.

Finding a Voice

Nurses in all health-care settings are saying, "Somebody's got to do something about this situation." The reality of the situation is that the "somebody" is nurses themselves. Once nurses identify exactly what it is that needs to be accomplished and understand what is possible within the political framework, then they can use their considerable political power to make changes that will benefit both the clients and the profession.

Rules for Radicals

Saul Alinsky, in *Rules for Radicals,* hypothesizes that human beings are divided into three groups: "the haves, the have nots, and the have a little and want mores." Nurses typically fall in the last group.[5]

Have a Little

One problem nurses in this group encounter is the ongoing conflict between the status quo and progress. They want to obtain more power and control, gain more benefits, earn more money, and have more respect as professionals. However, the strong desire to advance is counterbalanced by fear of jeopardizing their current jobs and their professional standing. Their motivation to be something more, to do something new, or to believe in something bigger is held back and pulled in another direction by their fear of change. The result of this internal tug-of-war is an attitude of inertia and ambivalence that has prevented nurses from organizing politically and effectively using their numerical power.

Want More

Despite the inertia and ambivalence problems of individuals in the "have a little and want more" category, some of the most notable revolutionaries in history have come from this group, including Thomas Jefferson, Napoleon Bonaparte, Martin Luther King, Jr., and Vladimir Lenin. Each of these individuals came from the working middle class with a belief that it could be made better. Nurses can use their actions as examples of what individuals can accomplish to raise their own motivation levels to a point where they overwhelm the inertia of the status quo.

Sit Back and Watch

A fourth group of people, who share the inertia found among the "have a little, want more" group, are the "do-nothings." These individuals can be heard saying things like, "I agree with what you are saying, I just don't agree with your means," "I'm not going to get involved in this," or "I'm too busy to belong to the organization." The do-nothings tend to watch the activities of others, and if their efforts are successful, then they will join in as beneficiaries because they feel they have supported the effort from an ideological standpoint. However, they avoid any active involvement in politics. The 18th-century British politician Edmund Burke recognized the danger of the do-nothings. He said, "The only thing necessary for the triumph of evil, is for good men [and women] to do nothing."

What Can One Nurse Do?

It is important to remember that politics is a free-market enterprise open to anyone who is willing to become involved and play the game. Success in the political arena is contingent on three elements:

1. Knowledge and understanding of the process
2. The ability to offer something of value to the political figure
3. The capacity to identify what will be necessary to accomplish the objective

Anyone who is interested in becoming politically active must recognize that all candidates and elected officials need three things: resources to run their political operation (money and volunteers), votes, and a means to shape public opinion.

Resources

Money

Sufficient resources are essential to running a political campaign. The first and most necessary resource is always money. Would-be candidates soon discover that a lack of money to fund a campaign will inevitably lead to political failure. An unfunded candidate cannot travel, send mailings, produce radio and television commercials, post signs, or organize a telephone bank.

Voters often fail to realize that political candidates are only as available as finances permit. Frequently, good candidates lose because they fail to garner the financial resources necessary to run an effective campaign. Nurses can gain a candidate's support for issues by donating to his or her campaign chest.

Volunteers

A second important resource in an election campaign is volunteers. Volunteers work in campaigns by manning telephone banks, making literature drops, placing signs, and conducting voter registration drives. Usually political candidates are very glad to have free help for their campaigns.

Although nurses may not be able to make large monetary contributions to a candidate's campaign, they can always volunteer some time. Working closely with a candidate on a volunteer basis allows individuals to discuss important issues and helps candidates who support issues important to nurses. Most candidates need a considerable amount of education about health-related issues because of their lack of knowledge about medical and nursing concerns.

Votes

Obviously, votes are essential to any candidate. If a candidate does not have votes, he or she will not be elected. One of the most significant activities nurses can become involved in is to join and support a political party. The chosen party should reflect the nurse's value system and fundamental beliefs.

Keep in mind that there is never a perfect fit with any political party. Almost everyone who belongs to a political party will disagree at some point with some element of the party, usually with the extremist views. However, differing opinions and beliefs should not be a barrier to membership in a political party. The only way to change a view or opinion is by active participation from within the party.

The ultimate political power is the vote. Nurses must be registered to vote and must go to the polls on election day. They can make the difference for a candidate who supports legislation that empowers nurses and who recognizes what is needed for beneficial health-care reform.

Shaping Public Opinion

Public Trust in Nurses

Candidates need endorsements from their constituents so they can build their support base. They generally consider endorsements from nurses as one of the most valuable assets to their campaign. By careful selection of candidates who support legislation favorable to nursing and health care, endorsements can give nurses the capacity to shape public opinion. Periodic polls conducted by national news magazines, asking readers to rank various professions by how much they are trusted, have consistently shown that the public views nurses very highly, in the same category as police officers, firefighters, and teachers.

Why the Governor Matters

Nurses should use endorsements by choosing candidates in campaigns that have an impact on important issues. Often the campaign for governor falls into this category, because governors, as chief executives, have a great deal of political power and can appoint people to a number of boards, committees, and other positions. Nurses need to recognize that the members of the board of nursing in their state, as well as other important appointed positions in health departments and other regulatory agencies, may be appointed by the governor and that this board has the final decision on the way that nurses practice.

When nurses establish a working political relationship with the governor, the governor is more likely to look favorably on them as those who have sustained him or her, provided financial support, and given endorsements during the political campaign. They will be the people the governor appoints to a board position.

Targeting endorsements will prevent nurses from making blind political decisions. Candidates should be assessed first on their willingness to support issues that nurses are interested in and then on their capacity to win the election.

Grassroots Effort

A model for individual political development encourages grassroots involvement in local issues. This model is based on the belief that grassroots efforts may be more fulfilling than involvement in partisan politics.[8] This model is an activity-oriented ladder, including activities at four distinct levels:

- Rung 1: Civic involvement. Children's sports, parent–teacher association (PTA), neighborhood improvement group.
- Rung 2: Advocacy. Writing letters to public officials and newspapers and making organized visits to officials to discuss local issues.
- Rung 3: Organizing. Independent organizing on local issues, incorporation of single-issue citizens' groups, and networking with similarly situated citizens' groups.
- Rung 4: Long-term power wielding. Campaigning for oneself or another, local government planning, and agenda setting.

Nurses in Office

Nurses usually shudder at the thought of running for political office. They tend to perceive political campaigns as something underhanded and tawdry and do not want to be involved. However, it is not impossible for nurses to achieve high status in public office.

One way that nurses can direct their political activities is to develop a political relationship with a legislator or a political operative who can mentor and guide the nurse in finding a route through the political maze. As discussed earlier, the principle of self-interest is one of the most critical elements in politics, and to establish a relationship with a political figure, nurses must demonstrate that the issues they support have value to both themselves and to the politician.

Making Alliances

There are several ways that a nurse can decide whom to support when becoming involved in the political process. A first step is to begin identifying the issues particular legislators are interested in and will vote for. Editorial opinion pieces in newspapers can give legislators a sense of the issues of concern.

It is a good idea to begin with local legislators and candidates, such as the state representative, state senator, or councilperson serving the neighborhood. Call their offices and find out when and where they are scheduled to speak, then go and listen to the speech to get a sense of who they are and what issues they support. Their speeches and the way they answer questions will reveal their ideology and partisanship. Also, during question and answer periods, ask elected officials what they think about issues important to you.

Another way to become familiar with prominent political figures is by attending some of the many partisan events that occur during an election season. A good way to visualize the local political landscape is by observing who is talking to whom at the event. Nurses can make their own assessments of political candidates by observing the candidates in action, calling their offices for information, reading published literature, and talking to people who know the candidates.

Beginning the process may seem difficult, but once you decide to become politically active, you'll become more confident.

Know the Issues

For nurses to be successful in the political process, they must know and understand the issues. At times an issue may be readily apparent in the nurses' community, for example, an increased number of homeless people. Other issues are easily identified by reading newspapers. Issues are generally presented in the editorial section; most newspapers also have a political watch section, which reports the results of any significant votes at the state and federal levels.

The American Nurses Association (ANA) newspaper, *American Nurse,* is an excellent source of information on issues of concern to the profession. In addition, the *American Journal of Nursing* Newsline feature and *Nursing and Health Care's* Washington Focus are excellent, easily readable sources of information in journals. *Capitol Update,* the ANA legislative newsletter for nurses, reports on the activities of its nurse lobbyists and on significant issues in Congress and regulatory agencies. This publication requires a subscription but is available in most nursing school and hospital libraries.

State nurses' associations and many specialty nursing groups also publish newsletters or legislative bulletins. Many of these are free to members but may be sent only when requested. Action alerts may also be sent to inform members of vital issues and the action needed by nurses. Most state legislatures now have online access to their proceedings so that bills of interest to nurses can be tracked as they progress through the legislative process.

Tactics

Tactics, essential tools for those who desire to be politically active, are the conscious and deliberate acts that people use to live and deal with each other and the world around them. In a political sense, "tactics" usually means the use of whatever resources are available to achieve a desired goal.

Hannibal, one of the great tacticians in political history, said, "We will either find a way or we will make a way." Nurses, with their long history of accomplishing much with few resources, are natural tacticians. As nurses learn how to organize themselves for political purposes, they can use their well-developed tactical skills to achieve important political goals. Listed below are some easy-to-use tactics for political action.

Engage in Bipartisan Tactics

Both Republican and Democratic nurses need to be politically active to achieve unified goals. Political action across the spectrum of issues and across partisan lines is necessary to achieve the goal of bipartisanship. Nurses should understand that only by supporting candidates who favor nursing and its agenda, whether Democrat or Republican, can the profession make changes that will advance its agenda. The most important thing, always, is the issue being addressed, not the personality or party of the candidate.

Lobbying

Sometimes communication with legislators takes the form of lobbying. Lobbying may be defined as attempting to persuade someone (usually a legislator or legislative aide) of the significance of one's cause or as an attempt to influence legislation. Lobbying methods include letter writing; face-to-face communication or telephone calls; mailgrams, telegrams, or e-mail; letters to the editor; and providing testimony (verbal or written).

To lobby effectively, one should be both persuasive and able to negotiate. Lobbying is truly an art of communication, an area in which nurses can become skilled. Before beginning any lobbying effort, it is vital to gather all pertinent facts.[7] If the

legislator asks you a question you do not know the answer to, be honest and reply that you will get that information. Then get back to the legislator as soon as you can.

In politics, getting the facts and laying the groundwork are analogous to developing a nursing care plan. Before visiting or writing a legislator, gather facts, delineate a problem or concern you wish to discuss, and develop a plan to articulate your concerns. Determine a method for evaluating your effectiveness.

If the plan is to visit the legislator's office, an appointment should be set up in advance. Usually, the meeting will actually be with the legislative aide, particularly at the federal level. This should not be discouraging, because this individual is often responsible for assisting in the development of position statements and offering committee amendments for the legislator.

To ensure that legislators listen to your concerns, it is important not only to be well prepared but also to show that others support your position. When one person speaks, legislators may listen, but when many people voice the same concern, legislators are much more likely to pay attention. Always leave a business card, contact sheet, or both with your personal information so that the legislator can contact you. Send a thank-you note expressing your gratitude for the meeting.

Collaborate with Constituency Groups

Nurses can increase their political power by making alliances with other powerful constituency groups that support similar issues, such as the AARP. The AARP is very interested in health-care issues, particularly managed care, national health insurance, and the decreased quality of care from the increased use of unlicensed personnel. Nurses who are organized into collective bargaining units can use an alliance with powerful unions. Unions are traditionally concerned with issues such as working conditions, including staffing patterns in hospitals, wages, job security, and benefits. Nurses are concerned about the same issues.

How to Organize

"Know thine enemy" is one of the most fundamental rules that tacticians must follow, whether in war or politics. Napoleon was successful as a tactician and general because, before he fought any battle, he walked the battlefield. He knew what the terrain was like and where the rocks and crevices were. He knew what to anticipate when he arrived on the battlefield. Nurses who want to be successful in a political battle must first learn the hills, valleys, rocks, and crevices of the primary political battlefield, their own state demographics.

Comparing numbers helps define the political landscape of a state. Important demographics for organizing nurses at the state level include:

- Total population of the state. This provides a demographic overview of the political arena.
- Total number of registered voters.
- Total number of registered voters by political party.
- Total number of likely voters in any given election cycle. To determine this number, the difference between an on-year election cycle and off-year election cycle should be understood. An on-year election cycle occurs when there is a major race in the state, usually during a presidential or gubernatorial race. An off-year cycle occurs when a major race is not being run. Lower levels of political activity are seen in an off-year election cycle.
- Total number of registered nurses. This information can be obtained from the state board of nursing. Comparing the number of actual voters with the number of registered nurses in a state provides an indication of the potential power of an RN voting block. For example, if there are 800,000 people who regularly vote in a state and there are 100,000 nurses in the state who are organized into a voting block about a particular issue, then that group of nurses represents a significant percentage of voters, and candidates running for statewide office will be interested in having nurses' support. Nurses must be encouraged to register and vote to increase the power of the block.

Important Characteristics of an Organizer

Many of the characteristics of an organizer listed in Box 19.3 are the same characteristics that are required of nurses on a daily basis in the practice of their profession. Although these characteristics may have varying degrees of value for the organizer, the one critical element a political organizer has to have is the capacity to communicate. Although nurses usually have a well-developed ability to communicate at the bedside, they may lack the

---

Box 19.3

Characteristics of an Organizer

- Curiosity
- Motivation
- Reverence
- Realism
- Flair for the dramatic
- Sense of humor
- Charisma
- Self-confidence
- Communication skills
- Clear vision of the future
- Capacity to change
- Persistence
- Ability to organize
- Imagination

---

confidence to communicate in the larger public and political arenas. Nurses need to recognize that the communication skills they use on a daily basis, as when explaining complicated medical jargon to clients, are the same skills they can use in translating health-care issues into language that the public and elected officials can understand.

One way to gain the public's interest and elected officials' support is to personalize health-care issues by stressing the fact that nurses are the professionals who provide the bulk of direct care for their mothers, fathers, siblings, and children. Communication of issues that touch people personally is usually the most effective method.

WHAT FOLLOWS ORGANIZATION?

Drafting Legislation and Creating Change

Certain critical questions must be asked. The first question always must be, "Who is the decision maker?" For example, if an issue needs to be resolved in the state board of nursing, the first step is to identify who makes the decisions at the board. Although the board members make decisions, it is important to remember that the people who sit on the board are appointed. Who appoints them and what is the basis of those appointments? If they are political appointees, they usually have some sort of political benefactor or a political relationship with someone in power.

Understanding these types of relationships makes it easier to determine the appointees' ideological and partisan positions on many issues. For example, if a nursing board is newly appointed by a recently elected Republican governor, it is probably safe to assume that most of the board members are Republicans who agree with the governor on many key issues.

The second question to address is, "How accessible is the appointee's benefactor?" Sometimes board members are appointed by the legislative leadership, not the governor. It is important to discover who appointed the board and whether or not individual voters have access to them. Generally, access by individual voters to the power figures who make these types of appointments is very limited. Organized groups, such as the ANA, provide the best avenue of access at the federal level.

> *Nurses need to recognize that the communication skills they use on a daily basis, as when explaining complicated medical jargon to clients, are the same skills they can use in translating health-care issues into language that the public and elected officials can understand.*

Questions About Health Care

Other questions that need to be answered include:

* How successful have nurses been in the past in achieving specific goals?
* What positions do nurses hold in government?
* What does the state board look like politically?
* Which legislators have supported nursing issues in the past?
* Which legislators traditionally oppose nursing and health-care issues?

Because of the failure to ask and answer these questions, numerous pieces of pro-nursing legislation have died in committee or lacked sponsors to move the bill through the process. In states where nurses are in tune with the political issues and powers, they have more success moving bills through the legislative process so that they become law than in states where nurses are apathetic about the political process.

If a Bill Doesn't Pass

Even if a bill favorable for nurses or health care does not pass the first time, the fact that it was brought to a vote is important for several reasons. First, it has brought an issue to the attention of the whole legislature that they might otherwise have dismissed as unimportant.

Second, the legislative process brings to light the proponents and opponents of the issue and allows nurses to specifically target legislators who voted against the bill. One of two approaches can be used at this point. Nurses can either communicate with the legislators to explain why the bill is important in hopes of changing their minds, or they can organize as a voting block and attempt to vote the opposing legislators out of office.

Third, after a bill has gone through the process the first time, it becomes much easier to identify the obstacles and sticking points in the language of the bill. Before the bill is reintroduced in a later session of the legislature, it can be modified and amended to eliminate those parts that may have caused ideological problems for specific legislators.

The Nurse as Political Ally

Very few nurses have sought or been elected to governmental positions. However, it is important to realize that not all nurses who hold elected positions are allies for nursing. Unless elected nurses identify themselves as nurses and support the profession, they may not be willing to support nursing issues politically.

For example, a nurse currently elected to Congress from a Southern state refused to speak to the nurses who participated in the March on Washington Nurses. Although she is a nurse and has had a number of articles published in nursing journals in the past, she refused to support the nurses who marched. Elected officials must always be judged by what they do and what they deliver, not by what they say, look like, or think, or by what people think they think.

Conclusion

There is nothing magical about nurses becoming involved in politics. It is simply a matter of hard work and use of the critical thinking skills nurses already possess. It is clear, however, that nurses can and do make a difference in the political arena. Nurses must ask how and where they can make a difference and how they can become involved in the process. Not every nurse will choose to run for political office, but each nurse can and should make a contribution. The willingness of nurses to become involved in politics is the key to developing legislative respect for the profession and improving health care.

Issues in Practice

How Do Politics Affect You and Your Family?

Why should nurses be involved in politics? Does it really make a difference who is elected and who makes the laws? Take a minute to go through the questions below and check the items you think may be affected by politics.

Between the time you wake up and the time you leave the house, several things usually happen to you. Do you think any of the following subjects are affected by politics?

• The water with which you wash your face and brush your teeth
• The electricity that lights the room
• The price and quality of food you have for breakfast
• The safety of the products you buy

As the average person's life span grows longer and the retirement age is lowered, these later years become more meaningful. Are any of the following decisions affected by our political systems?

• The age at which you can retire
• The income that you get during retirement
• The quality and cost of health care
• Our life expectancy

We value our leisure time and the chance to get away from it all. Are any of the following areas affected by politics?

• The parks and lakes where vacationers fish and swim
• The air you breathe
• The radio and television programs that entertain you

Take some time to think about these questions. The answers will make you think some more.

References

1. Webster's New Collegiate Dictionary. Simon & Schuster, New York, 2005.
2. Auerbach, DI, et al.: Better late than never: Workforce supply implications of later entry into nursing. Health Tracking 26(1):178–185, 2007.
3. National League for Nursing: Despite encouraging trends suggested by the NLN's comprehensive survey of all nursing program, large numbers of qualified applications continue to be turned down, 2006. www.nln.org/newsreases.
4. Upenieks, VV: Assessing nursing staffing ratios: Variability in workload intensity. Policy, Politics & Nursing Practice 8(1):7–19, 2007.
5. Alinsky, S: Rules for Radicals: A Practical Primer for Realistic Radicals. Random House, New York, 1971.
6. O'Donnell, DG: Unpublished material. 1996.
7. Lumpkin, B: Lobbying: Not a bad word, but a core competency. Imprint 54(2):40–43, 49, 2007.
8. Hoffman, CB, and Leavitt, JK: Policy & politics. Covering America's uninsured: Weighing the options. American Journal of Nursing 107 (4):75–79, 2007.
9. DoBias, M: Whistle-blower law tightened: Ruling demands first-hand knowledge of wrongdoing. Modern Healthcare 37 (14):8–9, 2007.

Bibliography

Brewer, C, and Kovner, CT: Is there another nursing shortage? What the data tell us. Nursing Outlook 49(1):20–26, 2001.
Burke, RJ: The ripple effect: Staffing post restructuring. Nursing Management 33(2):41–43, 2002.
Carlson, ED: Welfare reform: Policy implications for health. Texas Journal of Rural Health 19(2):42–48, 2001.
Clemons, T: Highlights from the Hill: NIWI 2000: Issues and opportunities. ORL—Head and Neck Nursing 19(2):22–23, 2001.
Des Jardin, K: Political involvement in nursing: Politics, ethics, and strategic action. AORN Journal 74(5):614–618, 2001.
Frank, IC: Policy perspectives: The nursing shortage. Journal of Emergency Nursing 27(4):391–393, 2001.
Higgs, ZR, et al.: Health care access: A consumer perspective. Public Health Nursing 18(1):3–12, 2001.
Malone, B: Making nursing's presence felt at the political party conferences. Nursing Standard 16(5):22, 2001.
O'Grady, ET: Health policy and politics. Access to health care: An issue central to nursing. Nursing Economics 18(2):88–90, 2001.
Rains, JW, and Barton-Krlese, P: Developing political competence. Public Health Nursing 18(4):219–224, 2001.
Roit, SM: When money talks, politicians listen. American Nurse 34(1):22, 2002.

20

Spirituality and Health Care

Roberta Mowdy

Learning Objectives

After completing this chapter, the reader will be able to:

- Develop a working definition of spirituality.
- Distinguish spirituality from religion.
- Describe what is meant by the nursing diagnosis spiritual distress.
- Describe research that supports the health benefit of spiritual practices.
- Describe the relationship between spirituality and one alternative healing modality used within nursing.

ROUGH SPOTS ON THE TRAIL

The road of life often is filled with twists and turns, ups and downs, and precipitous waysides. People who are facing potentially long-term or debilitating illnesses, confronting acute health crises, or suffering from loss and grief may find themselves reexamining the foundational beliefs they have held since childhood. Usually, at no other time in a person's life is he or she so focused on evaluating the spiritual self than during such crises. Yet the times when clients are most vulnerable also can be opportunities for personal and spiritual growth.

Nurses have the unique task of working with clients at various points throughout their life journeys. Often nurses encounter clients during the "rough parts of the trail." The holistic nursing perspective requires nurses to view each person as a biopsychosocial being with a spiritual core. Each component of the self (physical, mental, social, and spiritual) is integral to and influences the others (Fig. 20.1). Nurses spend more time with their clients than do other health-care workers. Therefore, the spiritual needs of clients must be recognized as a domain of nursing care. Holism cannot exist without consideration of the spiritual aspects that create individuality and give meaning to people's lives.[1] Thus, nurses must be sure to address the spirit along with the other dimensions to provide holistic care.

> "*Nurses have the unique task of working with clients at various points throughout their life journeys. Often nurses encounter clients during the 'rough parts of the trail.'*"

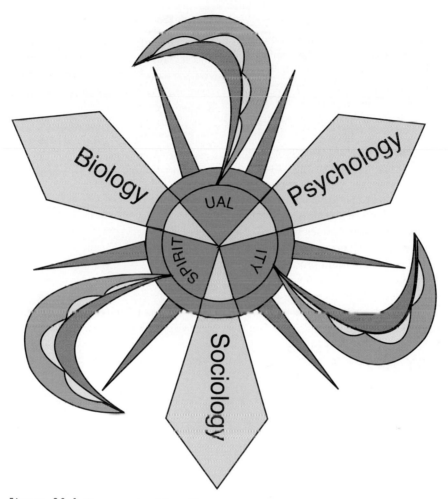

Figure 20.1 Components of the self.

NURSING AT LIFE'S JUNCTURES

It is universally true that the human life cycle is marked by a rhythm of transitions: birth, the entry of a child into society, puberty, sexual awakening, entry into adulthood, marriage, parenthood, illness, loss, old age, and death. In all cultures there are other rhythms that people honor, such as the solar and lunar cycles, the agricultural cycle, and the reproductive cycles. These cycles constitute the rhythm of human life.

Developmental Crisis

All people recognize the importance of transitions and in some way have ritualized them through their religions or through custom. People learn from their own cultural groups how to behave during each transition, and each cultural group has conceptualized an understanding of these human experiences. Their importance is universally recognized.

Nurses primarily have contact with clients in the health-care setting within the context of these transitions. Developmental crisis theory holds that transitions are times of anxiety and vulnerability for families. Therefore, nurses are required to treat people who are going through transitions with great tenderness and care. It is a sacred trust for nurses to be allowed into a family system in transition. Clients and families may seek spiritual support or may feel spiritual abandonment. Ideally, nurses can help people identify and find the spiritual support they require.

Science as Magic

Over a long period of time, from the enlightenment of the 17th century to the dawn of the 21st century, political leaders and educated people in Western cultures came to believe that all the answers to human suffering could be found in science and technology. For example, early in the 20th century, antibiotics were thought of as "magic bullets" that cured diseases and reduced suffering. People were eager to take part in research studies to solve their health-care problems.

It was in this context that the nursing profession embraced the Western scientific method as the measure for defining itself. Nurses believed, and some still do believe, that rigorous research involving testing of hypotheses would provide the theoretical base for the practice of professional nursing.

SOCIAL AND SCIENTIFIC EFFECTS ON SPIRITUALITY

To Be Fully Human

More recently, the horrors of terrorism, the harnessing of nuclear power, space exploration, and the mapping of the human genome are among the new capabilities that have given urgency to reconsideration of the question, "What does it mean to be fully human in the universe as it is now understood?" It is evident that science and technology cannot offer the solutions to all human problems; in fact, they have contributed to many of them.

Science, electronic communications, and the great social experiments of the past two centuries are among the influences directing humans to a consciousness that individuals are connected to the whole of creation and to all peoples. One of the ways in which both health-care consumers and professionals are responding to this realization is by reintegrating spirituality and spiritual modes of healing into health and illness practices. Another response is the growing inclination to examine and adopt the spiritual wisdom of traditions other than one's own.

> *Spirituality may be regarded as the driving force that pervades all aspects of and gives meaning to an individual's life.*

What Do You Think?

Make two lists: a list of the problems that science and technology have caused during the last 20 years and a list of the problems that have been solved by technology and science. Which list is longer? Why?

_____

_____

_____

_____

_____

_____

_____

_____

_____

_____

_____

Phenomenology

A feature of postmodernism is the realization that the concept of truth is relative, allowing for an appreciation of diverse perspectives on what is true. Science, including nursing science since the mid-1980s, has expanded its ways of discerning truth, leaving behind traditional hypothetico-deductive, quantitative research. The emergence of **phenomenology** within the discipline of philosophy is one major influence that has led nursing to appreciate qualitative methods of discovery. As a philosophical approach to understanding truth, phenomenology parallels and is closely related to existentialism, advocating the view that consciousness determines reality and truth in space and time.

In the health-care setting, a phenomenological approach recognizes the belief that the client's observations may be more objective than those of the nurse: they are attached to the client's past experiences and knowledge, which include rich descriptions of the person's life transitions. In nursing, intuition has emerged as a phenomenon worthy of further investigation. This change in viewpoint coincides with increased interest in complementary and alternative therapies and with the importance of spirituality in healing and wellness.

THE NATURE OF SPIRITUALITY

What Is Spirituality?

Spirituality is a broad and somewhat nebulous concept that has to do with people's search for answers to certain questions and issues (Box 20.1). Similar concerns have been identified among children of various cultural backgrounds in research on the development of spirituality.

A Diverse Heritage

A rich heritage of spiritual practices, including systematic reflection for growth toward wholeness, is found in all the major religions of the world. The roots of the great traditions, including each religion's prayer practices, can be traced to the shift in human consciousness that occurred around 500 B.C. During this period, many great teachers and spiritual leaders emerged, including Confucius; Lao-tzu; Siddhartha Gautama, who became the Buddha; Zoroaster; the Greek philosophers Socrates, Plato, and Aristotle; and the Hebrew prophets Amos, Hosea, and Isaiah.

Box 20.1

Spiritual Questions

Why are we here?

How do we fit into the cosmos?

What power or intelligence created and orders the universe?

What is the nature and meaning of divine or mystical experiences?

How are we to make meaning of suffering?

How are we to behave toward other people?

How are we to deal with our own shortcomings and failures?

What happens to us when we die, and where were we before we were born?

St. Augustine, a Roman Catholic bishop who lived in North Africa during the 5th century, is credited with first identifying the relationships among contemplation, action, and wisdom within the Christian tradition. For Augustine, the contemplative life was properly focused on the discernment of truth and was open to all people. Augustine equated truth, ultimately, with God.

Hope Through Compassion

Spirituality is often defined as integrative energy, capable of producing internal human harmony, or holism. Other definitions refer to spirituality as a sense of coherence. Spirituality also entails a sense of transcendent reality, which draws strength from inner resources, living fully for the present, and having a sense of inner knowing. Solitude, compassion, and empathy are important components of spirituality for many individuals.

The concept of hope is central to spirituality. Spirituality may be regarded as the driving force that pervades all aspects of and gives meaning to an individual's life. It creates a set of beliefs and values that influence the way that people conduct their lives. Spiritual activity involves introspection, reflection, and a sense of connectedness to others or to the universe. For many people, this connectedness focuses ultimately on a supreme being who is sometimes called God.

When providing spiritual care to their clients, nurses must base their actions on compassion, or sensitivity to the suffering of others. Compassion is a way of living born out of an awareness of one's relationship to all living creatures, a sensitivity to the pain and brokenness of others. The Greek word for compassion literally means "to feel in one's innards." Given this definition, one can easily see how compassion is part of spirituality and the life journey.

A Sense of Meaning

Traditionally, the term *spirituality* has been defined as a sense of meaning in life associated with a sense of an inner spirit. However, it is difficult to identify what such a spirit is like and how it can be observed. Spirituality can be defined from both religious and secular perspectives. A person with spiritual needs does not necessarily need to participate in religious rituals and practices.

Despite the lack of consensus regarding the definition of spirituality, several themes emerge from an interdisciplinary review of the literature:

• All human beings have the potential for spirituality and spiritual growth.
• Spirituality is relational.
• There is a necessary link among religion, moral norms, and spirituality.
• Spirituality involves lived experience; it is a way of life.

In some ways spirituality is a mystery. Although human beings can experience spirituality, appreciate it, and grow in it, there is much about spirituality that cannot be explained or reduced to human language.

On the basis of these themes, spirituality is defined as a way of life, usually informed by the moral norms of one or more religious traditions, through which a person relates to other persons, the universe, and the transcendent in ways that promote human fulfillment (of self and others) and universal harmony.

The Religious Perspective

From the religious perspective, spirituality can be defined as encompassing the ideology of the *imago dei* (image of God), or soul, that exists in everyone. The soul makes the person a thinking, feeling, moral, creative being, able to relate meaningfully to a supreme being and to others. This being or force may be called God, Allah, the divine creator and sustainer of the universe, the divine mystery, or other names that convey a profound sense of transcendence and awe. A religious perspective often entails a set of beliefs that help explain the meaning of life, suffering, health, and illness. These beliefs can be crucial to a believer's well-being.

Beyond Religious Practice

Spirituality is often mistakenly understood to mean just religious practice; however, it should be considered in the broader sense of the term. Religion can be an approach to or expression of spirituality, and spirituality is a component of religion, but the two concepts are different.

> *Occasionally, health-care professionals may encounter individuals whose spiritual practices are highly questionable or discomforting to witness (e.g., worshippers of Satan or those who seek to invoke harm to others through their prayers and rituals).*

It is quite possible for the members of a specific religion to be limited in their spirituality. Most people have known individuals who dutifully follow the rules of their religious tradition. They strongly believe that if they have adhered to the rules correctly, God will reward them with blessings such as health, success, affluence, social status, and power. For these individuals, adverse events like disease, death of a loved one, or loss of investments can be devastating, because they are perceived as a failure in religious practice or punishments from God. On the other hand, there are many deeply spiritual persons who do not belong to any organized religion but who may be profoundly reflective about the meaning of their life and experiences.

Specific Values and Beliefs

Current religious leaders attempt to help a diverse population appreciate religious traditions other than their own. They point out that all the world's major religions seek to answer the same questions: "Why are we here?" "What does it all mean?" and "What, if anything, are we supposed to be doing with our lives?" All religions taken together can be perceived like a stained-glass window that refracts the light in different colors and offers reflections of different shapes. Each of the world's religions is different because it has evolved to respond to unique histories and different cultural developments.

Definitions of religion usually identify a specific system of values and beliefs and a framework for ethical behavior that the members must follow. Religion can be thought of as a social construct that reflects its cultural context and specific philosophical influences. A religion evolves within a specific cultural group, situated in history, and attempts to discern what the group beliefs are and how the group has come to understand God's commandments.

Religion, as an institutionally based, organized system of beliefs, represents only one specific means of spiritual expression. Participation in a religion generally entails formal education for membership, an initiation ceremony, participation in worship gatherings, adherence to set rules of behavior, participation in prescribed rituals, a particular mode of prayer, and the study of that group's sacred texts. Religious groups vary widely in their tolerance of intragroup diversity of beliefs and behaviors as well as their respect for the belief systems of others. In addition, a specific religious group may encompass a wide range of understanding of what its practices represent.

Occasionally, health-care professionals may encounter individuals whose spiritual practices are highly questionable or discomforting to witness (e.g., worshippers of Satan or those who seek to invoke harm to others through their prayers and rituals).

The Secular Perspective

From a secular perspective, spirituality is seen as a set of positive values, such as love, honesty, or truth, chosen by the individual to ultimately become that person's supreme focus of life and organizing framework. These values have the capacity to motivate the individual toward fulfillment of personal needs, goals, and aspirations, leading ultimately to self-actualization.

Manifestation of Spirituality

The religious and secular perspectives can exist together in the totality of a person's life. A person's spirituality may be nourished by the ability to give and receive touch, caring, love, and trust. Spirituality may also entail an appreciation of physical experiences such as listening to music, enjoying art or literature, eating delicious food, laughing, venting emotional tension, or participating in sexual expression. A series of four developmental stages have been proposed for human spirituality:

- Stage 1: The chaotic (antisocial) stage, with its superficial belief system
- Stage 2: The formal (institutional) stage, with its adherence to the law
- Stage 3: The skeptic (individual) stage, with its emphasis on rationality, materialism, and humaneness
- Stage 4: The mystical (communal) stage, with its "unseen order of things"[2]

A SPIRITUAL TRADITION IN NURSING

Modern nursing has a rich legacy of the appreciation of spirituality in health and illness. Florence Nightingale's views of nursing practice were based on a spiritual philosophy that she set forth in *Suggestions for Thought*. She was the daughter of Unitarian and Anglican parents, and among her ancestors were famous dissenters against the Church of England. The skepticism fostered by her Unitarian upbringing may have influenced her to question and critique established religious doctrine. Her search for religious truth caused her to become familiar with the writings of Christian mystics (e.g., St. Francis of Assisi, St. John of the Cross) and also with various Eastern mystical writings, including the *Bhagavad-Gita*.

What Do You Think?

How would you define your spirituality—religious or secular?

_____

_____

_____

_____

_____

_____

_____

_____

_____

_____

_____

_____

The Lady of the Lamp

Most modern nurses consider Florence Nightingale (1820–1910) to be the mother of the nursing profession (see Chapter 2). Most know her as "the lady of the lamp," who almost single-handedly brought about sweeping changes in British medicine, care delivered on battlefields, and public health. Nightingale realized a call to care early in her life. She was a sickly child, and as the recipient of care from family members, she began to reciprocate in kind by nursing other sick relatives.

A Modern Prophet?

Nightingale sought places where she could learn to care for the sick and dying in a way that distinguished what she did from the work of common chambermaids. She attended the Institution of Deaconesses at Kaiserwerth in Dusseldorf, Germany. This was a Protestant training hospital that taught something akin to nursing as a call from God and a diaconal function. Through her time at Kaiserwerth and her contacts there, she came to believe that all persons on a mission or quest to become Christlike are given certain gifts and talents. Some say Nightingale was a modern prophet of God and saw herself as a liberated human being.

For Nightingale, spirituality involved a sense of a divine intelligence who creates and sustains the cosmos, as well as an awareness of her own inner connection with this higher reality. The universe, for Nightingale, was the embodiment of a transcendent God. She came to believe that all aspects of creation are interconnected and share the same inner divinity. She believed that all humans have the capacity to realize and perceive this divinity. Nightingale's God can be described as perfection or as the "essence of benevolence."[2]

> *Nightingale saw no conflict between science and mysticism. To her, the laws of nature and science were merely "the thoughts of God."*

The Thoughts of God

Nightingale saw no conflict between science and mysticism. To her, the laws of nature and science were merely "the thoughts of God." Spirituality, for Nightingale, entailed the development of courage, compassion, inner peace, creative insight, and other "God-like" qualities. Based on this belief, Nightingale's convictions commanded her to lifelong service in the care of the sick and helpless.

Nightingale endorsed the tradition of contemplative prayer, or attunement to the inner presence of God. All phenomena, Nightingale believed, are manifestations of God. A spiritual life entails wise stewardship of all the earth's resources, including human beings. She saw physical healing as a natural process regulated by natural laws, and as she stated in her *Notes on Nursing,* "What nursing has to do . . . is to put the client in the best condition for nature to act upon him."[3]

Spirituality and Religion in Nursing Theory

As nursing sought to establish itself as a profession with a legitimate knowledge base, the concern with human spirituality was downplayed and even consciously ignored until the early 1980s. Typically, the spiritual domain is assigned to the art rather than to the science of nursing, because its seemingly subjective nature is mistakenly equated with aesthetics and intuition. Paying attention to the spiritual domain in providing holistic care depends on the beliefs and values of both the nurse and the client.

There are 26 major nursing theories and conceptual frameworks that have been developed since the 1960s. Although 14 of them recognized the spiritual domain of health somewhere in their assumptions, only 2 theories mention it by name.

Energy Fields

Martha Rogers' Science of Unitary Human Beings is an example of a profoundly spiritual view of humanity that does not directly name the concept of spirituality. Rogers' framework suggests that there are unbounded human energy fields in interaction with the environmental energy field. Rogers' spiritual definitions can apply as well to the concept of the soul (discussed

> *At times clients make health-care decisions that conflict with the beliefs of their religious communities. These often produce high levels of spiritual distress that may affect the client's mental and physical well-being.*

later). Rogers, who grew up in Tennessee amidst fundamentalist Christians, was loath to be interpreted in that light; moreover, she had to establish her credibility at New York University during the 1950s, before nursing was accepted as a scientific discipline.

An Aspect of Holistic Health

Betty Neuman, in the later development of her theory, and Jean Watson are the only theorists who clearly acknowledged the impact of spirituality in the development of their theories (see Chapter 4). Watson alone defined and explained the spiritual terminology she used to discuss the spiritual aspect of holistic health.

Watson specifically identifies the awareness of the clients' and families' spiritual and religious beliefs as a responsibility of a nurse.[4] She advocates that nurses should appreciate and respect the spiritual meaning in a person's life, no matter how unusual that person's belief system may be. Watson states that nurses have an obligation to identify religious and spiritual influences in their clients' lives at home and to help clients meet their religious requirements in inpatient settings. For example, nurses can facilitate clients' use of measures, such as the lighting of candles (real or electric), put flowers and personal objects in the room, ensure privacy, and play music to promote increased comfort and to relieve anguish.

Spiritual Distress

Since 1978, the North American Nursing Diagnosis Association (NANDA) has recognized the nursing diagnosis of spiritual distress.[5] It has most recently been defined as "disruption in the life principle that pervades a person's entire being and integrates and transcends one's biological and psychosocial nature."

Defining characteristics of spiritual distress include concerns with and questions about the meaning of life and death, anger toward God, concerns about the meaning of suffering, concerns about the person's relationship to God, the inability to participate in preferred religious practices, seeking spiritual help, concerns about the ethics of prescribed medical regimens, black humor, expressing displaced anger toward clergy, sleep disturbances, and altered mood or behavior. Spiritual distress may occur in relation to separation from religious or cultural supports, challenges to beliefs and values, or intense suffering.

Illness as Punishment

Nurses should be aware that some individuals have been seriously harmed by their religious communities. Examples of harm might include being shunned or excommunicated, being told that they are evil, being forced into a rigidly controlled lifestyle by a cult, or being physically or sexually assaulted by members of the religious community. For these people, illness may be seen as punishment for some sinful action, and they may perceive any offer of spiritual support from the religious community as profoundly threatening. They may believe that God has abandoned them or that the idea of God is foolish or even destructive.

Given the rapid turnover of clients in most health systems, there may be little that the nurse can do other than to acknowledge their spiritual pain and accept them, with the assurance that "I am here for you now." If there is more time for contact, the nurse may be able to refer a client or family to appropriate support groups or clergy.

Going Against Tradition

At times clients make health-care decisions that conflict with the beliefs of their religious communities. These often produce high levels of spiritual distress that may affect both the mental and physical well-being of the client. Consider the following case study:

> When I was a nursing student in the early 1970s, I cared for a woman who was undergoing a therapeutic abortion because of several medical complications of her pregnancy. She had her first child before RhoGAM was available, and she, an Rh-negative mother, had borne an Rh-positive baby. She had only one kidney, and her physicians were concerned that the immunological complication of carrying a second Rh-positive baby would jeopardize that kidney's function. The decision was difficult for the woman and her husband to make, but they believed the first priority was to care for and raise their 7-year-old son. She needed to protect her kidney so that she could live and participate fully in the child's upbringing.
>
> The night before I cared for this woman, her clergyman came to the hospital and told her that she would go to hell for her decision. Being a devout church member, the woman

was extremely distressed the next day. The primary nurse assigned to this woman recognized the spiritual distress caused by the clergyman and requested that a hospital chaplain spend time with her. The chaplain talked and prayed with the woman for several hours. These actions brought great comfort to the woman, who proceeded with the abortion.

Clients often make choices that are difficult for nurses to accept. For instance, because of religious beliefs, clients may refuse commonplace treatments, such as blood transfusions, medications, and even minor surgeries. End-of-life decisions are often based on family members' spiritual beliefs and can be controversial among the health-care personnel who are involved in the decision. In some acute care settings, chaplains and psychiatrists conduct regular group sessions with staff nurses to assist them in understanding and accepting controversial client decisions. The Schiavo case in Florida demonstrates how well-meaning people with strong religious beliefs can be diametrically opposed when it comes to end-of-life decisions.

The Human Energy System and the Soul

Most religious traditions include a concept called "the soul." Religious traditions usually offer explanations of what the soul is, how and when human beings acquire a soul, and what happens to the soul after death, but "soul" need not be a religious concept.

Images of the Soul

Thomas Moore, a psychotherapist who has written extensively about spiritual development, describes the soul "not as a thing, but a quality or a dimension of experiencing life and ourselves. It has to do with depth, value, relatedness, heart, and personal substance . . . [not necessarily] an object of religious belief or . . . something to do with immortality."[6] Yet Moore observes that the soul must be nurtured, and religious practices can provide that nurturance. For Moore, spirituality is the effort a person makes to identify the soul's world view, values, and sense of relatedness to the whole of the person and of creation. The work of the soul is the quest for understanding or insight about major life questions.

Some people may depict the soul as an image of the person that extends several feet beyond the physical self, or characterize it by color and energetic

movement. Many people believe that the soul enters the body at some point during gestation and leaves the body at approximately the moment of death. Reincarnation, or the return of a soul for many earthly lifetimes, is a concept encountered in many religious frameworks, including certain mystical traditions within Judaism and Christianity, although not all denominations subscribe to it. The reason for the soul's return to earthly life is to learn, to develop, and to be purified. Some traditions express this process in terms of earning an improved position in the spiritual world to become closer to God after the final judgment.

The soul would seem to be an exquisitely precise and vast center for communication. Souls have the capacity to communicate with one another, with all living things, and with the divine source of all energy. Their capacity is not limited by the laws of physical matter. Some alternative modalities of healing rely on energy movement through the soul.

Examples of therapies that capitalize on knowledge of the soul and the movement of a divinely generated energy, life force, or grace (*chi* in Chinese, *ki* in Japanese, *prana* in Indian traditions) include therapeutic touch, Reiki, and shiatsu. Energy can move in many directions. When a person needs it, energy can be drawn from its divine source into the person. Excess energy can be moved from one person to another, and the flow of energy throughout the person's energy field can be balanced to achieve a state of health.

Human Energy Centers

Some alternative healing practices that use colors, herbs, aromas, and crystals can be regarded as consistent with a paradigm of repatterning the human energy field or altering the flow of energy throughout the person's body. The circulation of divine energy may be thought of as coming from God and circulating through all living things, the earth, and all the celestial bodies, thus interconnecting all creation.

Religious traditions of India and other Eastern cultures teach that the human energy system contains seven energy centers, or chakras. These can be considered the primary openings in the human energy system through which energy flows. Each center has or controls a unique type of energy and spirituality that it allows to enter or leave the body. The root chakra is located at the base of the torso or the perineum, and its energy has to do with the material world. The crown chakra, the highest level of energy at the top of the head, relates to spirituality.

Examining the religious art of many cultures, over many centuries, artists depict these areas of their subjects' bodies in similar ways. For instance, holy people are depicted with vivid, large, or colorful hearts, and their heads are surrounded by halos. At the very least, the chakras represent a paradigm for ordering the archetypal issues of human life.

What Do You Think?

What sources of religious energy do you have? When and how do you use them?

_____

_____

_____

_____

_____

_____

_____

_____

_____

_____

_____

Communication Between Worlds

Some individuals seem to be more aware of the nonphysical or spiritual realms than others. Many people have had a precognition or déjà vu experience during their lives. However, nurses may have more opportunities to glimpse a different reality than laypeople. Nurses have been involved in research on the near-death experience for more than 20 years.

The Near-Death Experience

Across religious and cultural traditions and throughout history, a common near-death experience has been documented, but only since the early 1980s has it gained credence among Western health professionals.

Many clients describe the experience of near death as a sensation of floating in the air while visualizing their body lying below on a hospital bed, at the scene of an accident, or where the near death occurred. They often watch health-care personnel who are working to resuscitate the body. The person

then experiences being drawn into a tunnel, perhaps accompanied by other forms or spiritual beings, and moving toward a bright light that exudes great energy or love. They also describe a communication with the light being, generally identified as God, about whether they are to remain there or return to the earthly body.

"Sir, the bright light you see is my penlight, not the afterlife."

Obviously, in cases of near death, the decision is made to return. Individuals who have experienced near death often report that they have developed a great inner peace, that they no longer fear death, and that their lives have been transformed by what they experienced.

Nurses who spend much of their time working with clients who are near death, such as hospice nurses, are most likely to have witnessed the experience of deathbed visions and gained a glimpse of a different realm of reality. Dying clients who are having a deathbed vision are often aware of multiple realities: the tangible here and now that family members and caretakers can observe, and "the other side," where they see loved ones who have died and are waiting for their arrival.

Some medical researchers attribute near-death and deathbed experiences to progressive hypoxia in specific brain centers. However, others give the experiences a spiritual interpretation. Could a husband, for example, really come to meet his wife of many years past? A vast amount of literature on angels and spiritual guides emphasizes that people need not feel alone or frightened by future situations or crises. Angels and other spiritual guides are available to comfort them just for the asking.

A Gown of Glowing White

Some authorities believe that children are more open to communication from the spiritual world than adults because they have not yet been contaminated by the laws of natural science that are generally accepted by Western society. For example, a young child related the following experience: When she was about 7 years old, she awoke in the middle of the night to find a beautiful lady in a gown of glowing white watching her. She had the experience at least one other time, but her mother, whom she called into the room at the time, was unable to see the lady.

Mysticism

Mystics are believed to be people who have a different relationship to time, space, matter, and energy than most of the population. It seems that they are able to understand the real nature and full capability of their souls and can apply that knowledge and ability to the physical world, producing changes that science has difficulty explaining and that some call miracles. For example, a current-day Hindu holy man in India, Sai Baba, generates ash that has brought miraculous healing to some people who have touched it. Also, many healing miracles were documented by physicians and scientists during the lifetime of the Italian Franciscan priest Padre Pio before his death in 1968.

The common message of mystics from around the world is that people are to live lives of love and compassion for all. The extraordinary love and compassion that most mark the early life of the Dalai Lama, a Buddhist holy man, are depicted in the historical films "Seven Years in Tibet" and "Kundun."

> *Some authorities believe that children are more open to communication from the spiritual world than adults because they have not yet been contaminated by the laws of natural science that are generally accepted by Western society.*

SPIRITUAL PRACTICES IN HEALTH AND ILLNESS

Nurturing the Spirit

The way that nurses care for and nurture themselves influences their ability to function effectively in a healing role with another person. The spiritual path is a life path. Attentiveness to one's own spirit is a key component of living in a healing way and is fundamental to integrating spirituality into clinical practice. Care of their spirit or soul requires nurses to pause, reflect, and take in what is happening within and around them; to take time for themselves, for relationships, and for other things that animate them; and to be mindful about nourishing their spirits. The many ways to nurture their spirits and respond to their spiritual concerns are the same as those that they suggest to their clients.

Spiritual Assessment Questions

Nurses may have some difficulty assessing the spiritual status of a client. Some questions that facilitate gathering this information include:

- What is strength for you?
- Where can you get your strength?
- Who gives you strength?
- How can you increase your inner strength?
- What does peace mean to you?
- Where do up feel at peace?
- Who makes you feel more peaceful?
- What situations will increase your sense of peace?
- When do you feel most secure?
- Where do you get your security from?
- Who makes you feel secure?
- How can you increase your security?[1]

A Professional Responsibility

Care of the spirit is a professional nursing responsibility and an intrinsic part of holistic nursing. Nurses must become confident and competent with spiritual caregiving, expanding their skills in assessing the spiritual domain and in developing and implementing appropriate interventions. The nursing profession must understand and support holistic care. Therefore, spirituality and the delivery of spiritual care become fundamental content areas for nursing students. Guidelines and policies must be developed to fully support nurse educators in their endeavors.[7]

A persistent barrier to the incorporation of spirituality into clinical practice is the fear of imposing particular religious beliefs and values on others. Nurses who integrate spirituality into their care of others need to recognize that, although each person acts out of and is informed by her or his own spiritual perspective, acting from this foundation is not the same as imposing these beliefs and values on another. In fact, many practitioners believe that the more grounded they are in their own spiritual understandings, the less likely they are to impose their values and beliefs on others.

A number of organizations and agencies encourage the incorporation of spiritual practices into health care (Boxes 20.2 through 20.5).

Prayer and Meditation

Prayer and meditation are spiritual disciplines practiced in many traditions, both cultural and religious. Appreciating the personal nature of these disciplines, the nurse, with respect and sensitivity, can help clients remember or explore ways in which they reach out to and listen for God or the absolute. Recalling the place and

> *Care of the spirit is a professional nursing responsibility and an intrinsic part of holistic nursing.*

meaning of prayer and the ways in which they experience the presence of and communion with God or the absolute provides clients with a rich resource.

In the clinical setting, both the nurse's and the client's understanding of prayer will determine its

Box 20.3

Parish (Congregational) Nursing

Parish (congregational) nursing is a movement of the past decade in which churches, synagogues, mosques, and other faith communities designate nurses to serve their membership. Parish nursing is viewed as a healing ministry, and parish nurses are attuned to spiritual issues raised by health transitions, as well as the healing nature of spiritual practice. They may assist people to remain in their own homes, connect them with other health services for which they are eligible, or provide needed health teaching and support. At times their role is to simply be present with them.

The International Parish Nurse Resource Center is located in St. Louis, Missouri. They can be contacted at 314-918-2559, 314-918-2527, 877-627-5653, or on the World Wide Web at www.parishnurses.org.

Box 20.2

American Holistic Nurses' Association

The American Holistic Nurses' Association (AHNA) was founded in 1980 by a group of nurses dedicated to bringing the concepts of holism to every arena of nursing practice. They define holism as wellness, that state of harmony between body, mind, emotions, and spirit in an ever-changing environment.

The AHNA offers certification in holistic nursing and has endorsed programs in aromatherapy, interactive imagery, and healing touch.

Visit the AHNA Web site at www.ahna.org.

Box 20.4

Office of Alternative Medicine

The Office of Alternative Medicine (OAM) was initiated at the National Institutes of Health in 1992 to evaluate the effectiveness of alternative medical treatment modalities. In addition to funding studies, they have developed a research database and a clearinghouse for disseminating information to the public.

The OAM's Web site is located at www.altmed.od.nih.gov/oam.

Box 20.5

International Center for the Integration of Health and Spirituality

The International Center for the Integration of Health and Spirituality (ICIHS) in Rockville, Maryland, disseminates research on the benefits of spiritual practices to health professionals through their publication, conferences, and speakers.

For further information about this resource, contact ICIHS at 310-984-7162, or visit their Web site at www.icihs.org.

role. Clarifying the client's understanding of and need for prayer is part of holistic nursing. Some clients want others to pray with or for them, while others do not believe in prayer. Nurses should support each client's request and needs for prayer, which may mean inviting others to take part in various forms of prayer with and for the client, or simply praying with the client themselves. Facilitating the appreciation and practice of prayer in a client's life is an important aspect of caring for the spirit.

Relief Through Imagery. When a person is physically confined to a hospital room, the practice of imagery may enable him or her to experience another space. Imagery can take a person to a temple, an ocean, a place of religious worship, a breakfast nook, or any "sacred space," that is, a life-giving and healing place for the client. In this other space, the client may feel more comfortable in spirit and more able to engage in prayer. Family and friends, as well as other clients and other staff, may be resources in this practice of imagery.

Exploring as many aspects of the prayer experience as possible enriches both the nurse's and the client's understanding of the nature and place of prayer. Sacred or inspirational readings, music, drumming, movement, light or darkness, aromas, and time of day are among the many factors that may be important considerations in one's prayer life.

The client's prayer life, in all of its fullness and meaning, nurtures the spirit, and the nurse may

be able to support the client's prayer needs by facilitating changes in the environment or schedule. It is wise to remember that merely the process of listening to and appreciating the prayer life of another nurtures the spirit and acknowledges the spiritual dimension of that person.

Relaxation Response

Remembered Wellness

The relaxation response and prayer have been demonstrated to affect illnesses. The ability of people to participate in their own healing through prayer or meditation may use a source of healing power called "remembered wellness,"[8] sometimes also called "the placebo effect." It is based on the belief that all people have the capacity to "remember" the calm and confidence associated with emotional and physical health and happiness. As a source of energy that can be tapped into, remembered wellness should not be regarded suspiciously but instead used for healing. However, its effectiveness depends on the individual's belief system.

Remembered wellness depends on three components: belief and expectation of the client, belief and expectation of the caregiver, and belief and expectation generated by a caring relationship between the client and the caregiver. A warm and trusting relationship seems to enhance the effectiveness of the care that is provided.

Everyone involved in providing health care is in a position to use remembered wellness as an energy source to enhance the healing process. One thing health-care providers can do to promote healing is to speak positively of treatments and medications being used. For example, positive reinforcement occurs when the nurse refers to the clients' medication as the "drug your doctor prescribed to help your heart" or the food tray as "nutrition to help your body fight your infection."

The Nocebo Effect

In contrast to the placebo effect, the "nocebo" (negative placebo) effect is the fulfillment of an expectation of harm. It is also an effect that health professionals can cause. Examples of the nocebo effect include advising clients that a medicine will probably make them sick, telling them that chemotherapy will drain their energy and cause their hair to fall out, or informing them that a certain percentage of people die from a given procedure.

Such warnings can actually bring about the complications.

A Quiet Focus

The relaxation response entails 20 minutes, twice each day, of quiet meditation on a word or image that is spiritually meaningful to the person. When an intrusive thought enters the person's consciousness, the person should lightly dismiss it, as if gently blowing a feather away, and return to the meditation word or image. Over time, individuals who use this method have lowered blood pressure, decreased incidents of dysmenorrhea, reduced chronic pain, and brought about improvement in a number of illnesses.

Peace Through Awareness

Relaxation, meditation, visualization, and hypnosis can help seriously ill clients, including many with cancer. Meditation is a technique of listening. However, listening is not a passive process. Rather, it is a way of focusing the mind in a state of relaxed awareness to pay attention to deeper thoughts and feelings, to the products of the unconscious mind, to the peace of pure consciousness, and to deeper spiritual awareness.

Some teachers of meditation suggest that the person select a spiritually symbolic word (e.g., God, love, beauty, peace, Mary, Jesus) on which to focus, whereas others suggest watching a candle flame. Still others teach practitioners to focus on their breathing. All these methods are intended to bring the person to a deeply restful state that frees the mind from its usual chatter. This is the experience of being centered. People may experience spiritual insights, but more often they experience a gradual enhancement of well-being.

Visualizing an Outcome

Visualization is the practice of meditating with an image of a desired outcome or the process of attaining it. It is preferable that the image be selected by the person using it rather than someone else. For example, a person with a tumor might visualize miniature miners mining the unhealthy tissue and carting it away. Hypnosis is a process of suggesting an image of a desired reality to someone. Both these techniques have been demonstrated to stimulate the immune system.

Researchers have also observed that some seriously ill people believe that they deserve their

> *Therapeutic touch (TT) is an active alternative healing modality that involves redirecting the human energy system.*

illness as a punishment for something they did in the past. Helping them forgive themselves often brings about dramatic improvements in their conditions. Releasing fear and hate has a similar effect. This process reflects back to Nightingale's belief that nurses need to help clients get out of the way of their own healing.

It might seem logical to conclude that clients who do not recover from illness, or who die, have failed to help themselves or did not adequately use their spiritual powers. That is not the case. Spiritual modes of healing do not always lead to cure. Spiritual healing takes a much broader view and includes enhanced comfort and an inner peace with disability or death.

Therapeutic Touch

Therapeutic touch (TT) is an active alternative healing modality that involves redirecting the human energy system. In recent years, TT has been retrieved from ancient traditions, studied, and refined.

Altered Wave Patterns

As a healing practice, TT is consistent with the Science of Unitary Human Beings developed by Martha Rogers. The Science of Unitary Human Beings defines people as energy fields interacting with the larger environmental energy field. The energy fields are characterized by patterns of waves. One way of altering the wave patterns of the human energy field is to use TT to move energy into and through it in deliberate ways.

The practitioner of TT acts with the intent of relaxing the recipient, reducing pain and discomfort, and accelerating healing when appropriate. Early controlled studies showed that the hemoglobin levels of a group of clients who received TT increased significantly more than the levels in a control group who did not receive TT.

The TT practitioner should approach the client with compassion and the intent to heal, and the recipient of care ideally approaches the healing encounter with receptivity and openness to change. The practitioner of TT first centers and then assesses the state of the recipient's energy field, noting energy levels and movement around the chakras. Cues may be determined through physical sensations in the practitioner's hands, direct visualization, inner awareness, or other intuitive modes of insight.

Issues in Practice

Religious Issues versus Care Issues

Angie and Edward are a young couple with two teenage children. They are a close and loving family who have a large network of family and friends. The entire family is active in their church, school, and other community groups.

Alan, 15 years old, has just been severely injured in a high school soccer game. Angie and Edward are summoned to the hospital where they are told that Alan has multiple fractured bones and possible internal injuries. While they are waiting for the surgical team to arrive, the couple keeps vigil at their son's bedside in the pediatric intensive care unit (PICU). The surgeon informs the distressed parents that there is evidence that Alan's injuries are more serious than previously diagnosed. Alan has active internal bleeding and will need a blood transfusion to survive. Although genuinely devastated, the parents adamantly refuse to sign for the lifesaving blood transfusion, stating that they are Jehovah's Witnesses and receipt of blood is against their religion. The surgeon asks you, Alan's nurse, to get the parents to change their minds. You talk with the couple, but they continue to refuse to sign the surgical consent form.

- What are the primary underlying spiritual principles involved in this dilemma?
- Do Alan's parents have the right to refuse their consent for a blood transfusion on the basis of religious beliefs?
- Do you think that the fact that Alan is a minor (under 18 years old) may make a difference in this situation?
- What actions do you think the charge nurse should take?
- How would you resolve this dilemma?

After assessing the recipient, the TT practitioner, working from the center of the client's energy field to the periphery, directs energy from the environment into the client's field as needed, stimulates energy flow through the client's field, clears congested areas in the energy field, dampens excess energetic activity, and synchronizes the rhythmic waves of the energy flow depending on the client's needs. The practitioner is not diverting his or her own energy into the client because it would be detrimental to the practitioner. Rather, the TT practitioner redirects the client's energy field or directs energy from the environment outside the client.

> *People working in the helping professions, whose work is rooted in compassion and concern for others, are prone to depression and burnout.*

An Expression of Care

Families and friends may need encouragement to share physical expressions of care and concern in the sometimes intimidating hospital environment. Nurses may encourage them with statements such as "It's OK to hold her hand; you won't interfere with the tubes." "He mentioned that you give a wonderful backrub; would you like to give him one today?" "She seems to know when you are in here holding her hand." "I can show you how to massage her feet." "Would you like to brush her hair?"

Persons vary in their degree of comfort with touch and the conditions in which they may want to share touch. The nurse's own personal feelings about and comfort with touch help in assessing the place and potential use of touch in the client's situation. At times when words cannot be found, or in circumstances where people are more comfortable with physical expression than with words, touch is a powerful expression of spirit and instrument of healing.

NURSING PRACTICE AND SPIRITUAL WELLNESS

Profession or Vocation?

Although the nursing profession is deeply rooted in religious traditions, modern nursing has spent considerable energy attempting to distance itself from this aspect of its history. Nursing as vocation has given way to nursing as profession (see Chapter 1). The current health-care system has required nurses to shift their identity from vocation to profession in order to achieve appropriate value in a system that is increasingly economically oriented.

Nursing as Spiritual Calling

Nursing is much more than the mere secular enterprise the modern world perceives it to be. Perhaps it is time that nurses re-evaluate the work they do and consider it a vocation, that is, a life calling in the spiritual sense of that word. The world's religions consistently allude to the symbolic and deep meaning of the work that nurses do. Nursing practice has the capacity to be richly imaginative and to speak to the soul on many levels. Nursing practice can be carried out mindfully and artistically, or it can be done routinely and unconsciously, like any other job. When nursing is practiced with deep consciousness and purpose, it nurtures the nurse as well as the client.[9]

Some experts perceive that nursing is directly connected to the nurse's fantasy life, family myths, ideals, and traditions. The profession of nursing may be one way nurses sort out their major life issues. Although the choice of nursing as a career may often seem to have been serendipitous, in the spiritual context it is reasonable to question whether anything really happens by accident. As nurses practice nursing, they craft themselves, undertaking the soul's lifetime work of self-definition and self-identification.

When the Well Runs Dry

As with most professions, at times it may become difficult, even impossible perhaps, to feel good about the work that one is doing. Negative attitudes about work are detrimental to a person's self-development and often cause people to become overly invested in the surface trappings of work, such as money, power, and success. The phenomenon of burnout among nurses has been identified and studied for many years (see Chapter 12). Burnout can be viewed from a spiritual perspective, in which the well runs dry, energy fields become unbalanced, or the person experiences a prolonged "dark night of the soul," or even feels that the nurse's life work is devoid of meaning.[10]

> *Only when nurses begin to slow down and start centering their energy fields will they have the capacity to be fully present and be able to attend with complete consciousness to their loved ones, colleagues, and clients and focus completely on the present moment.*

People working in the helping professions, whose work is rooted in compassion and concern for others, are prone to depression and burnout. A concerted effort at spiritual development, or the nourishment of the soul, is essential to nurses' overall mental and physical well-being.

> *Burnout can be viewed from a spiritual perspective, in which the well runs dry, energy fields become unbalanced, or the person experiences a prolonged "dark night of the soul," or even feels that the nurse's life work is devoid of meaning.*

Maintaining Balance

Self-restoration

In the attempt to maintain an internal state of balance, the first thing nurses need to do is take time to feed their spirit. Daily prayer or meditation is an important source of insight and energy. Belonging to a group or community that actively pursues spiritual growth is also a powerful source of spiritual nourishment. Many individuals find that their spirits are nourished within the setting of a formal religion, although not necessarily the one in which they were reared. It is not uncommon for people to seek a faith community in midlife or later life, perhaps after being away from one for many years. The experience of trying various religions and modes of worship is by itself a broadening, nurturing experience.

A Sense of Sacredness

Periodic retreat from the hustle and bustle of modern living can be highly restorative to the spirit. A retreat may be for a few hours, a half-day, a weekend, a week, or longer. For some people, keeping a journal is a retreat-like experience. For others, it may be a stroll through a beautiful park, a few hours watching waves on a beach, or a trip to the woods. Retreat is most effective when time is consistently set aside for introspection and reflection rather than for tasks.

A sense of sacredness can infuse everyday life with meaning and zest if nurses open themselves to it. It is a part of normal human activity to celebrate seasonal and family holidays with specific rituals, music, decorations, group gatherings, and foods. These types of activities honor life cycles that are greater than the individual and nurture important relationships that serve as a **support system.**

Enjoy Special Moments

Many people have routines for their weekends or days off that allow time for self-restoration. These special activities may include a large country breakfast while listening to favorite music; baking cookies, bread, or a pie; sitting for an extended period of time in a favorite easy chair; or even playing a physically demanding sport like basketball. Many people have favorite coffee mugs or dishes or special objects in their homes that are not only beautiful but may remind them of loved ones, wonderful trips, religious experiences, or other events that nourish them each time they view the object.

One of the most spiritual aspects of a person's life is the enjoyment of beauty. It costs little or nothing to plant or cut flowers or to listen to music. It is in these moments that a person's creativity and insight are most evident.

Regaining the Center

The hectic modern world continually urges people to enhance their capacity for dealing with multiple concerns at the same time. Some people even define success by looking at how many tasks they can juggle simultaneously. *Multitasking* is the new buzzword for the health-care environment of the 21st century. Nurses must be able to talk on the telephone, send faxes and e-mail, surf the net, and use a word processor for entering client data at the same time that they are developing care plans,

evaluating clients, answering call lights, supervising unlicensed assistive personnel, and providing physicians with information.

Although this is highly productive, the more nurses multitask, the more disconnected they become from themselves. Multitasking can be thought of as the antithesis of spiritual nurturance. Spirituality is about personal wholeness, whereas multitasking is about fragmentation.[10] Only when nurses begin to slow down and start centering their energy fields will they have the capacity to be fully present and be able to attend with complete consciousness to their loved ones, colleagues, and clients and focus completely on the present moment.

Conclusion

Spirituality within the nursing context needs to be seen as a broad concept encompassing religion but not equating with it. Fundamental to this concept is a search for meaning within life and its particular events such as ill health. Nursing students need to be made aware of the many forms that spiritual distress may take.

Nurses are in an ideal position to provide spiritual care that positively affects the mental and physical health of their clients. To be able to focus clearly on clients' spiritual needs, nurses must first consider their own spirituality as a starting point for self-knowledge. The means of supporting clients with spiritual problems must be explored. Teaching methods should be participatory and student centered; the means of assessing and meeting spiritual needs hinges on effective communication skills and determines whether the nurse is "being with" the client as opposed to merely "being there."

The meaning of the holistic moment emerges through the synergistic interaction among its elements (Fig. 20.2). Just as a person is greater than the sum of her or his parts, so is the holistic moment greater than the sum of its parts, namely spirituality, presence, and relationship to others.[11]

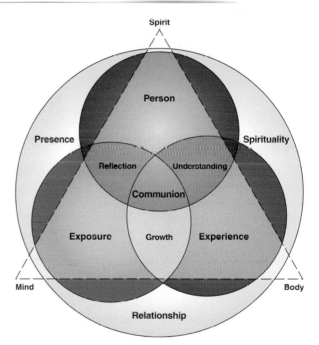

F i g u r e   2 0 . 2 Elements involved in experiencing spirituality and presence in the nurse–client relationship. (Adapted from Rankin, EA: Finding spirituality and nursing presence. Journal of Holistic Nursing 24(4): 286, 2006.)

Critical Thinking Exercises

Mrs. Jan Steiner, 73 years old, has outlived two husbands. Ted, her second husband, died 20 years ago. Reared in the Roman Catholic faith, Mrs. Steiner converted to Judaism when she married Ted. Her two daughters by her first husband were also reared in the Roman Catholic tradition. One of them, Kathy, continues to practice her religion. The other daughter, Judith, is Unitarian.

Mrs. Steiner experienced a stroke 2 years ago that left her moderately disabled. At that time she moved into a long-term care facility. She was still able to read and to enjoy visits with friends and family, but a second stroke 3 months ago left her incontinent and aphasic.

Mrs. Steiner has just had a major heart attack. Although bypass surgery could extend her life, she has never articulated any end-of-life desires. Her daughters are in conflict over how Mrs. Steiner's medical management should proceed. Kathy strongly believes that as long as Mrs. Steiner is alive, life should be actively supported. It would be morally wrong to do less than that. Judith, on the other hand, believes that what had been the "life" of Mrs. Steiner is essentially over and it is a waste of resources to merely delay the inevitable. The nursing staff, as they attempt to facilitate communication between the family and the medical staff, feel caught in the middle.

- What are your own spiritual beliefs about the proper approach to Mrs. Steiner's medical management?
- Analyze the positions of Kathy and Judith from both their ethical and spiritual contexts.
- What resources are likely to be available in the hospital or the community to help the daughters come to a decision?

Bypass surgery is not performed, and Mrs. Steiner returns to her long-term care facility. Her overall condition continues to deteriorate, and within 3 months she is very near death. She seems to have little awareness of her surroundings and she does not consistently recognize or respond to her daughters.

- Knowing the religious divergence within Mrs. Steiner's family, how might the nursing staff facilitate their preparation for the death of their mother and her funeral?
- What would happen within Mrs. Steiner's circle of family and friends if any "side"—Catholic, Jewish, or Unitarian—"won" in planning her end-of-life care?
- Have you seen blending of religious traditions in rituals of marriage or burial? What are the advantages and disadvantages of such an approach?
- What might be the outcomes of handling their mother's death in a strictly secular or nonsectarian way and allowing all relatives and friends to mourn privately in accordance with their own spiritual traditions?

References

1. Mitchell, D: Spiritual development of nursing students: Developing competence to provide spiritual care to patients at the end of life. Journal of Nursing Education 45(9):365–370, 2006.

2. Dossey, BM, et al.: Holistic Nursing: A Handbook for Practice. Aspen Publications, Gaithersburg, MD, 2000.

3. Nightingale, F: Notes on Nursing. Dover, New York, 1969. (Originally published in 1860.)

4. Watson, J: Nursing: Human Science and Human Theory of Care: Theory of Nursing. National League for Nursing, New York, 1988.

5. North American Nursing Diagnosis Association: Nursing Diagnosis: Definitions and Classification, 1997–1998. North American Nursing Diagnosis Association, Philadelphia, 1998.

6. Moore, T: Care of the Soul. HarperCollins, New York, 1992.

7. Lantz, C: Teaching spiritual care in a public institution: Legal implications, standards of practice, and ethical obligations. Journal of Nursing Education 46(1):33–38, 2007.

8. Beckman, S: Five strategies that heighten nurses' awareness of spirituality to impact client care. Holistic Nursing Practice 21(3):135–139, 2007

9. Lovanio, K: Promoting spiritual knowledge and attitudes. Holistic Nursing Practice 21(1):42–47, 2007.

10. Hoffert, D: Enhancing the ability of nursing students to perform a spiritual assessment. Nurse Educator 32(2):66–72, 2007.

11. Rankin, EA: Finding spirituality and nursing presence. Journal of Holistic Nursing 24(4):282–288, 2006.

Bibliography

Brillhart, B: A study of spirituality and life satisfaction among persons with spinal cord injury. Rehabilitation Nurse 30(1): 31–34, 2005.

Chesnay, M: Caring for the Vulnerable: Perspectives in Nursing Theory, Practice and Research. Jones & Bartlett, Boston, 2005.

Dameron, C: Spiritual assessment made easy . . . with acronyms! Journal of Christian Nursing 22(1):14–16, 2005.

Leininger, M: Culture Care Diversity & Universality: A Worldwide Nursing Theory. Jones & Bartlett, Boston, 2005.

McSherry, W: Meaning of spirituality: Implications for nursing practice. Journal of Clinical Nursing 13(8):934–941, 2004.

Ollier, C: Spirituality in nursing: An idea whose time has returned? Patient Care Staff Representative 4(12):4–5, 2004.

O'Mathna, DP, and Quiring-Emblen, JD: Making sense of complementary and alternative therapies. Journal of Christian Nursing 18(4):8–15, 2001.

Pesut, B: Developing spirituality in the curriculum. Nursing Education Perspective 24(6):290–294, 2003.

Sethness, R: Cardiac health: Relationships among hostility, spirituality, and health risk. Journal of Nursing Care Quarterly 20(1):81–90, 2005.

Wisnefske, K: The joy of parish nursing. Nursing Matters 15(12): 3, 9, 2004.

21

Cultural Diversity

Joseph T. Catalano

Learning Objectives

After completing this chapter, the reader will be able to:

- Define culture and identify its expression.
- Compare and contrast the "melting pot" and "salad bowl" theories of acculturation.
- Identify the components of an accurate cultural assessment.
- Distinguish between primary and secondary cultural characteristics.
- List and define the key aspects of effective intercultural communication.
- Name two sources of information about transcultural nursing.

TRANSCULTURAL NURSING

Culture is a powerful influence on how nurses and clients interpret and respond to health care. Both nurses and clients expect to be treated with respect and understanding for their individuality no matter what their cultural origins. Nurses who understand essential characteristics of transcultural nursing will be able to provide competent and culturally sensitive care for clients from all cultural backgrounds.

WHAT IS CULTURE?

Culture is defined and understood in several ways. Culture may be seen as a group's acceptance of a set of attitudes, ideologies, values, beliefs, and behaviors that influence the way the members of the group express themselves. For example, members of a political party, although diverse in other ways, may be viewed as a culture because of their beliefs and ideologies. Cultural expression assumes many forms, including language; spirituality; works of art; group customs and traditions; food preferences; response to illness, stress, pain, **bereavement,** anger, and sorrow; decision-making; and even world philosophy.

A Powerful Influence

An individual's cultural orientation is the result of a learning process that literally starts at birth and continues throughout the life span. Behaviors, beliefs, and attitudes are transmitted from one generation to the next. Although expressions of culture are primarily unconscious, they have a profound effect on an individual's interactions and response to the health-care system.

> Mrs. Su Sung, who is 74 years old, is brought into the emergency department (ED) by her family because of "very bad indigestion that won't go away." Three family members (a middle-aged man and woman and a younger woman)

accompany the elderly lady. They are discussing her condition in a mixture of English and another language the nurse does not recognize. Because the client does not seem to understand any English, the nurse attempts to address the family. The younger woman speaks only broken English but manages to explain that the client is her grandmother and that she is accompanied by her mother and father, who speak even less English than she does. By default, the granddaughter serves as the translator. After much prompting, she explains that her grandmother arrived in the United States for a visit only 2 days ago from a small mountain village in Korea where she has lived all her life. She had been having periodic episodes of "indigestion" for several weeks before the visit and used traditional herbal teas prescribed by the local healer to treat her condition. On the basis of further assessment and a diagnostic test, it is determined that Mrs. Sung had an extensive myocardial infarction at least 1 week before her trip and is currently in a mild state of congestive heart failure (CHF).

She is given medications for the chest pain and CHF and is started on anticoagulant medications in the ED. She is then transferred to the coronary care unit (CCU), where she is scheduled to have coronary angiography the next day. The angiogram shows multiple blockages in her coronary arteries and extensive myocardial damage. Because of her age and the extensive damage to her heart, the physician thinks it would be too risky to attempt bypass surgery and decides to monitor her closely and treat her medically until she is stable enough to have a balloon angioplasty.

When the CCU nurse assigned to Mrs. Sung enters the room at the beginning of her shift the day after the angiogram, she finds the client covered with four heavy blankets and a bedspread and sweating profusely. When the nurse attempts to remove the excessive bed covers, the client's daughter protests vehemently in Korean and puts the blankets back on as soon as the nurse leaves the room. The daughter seems to think that her mother is sick because she is too cold and gives the elderly woman hot herbal drinks from a thermos bottle she has brought from home.

When the granddaughter arrives, the nurse explains to her why excessive heat is harmful to the client's cardiac status and why she needs to follow the diet restrictions prescribed by the physician. The ingredients of the herbal drinks are unknown, and there may be some serious interactions with the numerous medications the client is receiving. The granddaughter translates this information to her mother, who seems to become even angrier with the nurse. Although she outwardly seems to comply with the restrictions, she continues the traditional folk treatments in secret, believing the Western hospital food is bad for her mother's health.

Mrs. Sung is very quiet and hardly ever asks for help. When she does talk to her family, the conversation is usually about the airplane flight to the United States and the belief that high altitude probably caused all Mrs. Sung's problems.

Her condition gradually deteriorates during her hospitalization, despite all the medical treatment. The nurse and physician tell the family about the client's worsening condition and the likelihood that she will not survive the hospitalization, but they refuse to relay the information to the client.

> *Culture is not a monolithic concept. Any individual probably belongs to several subcultures within his or her major culture.*

Although this situation is fictitious, it demonstrates some of the potential problems that nurses may encounter when interacting with clients who come from a strong traditional cultural background. Culture is, among other things, a belief system that has been developed over a person's lifetime and, like all strongly held belief systems, is difficult to change. In the case of Mrs. Sung, it is easy to see the futility of attempting to change her belief system in a short period of time with a limited number of interactions. Another important aspect of the situation is the effect of the family. Rather than being helpful to the care of this client or attempting to alter her belief systems to follow care recommendations, the family reinforced the client's beliefs.

Concepts of Culture

Culture is not a monolithic concept. Any individual probably belongs to several subcultures within his or her major culture. Subcultures develop when members of the group accept outside values in addition to those of their dominant culture. Even within a given culture, many variations may exist. For example, it is logical to conclude that people who live in the United States all belong to the American culture and would be very similar in most ways. However, teenagers living in the rural areas of Oklahoma may find it difficult to relate to teenagers raised in the inner city of Philadelphia. Even though they speak the same language and share some similar interests, they have so many different past experiences that change their perspectives on life that it may be difficult for them to relate to each other.

Culture can be considered a type of flawed photocopy machine that makes duplicates of the original document with minor differences. As a society attempts to preserve itself by passing down its values, beliefs, and customs to the next generation, slight variations in the practices inevitably occur. The key parts of the culture remain similar, but other parts change greatly owing to effects from both within and outside the group.

Diversity

Diversity is a term that is used to explain the differences between cultures. The characteristics that define diversity can be divided into two groups: primary and secondary.

1. Primary characteristics tend to be more obvious, including nationality, race, color, gender, age, and religious beliefs.
2. Secondary characteristics include socioeconomic status, education, occupation, length of time away from the country of origin, gender issues, residential status, and sexual orientation. These may be more difficult to identify, although they may have an even more profound effect on the person's cultural identity than the primary characteristics.

When individuals make generalizations about others based on the obvious primary characteristics and do not take the time to consider the secondary characteristics, they are stereotyping the other person. Stereotyping is an oversimplified belief, conception, or opinion about another person (or group) based on a limited amount of information.

MELTING POT VERSUS SALAD BOWL

The United States has traditionally been considered a melting pot of world cultures. Early in the history of the United States, most people who came from distant lands were eager to be assimilated into American culture. Many people Americanized their names, shed their traditional dress, learned American manners and customs as quickly as possible, and made heroic attempts to learn English without the benefit of formal schooling—all so they could "fit in" with their new homeland. Until recently, most people who immigrated to this country were very willing to acculturate (i.e., to alter their own cultural practices in an attempt to become more like members of the new culture). The end result was a blending, or melting pot, of cultures.

Multiculturalism

Since the early 1970s, the practice of intentional acculturation by immigrating cultures seems to have fallen by the wayside. Many individuals who migrate to the United States from other countries now cling tenaciously to their traditional cultural practices and languages, resulting in a phenomenon called multiculturalism. Rather than blending smoothly into the bigger pot as former immigrants have done, the modern immigrants maintain their own unique flavors and textures, much like the ingredients in a large tossed salad. As an ever-growing phenomenon, multi-culturalism is something that health-care providers need to be aware of; they must learn ways of adapting their health practices to allow for these differences.

Drawbacks and Benefits. There are drawbacks and benefits to both approaches. In the era of the melting pot, individuals who attempted to retain their native beliefs, customs, and languages were often ridiculed, scorned, and generally made to feel they were outsiders to the mainstream culture. When they did become homogenized into the American culture, learned the language of the dominant society, and made an effort to be seen as belonging, they were more likely to be accepted as equals and quickly advanced up the socioeconomic ladder.

Cultural Relativism

The current salad bowl trend has the advantage of allowing individuals in the dominant culture to gain an appreciation of other cultures for their unique contributions to society. The drawback of the salad bowl is that it tends to create pockets of culturally different individuals who live in, but only have minimal interaction with, mainstream American society. Because they do not speak the language or refuse to accept the customs of the dominant culture, it may be more difficult for them to advance their socioeconomic status.

The salad bowl process has also given rise to cultural relativism among some groups. Cultural relativism occurs when members of a strong cultural group understand their culture and group members only from their own viewpoint rather than from that of the larger culture. They do not try to understand the larger culture's unique characteristics, values, and beliefs.

Heritage Consistency

Some cultural groups manage to blend the melting pot and the salad bowl together through a rather complex process sometimes called heritage consistency. Outwardly, they may become acculturated to the point where they wear business suits, speak passable English, eat fast food, and go to movies. However, when they are at home, or with groups from their traditional culture, they speak their native language, wear their traditional clothes, eat ethnically correct meals, and generally follow their native customs.

> *Many individuals who migrate to the United States from other countries now cling tenaciously to their traditional cultural practices and languages, resulting in a phenomenon called multiculturalism.*

This approach to acculturation has the advantages of allowing them to fit in and advance in the larger culture while retaining many of the elements of their traditional culture that provide a sense of stability to their lives. It does, however, create in some individuals a type of cultural confusion that may lead to increased tension and anxiety.

U.S. ETHNIC POPULATION TRENDS

A Population Shift

Rapid population growth in ethnic groups has been the trend in the United States for many years. According to U.S. Bureau of Census statistics, in the year 2006 approximately 100 million, or 33 percent, of the entire U.S. population was composed of minority groups, up from 30 percent in the year 2000. If current trends continue, it is projected that by the year 2080, the Caucasian population will be a minority group constituting 48.9 percent of the total population of the

United States. In states such as California, the white population may be a minority as early as 2030.

Despite the relatively low number of minority nurses, it is expected that nurses from one culture should be able to give culturally competent care to individuals from any other culture.

Contributing to the rapid growth in minority populations is the increasing number of immigrants coming to the United States. Between 1920 and 2000, the number of legal immigrants each year increased from 500,000 to more than 6 million. Currently the largest numbers of immigrants are from Asia, Mexico, and Central and South America. Fewer immigrants have come from Africa and Europe than in previous years.

The Need for Transcultural Nursing

Culturally Competent Care

The percentage of minority nurses does not reflect the national population trends. Despite efforts on the part of the National League for Nursing (NLN), American Association of Colleges of Nursing (AACN), and other organizations concerned with nursing education, minority nurses have remained constant at approximately 10 percent of the RNs practicing in the United States. The latest reported statistics from the NLN demonstrate a leveling off of the number of minority students enrolled in basic nursing programs at about 15 percent. In a perfect world, the percentage of RNs from various minority groups should be approximately 33 percent and would mirror the percentage from each minority group.

Despite the relatively low number of minority nurses, it is expected that nurses from one culture should be able to give culturally competent care to individuals from any other culture. Being on the front lines of health care, nursing is the one profession that is continually confronted with cultural changes that result from ethnic shifts in the population. Nurses now recognize they can no longer use traditional ethnocentric models to guide their practice and protocols. Nurses are beginning to promote an understanding of individuals from other cultures and improve the overall quality of health care.

Coverage for Minorities

The Medicare and Medicaid laws that evolved out of the social programs of the 1960s have increased the number of culturally diverse clients with whom nurses come in contact. Historically, many minority groups tend to be among the poorest segments of the population. Before the Medicare and Medicaid legislation that expanded government-funded health care to cover all welfare recipients, some ethnic minorities were unable to afford health care and were seen in the health-care setting only when severely ill. Ethnic minorities are now covered by these laws and, by their increasing numbers in all levels and areas of health care, have prompted nurses to become more sensitive to the transcultural aspects of their work.

Since the 1970s, transcultural nursing has become an important subject in most nursing programs. However, nursing education has taken only the first unsteady steps on the path to seeking a true integration of cultural competence into daily practice. As technological and transportation advances bring more and more people from different cultures closer together, there will be an increased demand for nurses who can practice effectively in a culturally diverse society. Many challenges still lie ahead.

DEVELOPING CULTURAL AWARENESS

Developing cultural awareness is the first step in becoming a culturally competent nurse. One of the main challenges for nurses who practice in a culturally diverse environment is to understand the client's perspective of what is happening in the health-care setting. From a cultural viewpoint, it may be very different from what the nurse believes is occurring.

Awareness Begins at Home

A nurse develops cultural awareness only when he or she is able to recognize and value all aspects of a client's culture, including beliefs, customs, responses, methods of expression, language, and social structure. However, merely learning about another person's culture does not guarantee that the nurse will have cultural awareness. Nurses must first understand their own cultural background and

Issues Now

Minority Nurses Needed for the Future of Nursing

Recruiting, retaining, and reshaping the role of minority nurses has been a primary concern of the health-care industry for almost a decade. Initiatives have been implemented by both the private sector and governmental agencies to increase the numbers of minority nurses and meet the needs of the ever-shifting client demographics.

Recent studies have shown that there has been a 10% increase in the number of minority nurses. The number of minority nurses increased at a faster rate than the overall number of RNs. Based on the estimated number of 2.5 million licensed RNs in the United States, the following percentages are found in each minority group:

- African American, 4.2 percent (107,500)
- Asian, 3.4 percent (86,000)
- Hispanic, 1.6 percent (40,600)
- Native American, 0.5 percent (12,000)

Hospitals have been the primary employer of minority nurses and recognize that their employment is a matter of survival. In the competition to attract clients, hospitals cannot afford to have clients feel uncomfortable because of cultural diversity issues. A recent survey showed that 88 percent of minority nurses are employed in nursing, whereas only 82 percent of nonminority nurses are. Also, 85 percent of minority nurses are working full-time, but that number drops to 70 percent for nonminority nurses.

Although hospitals and health care in general acknowledge the need for more minority nurses, some nurses are experiencing barriers to their career mobility. Although the core issues are not unlike those that all nurses experience—understaffing, frustration with paperwork and regulations, and unappreciative administration and physicians—they also feel that their ethnic background may be hindering their chance for promotion. Sometimes their capabilities are questioned because of their differences, and that is a big deterrent.

The role of minority nurses continues to develop as an issue for the future of health care. Not only are they necessary because of the changing demographics of the population, but many in the health-care system believe that it is a sound economic policy to have more minority nurses. To help recruit nurses and retain those who are already practicing, several organizations have been established that nurses can contact. The National Coalition of Ethnic Minority Nurses Association and the Tennessee Hospital Association's Council on Diversity are available for assistance.

Sources: Cooper, S: Diversity requires more from role of minority nurses. Oklahoma City Nursing Times, May 6, 2002, p 17.

explore the origins of their own prejudiced and biased views of others. Several tools have been developed to measure a person's cultural awareness.

Cultural awareness begins with an understanding of one's own cultural values and health-care beliefs. To those unfamiliar with a particular culture's health-care beliefs, many of the health-care practices may appear meaningless, strange, or even dangerous.

Beliefs about health care are based in part on knowledge and are often related to religious beliefs. For example, if a particular society has no knowledge of bacteria as a cause of infection, then antibiotics may seem useless in achieving a cure for the disease. On the other hand, if a society believes that illness is caused by evil spirits entering the body as the result of curses by witches or medicine men, then practices such as incantations; use of ritualistic objects like bones, feathers, or incense; and even blood-letting and purgatives to release the spirit from the body are logical approaches to achieving a cure.

Cultural Belief Systems

The Purpose of Tradition

Cultural belief systems are highly complex. For example, some Native American groups attributed twin births to witchcraft and believed that one of the twin infants had to die so the other might live. These beliefs and practices are usually kept as closely guarded secrets among the group's members, and there may even be some type of sanction or punishment for members who reveal the belief.

Many cultural beliefs develop over time from a trial-and-error process that has both benefits and drawbacks. For instance, several Native American tribes that live in the Western desert have developed the practice of keeping infants in cradle boards until they begin walking. This practice, from a safety viewpoint, protects the crawling infant from injury and bites from creatures that are commonly found in the desert, such as scorpions, rattlesnakes, and poisonous insects or lizards. However, the practice tends to delay the leg muscle development of the child and increases the incidence of hip dysplasia because of the child's position in the cradle board.

Some cultural beliefs have a primary purpose of explaining unusual or unpredictable events. For example, many traditional Vietnamese-Americans believe that mental illness results from some action that offended one or more of the gods. They also believe that a family member who is mentally ill brings disgrace on the family, and thus knowledge of the illness must be kept secret, especially from strangers. As a result, traditional shamans, or priest-doctors, are sought to attempt to appease the offended deity through rituals and prayers. Only with great reluctance will a traditional Vietnamese-American family seek therapy or medication for a mental illness.

Cultural Values

The several sources of the development of cultural values include religious beliefs, worldview and philosophy, and group customs. The values that underlie any particular culture are powerful forces that affect all aspects of a person's life, ranging from individual actions and decision-making to health-care behaviors and life-goal setting. Values, which are discussed in Chapter 7, are the ideals or concepts that give meaning to an individual's life. They are deeply ingrained, and most individuals will strongly resist any attempt to change their value structure.

Cultural values are neither right nor wrong; they exist in a culture as the result of a long-term process of development that can often be traced back to a need for group survival. However, when judged from the perspective of other cultures, they may seem strange or perhaps harmful. Because it makes nurses feel secure and even superior, there is a tendency to transfer to clients health-care expectations based on the nurse's own cultural framework. This approach often leads the nurse to fail when trying to change health-care behaviors.

> *The values that underlie any particular culture are powerful forces that affect all aspects of a person's life, ranging from individual actions and decision-making to health-care behaviors and life-goal setting.*

Recognizing Health-Care Practices

Changing the Client's Values

It is important to recognize that one of the primary functions of nurses is to change clients' values, particularly values about health care. It is not an easy task. The first step, always, is to recognize that the nurse comes from a particular culture that has its own set of health-care values. Like all values, these have developed over time and are dependent on the nurse's education, upbringing, religious beliefs, and cultural background.

The next step is to identify the culture of the client and recognize specific health-care practices that are both similar to and different from those of the nurse. The nurse must then make a decision about whether it is desirable or possible to change the client's values and if the end result would be worth the effort.

When Is Persuasion Appropriate?

For example, many cultures have strong values concerning pregnancy and the birth of children. In traditional Middle Eastern families, the birth process is valued as an event strictly involving women, and the father is usually not present to either witness or assist in the delivery. However, midwives and obstetric nurses from the current American culture place a high value on the father's participation in the birth event as a way of promoting stronger family ties and starting the bonding process as soon as possible. The nurse who takes care of a Middle Eastern family must decide whether or not to try to convince the father to stay in the delivery room during the delivery. In any event, the ultimate outcome remains relatively unchanged. Even without the father in the delivery room, the child is delivered safely, and only the bonding process with the father is delayed.

Some African cultures have discovered over time that a woman who delivers a small infant will have a much easier time during labor and delivery. Small infants usually have fewer traumatic birth defects, and there are fewer stillbirths and a higher maternal survival rate. In some traditional central African homeland settings where there is little skilled health care available, the value of having small infants helps in the survival of the group. The custom of feeding pregnant women only a corn-mush cereal throughout their pregnancies ensures small babies at birth.

In the United States, where good prenatal nutrition is highly valued, this traditional practice is seen as dangerous to both the mother and the infant. Poor prenatal nutrition has been related to developmental delays, mental retardation, and skeletal deformities in infants as well as maternal malnutrition that can lead to infectious diseases and inability to breast-feed. In this situation, changing such practices of traditional African American women would be rewarded by healthier babies and mothers.

Assessing Culture

Obtaining accurate cultural assessments can be time consuming and difficult. However, the only way nurses can avoid imposing their cultural values and practices on others, and develop plans of care based on their knowledge about others' beliefs and customs, is to make a concerted effort to obtain this information. Several cultural assessment tools for clients have been developed—some short and directed, others lengthy and complicated. One of the most thorough cultural assessments developed to date is based on Purnell's Model for Cultural Competence (Box 21.1). Although this tool is lengthy, it can provide a good overview of the client's culture. Nurses should not neglect completing an assessment of their own culture, as well.

Beginning the Assessment

Most busy nurses do not have the time to complete this assessment on every client from a different

Other common reasons for noncompliance among culturally diverse clients include the lack of external symptoms of disease, inconvenient or painful treatments, and lack of external support from family members or close friends.

Respect for Healing Traditions

The nurse first needs to ask the client what traditional treatments are used in dealing with this disease. In some cases, where the traditional treatments are similar to the ones used by the health-care facility, the nurse may be able to demonstrate this similarity to the client.

> *. . . if culturally based alternative treatments do not interfere with the prescribed treatment plan or threaten the client's health, they can be used simultaneously with the standard medical treatments.*

In other cases, the treatments may be very different. However, if culturally based alternative treatments do not interfere with the prescribed treatment plan or threaten the client's health, they can be used simultaneously with the standard medical treatments. For example, nurses who work in the Native American health-care system and hospitals have become accustomed to finding bone fragments, feathers, and leather medicine pouches in the beds of their clients.

Cultural Synergy

Nurses who work actively to develop cultural synergy tend to be more successful in the delivery of competent transcultural care. *Cultural synergy* is a term that implies that health-care providers make a commitment not only to learn about other cultures but also to immerse themselves in those cultures. Nurses achieve cultural synergy when they begin to selectively include values, customs, and beliefs of other cultures in their own worldviews. The first step in cultural synergy is the desire to know everything there is about another culture and to purposely establish relationships with individuals from other cultures.

More Alike Than Different

Closely related to cultural synergy is the recognition that cultures are much alike in many aspects. It seems that most books and publications written about cultural diversity present only the diversity of cultures and not the similarities. Although recognition of cultural differences is important, it should be just one step toward the ultimate realization that there are more similarities than differences among diverse cultures.

Many colleges offer courses in comparative religions identifying the many similarities of the fundamental beliefs that underlie the major religions. However, many college courses on cultural diversity have not evolved past the point of identifying cultural differences. Perhaps this is due in part to the salad bowl approach to cultural communication that exists in current society. Perhaps a new approach to acculturation, based on the similarities between cultures rather than on the differences, needs to be developed.

INFORMATION SOURCES FOR TRANSCULTURAL NURSING

From a Conference . . .

The recent explosion of interest in cultural diversity and transcultural nursing has led to a proliferation of literature on the topic. The origins of the current transcultural movement can be traced back to 1974, when a transcultural conference on communication and culture was held at the University of Hawaii School of Nursing. Following the success of this conference, a series of transcultural conferences were planned over the next year to bring together nurses, sociologists, anthropologists, and other social scientists to discuss issues that would eventually form the basis for transcultural nursing.

Not long after the Hawaii conference, the Transcultural Nursing Society was organized. It was incorporated in 1981 and began publishing its semiannual official journal, *Journal of Transcultural Nursing,* in 1989. It is now being published four times a year. In 1976, the American Nurses Association (ANA) recommended that multicultural content be included in nursing curricula. Since then, the ANA has organized the Council on Intercultural

Issues in Practice

Case Study
Cultural Conflict Within a Family

In 1990, Jose Bisigan, aged 87 years, and his wife Carmen, aged 85, sold their small restaurant and immigrated to Los Angeles from a small town in the Visayan region of the Philippines. They came to join their firstborn daughter, nurse Felicia, aged 54, her husband, and their three children, aged 10 to 18. Mr. Bisigan speaks limited English and is in a poststroke rehabilitation unit. Since the stroke, he has had mild aphasia, mild confusion, and bladder and bowel continence problems. His hypertension and long-standing diabetes are controlled with medication and diet. His wife, daughter, and grandchildren have been supportive of him during this first hospitalization experience. Mr. Bisigan's family has cooperated with the health team, often agreeing with minimal resistance to the prescribed treatment management. The rehabilitation team recommended subacute rehabilitation treatment as part of the discharge plan.

As a businessman and the elder in the family household, Mr. Bisigan is looked to for counsel by the immediate and extended family. Mr. Bisigan's status, however, has caused friction between Felicia and her husband, Nestor, an American-born Filipino who works as a machinist. Nestor has accused Felicia of giving excessive attention to her mother and father. Felicia's worries about her parents' health have made Nestor very resentful. He has increased his already daily "outings with the boys." Felicia maintains a full-time position in acute care and a part-time night shift position in a nursing home.

Mr. Bisigan's discharge is pending, and a decision must be made before Medicare coverage runs out. Felicia has to consider the possible choices available to her father and the family's circumstances and expectations. Mrs. Bisigan, who is being treated for hypertension, has always deferred decisions to her husband and is looking to Felicia to make the decisions. Because of her work schedule, the absence of a responsible person at home, her mother's health problems, and intergenerational friction, Felicia considers nursing home placement. She is, however, reluctant to broach the subject with her father, who expects to be cared for at home. Mrs. Bisigan disagrees with putting her husband in a nursing home and is adamant that she will care for her husband at home.

Felicia delayed talking to her father until the rehabilitation team requested a meeting. At the meeting, Felicia indicated that she could not bring herself to present her plan to put her father in a nursing home because of her mother's objection and her own fear that her father will feel rejected. Feeling very much alone in resolving the issue about nursing home placement, she requested the team to act as intermediary for her and her family.

- Identify cultural family values that contribute to the conflicts experienced by each family member.
- Identify a culturally competent approach the team can use when discussing nursing home placement with the Bisigans.

(continued)

Issues in Practice (continued)

- How might the rehabilitation program be presented to Mrs. Bisigan and still allow her to maintain her spousal role?
- Discuss at least three communication issues in the family that are culture-bound and suggest possible interventions.
- Identify psychocultural assessments that should be done by the rehabilitation team to have a greater understanding of the dynamics specific to this family.
- Identify health promotion counseling that might be discussed with the Bisigans' grandchildren.
- Identify and explain major sources of stress for each member of this household.

Source: Purnell, LD, and Paulanka, BJ: Transcultural Health Care. F.A. Davis, Philadelphia, 1998, pp 269–270, with permission.

Nursing, which publishes the *Intercultural Nursing Newsletter.*

. . . to a Specialty
Since the 1980s, more and more universities and colleges have started offering graduate degrees in transcultural, cross-cultural, and international nursing. Graduates are now able to become certified transcultural nurses (CTNs) by completing oral and written examinations offered by the Transcultural Nursing Society. Nurses do not need to be from minority groups to obtain the CTN.

Society has not remained stagnant during this period of development and organization. Growing numbers of immigrants, changing governmental regulations, and grassroots movements all have contributed to the pressure placed on nursing to recognize and effectively care for clients from different cultures.

Conclusion

The major changes in U.S. demographics that began in the 1980s—and have been accelerating ever since—require nurses to provide culturally sensitive care. A fundamental belief of professional nursing holds that all individuals are to be cared for with respect and dignity regardless of culture, beliefs, or disease process. Therefore, nurses must actively seek multicultural education.

However, nurses need to keep in mind that cultural assessments and decisions about care are relative to the nurse's personal experiences, beliefs, and culture. There is a natural tendency to unconsciously stereotype individuals from other cultures on the basis of one's internal value system. There is also a tendency to batch all individuals from one culture into a single group, when in reality there may be wide variations within the group.

It is a well-accepted belief that nurses who value cultural diversity will deliver higher-quality care. Nurses who have a high level of cultural knowledge and sensitivity maximize their nursing interventions when they become coparticipants and client advocates for individuals who might otherwise be lost in an impersonal health-care system. Only when nurses can understand the client's perspective, develop an open style of communication, become receptive to learning from clients of other cultures, and accept and work with the ambiguities inherent in the care of multicultural clients will they become truly culturally competent health-care providers.

Bibliography

Anderson, K: Teaching cultural competence using an exemplar from literal journalism. Nursing Education 43(6): 253–260, 2004.

Aroian, K: Effective, efficient and equitable health care: What can cultural diversity teach us about sacred cows. Journal of Professional Nursing 20(6): 349–351, 2005.

Batnardi, M, and Perkel, L: Learning achievement programs: Fostering student cultural diversity. Nurse Educator 30(1): 17–21, 2005.

Brennan, S: Cultural immersion through ethnography: The lived experience and group process. Journal of Nursing Education 43(6): 285–288, 2004.

Briesacher, B, et al.: Racial and ethnic disparities in prescription coverage and medication use. Health Care Finance 25(2): 63–76, 2004.

Carol, R: Overcoming bias in the nursing workplace. Minority Nurse Winter, 28–33, 2005.

Carter, M: The ABCs of staffing decisions. Nursing Management 36(6): 16, 2004.

De Chesnay, M: Caring for the Vulnerable: Perspective in Nursing Theory, Practice and Research. Jones & Bartlett, Boston, 2005.

Flowers, D: Culturally competent nursing care: A challenge for the 21st century. Critical Care Nurse 24(4): 46–50, 2004.

Hascup, VA: Nursing out cultural stew. Advance for Nurses. 2006. www.advanceweb.com.

Health care disparities continue among minorities, the poor says HHS. Medical Ethics Advisor 20(2): 13–16, 2004.

Johnson, L: The role of cultural competency in eliminating health disparities. Minority Nurse Winter, 52–55, 2005.

Leininger, M: Culture Care Diversity & Universality: A Worldwide Nursing Theory, ed. 2. Jones & Bartlett, Boston, 2005.

Leishman, J: Perspectives of cultural competence in health care. Nursing Standard 19(11): 33, 2004.

Linnard-Palmer, L: Parents' refusal of medical treatment for cultural or religious beliefs: An ethnographic study of health care professionals' experiences. Journal of Pediatric Oncology Nursing 22(1): 48–57, 2005.

Marquand, B: Till death do us part. Minority Nurse Summer, 22–26, 2007.

Marquand, B: On the case. Minority Nurse Winter, 34–38, 2005.

Nokes, K, et al.: Does service learning increase cultural competency, critical thinking and civil engagement? Nursing Education 44(2): 65–71, 2005.

Purnell, LD, and Paulanka, BJ: Transcultural Health Care. F.A. Davis, Philadelphia, 1998.

Racial/ethnic and gender diversity in nursing education. Southern Regional Education Board, Council on Collegiate Education for Nursing, 2002.

Raiger, J: Applying a cultural lens to the concept of burnout. Journal of Transcultural Nursing 16(1): 71–76, 2005.

Spector, R: Cultural Care: Guide to Heritage Assessment and Health Traditions, ed. 3. Prentice Hall, Englewood Cliffs, New Jersey, 2004.

Spector, R: Cultural diversity in health and illness, ed 6. Prentice Hall, Englewood Cliffs, New Jersey, 2004.

Terhone, C: From desegregation to diversity: How far have we really come? Journal of Nursing Education 43(5): 195–196, 2004.

Williams, D: Recruiting men into nursing school. Minority Nurse Winter, 56–60, 2006.

22

Developments in Current Nursing Practice

Barbara Bellfield
Joseph T. Catalano

Learning Objectives
After completing this chapter, the reader will be able to:

- Discuss the nurse's role in forensics, bioterrorism, disasters, entrepreneurship, legal consulting, and case management.
- Discuss ways in which to develop a nurse-run business.
- Identify factors that indicate the need for case management.
- Discuss the importance of the nurse's early recognition of a bioterrorist attack.
- Give examples of organizations that nurses can become involved in to provide assistance in the event of a disaster.

NEW ROLES FOR THE NURSE

The profession of nursing is dynamic and ever-changing. Nursing roles evolve and develop in response to societal needs. This chapter will discuss the new and exciting practice roles in nursing. Included will be a discussion of forensic nursing, bioterrorism and disaster nursing, nurse entrepreneurs, nurse case managers, and legal nurse consultants.

FORENSIC NURSING

Forensic nursing is an emerging field that forms an alliance between nursing, law enforcement, and the forensic sciences. The term *forensic* means anything belonging to, or pertaining to, the law.

An Emerging Discipline
Forensic nursing, as defined by the International Association of Forensic Nurses (IAFN), is "the application of nursing science to public or legal proceedings; the application of the forensic aspects of health care combined with the bio-psycho-social education of the registered nurse in the scientific investigation and treatment of trauma and/or death of victims and perpetrators of abuse, violence, criminal activity and traumatic accidents." Forensic nurses provide a continuum of care to victims and their families beginning in the emergency room or crime scene and leading to participation in the criminal investigation and the courts of law.[1]

Nurses, particularly emergency room nurses, have long provided care to victims of domestic violence, rape, and other injuries resulting from criminal acts. They have collected, preserved, and documented legal evidence, often without formal training. It was not until 1992 that the term *forensic nursing* was coined.

> " *Nurses, particularly emergency room nurses, have long provided care to victims of domestic violence, rape, and other injuries resulting from criminal acts.* "

What Do You Think?

Do you know any nurses who are involved in forensic nursing? Is this a role that you might be interested in pursuing after graduation?

The IAFN was founded in the summer of 1992. Seventy-four nurses, primarily sexual assault nurse examiners, came together in Minneapolis, Minnesota, to develop an organization of nurses who practice within the arena of the law. This very diverse group includes, but is not limited to, legal nurse consultants, forensic nurse death investigators, forensic psychiatric nurses, and forensic correctional nurses.

The organization's membership tripled within its first year. By 1999, the IAFN had more than 1800 members. The American Nurses Association (ANA) recognized forensic nursing as a subspecialty in 1995, and the Scope and Standards of Forensic Practice was established in 1997. As this is a new field, the definition of the forensic nurse role is continuing to evolve. With the formation of the IAFN and the designation of the forensic specialty, nurses were given an identity and recognition for a role they have long been performing.

Forensic nurses specialize in several diverse roles and are beginning to find employment in a variety of settings. These roles include the sexual assault nurse examiner (SANE), the forensic nurse death investigator, the forensic psychiatric nurse, the forensic correctional nurse, and the legal nurse consultant.

Sexual Assault Nurse Examiner (SANE)

A SANE is a registered nurse trained in the forensic examination of sexual assault victims. A SANE has an advanced education and clinical preparation specialized in this area.

Clients who have been sexually assaulted have unique medical, legal, and psychological needs. As crime victims, they require a competent collection of evidence that assists in both investigation and prosecution of the incident. Their bodies and clothing become a key part of the crime scene and are essential for collection of evidence. The SANE offers the type of compassionate care that is often lacking among law enforcement personnel. The care provided by SANEs has been designed to preserve the victim's dignity and reduce psychological trauma. Research data collected in recent years indicate that the SANE's comprehensive forensic evidence collection leads to more effective investigations and more successful prosecutions.[2]

Usually SANEs work in a hospital or emergency room with other members of a sexual assault response team (SART). The other team members may include physicians, law enforcement personnel, social workers, child/adult protective service workers, and therapists.

In their training, SANEs learn all aspects of the care of sexually assaulted clients. Their responsibilities include interviewing the victim, completing the physical exam, collecting specimens for forensic evidence, and documenting the findings. They also provide emotional support for victims and family members. When the case goes to court, the SANE testifies as an expert legal witness about how evidence was collected and the physical and psychological condition of the client. The SANE may offer an opinion as to whether a crime occurred.

To become a SANE, an RN must complete an adult/adolescent SANE education program. These programs are available through a traditional university setting and online. The training includes either a minimum of 40 contact hours of instruction or three semester units of classroom instruction by an accredited school of nursing. Trainees also must have clinical supervision until they demonstrate competency in SANE practice. After successful completion of the program, the candidate is able to take the certification examination.

Legal Nurse Consultant

The legal nurse consultant is a licensed RN who critically evaluates and analyzes health-care issues in medically related lawsuits. Because the legal system is involved, nurses acting as consultants are considered to be practicing forensics. Nurses uniquely combine their medical expertise with legal knowledge to assess compliance with accepted standards of health-care practice.

Legal nurse consultants work in collaboration with attorneys and other legal and health-care professionals. They may have independent practices, work in the hospital setting in risk management, or be employed by law firms or health insurance companies.

The following is a list of activities performed by legal nurse consultants that distinguishes their specialty practice:

1. Drafting legal documents under the supervision of an attorney
2. Interviewing witnesses
3. Providing education to attorneys and other involved parties on health-care issues and standards
4. Researching nursing literature, standards, and guidelines as they relate to issues within a particular case
5. Reviewing, analyzing, and summarizing medical records
6. Identifying and conferring with expert witnesses
7. Assessing causation and issues of damages as they relate to the case
8. Developing a case strategy in collaboration with other members of the legal team
9. Providing support during the legal proceedings
10. Educating and mentoring other RNs in the practice of legal nurse consulting[3]

Forensic Nurse Death Investigator

The role of the nurse death investigator is to advocate for the deceased. In general, a death investigator is a professional with experiential and scientific knowledge who can accurately determine the cause of death. The forensic nurse death investigator is an RN with specialized education who is functioning in the death investigator's role.

The forensic nurse death investigator may assume several different titles such as forensic nurse investigator, death investigator, or deputy coroner. In some areas of the country, nurses actually practice as coroners. In the United States, there are currently no standard definitions of "nurse death investigator" or any national credentialing or education requirements. Each region of the country specifies the requirements in its own jurisdictions.

The basic knowledge and skills in which all nurses are educated, such as physical assessment,

> *Legal nurse consultants work in collaboration with attorneys and other legal and health-care professionals. They may have independent practices, work in the hospital setting in risk management, or be employed by law firms or health insurance companies.*

Issues in Practice

If You Were the Nurse on Duty, What Would You Do?

Below are scenarios that exemplify typical situations for the nurse in general practice. Identify your probable response. Critically analyze each situation in terms of what you know and do not know. What types of facts or skills are not part of your current knowledge base?

You are working on a maternity unit when a woman who is an inmate from a correctional institution is admitted in an advanced stage of labor. A correctional officer is in attendance; the woman is shackled at the feet and hands. As she is wheeled to the labor room, you note that the client has had 10 previous pregnancies and four live births.

- What factors make the care of this woman different from that of other pregnant women?
- Is she dangerous?
- How do you maintain confidentiality with this client?
- As an offender in custody, does she surrender any rights?

You work in a hospital setting that is experiencing an increase in workplace violence. Perpetrators of street, child, and domestic violence often follow their victims to the hospital and continue to pose a significant threat to the whole hospital community. It is important to assess the potential for violence.

- How will you contribute to the reduction of risk in the workplace?
- Identify risk factors and cues for violence.
- How would you implement strategies to assist violence management in the acute care setting?

A halfway house for paroled offenders is due to be constructed in your community. Residents are angry and afraid to have ex-convicts living in their neighborhood. A town meeting is scheduled in which the issue will be discussed. Does nursing have anything to contribute to the discussion?

- What do we know about mentally ill offenders, sex offenders, perpetrators of domestic violence, and others?
- What is the therapeutic outcome for those mentally ill offenders who have completed rehabilitation programs?
- What is the risk to the community?
- What stress management strategies are helpful to a community?

You work at a junior high school, providing sex education and health promotion programs for young teenagers. You notice that more and more young people are wearing gang colors and using gang-related language and hand signals.

- How does this affect your work?
- Does this change your priorities?
- Are there referrals or strategies that should be initiated because of the gang affiliations of your students?

pharmacology, anatomy, physiology, growth, and development, are minimum requirements for the death investigation role. This nursing knowledge allows the investigator to sort out factors involved in a death. Nurses also learn advanced communication skills and knowledge of the grief process during their education. These skills are required for notifying next of kin and interviewing witnesses.[4]

Forensic nurse death investigators have a number of responsibilities. They respond to scenes of deaths or accidents and work in collaboration with law enforcement. At the scene, they examine the body, pronounce death, and take tissue and blood samples. They take pictures of the body and evidence at the scene. Nurse death investigators must be able to recognize and integrate other evidence collected during the investigation, such as patterns of injury, types of wounds, and estimated time of death. They are responsible for record keeping and arranging for the transport of the body to the morgue or to the coroner's office to undergo autopsy for further examination. Nurse death investigators work with the forensic pathologist to collect additional evidence in the lab during the autopsy.

What Do You Think?

Have you ever been involved in a court case or lawsuit? What was your role? How would being a nurse trained in legal issues have changed what you did or said?

Forensic Psychiatric Nurse

Forensic psychiatric nurses work with individuals who have mental health needs and who have entered the legal system. These nurses generally practice in state psychiatric institutions, jails, and prisons.

Nurses in this role perform physical and psychiatric assessments and develop care plans for the clients entrusted to their care. At the most basic level, forensic psychiatric nurses assist clients with self-care, administer medical care and treatment, and monitor the effectiveness of the treatment. Psychiatric interventions are developed to promote coping skills and improve mental health in a therapeutic environment.[5]

Forensic psychiatric nurses may also have advanced practice certification. Registered nurses who have master's degrees in psychiatric–mental health nursing practice as clinical nurse specialists or nurse practitioners. Nurses in this role are able to diagnose and treat individuals with psychiatric disorders and often are allowed to prescribe medications. They may function as primary care medical and mental health providers, psychotherapists, and consultants. Advanced practice forensic psychiatric nurses may practice independently, in mental health centers, state facilities, and health maintenance organizations (HMOs).

Forensic Correctional Nurse

Correctional facilities reflect the demographics of the general population, with an increasingly aging incarcerated population who have age-related health-care problems. Forensic correctional nurses provide health care for inmates in correctional facilities such as juvenile centers, jails, and prisons. They manage acute and chronic illness, develop health-care plans, dispense medications, and perform health screenings and health education. Forensic correctional nurses conduct psychiatric assessments and respond to emergency situations. The role of the forensic correctional nurse offers a high level of autonomy compared with other nursing roles.

Evolving Requirements

There is no official certification as a forensic nurse in the United States except for the SANE certification. Many nurses working in forensic roles believe certification requirements will develop as the specialty of forensic nursing continues to evolve and becomes better defined. In the near future, nursing education will be required to develop classes that teach forensic nursing as a part of their curriculum.

NURSE ENTREPRENEUR

Should You Be Your Own Boss?

An entrepreneur is someone who establishes and runs his or her own business. A nurse entrepreneur starts a business by combining nursing experience and knowledge with business knowledge. Starting a business can be risky financially and certainly is far different from the nurse's traditional role as an employee in an institution.

The role of the forensic correctional nurse offers a high level of autonomy compared with other nursing roles.

However, nurses are educated to think independently and are sometimes willing to take risks for the benefit of their clients. As professionals who can translate their expertise and confidence into new arenas, nurses are capable of achieving personal and financial success running their own businesses.[6]

Historically, nurse-run businesses have usually focused on temporary staffing agencies, nursing education, or consultant roles. Nurse entrepreneurs can also include nurse attorneys, nurse case managers, nurse educators, nurse death investigators, nurse midwives, nurse paralegals, psychiatric nurses, legal nurse consultants, and sexual assault nurses. Nurse practitioners in rural areas set up their own primary care clinics and provide care for populations who do not have access to any other type of primary care.

Assess Your Nursing Skills

In making the decision to start a business, nurses need to first assess their nursing experience to determine what type of business would be appropriate for their skill and knowledge levels. For example, a SANE may contract services to emergency rooms or law enforcement agencies. A critical care nurse may start a home care agency offering high-tech services. Nurses may develop self-defense courses they can market to high-risk professions, such as forensic psychiatric and forensic correctional nurses.

After nurses determine what skills and knowledge they possess, they need to develop a plan on how to establish the business. A basic level of knowledge about finances and the business start-up process is essential for success. The hopeful entrepreneur needs to consider the customer who will be seeking his or her services, what customers need and desire, what start-up costs will be, and who the competition may be. Answering these questions will allow the nurse to assess the potential success of the business.[7]

Any nurse can start a business. Generally, no advanced degrees are required unless the business involves diagnosis and treatment. Key qualities needed for success are a high degree of self-motivation and a passion for the business to succeed. Nurse entrepreneurs are limited only by their creativity and desire to succeed.

CASE MANAGEMENT

The Case Management Society of America (CMSA) defines case management as ". . . a collaborative process of assessment, planning, facilitation and advocacy for options and services to meet an individual's health needs through communication and available resources to promote quality, cost-effective outcomes."[7] Effective collaboration among all members of the health-care team is essential to meet the needs of clients in today's complex heath-care system.

A Care Coordinator

Nurse case managers act as advocates for clients and their families by coordinating care and linking the client with the physician, other members of the health-care team, resources, and the payer. The goal of the nurse case manager is to help the client obtain high-quality, cost-effective care while decreasing the duplication and fragmentation of care. Research data indicate that active participation by a nurse case manager in the care of a client positively affects the outcomes experienced by the client.

Nurses are uniquely prepared by their education and professional experiences to fulfill the role of case manager. The holistic health-care approach has been an underlying principle of nursing care since the time of Florence Nightingale. Nurses have experience in arranging referrals, providing client education, and acting as a liaison between physicians and specialty care.

Any client who may face challenges regarding care and recovery can benefit from case management. Included are hospitalized clients, those with complex medical conditions, those requiring specialty care, and those who have personal or psychological circumstances that may interfere with recovery. Factors that indicate the need for a nurse case manager include:

1. A complex treatment plan that requires coordination or a plan that is unclear
2. An injury or illness that may permanently prevent the client from returning to a previous level of health
3. A pre-existing medical condition that may complicate or prolong recovery
4. A need for assistance in accessing health-care resources
5. Environmental stressors that may interfere with recovery

Physicians Catch Up

The Case Management Society of America Standards of Practice for Case Management cites the physician and case manager collaboration as essential for successful case management.[8] Although recent research shows that clients benefit from case management, it has been underused by physicians. Case managers and physicians met in 2003 to identify barriers to the use of case management and to explore ways to increase the use of case managers. One result of this meeting was the development of the Consensus Paper of 2003 Physician and Case Management Summit: Exploring Best Practices in Physician and Case Management Collaboration to Improve Patient Care. This paper identified both barriers and ways to promote effective, collaborative use of case management by physicians (Box 22.1).

The research that attributes improved client outcomes directly to case management is compelling. It appears that nurse case managers will continue to expand their role in the health-care system of the future.

BIOTERRORISM

An Acute Health Issue

Bioterrorism is the use of microorganisms with the deliberate intent of causing infection to achieve military or political goals. Biological weapons are relatively easy and inexpensive to produce. The use of microorganisms is a particularly effective means of killing large numbers of people. After being released, microorganisms can go undetected for an extended period because their effects are not immediate and the initial symptoms are often nonspecific or "flu-like." Person-to-person transmission may continue for days or even weeks before the source is detected.

> *Nurse case managers act as advocates for clients and their families by coordinating care and linking the client with the physician, other members of the health-care team, resources, and the payer.*

Box 22.1

Collaboration of Case Managers and Physicians

Barriers to the Use of Case Managers by Physicians
1. Lack of resources and financial incentives in medical practice to integrate case management
2. Resistance to change by, and time pressures imposed on, physicians
3. Insufficient awareness of the role of the case manager among physicians and consumers
4. Insufficient promotion of their value by case managers
5. Lack of evidence of the value of case management

Facilitators of the Use of Case Managers by Physicians
1. Recognition, understanding, and use of case management
2. Standardization of the education and definition of case managers
3. Education for physicians and consumers about case management
4. Compensation for physicians who use case manager services
5. Education of clients in accessing case management
6. Validated research on the effectiveness of case management
7. Recognition of the CMSA Standards of Practice for legitimacy and credibility of the nurse case manager role.

The vulnerability of the United States to a biological attack became painfully apparent with the delivery of anthrax spores through the postal system as an infective agent after the 9/11 attacks.[9] The need to protect a vulnerable American population from further terrorist attacks became an acute public health issue. Also, the offensive biological weapons programs of the former Soviet Union produced some weaponized biological agents that cannot be located; this knowledge has increased the national anxiety level concerning bioterrorism in the United States.

Since 1998 the ANA has worked in conjunction with the American College of Emergency Physicians (ACEP) to develop strategies for health-care providers to use in responding to nuclear, biological, and chemical incidents.

Early Recognition
For nurses and other clinicians, the key to an effective response is training in the early recognition of a bioterrorist attack. Recognizing and treating outbreaks as early as possible is critical for rapid implementation of measures to prevent the spread of disease. Response to bioterrorist attacks is similar to the traditional public health response to naturally occurring outbreaks of communicable diseases, but the focus must be on early detection. However, early recognition is challenging because terrorists may use weaponized biological agents that cause highly variable initial symptoms.

Clinical Presentation
Nurses and other clinicians must be familiar with the specific symptoms and clinical syndromes caused by bioterrorism agents (Box 22.2). One of the first indications of a biological attack will be an increase in the number of individuals seeking care from Public Health Agencies, primary care providers, and emergency rooms. Hospitals, doctors, nurses, and public health professionals will be on

Box 22.2

Epidemiological Clues to a Biological Attack

Presence of a large epidemic

Unusually severe disease or unusual routes of exposure

Unusual geographic area, unusual season, or absence of normal vector

Multiple simultaneous epidemics of different diseases

Outbreak of zoonotic disease

Unusual strains of organisms or antimicrobial-resistant patterns

Higher attack rates in persons exposed

Credible threat, as determined by authorities, of biological attack

Direct evidence of biological attack

the front lines of any attack. A heightened level of suspicion, plus knowledge of the relevant epidemiological clues, should help in the recognition of changes in illness patterns.[10]

Biological Agents

The Centers for Disease Control and Prevention (CDC) developed a list of biological agents that are considered the most likely to be used in a bioterrorist attack (Table 22.1). Infective agents were included for their ability to produce widely disseminated infections, high mortality rates, potential for major public health impact, and ability to cause panic and social disruption. Those that require special action for public health preparedness were also included. Category A agents possess the highest immediate risk for use as biological weapons; category B agents pose the next highest risk. Category C agents have a potential for use, but are not considered an immediate risk as biological weapons.

Effective Response

Identification and Management

In the event of a widespread bioterrorism attack, nurses in all levels and types of

health-care settings have the potential to become involved. To develop a prompt and effective response, nurses and other health-care providers must know the modes of transmission, incubation periods, symptoms, and communicable periods of these diseases as outlined by the CDC.

Once a potential outbreak is detected, it must be brought to the attention of the appropriate health-care agencies or specialist in infective diseases. All nurses should have accurate around-the-clock information on the resources available for their geographic area. Once appropriate notifications have been made, nurses will use their skills of clinical evaluation and history taking to identify the infective organism, mode of transmission, and source of exposure. In addition, nurses play a critical role in managing post-exposure prophylaxis and its complications, as well as psychological and mental health problems brought on by the event.

What Do You Think?

Have you received any specialized training in disaster or bioterrorism preparedness? If you have, how does it make you better able to care for victims of disaster or bioterrorism? If you have not, why? Do you feel prepared to care for these victims?

_____

_____

_____

_____

_____

_____

_____

_____

_____

_____

_____

_____

_____

> *Since 9/11 the need to protect a vulnerable American population from further terrorist attacks has become an acute public health issue.*

Response Training

The American College of Emergency Physicians in alliance with the American Nurses Association submitted a

Table 22.1   Critical Biological Agent Categories for Public Health Preparedness

Category	Biological Agent	Disease
A: Highest immediate risk	*Variola major*	Smallpox
	Bacillus anthracis	Anthrax
	Yersinia pestis	Plague
	Clostridium botulinum (botulinum toxins)	Botulism
	Francisella tularensis	Tularemia
	Filoviruses and arenaviruses (Ebola and Lassa virus)	Viral hemorrhagic fevers
B: Next-highest risk	*Coxiella burnetii*	Q fever
	Brucella species	Brucellosis
	Burkholderia mallei	Glanders
	Burkholderia pseudomallei	Melioidosis
	Alphaviruses	Encephalitis (VEE, EEE, WEE*)
	Rickettsia prowazekii	Typhus fever
	Toxins (e.g., ricin, staphylococcal enterotoxin B)	Toxic syndromes
	Chlamydia psittaci	Psittacosis
	Food-safety threats (e.g., Salmonella species, *E. coli* 0157:H7)	Salmonellosis Diarrheal illness, sepsis, hemolytic uremic syndrome
	Water-safety threats (e.g., *Vibrio cholerae, Cryptosporidium parvum*)	Cholera Cryptosporidiosis
C: Potential, but not an immediate risk	Emerging-threat agents (e.g., Nipah virus, hantavirus)	

*EEE = eastern equine encephalitis; VEE = Venezuelan equine encephalitis; WEE = western equine encephalitis.

list of recommendations to the Health and Human Services Office of Emergency Preparedness in April 2001. Included was the recommendation that all basic nurse education programs include information on how to respond to mass casualty events. The task force also recommended that self-study modules and other types of specialty programs be developed for ER nurses that would contain more in-depth information on the detection and management of bioterrorism.

The ANA is actively involved in developing ways to better prepare nurses to respond to bioterrorist events. In collaboration with the Department of Health and Human Services, they established the National Nurses Response Team (NNRT). This joint effort was unveiled at the ANA's 2002 biennial convention.

Activation and Deployment

In the event that the president declares a bioterrorism state of disaster, the NNRT will be activated to respond by providing mass immunization or chemoprophylaxis to a population at risk. The NNRT, under the auspices of the Department of Health and Human Services, will be quickly deployed in response to a major national event.

The goal of the ANA and federal officials is to recruit 10 regional teams of 200 nurses. The ANA is working to recruit these nurse teams and will provide ongoing education to the NNRT in disaster response. The Department of Health and Human Services is responsible for the screening and processing of potential nurse team members after they have been recruited by the ANA.

When the NNRT teams are deployed, the members become "federalized," and the federal government will pay their salaries, reimbursement for travel, and housing costs during the duty period. In case of a terrorism disaster, the deployment will be limited to 2 weeks to minimize the impact on the nurses' employers.

The nursing profession faces serious challenges in the response to threats of bioterrorism. The nation is counting on nurses to play a vital role in bioterrorism preparedness and response. The public depends on nurses to be the frontline responders and to protect them from the effects of bioterrorism. Nurses must be able to communicate medical information and educate the public quickly after a crisis. It is imperative that the nursing profession train nurses in appropriate, effective responses to ensure the best outcome in a frightening, unfamiliar event.

DISASTER NURSING

The United States has witnessed an increase in terrorism-related disasters during the past decade. However, the vast majority of disasters are still considered natural. These range from the catastrophic failure of manmade structures, such as bridge collapses, to weather-related catastrophes, such as hurricanes and floods. Simply defined, a disaster is a catastrophic event that leads to a large number of injuries, displaced individuals, or major loss of life. The American Red Cross defines a disaster as ". . . an occurrence such as a hurricane, tornado, storm, flood, high water, wind-driven water, tidal wave, earthquake, drought, blizzard, pestilence, famine, fire, explosion, building collapse, commercial transportation wreck, or other situations that cause human suffering or create human needs that the victims cannot alleviate without substantial assistance."[11]

Many Roles for the Nurse

Every disaster poses its own unique challenges. The role of the nurse in a specific disaster depends on its nature and on the type and numbers of injuries. Although most nurses are familiar with the type of disaster aid provided by the Red Cross, they may assume many other roles when a disaster strikes. Often in disaster situations, nurses function outside their usual practice setting and may assume a variety of roles in meeting the needs of the disaster victims. Nurses must be able to perform under stressful and sometimes physically dangerous conditions.

After the hurricanes in Florida in 2005, large numbers of disabled and elderly clients who had been living in nursing homes and extended care facilities were displaced to schools and shelters. Nurses assumed the primary responsibility for caring for these individuals who, because they could not care for themselves and lacked essential medications, needed care at a level above what rescue workers could provide.

When the number of injured is very large, more than 1000, the incident is classified as a mass casualty, and multiple agencies, from the local to federal, become involved. Many times a nurse functions as a triage practitioner, assessing victims and prioritizing care for the best use of resources. However, in mass casualty situations, the traditional classification of clients into low risk, intermediate care, and immediate care is reordered. To provide care for the greatest numbers of victims, often workers give only palliative care to those with critical injuries, allowing more resources to be used for those with a better chance of surviving the disaster.

Nurses also provide direct treatment, which may be brief, or may be involved in more complex roles, such as mobile surgical units (Box 22.3).

Box 22.3
Responsibilities of the Disaster Nurse

Short term
1. Provides emergency medical assistance. Special attention is given to vulnerable groups, such as the handicapped, children, and the elderly.
2. Provides assistance in the mobilization of necessary resources such as food, shelter, medication, and water.
3. Works in collaboration with existing organizational structures and resources.

Long term
1. Provides assistance with resettlement programs and psychological, economic, and legal needs.
2. Partners with independent, objective media; local and national branches of government; international agencies; and nongovernmental organizations.

However, in the early stages of many disasters, nurses may find a lack of essential resources. Nurses have a long history of being able to improvise and get by with what is available, and a disaster will certainly challenge their creativity.

Disaster Phases

Preparing for Impact

Certain types of natural disasters are preceded by a warning period. For a tornado, this may range from a few minutes to as much as an hour; for hurricanes, it may be as long as several days. During the warning stage, also called the preimpact phase, the focus is on preparation for the aftereffects of the event. This preparation is primarily at the local level.

Even before a catastrophic event is predicted, communities in disaster-prone regions practice with disaster drills. These drills provide valuable training in a low-stress environment and identify the types of resources that may be needed during a disaster. This type of training helps identify unique risk situations for the community and builds the skill and knowledge disaster responders must have to meet the needs of the population. When the disaster becomes imminent, and a warning is issued, preparations such as evacuations are put into operation.

Communication is Critical

One key element, brought to the forefront by recent disasters, is the ability of the various agencies involved to communicate with each other. Fire and rescue, first responders, law enforcement, public health, and health-care services must be able to exchange essential information to provide the highest-level care possible. Good communication leads to a well-coordinated response. All agencies must have agreements in place and understand the role that each one is to play in the disaster. This preparation will eliminate the turf arguments sometimes seen among agencies. In rural areas, agreements with nearby communities also become important.

Planning for the news media and the flow of information is often overlooked in disaster preparations. Nurses are likely to hear about a disaster from breaking news reports before they learn about it through official channels. One fear that can become real is group panic. Generally, all information released from a health-care facility should go through the public relations representative or the designated spokesperson for the facility.

Before any information is released, it should be determined how the news will affect particular populations. Families of victims often cling to every word and may misinterpret what is being said.

Persons designated to speak for the health-care facility should have experience with public speaking and be able to convey the information clearly and in terms that the general public can understand. They should also be able to "think on their feet" when responding to questions. However, question-and-answer sessions should be severely limited, especially when national media are involved. When people are under stress or have high levels of anxiety, communication must be direct, honest, and to the point. Long technical explanations will only confuse the facts. The public should also be calmed by reassurances that everything possible is being done. Regular updates every 30 to 60 minutes, even if there is little new information, are helpful in reducing anxiety levels.

The following agencies can help with planning during the preimpact phase:

- Disaster Medical Assistance Team (DMAT): A group of frontline medical personnel, including nurses, who provide health care after a disaster. These may include terrorist, natural, or environmental disasters.
- Medical Reserve Corps: Part of the USA Freedom Corps, which was developed in 2002 in response to Americans' desire to volunteer and serve their communities in the wake of the 9/11 terrorist attacks.
- American Red Cross: Registered nurses can join their local Red Cross and receive specialized training in disaster and bioterrorism preparedness.
- Commission Corps Readiness Force: Deploys teams to respond to public health emergencies.[12]
- National Disaster Medical System (NDMS): Mobilizes comprehensive disaster relief and works closely with local fire, police, and emergency medical services. NDMS also uses volunteer disaster response teams called International Medical/Surgical Response Teams (IMSURTs), of which nurses are an essential component. The IMSURTs provide emergency medical services at any place in the world where there is a lack of resources.

The Impact Phase

When the actual disaster strikes, the impact phase begins. The goal during the impact phase is to respond to the disaster, activate the emergency response, and reduce the long-term effects of the disaster as much as possible. Activation of the emergency response plans developed during the preimpact phase mobilizes all agencies involved. Because fire, rescue, and police are usually the first on the scene, they provide and establish the command post from which all other efforts will be coordinated. Their goal is to identify and remove victims from dangerous situations, deal with unstable structures, and provide first aid to those who have been injured.

Because of the recent heightened concern over acts of terrorism, law enforcement may initially take control of the disaster until it can be determined that the cause was not a criminal act. Nurses working in the early stages of disasters sometimes feel frustrated by law enforcement officers, who may limit their ability to provide care. It is important to remember that law enforcement is concerned with identifying a crime and preserving evidence that may be used later in criminal prosecutions. The whole disaster area is considered a crime scene until released by law enforcement.

The Incident Management System (IMS) is an effective tool in bringing some order to the confusion that always surrounds any disaster event. Based on a military model, IMS is a hierarchy with a well-defined chain of command. At the top is the incident commander or manager, who is responsible for coordinating all rescue efforts. A "job sheet," really a vertical organizational chart, lists all the key people from all the key agencies involved. It also outlines the responsibilities of each person and agency and must be followed throughout the disaster event for the best coordination of emergency services. Most IMS plans now include hospitals within the service area. Information flows freely from the commander down to paramedics and from the street level back to the top.

Medical assistance is provided in hospitals, local clinics, or the field. Deployable Rapid Assembly Shelter Hospitals (DRASHs) are mobile shelters that can be used by the IMSURT team as a small independent hospital. The DRASH is designed with triage emergency care, intensive care units, and surgical rooms.

Protection for First Responders

Nurses and other first responders must always be aware of the potential dangers of any disaster. If the health-care providers become injured during rescue attempts, they can no longer provide care to the victims. As a result, protecting the lives and health of the first responders takes priority over rescue efforts. Because of the wide range of potential hazards, including chemicals such as nerve gas or toxins, biological substances, radioactive agents, and explosive devices, care providers must wear appropriate protective equipment. Images of rescue personnel wearing bulky white biohazard suits have become ingrained in the public consciousness. The biohazard suits, otherwise known as personal protective equipment, actually have a range of protective ability against many types of substances (Box 22.4).

> *Often in disaster situations, nurses function outside their usual practice setting and may assume a variety of roles in meeting the needs of the disaster victims. Nurses must be able to perform under stressful and sometimes physically dangerous conditions.*

Box 22.4
Protective Levels of Biohazard Suits

Level A: Resistant to all types of chemicals and biological and radioactive substances and is used in situations where splashing or exposure to unknown agents is possible. Totally encapsulates personnel and has its own internal air supply.

Level B: Has a hood but does not totally encapsulate personnel. Is splash resistant to most chemicals. Has its own internal air supply.

Level C: Has a hood but does not totally encapsulate personnel. Is less resistant to chemical penetration than previous levels. Equipped with a respirator that can filter out most chemical contaminants and biological and radioactive substances.

Level D: Used when there are no chemicals or agents that can affect the respiratory system or penetrate through the skin. Generally consists of a jump suit or scrub suit.

Source: Firstrespondernetwork.com

Most nurses have not received training in donning, wearing, or performing procedures in biohazard suits. If nurses find themselves in situations in which they may be required to wear such protection, it is important to recognize some of the limitations. The heavy gloves reduce manual dexterity significantly, and even routine procedures, such as starting IVs or dressing wounds, become extremely difficult if not impossible. The hood restricts peripheral vision and the plastic view plate may distort the visual field. Even cursory physical examination, including the ability to use a stethoscope, becomes more difficult. Nurses may also find that the suit itself causes claustrophobia. The unusual taste and smell of the self-contained breathing equipment have been known to cause nausea.

After exposure to any type of chemical, biological, or radioactive agent, personnel must go through a decontamination procedure. These procedures vary widely depending on the type of agent. They range from simply removing clothes and showering with water to extensive treatment with various neutralizing agents. Most emergency response teams have a decontamination tent that provides some privacy and contains the equipment necessary for thorough decontamination.

...AND THIS WILL BE THE NEW NURSING UNIFORM TO BE WORN AT ALL TIMES!

After the Disaster

The postimpact phase may begin as little as 72 hours after the incident and in some cases may last considerably longer. It may continue for years, as in the aftermath of hurricane Katrina in New Orleans. The activities focus on recovery, rehabilitation, and rebuilding. One of the key activities during the postimpact phase is the evaluation of the disaster preparations and of how rescue and recovery efforts could be improved.

Conclusion

Florence Nightingale wrote in 1859 that "no man, not even a doctor, ever gives any other definition of what a nurse should be than this 'devoted and obedient.' This definition would do just as well for a porter. It might even do for a horse!"[14] The profession of nursing has come a long way since Nightingale made the first efforts to move it out of its position of servitude to physicians.

Nursing is constantly evolving and defining itself as it strives to include expanded roles of practice. Of the many new and exciting roles for nurses, forensic, bioterrorism, disaster, entrepreneur, case management, and legal consultant have developed in response to the needs of society.

The tragic events of September 11, 2001, in New York City, Washington, DC, and Pennsylvania revealed how poorly prepared the United States was to deal with disasters. In response, legislation was enacted on federal and state levels that began to address the many issues associated with terrorist acts. Large sums of money were expended for the purchase of equipment and to train health-care workers to be better able to deal with a variety of potential disasters. Collaboration between groups that often had little to do with each other in the past became an essential component of these plans. The Department of Health and Human Services and the ANA have been working closely to educate nurses in disaster and bioterrorism responses. However, the country still remains woefully unprepared for major disasters, as was seen in the events following Hurricane Katrina.

Although nurses have practiced in these areas for many years, they are only now beginning to be recognized for the unique skills and qualities they bring to these roles. For example, the job description of an emergency room nurse has long included interviews and assessments of crime victims, collection and proper handling of evidence, and accurate and complete documentation of injuries and information provided by crime victims. In the role of client advocate, nurses have always been case managers through assessment of client needs, coordination of referrals for specialized or long-term care, and coordination of non-nursing services such as diet teaching and social services.

All nurses have the knowledge of anatomy, physiology, growth, and development that is required for the death examiner position. As more nurses seek the specialized training now available for many of these roles and obtain nationally recognized certification as a demonstration of their knowledge, they will gain acceptance as highly qualified and valuable members of these specialized health-care teams.

Issues in Practice

Authorization of Subspecialty Roles to Be Limited in Texas
Rethinking Advanced Practice

The Texas Board of Nurse Examiners is responsible for authorizing Advanced Practice Nurses (APNs) to practice as clinical nurse specialists or nurse practitioners in the state of Texas. The board bases its authorization on the individual's educational preparation. The board has expressed concerns regarding the increasing number of subspecialty areas in which nurses were seeking advanced practice authorization. Some of the areas of concern included ophthalmology, diabetes management, and forensics subspecialty. The primary concern cited by the board was that the educational preparation in the subspecialty areas may result in individuals who are not prepared to recognize a broad range of conditions and diseases because of the narrow focus of their training. They also expressed concerns that APNs may be unable to find employment because of the limitations of their training.

The board expressed its belief that subspecialty practices are valuable and should continue. They also believe, however, that it is in the best interest of the public that the APNs have a broad-based foundation to enter into practice. The subspecialty training is to be considered an additional expertise and will not require further recognition by the board.

In April 2003, the board requested that the Advanced Practice Nursing Advisory Committee (APNAC) review the APN titles that were currently recognized. They were to then advise the board of the titles that should continue to be recognized. The APNAC recommended that the board recognize only those titles for which there is a national certification examination specifically targeted to that role and to specialty areas that include broad-based educational preparation.

The committee also recommended a time-limited exception to these recommendations to individuals currently enrolled in advanced practice education programs. These exceptions are for roles that were currently recognized by the board, but would not continue to be recognized in the future. Under these exceptions, nurses could practice in their specialty area but only in the state of Texas. In July of 2004, the board voted to propose amendments relating to advanced practice titles and published these proposals to notify the public.

A Public Hearing

A public hearing regarding these proposed amendments was held October 20, 2004. Testimony was heard from 11 organizations and five individuals. Among the organizations represented were the ANA, the Texas Nurses Association, and the National Association of Clinical Nurse Specialists. The ANA expressed concerns that the nursing profession should not be wed to the idea that nurses should be generalists and not specialists. They stated that there are mechanisms already in place, such as defined scope and standards of practice, to protect clients and ensure appropriate training of APNs. They also stated that proposed amendments could be

(continued)

Issues in Practice (continued)

construed as restraint of trade and hamper the recognition of APNs as accepted members of health-care delivery systems.

Multiple concerns were expressed by other organizations attending the hearing. There were concerns that changes would have a negative economic impact on the state and discourage nurses from coming to Texas to practice. Some felt that enrollment numbers in nursing programs would decline. Concerns were expressed that the board was exceeding its authority. Others felt that the board had not adequately collaborated with national and state leaders in these roles before recommending the changes. Several of the attendees expressed agreement with the proposed amendments. Each comment expressed by those present at the hearing was responded to by the board. A summary of the hearing can be found at www.sos.state.tx.us.

The initially proposed amendments were withdrawn January 27, 2005. The board integrated some of the proposed changes made during the October 20, 2004, meeting. The changes that were made do not change the limitations on the APN roles that the board will recognize. On February 11, 2005, the Texas Board of Nurse Examiners formally approved amendments to Chapter 21, Advanced Practice Nurses, 22 TAC 222.2 and 221.7. These changes became effective January 1, 2006.

Sources: American Nurses Association: Texas Board of Nurse Examiners: Restrictive Proposed Changes to Limit Advanced Practice Specialties, 2004. www.nursingworld.org/gova/state.htm. Texas Register: Proposed Rules: Board of Nurse Examiners 30(6):635–645, 2005.

Critical Thinking Exercises

pplication of Human Rights

What information do you need to make a decision? The reader is encouraged to explore applications of human rights from the point of view of the victim and the perpetrator of the crime. Think about how the issue of human rights would be defined and protected in the following examples. What is the nurse's role?

- A married father of two, an upstanding member of the community, is accused of child molestation and is admitted to the unit for psychiatric evaluation and submission of tissue samples.
- A female inmate becomes pregnant in prison and does not want anyone to know who the father is.
- A young man has a history of substance abuse and mental illness. He refuses medication to control psychotic behavior and is confined in a forensic psychiatric facility because of the claim that he is incompetent to stand trial for car theft.
- A mother of an infant is being interviewed in a suspected child abuse case. She admits that she was sexually and physically abused as a child and throughout her marriage. The priority is to establish her role in the current charges involving injury of her 3-month-old infant.

References

1. Miller, PJ: Enhancing effectiveness in assessing forensic nursing staff competency. Journal of Forensic Nursing 3(2): 72–6, 86, 2007.
2. Campbell, R: Sexual assault nurse examiners' experiences providing expert witness court testimony. Journal of Forensic Nursing 3(1): 7–14, 2007.
3. Milazzo, VL: Legal nurse consultants keep the healthcare system healthy. Imprint 54(1): 46–49, 2007.
4. Kopishke, L: Forensics corner: Mitigation specialist: A natural role for the LNC. Journal of Legal Nurse Consultant 15(3): 22–23, 2004.
5. Whitehead, E: Assessment of risk and special observations in mental health practice: A comparison of forensic and non-forensic settings. International Journal of Mental Health Nursing 15(4): 235–241, 2006.
6. Elango, B: Barriers to nurse entrepreneurship: A study of the process model of entrepreneurship. Journal of the American Academy of Nurse Practitioners 19(4): 198–204, 2007.
7. O'Donnell, LT: Ethical dilemmas among nurses as they transition to hospital case management: Implications for organizational ethics. Professional Case Management 12(3): 160–169, 2007.
8. Better defining the role of public health nurses can improve disease surveillance necessary for bioterrorism preparedness. Nursing Economic 25(2): 120, 2007.
9. Syrett, JI: Will emergency health care providers respond to mass casualty incidents? Prehospital Emergency Care 11(1): 49–54, 2007.
10. Rogers, B, and Perce KH: Disaster preparedness: Occupational and environmental health professionals' response to Hurricanes Katrina and Rita. American Association of Hospital Nurses Journal 55(5): 197–207, 2007.
11. Weeks, SM: Mobilization of a nursing community after a disaster. Perspectives in Psychiatric Care 43(1): 22–29, 2007.
12. Reineck, C: The readiness estimate and deployability index: A self-assessment tool for emergency center RNs in preparation for disaster care. Topics in Emergency Medicine 26(4):349–356, 2004.
13. Goodnow, M: Outlines of Nursing History. W.B. Saunders, Philadelphia/London, 1935.
14. Nightingale, F: Notes on Nursing. Dover Press, Oxford, England, 1860.

Bibliography

Bemis, P: Being your own boss: It's more than just a pipe dream. Nursing Spectrum, 2004. www.communitynursingspectrum.com/Magazinearticles/articles.cfm?AID=9882.

Berkowitz, B: One year later: The impact and aftermath of September 11. Public Health Nursing Practice: Aftermath of September 11, 2001. Online Journal of Issues in Nursing 7(3), 2002. wwwnursingworld.org/ojin/topic19/ tcp19_4.htm.

Campbell, M: Nurse entrepreneur gives new face to care. Nursing Matters 15(5): 14, 22, 2004.

Chang, P: The development of intelligent, triage-based, mass-gathering emergency medical service PDA support systems. Journal of Nursing Resources 12(3): 227–235, 2004.

Cogar, S: The legal nurse consultant's role in defending law enforcement officers. Journal of Legal Nurse Consultant 15(1): 3–6, 2004.

Cox, E: Disaster nursing: New frontiers for critical care. Critical Care Nurse 24(3): 16–18, 20–24, 2004.

Hayward, M: Facing danger. Nursing Standard 19(3): 20–21, 2004.

Heitkemper, M: Clinical nurse specialists: State of the profession and challenges ahead. Clinical Nurse Specialist 18(3): 135–140, 2004.

Nash, D, et al.: Consensus paper of the 2003 Physician and Case Management Summit: Exploring Best Practices in Physician and Case Management Collaboration to Improve Patient Care. Case Management Society of America, 2003.

Pasqualone, G: Perspectives on the Future of Forensic Nursing. Online Forensic Nurse Magazine 2005. www.forensicnursemag.com/articles/3b1cover.html.

Wessling, S: The Case for Forensic Nursing. Minority Nurse.Com, 2003. www.minoritynurse.com/.

Young, C: Biological, chemical, and nuclear terrorism readiness: Major concerns and preparedness of future nurses. Disaster Management Response 2(4): 109–114, 2004.

Associations and Web Sites

American Academy of Forensic Sciences: www.aafs.org

American Association of Legal Nurse Consultants: www.aalnc.org

American College of Forensic Examiners International: www.acfei.com

American Forensic Nurses: www.amrn.com

American Psychiatric Nurses Association: www.apna.org

Forensic Nurse Magazine: www.forensicnursemag.com

International Association of Forensic Nurses: www.forensicnurse.org; www.iafn.org

Legal Nurse Consultant Certificate Program: www.continuing-legal@udel.edu

National Alliance of Sexual Assault Coalitions: www.taasa.org

National Association of Correctional Nursing: www.correctionalnursing.org

National Association of Independent Nurses: www.independentrn.com

National Commission on Correctional Healthcare: www.ncchc.org

National Nurses in Business Association: www.nnba.net

Nurse Entrepreneur Network: www.Nurse-Entrepreneur-Network.com

Nursing Entrepreneur: www.nursingentrepreneurs.com

Office for Victims of Crime: www.ojp.usdoj.gov/ovc

Office for Victims of Crime Resource Center: www.ncjrs.org

Public Health Functions Projects: www.health.gov. phfunctions/public.htm

Rape, Abuse and Incest National Network (RAINN): www.rainn.org

Sexual Assault Resource Service (SARS): www.sane-sart.com

Violence Against Women Office: www.ojp.usdoj.gov/vawo

23

Client Education: A Moral Imperative

Mary Abadie
Cynthia Bienemy
Joan Anny Ellis
Anita H. Hansberry
Sharon W. Hutchinson
Janet S. Rami

Sharon M. Bator
Sandra Brown
Betty L. Fomby-White
Jacqueline J. Hill
Anyadie Onu
Enrika K. Singleton

Learning Objectives

After completing this chapter, the reader will be able to:

- Explain the philosophical reason for using the term "client" rather than "patient."
- Describe the quality requirements for computer-based client health teaching.
- Discuss ways to enhance communication with different cultures.
- Discuss the basic literacy requirements for self-management of health care.
- Use the three domains in learning and the six domains in level of understanding to develop a client teaching plan.
- Discuss commonly used teaching strategies and methods appropriate for clients of all ages.
- Describe the nursing skills needed to provide appropriate client teaching.
- Compare the nursing process and teaching process for client teaching.

INTRODUCTION

Some indicators of the considerable growth of nursing as a profession include the expectations of nurses to provide client education, the increased emphasis on ethics, and the legal accountability for safe and high-quality nursing care. (See Chapters 7 and 9.) For example, 50 years ago, nurses were prohibited from teaching clients (then referred to as patients) in the U.S. hospital system without direct orders from physicians. Many physicians believed that client teaching in general was not relevant or effective, nor were there third-party payments available for client teaching.[1]

> *The jewel in the crown of nursing practice is without a doubt patient education.*
> S. Rankin and K. Stallings

In the current health-care system, client teaching is not only an expectation but an ethical and legal requirement. In recent years, several lawsuits have resulted from the failure of nurses to provide adequate client teaching (Box 23.1).

Physician authors advise clients to be "smart" and learn as much as possible about their health-care needs.[2] Expert nurses have modeled ways to incorporate client education as a priority in care,[3] and nurse theorists provide world views and theories imbued with the primacy of client education.

Box 23.1

Documenting What You Teach

Always document what you teach clients and their families and include their understanding of what you taught. The court in *Kyslinger versus United States* (1975) addressed the nurse's liability for client teaching. In this case, a Veterans Administration (VA) hospital sent a hemodialysis client home with an artificial kidney. The client eventually died (apparently while connected to the hemodialysis machine) and his wife sued, alleging that the hospital and its staff failed to teach her or her husband how to properly use and maintain a home hemodialysis unit.

After examining the evidence, the court ruled against the client's wife as follows: "During those 10 months that plaintiff's decedent underwent biweekly hemodialysis treatment on the units (at the VA hospital), both plaintiff and decedent were instructed as to the operation, maintenance, and supervision of said treatment. The Court can find no basis to conclude that the plaintiff or plaintiff's decedent were not properly informed on the use of the hemodialysis unit."

ETHICAL CONSIDERATIONS OF HEALTH SELF-MANAGEMENT

In the United States there has been a lack in adequate preparation for educating clients with self-management concerns, particularly clients with chronic illnesses. This lack of education is a serious violation of ethical responsibilities by health-care providers at all levels. It has the potential to produce harm, such as increased pain, disability, and premature death. For people in poverty conditions, the negative outcomes can be far worse. The unhealthy outcomes produced by lack of adequate education also cause greater monetary loss and greater loss of productivity. [4]

MANAGED CARE

Managed care, with its focus on clients' taking greater responsibility for their own health and self-care, has contributed to the increased need for client education.[5] The Institute of Medicine (IOM) has harshly criticized the chasm in quality of health care and strongly recommends placing clients at the center of control, with clients' choices based on the best information and knowledge available to them. The IOM established 10 rules, four of which relate to client teaching (Table 23.1).[6] For many years, the rules for redesigning health care to empower consumers and advocate for their specific health

Table 23.1 Building Responsiveness into Health-Care Systems

Rule	Description
1. Care is based on continuous healing relationships.	Clients should receive care whenever they need it and in many forms, not just face-to-face visits. The health-care system must be responsive at all times, and access to care should be provided over the Internet, by telephone, and by other means in addition to in-person visits.
2. Care is customized according to client needs and values.	The system should be designed to meet the most common types of needs, but should have the capability to respond to individual client choices and preferences.
3. The client is the source of control.	Clients should be given the necessary information and opportunity to exercise their chosen degree of control over health-care decisions that affect them. The system should be able to accommodate differences in client preferences and encourage shared decision-making.
4. Knowledge is shared and information flows freely.	Clients should have unfettered access to their own medical information and to clinical knowledge. Clinicians and clients should communicate effectively and share information.

needs have been backed by many nursing theorists and by nursing research.[4,7]

The Joint Commission on Accreditation of Healthcare Organizations (JCAHO) has taken steps to regulate client teaching because it is essential to high-quality care. Not only do JCAHO representatives make unannounced visits, they also look for evidence that education standards are being met.[2] The JCAHO Standards PC.6.1 requires the hospital staff to serve as critical resources by acting as skilled client educators. Additionally, JCAHO determines whether learning activities relate to assessment of the client's learning needs and any areas in which the client would like more information. The standard requires all providers to communicate whether the client's teaching needs are being met (Box 23.2).[5]

Box 23.2

JCAHO Focus on Standard PC.6.1

Standard
- Client receives appropriate education and training specific to needs.

Rationale
- Clients are given sufficient information to make decisions and to take responsibility for self-management. Families are educated to improve outcomes.

Elements of Performance
- Education is appropriate to client's needs
- Cultural and religious beliefs, emotional barriers, motivation, physical or cognitive barriers to communication are assessed.

Educational Content
- Plan for care, treatment, services
- Basic health practices and safety
- Safe and effective medication use
- Nutrition and diet, oral health
- Use of equipment or supplies
- Pain assessment and management
- Habilitation/rehabilitation toward maximum independence

Source: Joint Commission on Accreditation of Healthcare Organizations, 2005, pp C–26, C–27.

IMPLICATIONS OF TECHNOLOGY

Electronic Records
Electronic charting systems currently help track the teaching standards recommended by JCAHO and IOM. As is shown in Table 23.1, the IOM suggests that care should be continuous, customized to each client, and keep the client in control, with freely shared information. Electronic records and charting systems assist in tracking required information. (See Chapter 18 for more detailed information of electronic charting.)

Other technologies include telehealth, biodefense systems, and universal access to the Internet, all of which can serve as teaching tools for improving client care.[8] Clients at some hospitals, such as the University of Minnesota Health Care Services, can now log onto the Web site and access their own electronic hospital records. Such advances are also good marketing tools for medical facilities: Well-educated learners can use them successfully in programs such as "weight reduction, stress abatement, parenting and women's health issues."[5]

Working With the Internet
The Internet is the fastest-growing source of health information. Access to the latest information in virtually any subject is just a click away. Electronic networking has created a worldwide learning community that clients and health-care providers can tap into. This technology better enables clients to increase their own level of responsibility for their health care. This factor in itself will change nursing practice profoundly. According to O'Neil et al., "the original purpose of the Web was to communicate and share information, and its development has . . . changed the practice of nursing."[9] Web sites such as WebMD, with 16 million users each month; online "Ask-a-Nurse" sites; and "Tele-Medicine," to name a few, strongly enhance nursing practice. Note that only a few health information Web sites follow privacy policies; it is common for them to share personal health information without the client's permission or even personal knowledge.[4]

In this growing, complex society, demands from the client for sophisticated and better health care have increased, and online Web-based classes can impart information as never before. Nursing must keep abreast of these trends and devise more Web-based learning opportunities to improve the quality and outcomes of client care.

Using Technology in Teaching

Widespread access to the Internet, and its huge volume of available information, makes it a useful and widely sought tool for both clients and caregivers. The Internet can provide contact with medical publications, caregivers, prescription and nonprescription drug information, other clients or family members, and an almost limitless variety of related sources.

Searching for Information

More than half of Americans who have gone online have searched for health or medical information. On a daily basis, far more people seek such information online than actually visit health professionals. They can also enhance their own knowledge through proper use of the Internet.

Some medical professionals have expressed concern about the poor quality control of Internet information, and about the possibility that clients seeking health-care information will be misinformed. The JCAHO has a Web site, www.jointcommission.com, with an icon labeled "Health on the Net Foundation." This icon, used with the Search button, connects the user to any Internet site. If the site meets the rigorous JCAHO criteria, additional information about the Web site will appear. If nothing appears, the site does not meet the criteria and should be viewed as unreliable.

Table 23.2 lists some helpful online health and medical directories. This list is not comprehensive.

Evaluating Results

Evaluation of the search results is important, and a partnership between caregiver and client is the best way to undertake it. Both the client and caregiver should ask: Does the site or information have credibility? Is it published by a marketing firm or drug manufacturer with a primary focus on sales rather than education? Is the content accurate and aligned with the answer being sought? Can it be checked for accuracy elsewhere? Is it scientifically based or anecdotal? Are disclaimers present, and if so, do they state appropriately that the information is for general use and not diagnostic?

Table 23.2 Online Health and Medical Directories

Name	URL Address	Description
Harden Meta Directory	www.lib.uiowa.edu/hardin/md	Health sites listing, selected for connectivity
Health A–Z	www.healthAtoZ.com	Consumer health site maintained by health-care professionals
HealthFinder	www.healthfinder.gov	U.S. government–maintained site; uses colloquial language
Medhunt	www.hon.ch	Sponsored by Health on the Net Foundation, for professionals and clients
MedicineNet	www.medicinenet.com	Doctor-produced information
Mayo Clinic	www.mayoclinic.com	General health information
Government	www.nutrition.gov	General nutrition information
Agency for Healthcare Research and Quality	www.ahrq.gov/consumer	Primarily aimed at health-care professionals; informative for some clients
CDC Health Topics A to Z	www.cdc.gov/ncidod/diseases	Information about infectious diseases studied by the Centers for Disease Control and Prevention (CDC)
Safe Medication (American Society of Health System Pharmacists)	www.safemedication.com	Information to help clients use medications safely and correctly

To provide the best of care, nurses will need a thorough understanding of all these Internet learning tools.[5] Of course, nurses must also recognize that some clients, such as economically disadvantaged ones, do not have Internet access. In such cases, the nurse will need to substitute more traditional methods of obtaining information.

To provide appropriate level reading materials, the nurse must know the client's literacy level.[11] The Joint Commission Public Policy Initiative has a Web site that helps nurses evaluate literacy for client education quality. The link is http://www.jointcommission.org/PublicPolicy/health_literacy.htm.

HEALTH PROMOTION FOR OUR TIME

The need for enhanced communication has created a new emphasis on health promotion. One example is the Healthy People 2010 objectives, created by the U.S. Department of Health and Human Services. Healthy People 2010 set two main goals: 1.) Increase the quality and the length of healthy lives; and 2.) Eliminate health-care disparities related to gender, race or ethnicity, education or income, disability, geographic location, or sexual orientation.[12] The importance of culturally sensitive collaboration between health-care providers, clients, and communities is implicit.

Unfortunately, nowhere does this benchmark of health care discuss ways of teaching people to make healthy choices.[13] This educational gap is reflected by the unacceptable health-care disparities among minority groups. Also, the goal for reducing smoking has not been accomplished; the number of teenagers who smoke has even increased significantly.

The Centers for Disease Control and Prevention (CDC) has taken the lead role in achieving the Healthy People 2010 objectives, convening conferences and forming committees to address health disparities and then informing Congress of the progress. Also, the American Medical Association (AMA) has investigated health-care disparities and has published articles explaining how physicians are addressing them.[14] Nurses are participating in the effort by designing nursing interventions to help people make choices and develop a self-management support system.[15]

Some people find it difficult to make choices because they have not learned to think critically. A new theory of choices is emerging in the nursing literature, led by the work of Dr. Betty Fomby-White, with the purpose of helping clients make informed choices for equitable care.[16] Chapter 6 discusses critical thinking in greater depth.

CARING RELATIONSHIPS MATTER

If clients feel loved by themselves and others, they will want to learn more and will have more faith in their own ability to learn.[7] Abundant information demonstrates that drug abuse and other destructive habits are linked to lower self-worth. Helping clients develop healthy lifestyles and choices is "one of the most important responsibilities of contemporary nurses."[17]

In the midst of health reform, sustaining a caring orientation is critical for both the health-care provider and the client. "… the quality of the relationship is what facilitates health and makes it possible for nurse and patient to connect in a way that is transforming."[18] A non-nurturing interpersonal relationship is profoundly negative to body, mind, and spirit for the health-care provider as well as the client. Tables 23.3 and 23.4 reflect the dramatically different consequences of caring and noncaring relationships between nurses and clients. (See Chapter 4 for caring theory and models and their impact on care; see Chapter 14 for ways to improve communication.)

Research studies show that competent, appropriate interweaving of spirituality and prayer enhances healing. Spirituality can provide support in conditions that include hypertension, stress, cancer, and depression.[20] See Chapter 20, "Spirituality and Health Care," and Chapter 25, "Alternative and Complementary Healing Practices."

> *All we do is behave, all behavior is chosen, and we are driven by our genes to satisfy five basic needs: survival, love and belonging, power, freedom, and fun.*
> *William Glasser, 1998*

> *The strongest principle of growth lies in human choice. George Eliot*

Table 23.3 Empirical Outcomes of Caring: Clients

Effects of Caring Relationships on Clients (Summary of Findings)	Effects of Noncaring Relationships on Clients (Summary of Findings)
Emotional and spiritual well-being (dignity, self-control, personhood)	Humiliation, fear, despair, perceived lack of control and helplessness, alienation, vulnerability, lingering bad memories
Enhanced healing, more lives saved, increased safety, more energy, fewer costs, more comfort, less sense of loss	Decreased healing
Trusting relationship, decrease in alienation, closer family relations	

Source: Swanson: Meta-analysis of 130 empirical studies. *In* Watson, J: Assessing and Measuring Caring in Nursing and Health Science. Springer, New York, 2002, p 11.

CLIENT-TEACHING IMPLICATIONS FOR NURSING EDUCATION

Shared power is essential for building a constructive sense of community. Therefore, educators should emphasize the importance of sharing power with clients. Nursing education is essential for mentoring collaboration, increasing cultural competence, and decreasing prejudice and stereotyping.

Mentoring is a highly effective way of becoming an expert nurse.[21] By mentoring partnerships and increasing their own cultural competence, health-care providers expand and update their own educational process.

The Nurse's Evolving Role

The National Institute for Nursing Research (NINR) has been given a mandate from the Congressional Committee (which appropriated $435,630,000 to the Institute) to investigate selected health issues. Among these issues is the need to eliminate disparities in access to health care and quality of health care being provided. In its mandate, the Committee states that "reducing, and ultimately eliminating, health disparities is a critical priority for all areas of health-care research." To stimulate research on health-care disparities, NINR is encouraging the development of new nurse scientists from underserved populations.[22]

Table 23.4 Empirical Outcomes of Caring: Nurses

Effects of Caring Relationships on Nurses (Summary of Findings)	Effects of Noncaring Relationships on Nurses (Summary of Findings)
Sense of accomplishment, satisfaction, purpose, gratitude	Hardened affect and feeling of failure
Preserved integrity, fulfillment, wholeness, self-esteem	Obliviousness and apathy
Satisfaction in living own philosophy	Depression
Respect for life and death	Fear of death
Opportunities for reflection	Worn-down feeling
Love of nursing and increased knowledge	Burnout and indifference

Source: Swanson: Meta-analysis of 130 empirical studies. *In* Watson, J: Assessing and Measuring Caring in Nursing and Health Science. Springer, New York, 2002, p 11.

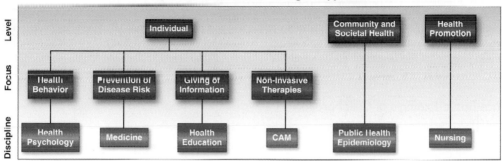

Figure 23.1   The interaction of different health professions with the community. CAM = complementary and alternative medicine. (From Leddy, S: Health Promotion. F.A. Davis, Philadelphia, 2006, with permission.)

Collaborative Client Teaching for Healthy Communities

Sensitivity and Empowerment

The Pew Commission Final Report stressed that relationship-centered interactions must become central to the education of health professionals.[23] The report emphasized that constructive interpersonal encounters—culturally sensitive, caring, collaborative, and relationship centered—

> *Nursing science is a new product . . . is open-ended; constantly evolving; never finished. . . . To actively and creatively participate in realizing the future, whatever it may hold, demands unparalleled vision, a greatly expanded human compassion, the capacity to enjoy uncertainty, and the courage to stand up and be counted; to initiate; to set direction that mankind may benefit. There is vast promise for those of wisdom, imagination, and daring whose social concern transcends personal gain and whose integrity does not vacillate.*
> *Martha Rogers*

are critical to the promotion of preventive health care. See Chapter 4 for a fuller discussion of the Pew Commission Final Report, including "Twenty-one Competencies for the 21st Century."

For effective partnership and interaction with other health-care professionals, a picture of the health team can show how different professions view their focus on client care (Fig. 23.1).

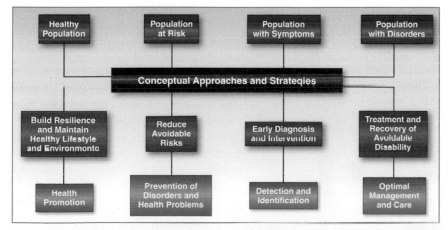

Figure 23.2   Health care for different populations. (From Rankin, S, et al.: Patient Education in Health and Illness. Lippincott Williams & Wilkins, New York, 2006, with permission.)

Health professionals also can use population approaches in client teaching (Fig. 23.2). Effective decision-making and problem-solving are critical and occur when a community is empowered. Such empowerment improves the health of all community members.

An Evidence-Based Example of Collaboration and Partnership

Few social programs can boast scientifically demonstrated outcomes through randomized controlled trials. Even fewer have demonstrated multigenerational outcomes that benefit society economically and reduce long-term social service expenditures. Box 23.3 summarizes the results of a teaching partnership involving nurses, other health professionals, and first-time parents.[24]

For 30 years, Dr. David Olds conducted a model for a Nurse–Family Partnership (NFP) in collaboration with schools and with the fields of medicine, psychology, and public health. This teaching study tracked the effectiveness of home visiting by nurses in improving maternal and child health. First-time parents volunteered to take part in the study.

The Nurse–Family Partnership is committed to enduring improvements in the health and well-being of low-income, first-time parents and their children. Nurses were chosen for this program because of the high public trust of nurses

---

Box 23.3

Nurse–Family Partnership: Helping First-Time Parents Succeed

At an average savings of $17,500 per client being returned to the government, the following consistent outcomes occurred:

- Improved prenatal health
- Fewer childhood injuries
- Fewer subsequent pregnancies
- Increased intervals between births
- Increased maternal employment
- Improved school readiness

Source: Olds, DL, et al.: Home visiting by paraprofessionals and by nurses: A randomized, controlled trial. Pediatrics 110(3):486, 2002.

and because nurses can relate to clients in a caring manner. The NFP has evolved to serving 270 counties across 22 states within the United States.[25]

A Denver trial conducted in 1994 compared home visits by nurses with paraprofessionals (workers with no formal education in caregiving professions). The visits by nurses produced significantly greater benefits to the participants' health and welfare; the paraprofessionals' visits produced small effects that rarely achieved statistical or clinical significance. The study concluded that caution should be used in allowing health-care providers other than registered nurses to make home visits, at least until consistent new evidence indicates that other helping paraprofessionals can become effective home visitors.[27]

Cultural Aspects of Teaching

Given the cultural diversity of the United States, nurses and other health-care providers must accommodate to different cultural behaviors. A client's cultural background strongly influences attitudes and beliefs about health. The nurse's knowledge of diverse cultural groups can facilitate a therapeutic approach to the client.

Communication Style

Communication and a caring relationship are profoundly affected by culture. Table 23.5

T a b l e 2 3 . 5 Cultural Differences in Communication Styles

Native Americans	Asian-Americans, Hispanics	Caucasians	African Americans
1. Speak softly, more slowly	1. Speak softly	1. Speak loudly and fast to control listener	1. Speak with affect
2. Indirect gaze when listening or speaking	2. Avoid eye contact when listening or speaking to high-status persons	2. Head nods, nonverbal markers	2. Direct eye contact (prolonged) when speaking, but less when listening
3. Interject less, seldom offer encouraging communication	3. Similar rules	3. Head nods, nonverbal markers	3. Interrupt (in turn, when convenient)
4. Delayed auditory response (silence)	4. Mild delay	4. Prompt response	4. Prompt response
5. Manner of expression low-keyed, indirect	5. Low-keyed, indirect	5. Objective, task oriented	5. Affective, emotional, interpersonal

Source: Adapted from Sue, DW, Sue, D: Counseling the Culturally Different: Theory and Practice, ed. 2. John Wiley, 1990.

outlines differences in, and nuances of, some communication styles.

Language

The client's primary language may influence his or her ability to learn, especially if the nurse does not know the language. In conducting a language assessment, the nurse must determine the client's fluency in the primary as well as the secondary language.

Brochures that have been translated directly from English may not convey the intended message, or the words used may not be familiar to the client. In that case, an interpreter may be needed. It is important to ascertain that the interpreter speaks a dialect familiar to that particular client. The following example provides an example of the fine discrimination needed in client teaching:

> In the Hispanic groups there are variations to the Spanish language. One example is the word *caretta,* which for Mexicans means a cart used by farmers and pulled by oxen. For many Central Americans, *caretta* means a taxicab. Using the wrong word can adversely affect a

Hispanic individual trying to leave the emergency room to go home.[26]

> *To be a good teacher, one needs to understand one's self, and to understand one's self, one must understand one's own culture and one must then understand other cultures, their verbal and non-verbal language and communication, as well as their environment.*
> *Anyadie Onu, Nurse Educator*

A person may understand elementary English and yet be unable to translate a lengthy or rapidly spoken explanation. When the nurse and client are from different cultures with language variations, more sensitivity and understanding than usual are required. Although television has contributed to wide recognition of terms such as "malignancy" and "cholesterol," the nurse should not take for granted that a client understands such terms and their implications in the same way a nurse does. Nor should the nurse expect the a client receiving an explanation will be brave enough to speak up and ask for clarification, particularly if the client has been hiding a literacy problem for years. The following passage illustrates the frustration and fear that can occur in a chaotic cultural misunderstanding:

> A nursing acquaintance tells of a client who became hysterical when an explanation about the presence of a hydatidiform mole aroused fears of a brown, furry animal growing inside

her. The client was too fearful and ashamed to tell her husband. She did not follow through on treatment for a long period of time, until a translator determined what the misapprehension was. Then a priest as well as the health-care providers were needed to help the client overcome her emotional turmoil and stress that could have been avoided with a more sensitive communication.[26]

The Office of Minority Health (2001) supports standards needed for cultural competence, language access, and organizational support and recommends the adoption of the National Standards for Culturally and Linguistically Appropriate Standards.

Educational Level and Motivation

The higher a person's educational level, the more likely that person is to have received some formal health education. Research also shows that the higher a person's educational level, the higher the motivation to learn. Physicians often speak of well-educated clients whom have surfed the Internet and taught themselves new information about a disease(s).

The nurse should ask the following questions before teaching a client: What is the client's level of motivation to learn? What factors will motivate the client to learn healthy behaviors? Outstanding motivational success occurred in the nurse–family partnership when the following five principles were followed (Box 23.4).[27]

> " *Patient education is not an extra task—it's the one thing you do that makes all your other interventions work . . .*
> *Exit Care Patient Information System* "

Box 23.4

Olds' Principles of the Nurse–Family Partnership

1. The client is an expert on his or her own life.
2. Follow the client's heart's desire.
3. Focus on strengths.
4. Focus on solutions.
5. Only a small change is necessary.

Source: Olds, DL, et al.: Home visiting by paraprofessionals and by nurses: A randomized, controlled trial. Pediatrics 110(3): 486, 2002.

These simply stated five principles concur with Peplau's notion of the importance of interpersonal relationships to the practice of nursing.[28] Authoritarian, oppressive, negative communications result in a lack of healing. Simple, sincere, positive exchanges create and reinforce a new health-care communication style and healing.

THE NUTS AND BOLTS OF CLIENT TEACHING

Imagine the best-case scenario: caring communication, cultural and environmental sensitivity, attention to educational and economic considerations, and advanced technology. In these circumstances, nurses can rely on the teaching–learning process just as they do on the nursing process. In fact, the two processes are very similar.

The need for certain collaborative skills is implicit in the teaching–learning process. Health-care providers need these skills to empower their clients and help them achieve the best possible quality of life. Haber[4] recommends the following collaborative skills:

1. Consider yourself a consultant and help clients remain in control of their own health choices.
2. Counsel all clients, and especially reach out to those who differ from you in age, educational level, gender, and ethnicity.
3. Make sure your clients understand the relationship between behavior and health. Understand, though, that knowledge is necessary, but not sufficient to change clients' behaviors.
4. Assess clients' barriers to change, including their lack of skills motivation, resources, and social support.
5. Encourage clients to commit themselves to change, involving them in the selection of risk factors to eliminate.
6. Use a combination of strategies, including behavioral and cognitive techniques, the identification and encouragement of social support, and appropriate referrals.
7. Monitor progress through follow-up telephone calls and appointments, and activate your health-care team, including the receptionist and other office staff.
8. Be a role model.

Table 23.6 Comparison of the Teaching–Learning Process with the Nursing Process

Teaching–Learning Process	Nursing Process
I. Assessment 　A. Learner characteristics 　B. Learner needs	I. Assessment
II. Development of expected learning 　outcomes through objectives	II. Diagnosis and planning
III. Development of a teaching plan 　A. Content 　B. Teaching strategies and learning activities	III. Implementation of the nursing plan
IV. Implementation of the teaching plan	IV. Evaluation
V. Evaluation of expected outcomes 　A. Achievement of learning outcomes 　B. Effectiveness of the teaching process	

Source: Adapted from Edelman, C, and Mandel, C: Health Promotion Throughout the Life Span. Mosby Elsevier, Philadelphia, 2006, p 225.

Table 23.6 outlines the five steps of the teaching–learning process and compares them with the four steps of the nursing process.[28] The following discussion of the teaching–learning process examines each step in detail.

I. Assessment

　A. Learner Characteristics

In assessing learning needs and learning readiness, nurses should focus on cultural and literacy issues and on the client's age and gender. People with learning disabilities also require special attention.

　　The term "**health literacy**" refers not only to reading comprehension level, but also to the ability to act on instructions. Problems with health literacy are associated more commonly with ethnic minorities, who have worse outcomes than the majority of the U. S. population.[29] However, even the most educated may have difficulty understanding health-care instructions. One well-educated elementary school teacher thought the instruction to take pills with food meant wrapping her pills in cheese and then taking them.[30]

　B. Learner Needs

The most effective learning occurs when the client is involved in the process. **Passive learning** does not change behaviors or attitudes and therefore does not change the

outcome.[31] Although passive learning is useful when new knowledge must be gained, it becomes unbalanced and lost for lack of application. In either case, the nurse must determine the performance level of any tasks or skills the client may need to learn.[32]

II. Development of Expected Learning Outcomes Through Objectives

Without learning objectives, measurement of learning outcomes is compromised and ineffective. By developing behavioral objectives, the nurse clarifies what behaviors or actions are expected. The best objectives are created by the client in collaboration with, first, the health-care team, and second, the family or community to which the client returns. Clients are energized by accomplishing simple behaviors conceived collaboratively.

Objectives fall within three domains, or categories: affective, cognitive, and psychomotor. The **affective** domain concerns the feelings, values, and attitudes necessary for a positive effect on the client's life. Affective skills include positive attitudes, constructive feelings, and values (ethics) that underlie the rapport with the client.

Cognitive objectives outline the knowledge the client will need, accounting for intellectual ability and age. Cognitive skills include evidence-based knowledge, logical thought processes, and sufficient clarity of vision to understand the client's perception of his or her self-management care needs. The last point is important for promotion of the greatest possible independence.

The cognitive area also involves understanding of both acute and chronic illnesses. Many Web sites offer suggestions for teaching clients about managing illness. The cognitive domain is divided into levels of understanding, from simple to complex. Box 23.5 shows the different levels of learning.

The **psychomotor** domain comprises expected behaviors, such as a change in diet or weight. For behavioral change to occur, memory from the cognitive domain must be present. Psychomotor skills include modeling the skills clients will need for self-care. For example, an obese 92-year-old Caucasian female diabetic, suffering from retinal damage and renal failure caused by untreated hypertension, will need to give injections, take her own blood pressure, check her urine for protein and glucose, and increase possible exercise options, along with trying to improve her deteriorating vision and following a renal diet. A nurse could model these behaviors or involve her with a support group of individuals needing to learn the same skills.[31]

Box 23.5

The Cognitive Domain: Levels of Understanding

- Knowledge: recall of facts and concepts
- Comprehension: understanding of what concepts mean
- Application: use of a concept
- Analysis: ability to examine or explain a concept
- Synthesis: integration of a concept with other learning
- Evaluation: judging or comparison of concepts

Source: Adapted from Bastable, SB: Behavioral objectives. *In* Bastable, SB, ed.: Nurse as Educator: Principles of Teaching and Learning for Nursing Practice. Jones and Bartlett, Sudbury, MA, 2003, p 226.

III. Development of a Teaching Plan

A. Content

Nurses can gather the content they need from many resources. Some underused but critical sources are nursing organizations and disease-oriented Web sites, such as that of the American Cancer Society. Good content also helps clients get answers about medical decisions; self-care information; and more complete understanding of their condition, their care, or any area of wellness that needs improvement.[33]

B. Teaching Strategies and Learning Activities

Tables 23.7 and 23.8 summarize this part of the outline.

Table 23.7 Commonly Used Teaching Strategies and Methods

Strategy/Method	Description
Case study	An actual or hypothetical account of a situation to help the learner apply principles. Useful for critical thinking exercises in the classroom. Useful in the clinical setting for comparison with actual situations. Helpful in problem-solving. The learner moves from a simple formulation of a problem to a complex understanding of it.
Computer instruction (PowerPoint™, Internet) (also called **e-learning**)	Use of computers in the classroom or clinical setting. Adds color to presentations. Key words are important in PowerPoint presentations. Includes blogs, iPods, and video games for younger learners.
Demonstration	A skill performed by the teacher and repeated by the learner. Useful for developing motor skills in both the classroom and clinical settings.
Discussion	Verbal communication of ideas; information with participation by both teacher and learner. Useful in classrooms with fewer than 20 students. Useful in clinical settings with an audience of 1 or more. Allows for assessment of values and knowledge of the topic. Elicits decision-making regarding a situation or a piece of information.
Lecture	Formal oral presentation by the teacher. Useful for a group of more than 30. Best if oral presentation is accompanied by a handout (e.g., outline, notes, with space to write more notes). Handouts help the learner stay focused.
Media	Use of audiotapes, videotapes, or filmstrips; may be auditory or visual. Useful for testing motor-skill development, discussing a particular topic, or assessing comprehension of content.
Modeling	Teaching by example; learners observe the teacher's behavior.
Trial and error	Learning by experience; used sometimes when the learner has little knowledge of content or of a situation. Sporadically useful during practice with a computer, engine, or other machine. Trial-and-error learning is time consuming and frustrating to learners (especially adults) and should be minimized.
Visual aids	Use of overhead transparencies, slides, pictures, paintings, posters, handouts, brochures. Useful for determining knowledge about, e.g., objects and organs. Useful as adjunct to verbal explanation of concepts.
Role-playing	Acting the part of another person; usually followed by discussion of perceptions or feelings. Provides a change in perspective. Useful in both classroom and clinical settings.

Table 23.8 Matching Teaching Strategies to Learners

Strategy/Method	Learner
Case Study	Adolescents, young adults, adults
Computer	All ages; especially appropriate for young learners (born after 1982)
Demonstration	All ages
Discussion	Pre-adolescents, adolescents, young adults, adults, older adults
Lecture	Adults, older adults
Media (e-learning)	All ages; especially appropriate for young learners (born after 1982)
Modeling	All ages
Trial and Error	Adolescents, young adults
Visual Aids	All ages
Role-playing	Children, adolescents, young adults

IV. Implementation of the Teaching Plan

Client education is difficult when tasks outweigh the time needed to do an effective job. Hospitals should introduce a new position: Client Teacher Practitioner. This person would devote the needed time to creating and maintaining the required environments at a primary, secondary, or tertiary setting.

A study at Georgetown University found that, on an average, $3 to $4 was saved for every dollar invested in client education. A Danish hospital study of clients with COPD found a savings of $2583 per client. Centers that specialize in asthma care (The Community Asthma Care Centers) save $1.07 million in health-care costs when clients are able to carry out self-care measures properly.

V. Evaluation of Expected Outcomes

A client's ability to meet co-created objectives can be easily monitored if follow-up and communication are embedded in the teaching–learning process. Technology- and computer-based learning programs need further study. That, and time, will determine their contribution to saving lives and improving quality of life for clients, families, and communities.

Conclusion

> *The economic future of our nation is dependent on our ability to take the quantum leap in the way we value the health of our citizens. The ways a nation cares for its sick can (and will) serve as a 'social mirror'... through this mirror we can learn about the society's values.*
> *Edward Beardsley*

Everyone in our society will benefit if client education is successfully planned and instituted, and if disparities of race, culture, age, and other factors are eliminated.

Critical Thinking Exercises

- Take the computer-based learning sites in Table 23.2 and plug them into the JCAHO icon to determine which ones are approved.
- Look back at your own client teaching and critique what you did well and what could have been improved. Refer to the JCAHO requirements in Box 23.2.
- Review Chapter 7, "Ethics in Nursing," and apply the concepts to the moral imperative for client teaching.
- Review the legal caveat in charting for client teaching. Reflect on your own client teaching charting and describe your strengths and weaknesses in this area.

References

1. Rankin, S, and Duffy, K: Patient Education: Issues, Principles, and Guidelines. JB Lippincott, St. Louis, 1983.
2. Roizen, M, and Oz, M: You, The Smart Patient. Free Press, New York, 2006.
3. Benner, P: From Novice to Expert. Prentice Hall, Upper Saddle River, NJ, 2001.
4. Haber, D: Health Promotion and Aging: Practical Applications for Health Professionals. New York: Springer, 2003.
5. Leddy, S: Health Promotion. F.A. Davis, Philadelphia, 2006.
6. Rankin, S, et al.: Patient Education in Health and Illness. Lippincott Williams & Wilkins, New York, 2006.
7. Redman, BK: The ethics of self-management preparation for chronic illness. Nursing Ethics 12(4):360–369, 2005.
8. Institute of Medicine: Crossing the quality chasm: A new health system for the 21st century. National Academy Press, Washington, DC, March 2001.
9. Hoggard-Green, J: How the consumer defines health care. Unpublished dissertation. University of Utah, 2000.
10. Stone, John H: Communication between physicians and patients in the era of e medicine. New England Journal of Medicine 345(24), 2007.
11. O'Neil, C, et al.: Developing an Online Course. Springer, New York, 2004.
12. Edelman, C, and Mandel, C: Health Promotion Throughout the Life Span. Mosby Elsevier, Philadelphia, 2006, p 223.
13. U.S. Department of Health and Human Services, January 2002.
14. Fomby-White, B: Education and the theory of choice. Unpublished treatise. November 2006.
15. Cooper-Patrick, L, et al.: Race, gender, and partnership in the patient-physician relationship. Journal of the American Medical Association 282(6): 583–589, 1999.
16. Fomby-White, B: Choice theory. Unpublished treatise. 2007.
17. Creasia, J, and Parker, B: Conceptual Foundations: The Bridge to Professional Nursing Practice. Mosby Elsevier, Philadelphia, 2006, p 347.
18. Watson, J: Assessing and Measuring Caring in Nursing and Health Science. Springer, New York, 2002, p 11.
19. Swanson: Meta-analysis of 130 empirical studies. In Watson, J: Assessing and Measuring Caring in Nursing and Health Science. Springer, New York, 2002, p 11.
20. Bienemy, C: Examining relationships between chronic stress, clinical depression, blood pressure in clinically diagnosed hypertensive African American women. Unpublished dissertation, Southern University, 2003.
21. Hill, J, et al.: Getting Your First Job. In Jones, R: Nursing Leadership and Management: Theory, Processes, and Practice. F.A. Davis, Philadelphia, 2007.
22. Hill, J: Mentoring African American women leaders in nursing. Unpublished dissertation, Louisiana State University, Baton Rouge, LA, 2003.
23. Pew Commission: Report of the Pew-Fitzer task force on advancing psychological health education: Relationship-centered care. Robert Wood Johnson Foundation, Washington, DC, 1998.
24. Goodman, A: The story of David Olds and the nurse home visiting program. Robert Wood Johnson Foundation, Washington, DC, July 2006.
25. Mills, K: Presentation to Baton Rouge District Nurses Association, Baton Rouge, LA, November 8, 2006.
26. Joyce, E: Matching teaching to the learner. Unpublished treatise. New Mexico State University, Los Cruces, New Mexico, 2006.
27. Olds, D, et al.: Home visiting by paraprofessionals and by nurses: A randomized, controlled trial. Pediatrics 110(3):486, 2002.
28. Peplau, H: Interpersonal relations in Nursing. Sage Publications, Newbury Park, CA, 1991.
29. Edelman, C, and Mandel, C: Health Promotion Throughout the Life Span. Mosby Elsevier, Philadelphia, 2006.
30. Domrose, C: Patient Teaching. NurseWeek 8(12):10, 2007.
31. Nunnery, R: Advancing Your Career: Concepts of Professional Nursing. F.A. Davis, Philadelphia, 2005.
32. Yoder-Wise, P: Leading and Managing in Nursing. Mosby Elsevier, St. Louis, 2007.
33. Patient Teaching Made Incredibly Easy. Springhouse, Springhouse, PA, 1999.

Bibliography

Beardsley, E: Health, Biology, Bioethics: A History of Neglect. University of Tennessee Press, 1987.
Dossey, B, et al.: Holistic Nursing. Jones & Bartlett, Boston, 2005.
Exit Care Patient Information System. www.exitcare.com.
Ferguson, VC: Educating the 21st Century Nurse. National League for Nursing Press, New York, 1997.
Greene, M: The Dialectic of Freedom. Teachers College Press, New York, 1988.
Rankin, S, et al.: Patient Education in Health and Illness. Lippincott Williams & Wilkins, New York, 2006.
Rogers, C: Freedom to Learn. Charles E. Merrill, Columbus, OH, 1969.
University of Minnesota Health Science Center Web Page at www.ahc.umn.edu

24

Nursing Research and Evidence-Based Practice

Mary Ann Remshardt

Learning Objectives

After completing this chapter, the reader will be able to:

- Discuss the necessity of nursing research as an essential component of comprehensive client care.
- Describe ways in which nursing research can be used to enhance communication and understanding between cultures.
- Demonstrate the ability to identify the basic similarities and differences related to qualitative and quantitative research designs.
- Identify at least four strategies that may help promote implementation of valid research findings in clinical settings.
- Define and describe the concept and utility of evidence-based practice.
- Discuss the research–practice gap as this relates to nursing research and identify some ideas for promoting change.

A UNIQUE BODY OF KNOWLEDGE

One characteristic that defines a profession is the creation of a unique body of knowledge and related skills to guide its practitioners. There are many ways of obtaining knowledge. In the nursing profession, the development of a distinct body of nursing knowledge is an ongoing process. Nursing has a long and dignified history as a service and caring profession. In contrast, nursing as a scientific discipline is just now taking its first unsteady steps. As with every profession, nursing continues to evolve to meet the needs of a changing society and the rapid development of new health-care technology.

TRIAL AND ERROR

In the past, much of what constituted the practice of the nursing profession was based on the edicts of those in authority. Founded on experiential learning, nursing focused on doing exactly what was prescribed by a person in charge, usually the physician. Before we built our own body of knowledge, it made sense to rely on the judgment of those who were considered by society to be authorities on issues such as health and illness and with whom nurses worked closely.

In the past, when skills used in the promotion of health and healing were developed, often through trial and error, they were then passed on by tradition. The trial-and-error method (supported by early science) historically served as a primary source of health-care knowledge.

Today the *search* for knowledge within what is *known* is being systematically replaced by *research* that reveals what is *best* in nursing practice. Research is the approach through which nursing knowledge, although not infallible, may be judged much more reliable and transferable than that afforded by authority, tradition, or past experience. Nursing as a science depends on valid research evidence to support best practice. Research provides the crucial link between theory and practice.

This chapter presents an overview of pertinent issues regarding the critical nature of research as scientific support for the profession of nursing.

> *In theory, there is no difference between theory and practice. But, in practice, there is. Jan L. van de Snepscheut*

> *If you can change your mind, you can change the world. Joe Reimer*

NURSING RESEARCH DEFINED

Nursing research defines nursing as a profession and as such must be embraced by nursing professionals. As one of a number of professions involved in providing health care, nursing accepts responsibility for defining its own uniqueness. Scientific inquiry is the tool of choice for tasks related to professional clarification, justification, extension, and collaboration.

The Goals of Inquiry

Nurses are held accountable for their actions and must equip themselves to defend the interventions they initiate through strong empirical evidence. At the very minimum, nursing care must be safe. With contemporary cost-containment issues, nursing interventions are expected to demonstrate practicality as well as cost effectiveness. Research can show which approaches to nursing care are most effective and which do not work. The profession of nursing will not experience a true renaissance until scientific inquiry becomes as much a part of daily practice as caring interventions.

More than a method of inquiry, nursing research is a systematic process for answering

questions through the discovery of new information with the ultimate goal of improving client care.[1] The purpose of nursing research is "to test, refine and advance the knowledge on which improved education, clinical judgment, and cost-effective, safe, ethical nursing care rests."[2]

Beyond Clinical Practice

Some authors would limit the scope of nursing research to the clinical practice of nursing. In its fullest meaning however, nursing research involves a systematic quest for knowledge designed to address questions and solve problems relevant to the profession including issues related to nursing practice, nursing education, and nursing administration.[3] Nursing research is conducted to expand and clarify the body of knowledge unique to the discipline of nursing.

Redefining the Client. Nurses know that clients are more than just individuals receiving nursing care within selected clinical settings. Nursing clients are family units, communities, organizations, institutions, corporations, local and state agencies, and citizens of a country as well as the global community. To accurately measure how effectively it meets the needs of an expanding and diverse consumer base, the nursing profession must integrate an expanding and diverse body of scientific knowledge into its daily practice. Nurses must focus on promoting better understanding of the research process and encouraging their colleagues to seek the evidence needed to explain, modify, and improve nursing practice.

Setting Priorities and Directions. Clinical decisions and the resulting nursing interventions are justified by scientifically documented findings. Using nursing research, nurse investigators not only address issues related to cost, safety, quality, and accessibility of health care, but look ahead to establish priorities and to define the future direction of the nursing profession.

Crossing Cultural Boundaries. One critical requirement for a dynamic profession is to understand and address cultural issues involved in nursing care and to understand the various cultures within the communities where nurses practice. We must also learn to look beyond perceptual and geographic boundaries to promote dialogue, investigation, and collaboration with our many international nursing colleagues in the interest of culturally sensitive and global concerns. Culturally related issues provide numerous opportunities for nursing research (see Chapter 21).

DEVELOPMENT AND PROGRESSION OF RESEARCH IN NURSING

The Origin of Nursing Research

Florence Nightingale is viewed as the person who first elevated nursing to the status of a profession, as presented in her first book, *Notes on Nursing* (1859).[4] She is also credited with introducing research to the profession. Nightingale believed in the importance of "naming nursing" through the collection and use of objective data to support the need for health-care reforms, including those related to nursing education. Nightingale recognized the impact of combining strong logical thinking and empirical research in developing a sound scientific base on which to build the practices of the nursing profession.

Methodical Observation

As the first recognized nurse epidemiologist, Florence Nightingale systematically collected objective data and in 1855 described environmental factors that affected health and illness. During the Crimean War, appalled by what she observed of the care of soldiers, Nightingale was forward thinking enough to implement and then demand scientific inquiry in the practice setting. She methodically gathered facts, eventually supporting her claims that lack of cleanliness, fresh air, proper rest, and nutrition contributed to high levels of disease and death seen in the frontline "hospital" during the war.

As a result of her research, she petitioned forcefully for more supplies, better food, and cleaner conditions. Her advocacy lowered the mortality rate

> *All research is primarily done for one of three reasons: altruism, curiosity, or vanity. Author unknown*

among wounded soldiers from 42 percent to 2 percent. Her work during the 1800s was not fully appreciated until more than a century later.[4]

The Development of Research

Even today, the full importance of this one woman's work for the profession of nursing is still being evaluated. Nightingale had few professional role models, relatively little education, a military organization that doubted her value, and meager financial support. Her accomplishments, in view of the challenge, were phenomenal. It is interesting to speculate about how much more progress would have been made in building the unique body of nursing knowledge if other nurses had heeded Nightingale's earliest call for research.

A Look at Nursing Education

During the 1940s, many studies concerning nursing education came to the forefront because of the tremendous demand for educated nurses during World War II. Nursing education practices were evaluated in a study commissioned by the National Nursing Council for War Service. Findings from this study and others at the time uncovered weaknesses in nursing education. This relatively new wave of research spawned several other studies that looked at nurses' functions, roles, attitudes, acceptance, and interactions with clients.

A Center for Nursing Research

Several events that occurred during the 1950s prompted those conducting nursing research to carve out an ever-expanding path for the profession of nursing that continues to widen today. Nurses with advanced degrees were increasing in numbers. A center for nursing research was formed at the Walter Reed Army Institute of Research.

Creation of the American Nurses' Foundation and the journal *Nursing Research* allowed publication of nursing research findings that gave both a face and a voice to the studies. Many of these studies became both the mirror and the microscope through which nurses studied themselves. This self-appraisal was an unprecedented research approach for any profession.

A New Definition of Nursing

In the 1960s, phrases such as *conceptual framework, conceptual model,* and *nursing process* made their first appearances in textbooks and other nursing literature (see Chapter 4). Nursing leaders, now becoming more focused on theoretical support for nursing, continued to lament the relative lack of research.

Many professional nursing organizations set priorities for research during this time. It was also during this time that another visionary nurse heeded the call to logical reasoning and empirical research. Virginia Henderson, one of the early nursing theorists, defined the role of nursing as "to assist individuals (sick or well) with those activities contributing to health, or its recovery or to a peaceful death, that they perform unaided, when they have the necessary strength, will, or knowledge; to help individuals carry out prescribed therapy and to be independent of assistance as soon as possible."

This definition was so conceptually clear that it was accepted by the International Council of Nurses (ICN) in 1960, and Henderson's work went on to identify many relevant research questions for the practice of professional nursing.

A Growth in Research Programs

In the 1970s, the number of graduate nursing programs experienced tremendous growth, and so did the number of nurses conducting research. Increases in the number of ongoing research studies pointed out the need for an improved way to give those studies voice. Three more research journals were developed: *Advances in Nursing Science, Research in Nursing and Health,* and the *Western Journal of Nursing Research.* During this time the research focus began to change from the study of nurses to the study of client care needs. Clinical challenges were identified as having the highest priority for nursing research.

A Source of National Data

The 1980s witnessed another information explosion with the continued growth rate of research-trained, graduate school–educated nurses and the introduction of computers. Research and writing were both enhanced by electronic databases and the expanding World Wide Web. In 1983, the American Nurses' Association created the Center for Research for Nursing.

The mission of this center is to serve as a source of national data for the profession. In 1986, The National Center for Nursing Research (NCNR) at the National Institutes of Health was established by congressional mandate. The mission of this organization is to support clinical (applied) and basic research to create a scientific foundation for the care of individuals across the lifespan. During the 1980s, a journal with the specific intention of providing research directed toward the practicing clinical nurse took form in *Applied Nursing Research.*

A New Focus on Practice

In 1993, the NCNR was awarded full institute status, and the National Institute of Nursing Research (NINR; www.nih.gov/ninr.org) came into being. In 1996, NINR had a reported $55 million budget, and it was poised to promote and support research priorities established during that decade. Since the late 1990s, studies have become more focused on the practice of nursing, the outcomes of nursing and other health-care services, and the building of a stronger knowledge base by replicating previous research using a variety of settings and situations.

THE NEXT STEP IN NURSING PRACTICE

Evidence-Based Practice

Today, the movement to achieve cost-effective, high-quality care based on scientific inquiry generates the drive for evidence-based practice (EBP). Evidence-based practice is today's nursing issue of priority. Because of the volume of literature being published by all health-care professions, including nursing, it is important to develop critical discernment skills. Critical discernment requires the nurse to understand the research process and to sift through and carefully assess all available and credible research findings. Once the research has been analyzed and judged, recommendations for using the best practice techniques can be made on the basis of best evidence.

Although nurses have been using evidence-based nursing practice in some form since the early days of nursing, it is only recently that the process has become formalized and widespread as a methodology. The current use of EBP in nursing requires a transition from nursing care that is based on opinions, past practices, and precedent to decisions that are based on scientific research and proven evidence. The goal of nurses using EBP is to obtain the best information available and to integrate it into nursing practice. Such practice includes the client's values and self-determination in providing care, as well as those of the client's family. The ultimate outcome sought is improved quality of care.

"ARE YOU SURE THIS NEW BATH TECHNIQUE WAS ON THE EVIDENCE-BASED PRACTICE LIST?"

Evidence Reports

Nurses can use numerous sources when incorporating EBP into their care provision. Research reported in the literature is a primary source of high-quality information, but not the only one. Other sources include expert opinion, collaborative consensus, published standards, historical data, local quality assurance studies, and institutional reports including cost effectiveness and client–family preferences and input. The key to using these various sources of information is the ability to grade or rank them so that nursing practice is based on the *best* information available. An excellent way to sort out the quality of information is to visit the Web site www.guideline.gov. for evidence reports.

The evidence reports contained at this site provide a scientific basis for a disease or a nursing practice and then integrate the data into actions used

in practice. The reports synthesize previous and current knowledge related to the topic, review the information for quality and documentation, explain how EBP is currently being used, and discuss how useful the EBP is to the clinical practice. The reviews in evidence reports are more detailed than a typical literature review and include broad-based information that is translated into specific approaches to client care. Although currently the data are somewhat limited, new data are constantly being added to the site.

Nurses should look for several key elements in evidence reports when attempting to integrate EBP into their care. The first part of the report should include a structured summary statement of the problem, practice, or disease that describes what is in the evidence report. The second part should include a lengthy and detailed analysis of the published and unpublished data, including reviews of articles and reports, the populations included in the studies, and the nature of the nursing actions investigated. One of the most important elements in the second part of the evidence report is the ranking or grading of the quality of the evidence.

The level of quality of the evidence is sometimes referred to as the "level of recommendation for use" and answers the nurse's question, "Should I value this information and use it in my practice?" Integrative reviews in evidence reports should provide both the type of evidence included and the strengths and consistencies of the information.

Types of Evidence Used

Five types of evidence can be present in an evidence report, ranked from I (strongest) to V (weakest). They are:

  I. Meta-analysis of multiple well-designed, controlled studies that examines and synthesizes many studies to find similar results
 II. At least one well-designed experimental study with a random sample, control group, and intervention
III. Well-designed, quasi-experimental studies, such as nonrandomized controlled, single-group pre- or post-test group, cohort studies, or time series studies
IV. Well-designed nonexperimental studies, such as comparative and correlational descriptive studies and controlled case studies
 V. Case reports and clinical examples

The strength and consistency of evidence are also ranked on a five-point scale ranging from A (best) to E (poorest). In general, a "B" or higher should be present before a nurse integrates the data into EBP. The rankings are:

A. There is evidence of type I or consistent findings from multiple studies of types II, III, or IV.
B. There is evidence of types II, III, or IV, and the findings are generally consistent.
C. There is evidence of types II, III, or IV, but the findings are inconsistent.
D. There is little or no evidence or there is type V evidence only.
E. Panel Consensus: Practice recommendations are based on the opinions of experts in the field.

One of the potential problems in using these ranking systems is that they may not be the best method of analyzing the strength of the evidence. In nursing, much of the research is qualitative or descriptive, or even narrative, because of the difficulty in performing controlled studies with large groups of clients. The nurse needs to check the consistency of the results, even though there may not be any type I, II, or III studies in the evidence report.

The next section of the evidence report focuses on clinical practice and should include practice-focused guidelines or recommendations for specific clinical interventions. Often this section begins with a statement such as "There is very good evidence that . . ." or "There is no evidence that . . ." The practices outlined should be specific and relevant to the care being given.

The last section of the evidence report is the report source. Reports should be specific and current and should come from high-quality, refereed professional journals.

Evaluating an Evidence Report

The nurse can evaluate the evidence report by asking three questions. Only after answering these questions will the nurse be able to decide what to do with the information.

1. *Is this the best available evidence?* Best sources include peer-reviewed journals and reports no more than 3 to 5 years old.
2. *Will the recommendations work for my practice given the client population and problems?* If the study population is of young adult white males

and the nurse's primary work population is elderly females, then the data generated may not apply.
3. *Do the recommendations fit well with the preferences and values of the clients I commonly work with?* If the values of the nurse's primary group vary greatly from those of the study group, it is likely the recommendations may not work well.

Nurses can locate evidence reports from numerous sources:

Clinical Journals

Evidence-Based Nursing
Online Journal of Clinical Innovations
Reformatted STTI *Online Journal for Knowledge Synthesis in Nursing*

Other Sources

National Guideline Clearinghouse (U.S. Agency for Healthcare Research and Quality): A repository for clinical practice guidelines.
The Cochrane Collaboration (international): Develops and maintains systematic reviews.
SUNY Web site: Lists the best sites for information.

When nurses begin to take the next step and integrate EBP into the care they provide, they will make a major leap toward raising the level of professionalism in nursing practice. Through the use of EBP in nursing, the quality of client care will improve when that care is based on validated evidence that focuses on what works best.

Source: L. Benefield, Evidence-Based Nursing Practice: How to Dance to the Tune. (Presentation at the NSNA National Convention, Phoenix AZ, 4/23/03)

The future is here. It is just not widely distributed yet. William Gibson

Currently, nurses have not only been given the responsibility to conduct research but to evaluate, critique, and apply the research findings of other nurses and health-care professionals in their own practice. Understanding research is more than merely learning simple methods of inquiry.

THE RESEARCH PROCESS

Nursing students, long before graduation, often notice something in the clinical setting that grabs their attention. They may simply wonder if a different approach would work better in a particular situation or if the best technique is currently being used, and what evidence exists to support a particular technique or intervention as "best."

As neophytes, students may question interventions or solutions that seasoned nurses may take for granted. Students may see the experienced nurse's familiar world differently, and their minds may be open to possibilities that others may not see. Questioning the status quo is a key first step in the research process. Employing critical thinking often leads to visualization of a research project, the development of a plan, the implementation of that plan, and finally, sharing of the findings with others. This process follows a logical progression from abstract ideas to concrete actions.

Research Designs

The word *design* implies both creativity and structure. The design for a research study can be seen as a road map or a recipe. It serves as a fairly flexible set of guidelines that will provide the researcher with answers to the questions of inquiry.

To choose a research design, the nurse must first develop a vision of the overall plan for a study, including a general idea of the type of data needed to answer the research question. The design is a critical link that connects the researcher's framework with appropriate types of data. The level of pre-existing knowledge in the area of inquiry also helps determine the research design. If little is known about a specific subject, an exploratory study may be the best method for uncovering new information. In exploratory research, there is usually more interest in the qualitative characteristics of data. Hypotheses are usually not required for these studies.

If the researcher is looking at variables that are independent, objective, or demonstrate cause and effect, then a quantitative design is best. If the question invites discovery of meanings, perceptions, and the collection of subjective data, then qualitative designs should be used.

> *Not everything that can be counted, counts and not everything that counts can be counted. Albert Einstein*

Quantitative versus Qualitative Research

Historically and in the tradition of scientific inquiry, quantitative experimental research designs were the most highly respected. These designs are guided by a somewhat rigid set of rules that gives the most importance to the *process* of inquiry. However, the past decade has seen a growing interest in, and respect for, qualitative approaches in research, especially in the social sciences. Social researchers see human interactions as complex, highly contextual, and too intricate to be studied using a rigid framework or standard instrument. Also, attempting to conduct quantitative research on human subjects often produces serious ethical dilemmas.

Qualitative Designs

The purpose of qualitative inquiry is to gain an understanding of how individuals construct meaning in their world, visualize a situation, and make sense of that situation. For example, to nurses, the concept of "caring" is very important, yet the nurse will probably perceive caring differently than the client. The nurse researcher wishing to measure "caring interventions" might find this concept very difficult to quantify, but a qualitative method could yield much usable information.

Because of the nature of nursing and the usual subject matter (human beings), qualitative designs are best suited to answer questions that interest nurses. The most commonly used of these designs are shown in Box 24.1.

Semistructured interviews using open-ended questions and observations are the most commonly used data collection methods in qualitative studies. Knowledge generated by qualitative research answers questions related to the meaning and understanding of human experiences.

Box 24.1

Qualitative Research Designs

Phenomenology
Ethnography
Grounded Theory
Historical Studies
Case Studies

Quantitative Designs

Quantitative designs are approaches that seek to verify data through prescriptive testing, correlation, and sometimes description. These designs imply varying degrees of control over the research material or subjects. Control of the research design can range from very tight to somewhat loose.

The design in quantitative research becomes the means used for hypothesis testing. The design also optimizes control over the variables to be tested and provides the structure and strategy for answering the research question. More highly controlled quantitative designs try to demonstrate causal relationships, and more flexible designs address relationships between and among variables. Box 24.2 summarizes and classifies quantitative research designs.

In quantitative experimental design, a comparison of two or more groups is required. The groups under study must be as similar as possible so that results can be credited to the treatment of the variables and not to differences between the groups. The independent variable is the one managed or manipulated by the researcher. The dependent variable *depends on,* or is altered as a direct result of, the researcher's manipulation.

In research, it is good to remember that neither the quantitative nor the qualitative research school is better. Each research approach is useful in different ways and both expand understanding of health care and the nursing profession. What *is* important is to choose the methodology that best

" *Statistics are no substitute for judgment. Henry Clay* "

addresses the questions the researcher is asking and collects whatever data are most useful.

NARROWING THE RESEARCH–PRACTICE GAP

Two Different Cultures

More and more, nurses are becoming academically astute in the area of research. Unfortunately, education alone does not ensure transfer of what is learned into the daily practice of nursing. Like the basic but critical skill of sterile asepsis, research will become a part of each nurse's practice only when it becomes a part of each nurse's ideology.

Academic and practice arenas are often, in reality, two entirely different cultures. The critical and creative thinking so valued and promoted in the academic environment may fall victim to time and budget constraints within the clinical setting. To support what is best for clients, clinical practice areas such as hospitals must find ways to ensure that research finds safe harbor in the culture of practice. The implementation of research in practice will depend on inquisitiveness, development of cognitive skills, the ability to question one's own practice, and professional discipline. Nurses must also understand that sometimes research findings may conflict with practices rooted in tradition.[5]

Box 24.2

Research Designs

Experimental Designs
Pretest/post-test control group
Post-test only control group
Solomon four group

Quasiexperimental Designs
Nonequivalent control group
Time series

Pre-experimental Designs
One group pretest/post-test

Nonexperimental Designs
Comparative studies
Correlational studies
Developmental studies
Evaluation studies

Meta-analysis Studies
Methodological studies
Needs-assessment studies
Secondary analysis studies

Survey studies
One-shot case study

Barriers to Research in Practice

Experts are now asking, "Why generate more research when the research already generated has not been adapted to practice?" The research–practice gap remains a bewildering challenge to the nursing profession.

An Isolated Skill

A challenge to the use of research in practice is that research skills are often taught to nursing students in isolation from other nursing subjects. This type of teaching may broaden the division between research and practice by separating the two elements early in the nurse's development and education. Unless ways are found to focus inquiry and link research findings to clinical practice early in the education process, the research–practice gap will likely remain.

As the situation currently stands, even though there has been an emphasis on nursing research for more than two decades, there are few indications that nurses on the front lines of clinical practice actively use research as a way to inform their practice.

Lack of Understanding

There are several barriers to the implementation of research in the health-care setting. Often, nurses skilled in clinical nursing may not be skilled in conducting research. Nurses who attempt to use research studies to answer practice questions may feel that the research does not provide the practical solutions for which they are looking. This concern may be valid because some researchers do not understand practice issues from the bedside nurse's viewpoint.

Conversely, practicing clinical nurses may lack the knowledge to understand or interpret the language of research. Published research often appears so esoteric and complicated that the message cannot be found in the bottle. The information should be easily accessible to those who provide direct care to clients. Researchers must find ways of packaging the conclusions so that practicing nurses may easily understand and implement clinical solutions to the care issues they are facing.

Unquestioned Practices

Entrenched nursing practices present another challenge. In the not-too-distant past, traditional nursing practices appear to have had a half-life longer than uranium. A few nursing traditions remain so widely accepted as fact that they are never questioned, and they therefore evade the scrutiny of testing. Best practice may never become evident without testing approaches to practices that have been accepted as necessary, preeminent, and sacrosanct.

Lack of Incentive

With the real challenges of time and budget limitations, very few hospitals or other agencies offer encouragement or rewards to nurses who *are* willing to seek out and use research findings in an effort to improve practice. One survey, conducted to identify barriers to implementation of research from clinicians' perspectives, revealed "insufficient authority and insufficient time" as the two obstacles most often cited.[1]

Resistance from Managers

Some researchers suggest that unit managers may view an environment of updates and change as unfavorable to maintaining a committed and cohesive staff. Some describe change as a threat to the constancy necessary for safe and expeditious client care.[6] Nurses willing to incorporate best practice evidence into clinical protocols must have confidence in their own professional judgment and the courage to stand against nurses who find comfort in unchanging traditional practices.

Incorporating Best Practice

Several strategies can help nurses conduct and use research for the improvement of nursing care, such as attending conferences in which clinical research findings and ideas for practice are presented. Other strategies proposed include but are not limited to:

1. Incorporating research findings in textbooks, basic and continuing nursing education programs, and clinical policy and procedure manuals
2. Explicitly connecting research use to institutional goals and objectives
3. Developing joint committees between colleges of nursing and hospital nursing departments
4. Inviting staff nurses to find and present summaries and abstracts, during unit meetings and clinical case conferences, in an effort to increase the interest of colleagues working on their units[7]

Several of the most widely read clinically focused nursing journals, such as *American Journal of Nursing, Nursing 2008,* and *RN,* are beginning to add research sections. These increase the ease of access to research, ensure a wider distribution of current clinical research findings, and promote the incorporation into clinical settings of best practices based on credible evidence. This mission serves the profession by simplifying some of the language of research and by giving voice to the importance and practical nature of clinical research.

> " *No problem can be solved by the same consciousness that created it. We must see the world anew. Albert Einstein* "

EVIDENCE-BASED PRACTICE

Improvement of client care is the primary reason for conducting nursing research. Nursing interventions must be supported by accurate information. The current philosophy in nursing and health care is that professionals must use research evidence when making decisions about the clinical management of clients. Health-care decisions can be logically based on primary research, systematic reviews of research literature, or both.

Systematic Reviews

Systematic reviews present reliable summaries of past research. The role of such reviews has become more important as the volume of health-care literature has expanded. Other factors favoring reviews include the inconsistent quality of some research produced, the increased number of treatment approaches resulting from the availability of the numerous pharmaceuticals and health-care products on the market today, and the exponential growth of health-related technology.

Consideration of these factors has prompted the proposal that systematic reviews of existing literature replace primary research as a main source of evidence for clinical decision-making. One review of this type could replace many individual studies and free those making clinical decisions from finding, interpreting, and evaluating a collection of published primary research reports and articles.

Some believe that systematic reviews would represent the "gold standard" in research summaries.

However, those eager to jump on the review-only bandwagon need to keep in mind that methods currently used for literature review may not most accurately reflect some of the nursing research being reviewed. The challenge exists in the "narrowly defined concept of what constitutes good evidence."[8]

Primary Research

What about only using nursing research studies as a source of information? One recurring criticism of primary nursing research is that much of it is accomplished as single studies. Some nursing researchers believe that many excellent qualitative studies are not followed by rigorous quantification.[9] Other nursing leaders continue to urge nurse researchers to make replication studies a high research priority, particularly for research addressing clinical nursing issues. A single study is rarely adequate for making decisions regarding clinical practice.[10]

The Best of Practice

Evidence-based practice is believed to constitute the best of practice and has garnered the attention of health-care administrators because of its potential to decrease the cost of health-care delivery. Standards of nursing practice, clinical guidelines, and routine performance audits promote the use of research findings to some degree. The availability of electronic databases and emphasis on the teaching of research in nursing curricula, along with such support organizations as the Cochrane Collaboration (www.cochrane.org), Best Evidence (www.acponline.com), and the Centers for Health Evidence (www.cche.net), all endorse the expectation that nurses must be able and willing to use evidence to inform their practice.

How Useful Is It?

Successful implementation of EBP also depends on how practical and useful the information is to the practicing nurse. The usefulness of information requires the nurse to evaluate several factors, including potential benefits versus possible harm, cost effectiveness, availability of ongoing support

Issues in Practice

Short Staffing in an Emergency

Halley had been working on the medical–surgical unit since her graduation from an ADN nursing program 2 months ago. She had also had clinical rotations at the same unit while in nursing school and felt comfortable and confident with the unit's procedures and her own skills. One Sunday evening the house supervisor stopped her just before the beginning of her shift and explained that the RN on the eight-bed maternity unit had called to say that she was going to be late because of a family emergency. Because of the overall short staffing on weekends at this hospital, Halley would need to be pulled to the maternity unit for no more than 2 hours to cover the RN position and pass medications until the regular nurse could arrive for her shift. That would leave the medical–surgical unit short staffed, but it was relatively quiet and only about three-quarters full.

Halley hurried to the maternity unit and received an abbreviated report from the staff who were waiting to go home. All the clients were stable, and the only potential problem was a client in the emergency department (ED) who was 36 weeks pregnant and might be in the early stages of labor. Although they hadn't received report on the client in the ED, the departing staff joked that it would probably be the next morning before "anything happened."

After conducting an abbreviated initial assessment of the clients on the maternity unit, Halley called the ED to receive report on their client. The client was a 36-year-old woman who had three children, aged 12, 9, and 2. The ED nurse also reported that the client's old charts revealed a history of "precipitous labor" (a very rapid labor with the sudden birth of the baby). Given the client's history and the relatively short time of her last delivery, Halley recognized that she did not have the skills or experience to provide safe care for this client.

Halley called the nursing supervisor and explained that she would need a nurse more experienced in obstetrics to help admit and care for this new client. The supervisor responded that the whole hospital was short of nurses and she had no one she could send. Halley would just have to do her best until the regular maternity unit nurse arrived.

A few minutes later, the ED nurses brought the client to the maternity unit. After she was transferred to a unit bed, Halley did an initial admission assessment with the following results: blood pressure 166/123; pulse 134; contractions 2 to 3 minutes apart, regular and strong; fetal heart rate 166, faint but regular; amniotic fluid leaking from the vagina. After making her assessment, Halley again called the supervisor and demanded that she come to the maternity unit immediately to help with this client, who Halley felt was going to deliver her baby very soon. The supervisor responded that she was in the middle of a code blue in the ICU and that Halley would just have to hang on for the half hour or so until the maternity nurse was due to arrive.

- What are the primary underlying ethical principles involved in this dilemma?
- How do an individual nurse's ethical obligations differ from those of a hospital's administration?
- What type of research data would help resolve this issue?
- Do you think this case study reflects a realistic situation?

resources, and willingness of the health-care staff and clients to accept change.

With the emphasis on the urgency for implementing EBP, critical and creative thinking have become even more important for the following reasons:

• Nurses must access, understand, evaluate, and disseminate a rapidly expanding body of nursing and other health-related information.
• Nurses must be able to recognize commonalities and uncover inconsistencies regarding the values of the profession, the values of the organization that employs them, the needs of clients for whom they advocate, and even the popular culture that exerts pressure on the public's ability to make safe choices.
• Nurses recognize that it takes critical and creative thought to support research into complex health-care issues and to promote successful implementation of changes in professional practice.

The goals of EBP include cost-effective practice based on the data produced by research, the dissemination of data, and the implementation of best practice interventions into the nurse's practice. The following have been identified as essential features of EBP:

• EBP is problem based and within the scope of the practitioner's experience.
• EBP narrows the research–practice gap by combining research with existing knowledge.
• EBP facilitates application of research into practice by including both primary and secondary research findings.
• EBP is concerned with quality of service and is therefore a quality assurance activity.
• EBP projects are team projects and therefore require team support and collaborative action.
• EBP supports research projects and outcomes that are cost effective.[11]

> *Leaders and educators within the profession of nursing agree that there is a role for every nurse in research, regardless of level of education.*

In summary, evidence-based researchers conduct systematic reviews of existing literature. These reviews are necessary because of the large quantity of health-care literature already in existence that has not been assimilated into practice. The mission of EBP researchers is to evaluate and present the evidence that is available on a specific topic in a clear and unbiased way. Clinical recommendations evolving from this process present nurses with sound decisions based on best evidence. Consequently, researchers will not only know what questions have been satisfactorily answered, but will also be better able to identify where gaps in the knowledge still exist.

Networking: Where to Begin

As more evidence becomes available to guide practice, agencies and organizations are developing EBP guidelines. The Agency for Healthcare Research and Quality funds several EBP centers that are accessible through its Web site (www.ahrq.gov) and sponsors a National Guideline Clearinghouse where abstracts for EBP are available at www.guideline.gov. The American Pain Society (www.ampainsoc.org), the Oncology Nursing Society (www.ons.org), and the Gerontological Nursing Interventions Research Center (www.nursing.uiowa.edu/gnirc) also provide material. The Best Practices Network presents information from several organizations and is available at www.best4health.org.

RESEARCH ROLES BY EDUCATIONAL LEVEL

Leaders and educators within the profession of nursing agree that there is a role for every nurse in research, regardless of level of education. A minimal requirement for all 21st-century nurses is the ability to develop *and use* basic research skills. Nurses striving to improve their individual practice are increasingly committed to building a body of knowledge specific to nursing. Findings from scientific inquiry define the unique and valuable roles and the challenges of nursing.

Areas of Competency

One of the hallmarks of success in the field of research is the identification of research competencies for nurses at each educational level of preparation. In its classic document, *Commission on Nursing Research: Education for Preparation in Nursing Research,* the American Nurses Association (ANA) identified research competencies for each classification of the nursing education program. It is presumed that professional nurses committed to lifelong learning will cultivate their research expertise throughout their careers. Following are the expected research roles by educational level:

Associate Degree Nursing Graduate

1. Demonstrates awareness of the value or relevance of research in nursing
2. Assists in identifying problem areas in nursing practice
3. Assists in collection of data within an established structured format

Associate degree nurses are expected to demonstrate an awareness of the value of research in nursing by becoming knowledgeable consumers of research information and by helping identify problems within their scope of nursing practice that may warrant exploration.

Baccalaureate Degree Nursing Graduate

1. Reads, interprets, and evaluates research for applicability to nursing practice
2. Identifies nursing problems that need to be investigated and participates in the implementation of scientific studies

3. Uses nursing practice as a means of gathering data for refining and extending practice
4. Applies established findings of nursing and other health-related research to practice
5. Shares research findings with colleagues

Nurses with a baccalaureate education are expected to be intelligent consumers of research by understanding each step of the research process to interpret, evaluate, and determine the credibility of research findings. The baccalaureate nurse is able to distinguish between findings that are merely interesting and findings supported by enough data to be included in the nurse's practice. Baccalaureate-prepared nurses also participate in one or more phases of research projects. These nurses must be alert to and uphold the ethical principles of any research involving human participants and oversee the protection of individual rights as specified in the ANA Code of Ethics.

Master's Degree in Nursing

1. Analyzes and reformulates nursing practice problems so that scientific knowledge and scientific methods can be used to find solutions
2. Enhances quality and clinical relevance of nursing research by providing expertise in clinical problems and by providing knowledge about the way in which these clinical services are delivered
3. Facilitates investigation of problems in clinical settings by contributing to a climate supportive of investigative activities, collaborating with others in investigations, and enhancing nurses' access to clients and data
4. Investigates for the purpose of monitoring the quality of the practice of nursing in a clinical setting
5. Assists others in applying scientific knowledge in nursing practice

Doctorate Degree in Nursing or a Related Discipline

1. Provides leadership for the integration of scientific knowledge with other types of knowledge for the advancement of practice
2. Conducts investigations to evaluate the contributions of nursing activities to the well-being of clients
3. Develops methods to monitor the quality of the practice of nursing in a clinical setting and to evaluate contributions of nursing activities to the well-being of clients

Graduate of a Research-Oriented Doctoral Program

1. Develops theoretical explanation of phenomena relevant to nursing by empirical research and analytic processes
2. Uses analytic and empirical methods to discover ways to modify or extend existing scientific knowledge so that it is relevant to nursing
3. Develops methods for scientific inquiry of phenomena relevant to nursing[12]

ETHICAL ISSUES IN RESEARCH

The Nuremberg Code

Although guidelines that govern human behavior have always been a part of recorded history, the need for ethical standards in research came to the public's attention in a dramatic way following World War II when evidence of the Nazis' experimentation and

> *We may all have come on different ships, but we're in the same boat now.*
> *Martin Luther King, Jr.*

torture of selected groups of victims was revealed.

During the trials of Nazi war criminals, the U.S. Secretary of State and the Secretary of War discovered that the defense was trying to justify the atrocities committed by Nazi physicians as merely "medical research." As a result, the American Medical Association was asked to develop a code of ethics for research that would serve as a standard for judging the Nazi war crimes. This standard remains valid to this day and is known as the Nuremberg Code (Box 24.3).

National Research Act

Ethical issues are critical to all research, and researchers from all disciplines are bound by ethical principles that protect the rights of the public. One set of principles addressing the conduct of research came from the 1974 National Research Act. This act established the National Commission for Protection of Human Subjects in Biomedical and Behavioral Research.

Box 24.3

Articles Adapted from The Nuremberg Code

1. The voluntary consent of human subjects is absolutely necessary.
2. The experiment should yield fruitful results for the good of society.
3. The experiment should be so designed and based on results of animal experimentation and knowledge of ... the disease or problem under study that the anticipated results will justify performance of the experiment.
4. The experiment should be conducted so as to avoid all unnecessary physical and mental suffering and harm.
5. No experiment should be conducted where there is an a priori reason to believe that death or ... injury will occur.
6. The degree of risk ... should never exceed that determined ... by the importance of the problem to be solved by the experiment.
7. Proper preparations should be made ... to protect the experimental subject against even remote possibilities of injury, disability, or death.
8. Scientifically qualified people must only conduct the experiment. The highest degree of skill and care should be required through all stages of the experiment.
9. During the course of the experiment, the subject should be at liberty to bring the experiment to an end ....
10. During the course of the experiment, the scientist ... must be prepared to terminate the experiment at any stage ....

Source: Adapted from Trials of War Criminals before the Nuremberg Military Tribunals under Control Council Law No. 10, Vol. 2, pp 181–182. U.S. Government Printing Office, Washington, DC, 1949.

Part of that act mandated the establishment of Institutional Review Boards (IRBs), whose primary responsibility is to safeguard, in every way, the rights of any individual participating in a research study. Institutional Review Boards are panels that review research proposals in detail to ensure that ethical standards are met in the protection of human rights. The mission of the IRB is to ensure that researchers do not engage in unethical behavior or conduct poorly designed research studies.

Every university, hospital, and agency that receives federal monies must submit assurances that they have established an IRB composed of at least five members. These members should reflect a variety of professional backgrounds, occupations, races, and cultures in an effort to uphold complete and unbiased project reviews.

> *In nurses' position of trust with clients, nurses possess a great deal of influence over a population that is especially vulnerable because of health issues and needs.*

Code of Ethics for Nurses

The profession of nursing also has its own code of ethics to which all nurses are legally and ethically bound. The development of this code was initiated by the ANA Board of Directors and the Congress on Nursing Practice in 1995. In June 2001, the ANA House of Delegates voted to accept a revised Code of Ethics, and in July 2001 the Congress of Nursing Practice and Economics voted to accept the new language, resulting in a fully approved Code of Ethics for Nurses with Interpretive Statements. A read-only version of this document is available at www.nursingworld.org/ethics/ecode.htm. Specific ANA position statements on selected ethics and human rights issues may be viewed at www.nursingworld.org/readroom/position/ethics (see Chapter 7).

The moral authority nurses possess by reason of their license and position in the health-care structure must be used to guard against those who may try to minimize the importance of that responsibility or, for any reason, attempt to convince nurses to set aside their responsibilities. Nursing research most often addresses the needs and behaviors of human beings. Embedded in

nurses' professional code of ethics is the charge to protect every person from harm. This responsibility extends beyond nursing *research* to include any client-related issue, any type of behavioral or biomedical research, or any questionable procedure.

In nurses' position of trust with clients, nurses possess a great deal of influence over a population that is especially vulnerable because of health issues and needs. This unique position of trust gives nurses a higher responsibility to protect and defend those in their care.

Informed Consent

Protection of human subjects underpins the conduct of research and implies that individuals have the information they need to make informed decisions (Box 24.4). They have the right to be fully informed, not only about the care they receive but also about any research in which they participate. Informed consent is both an ethical and a legal requirement in the research process. The ethical principle of self-determination is central to the process.

Besides those with special health considerations, certain groups of individuals are considered particularly vulnerable owing, in part, to their lack of ability to give informed consent or their potential susceptibility to coercion. These groups include children, the mentally retarded, the elderly, those with terminal diseases, the homeless, and those who may have altered levels of consciousness as the result of condition, medication, or sedation.

Nurses are well aware of the need for informed consent and the provision of information prior to procedures. This knowledge can serve nurses well in their obligation to obtain informed consent prior to conducting research. The key elements of informed consent for research can be found in Box 24.4.

The language of the consent form must be clear and understandable, written in the primary language of the client, and designed for those with

Box 24.4

Key Elements of Informed Consent

1. Researcher is identified and credentials presented.
2. Subject selection process is explained.
3. Purpose of the research is described.
4. Study procedures are discussed.
5. Potential risks are identified.
6. Potential benefits are described.
7. Compensation, if any, is discussed.
8. Alternative procedures, if any, are disclosed.
9. Assurances regarding anonymity or confidentiality are explained.
10. The right to refuse participation or withdraw from the study at any time is assured.
11. An offer to answer all questions honestly is made.
12. The means of obtaining the study results is described.

Source: Nieswiadomy, RM: Foundations of Nursing Research, 4th edition, copyright 2002. Adapted by permission of Pearson Education, Inc., Upper Saddle River, NJ.

no more than an eighth-grade reading level. Technical language should never be used. The Code of Federal Regulations states that subjects must never be asked to waive their rights or to release the investigation from liability or negligence. It is important to note that various institutions and researchers, in an extended effort to protect research participants, include more than the 12 elements listed in Box 24.4.

Process Consent

In qualitative research, an important concept is process consent, which requires that the researcher renegotiate the consent if any unanticipated events occur.[13] An example of this might be a situation in which two parents with a small child in the hospital have given consent for the taping and study of "a day in the life of a hospitalized toddler."

During taping of the event, the parents are informed by the physician that a diagnosis is being questioned and their child must subsequently

undergo an unexpected lumbar puncture. The parents may become visibly upset by this turn of events. In such a case the researcher should find a way of reconfirming the couple's ongoing interest in being part of the research study. When this family is given the opportunity to renegotiate the original agreement, the nurse researcher is confirming his or her role of advocate and proceeding in the best interest of all participants.

Detecting the Ethical Components of Written Research

It may be difficult to critique the ethical features of written research reports, but if there is evidence that permission to conduct the study was granted by an IRB, it is highly likely that the participants' rights were protected. Nurses have the responsibility of protecting the privacy and dignity of every individual, and the integrity of the nursing profession depends on doing what is right even when no one is watching.

Box 24.5 provides the guidelines for critiquing ethics in research.

Box 24.5

Guidelines for Critiquing the Ethical Features of Research

1. Was the study approved by an institutional review board (IRB)?
2. Was informed consent obtained from every subject?
3. Is there information regarding anonymity or confidentiality?
4. Were vulnerable subjects used?
5. Does it appear that any coercion may have been used?
6. Is it evident that potential benefits of participation outweigh the possible risks?
7. Were participants invited to ask questions about the study and told how to contact the researcher, should the need arise?
8. Were participants informed how to obtain results of the study?

Source: Nieswiadomy, RM: Foundations of Nursing Research, 4th edition, copyright 2002. Adapted by permission of Pearson Education, Inc., Upper Saddle River, NJ.

IMPLEMENTING RESEARCH IN THE PRACTICE SETTING

Knowledge that is generated by research and then translated into policy and procedure becomes the ultimate guide to the scientific practice of nursing. A primary responsibility of every nurse conducting research is the distribution of the findings (evidence) that have application in the client care setting. Conversely, the professional responsibility of every nurse caring for clients requires that all nursing interventions be planned on the basis of reliable research findings.

> *There is no such thing as a minor lapse of integrity. Tom Peters*

Nursing research is of no value to the profession, or to the client, if the practice supported by the research is not used in the clinical setting. Unlimited opportunities for the generation and the dissemination of new knowledge exist in nursing, but the truly daunting task addresses the challenge of transforming that knowledge into practice.

> *All truth passes through three stages: Ridicule, opposition and then acceptance as being self-evident. Arthur Schopenhauer*

The Call for Implementing Research

Research is critical to the professional practice of nursing. The Joint Commission on the Accreditation of Healthcare Organizations (JCAHO) accreditation guidelines specify that client care intervention must be based on information from scientifically valid and timely sources.

The mandate of the modern health-care system is that nurses make practice decisions based on the best scientific information available. Standard VII of the American Nurses Association (ANA) Standards of Clinical Nursing Practice states that "the nurse uses research findings in practice." Nurses may participate in research activities in a number of ways. They can conduct reviews of literature, critique research studies for the possibility of application to practice, or "[use] research findings in the development of policies, procedures and guidelines for client care."[14]

Approaches to Using Research

Nursing is not the only profession experiencing reluctance in transforming research into practice.

Even though new knowledge is expanding at an exponential rate, every discipline seems to have some type of research–practice gap. Nurses are often hesitant to change current traditional practice to EBP. They often identify significant difficulties involved in the changeover. Currently there are several models to help nurses apply research findings that support EBP. One model that appears both practical and relatively uncomplicated is found in Box 24.6.[15]

Promoting Change

It is often difficult for nurses to promote an environment conducive to change. In many hospitals, maintaining the status quo often appears to carry incentives that may intimidate even the most intuitive and confident change agent. The professional nurse committed to using "best evidence" to provide the best client care can be most effective by finding simple approaches that create an environment receptive to new research findings. Some helpful tactics include:

- Reading clinical journals regularly but also critically. Nursing professionals are well informed and believe in the concept of lifelong learning.
- Attending clinically focused nursing conferences where the latest client care interventions are presented and discussed.
- Learning to look for evidence that clearly supports the effectiveness and the feasibility of updating nursing interventions.
- Seeking work environments that promote the use of research findings and evidence-based care.
- Collaborating with a nurse researcher. Apprenticeship to one who masters a skill is an old but venerated means of learning that skill.
- Learning to critically scrutinize the status quo. Many worthwhile ideas for change come from those students and nurses "in the trenches" and at the bedside.
- Pursuing the possibility of a proposal and implementation of a project. If the nurse finds a research-based idea for clinical care interesting, then taking the steps to research it can be productive.

Box 24.6

Rosswurn and Larrabee Model for Application of Nursing Research

Assess the need for practice changes
(a) Involve all nurses that have a stake in the intervention or change.
(b) Identify problems associated with the current practice.
(c) Compare available information.

Link the problem intervention and outcomes
(a) Identify possible interventions.
(b) Develop outcome indicators.

Produce best evidence for consideration
(a) Conduct a review of existing literature.
(b) Compare and contrast the evidence found.
(c) Determine feasibility (including cost in dollars and time).
(d) Consider benefits and risks.

Design a proposed practice change
(a) Define the anticipated change.
(b) Identify necessary resources.
(c) Develop a plan based on desired outcomes.

Implement and evaluate the proposed change
(a) Conduct a pilot study.
(b) Assess the process and the outcomes.
(c) Make a decision to alter, accept, or reject the proposed change.

Support the change with ongoing evaluations of the outcomes
(a) Communicate the desired change to those involved.
(b) Conduct in-service education sessions.
(c) Revise standards of practice (policy/procedures) reflecting the change.
(d) Monitor the ongoing process and results.

Source: Rosswurm, M, and Larrabee, J: A model for change to evidence-based practice. Journal of Nursing Scholarship 31(4):317–322, 1999, with permission.

Conclusion

Modern health care has become so complex and demanding that simple trial-and-error approaches do not provide the high-quality information required for the safe, effective, and economical care demanded by well-informed consumers. The nursing profession is quickly moving away from the "I do it because it's always been done this way" method of care to scientifically rooted care practices based on research. As a result, nurses are gaining increased recognition as key members of the health-care team.

Also, nurses are now required to be able to analyze and evaluate research findings to determine which studies are of high quality and which can be used as a guide for nursing practice. Similarly, nurses are required to contribute to the body of nursing knowledge by participating in nursing research studies conducted at their facilities. It is presumed that nurses with advanced degrees will initiate and conduct high-quality research.

The ability of nurses to make thoughtful use of research is an important first step in the development of EBP. Society's call for cost containment, high-quality care, and documented outcomes of health-care services will continue to fuel the engine of positive health-care developments. As nursing looks to its future, research and EBP will increase in importance as factors that guide and inform the day-to-day practice of nurses.

GLOSSARY OF TERMS USED IN RESEARCH

Bias An influence that produces a distortion in the results of a research study.

Case study An in-depth qualitative study of a selected phenomenon involving a person, a group of people, or an institution.

Causal relationship A relationship between variables in which the presence or absence of one variable (known as the "cause") will determine the presence or absence of the other variable (known as the "effect").

Collaboration A cooperative venture among those with a common goal.

Conceptual framework A framework of concepts that demonstrate their relationships in a logical manner. Although less well developed than a theoretical framework, this framework may be used as a guide for a study.

Conceptual model A set of abstract constructs that explains phenomena of interest.

Correlation The degree of association between two variables.

Empirical evidence Objective data gathered through use of the human senses.

Epidemiologist One who studies the distribution and determinants of health and illness and the application of findings as a means of promoting health and preventing illness.

Ethical standards Standards determined by principles of moral values and moral conduct.

Ethnography A qualitative research approach involving the study of cultural groups.

Evidence-based practice (EBP) The selective and practical use of the best evidence, as demonstrated by research, to guide health care implementation and decisions.

Experimental research design A quantitative research design that meets all of the following criteria: an experimental variable that is manipulated, at least one experimental and one comparison group, and random assignments of participants to either the experimental or the comparison group.

Exploratory study The descriptive examination of available data to become as familiar as possible with the information.

Grounded theory An inductive approach to research using a systematic set of procedures to develop a theory that is then supported by, or "grounded in," the data.

Historical study Qualitative research involving the systematic collection and synthesis of data regarding people and events of the past.

Hypothesis A formal statement of the expected relationship between variables in a selected population.

Informed consent Consent to participate in a study given by one who has full understanding of the study before the study begins. Informed consent is based on the principle of the right of each individual to self-determination.

Institutional review board (IRB) A panel established at an agency, such as a hospital or university, to review all proposed research studies and to set standards for research involving human subjects.

Nonprobability sampling A sampling process in which a sample is selected from elements of a population through methods that are not random. Convenience, quota, and purposive sampling are examples.

Nuremberg code A code of conduct that serves as one of the recognized guides in the ethical conduct of research.

Nursing research A process that permits nurses to ask questions directed at gaining new knowledge to improve the profession, including elements of client care.

Phenomenology Qualitative research studies that examine lived experiences through descriptions of the meanings of such experiences by the individuals involved.

Primary research source A report or account of a research study written by the researcher(s) conducting the study. In historical research a primary source might be an original letter, diary, or other authenticated document.

Process consent A version of informed consent that supports renegotiation when a situation originally consented to undergoes change.

Qualitative research design A systematic but subjective research approach implemented to describe life experiences and give them meaning.

Quantitative research design A systematic and objective process used to describe and test relationships and evaluate causal interactions among variables.

Quasiexperimental design A type of experimental design in which there is either no comparison group or no random assignment of participants.

Random sample A selection process that ensures that each member of a population has an equal probability of being selected.

Reliability The dependability or degree of consistency with which an instrument measures what it is intended to measure.

Replication study A research study designed to repeat or duplicate earlier research. A different sample or setting may be used while the essential elements of the original study are kept intact.

Research design A blueprint for conducting a research study.

Research process A process that requires the comprehension of a unique language and involves the ability to apply a variety of research processes.

Review of literature An exploration of available information to determine what is known and what remains unknown about a subject.

Sample A subset of a population selected to participate in a study as representative of that population.

Scientific inquiry A logical, orderly means of collecting data for the generation and testing of ideas.

Theoretical framework A framework based on propositional statements derived from one theory or interrelated theories.

Validity The ability of an instrument to measure the variables that it is intended to measure.

Variable Any trait of an individuals, object, or situation that is susceptible to change and that may be manipulated or measured in quantitative research.

References

1. Fain, A: Reading, Understanding, and Applying Nursing Research. F.A. Davis, Philadelphia, 2004.
2. American Association of Colleges of Nursing, 1999. www.aacn.nche.edu/Publications/positions/rscposst.htm.
3. Polit, D, and Hungler, B: Nursing Research Principles and Methods. Lippincott, Philadelphia and New York, 1999.
4. Goodnow, M: Outlines of Nursing History. W.B. Saunders, Philadelphia and London, 1935.
5. Seymour, B, et al.: Valuing both critical and creative thinking in clinical practice: Narrowing the research-practice gap. Journal of Advanced Nursing 42(3): 288–297, 2003.
6. Le-May, A, et al.: Bridging the research-practice gap: Exploring the research cultures of practitioners and managers. Journal of Advanced Nursing 28: 428–437, 1998.
7. Fain, A: Reading, Understanding, and Applying Nursing Research. F.A. Davis, Philadelphia, 2004.
8. Evans, D: Systematic reviews: Gatekeepers of nursing knowledge. Journal of Clinical Nursing 10(5): 593–600, 2001.
9. Evers, G: Naming nursing: Evidence-based nursing. Nursing Diagnosis 12(4): 137–142, 2001.
10. Nieswiadomy, R: Foundations of Nursing Research. Prentice Hall, Englewood Cliffs, NJ, 2002.
11. French, P: The development of evidence-based nursing. Journal of Advanced Nursing 29(1): 72–79, 1999.
12. American Nurses' Association Commission on Nursing Research: Guidelines for the Investigative Function of Nurses. American Nurses' Association, Kansas City, MO, 1989.
13. Munhall, P: Ethical considerations in qualitative research. Western Journal of Nursing Research 10(2): 150–162, 1988.
14. American Nurses Association Standards on Clinical Practice, 1991, p 16.
15. Rosswurm, M, and Larrabee, J: A model for change to evidence-based practice. Journal of Nursing Scholarship 31(4): 317–322, 1999.

Bibliography

Aroian, K: Effective, efficient and equitable health care: What can cultural diversity teach us about sacred cows. Journal of Professional Nursing 20(6): 349–351, 2005.

Ax, S, and Kincade, E: Nursing students' perceptions of research usefulness, implementation and training. Journal of Advanced Nursing 35(2): 161–170, 2001.

Brink, P, and Wood, M: Basic Steps in Planning Nursing Research. Jones and Bartlett, Boston, 2001.

Brockopp, D, and Hastings-Tolsma, M: Fundamentals of Nursing Research. Jones and Bartlett, Boston, 2003.

Burns, N, and Grove, S: The practice of nursing research conduct, critique and utilization. Elsevier Saunders, St. Louis, 2005.

Callister, M, et al.: Inquiry in baccalaureate nursing education: Fostering evidence-based practice. Nursing Education 44(2): 59–65, 2005.

Chesnay, M: Caring for the Vulnerable: Perspectives in Nursing Theory, Practice and Research. Jones and Bartlett, Boston, 2005.

Dempsey, P, and Dempsey, A: Using Nursing Research. Lippincott, Philadelphia and New York, 2000.

Ellett, M, et al.: Ethical and legal issues of conducting nursing research via the internet. Journal of Professional Nursing 20(1):68–72, 2004.

Ferguson, L, and Day, R: Evidence-based nursing education: Myth or reality? Nursing Education 44(3): 107–116, 2005.

Karigan, M: Ethics in clinical research: The nursing perspective. Amercian Journal of Nursing 101(9): 26–31, 2001.

Katz, J, et al.: Essential qualifications for nursing students. Nursing Outlook 52(6): 277–289, 2004.

Larrabee, J: Advancing quality improvement through using the best evidence to change practice. Journal of Nursing Care Quality 19(1): 10–13, 2004.

LoBiondo-Wood, G, and Haber, J: Nursing Research Methods, Critical Appraisal, and Utilization. Mosby, St. Louis, 2002.

Long, K: Preparing nurses for the 21st century: Re-envisioning nursing education and practice. Journal of Professional Nursing 20(2): 82–89, 2004.

Manojlovich, M: Predictors of professional practice behaviors in hospital settings. Nursing Research 54(1): 41–47, 2005.

Mitchell, P: The "so what" question: The impact of nursing research. Journal of Professional Nursing 20(6): 347–349, 2005

Pare, R, and Elovitz, L: Data warehousing: An aid to decision-making. T.H.E. Journal 43(9): 32–34, 2005.

Streubert, H, and Carpenter, D: Qualitative Research in Nursing. Lippincott, Philadelphia, 1995.

Szirony, T, et al.: Perceptions of nursing faculty regarding ethical issues in nursing research. Nursing Education 43(6): 220–280, 2004.

25

Alternative and Complementary Healing Practices

Lydia DeSantis

Learning Objectives

After completing this chapter, the reader will be able to:

- Compare the philosophy and objectives of alternative and complementary healing modalities with those of conventional Western medicine.
- List major reasons why a growing number of people use alternative and complementary healing modalities.
- Describe major types of alternative and complementary healing modalities.
- Summarize methods by which nurses and clients can obtain information about alternative and complementary healing modalities.
- Evaluate a client for use of alternative and complementary healing modalities.
- Identify the strengths and weaknesses of alternative and complementary healing modalities.

A DIFFERENT KIND OF HEALING

Complementary and alternative health-care practices are widely used by a large percentage of the population. Their popularity continues to increase dramatically with clients of all ages and backgrounds. It is important for nurses to have a good understanding of this type of health care to ensure their clients' safety and well-being and to be supportive of their practices.

According to the World Health Organization (WHO), 80 percent of the world's population uses what Americans call "alternative" practices as their primary source of health care. Because of the widely accepted use of these practices, WHO has officially sanctioned the incorporation of "safe and effective [alternative] remedies and practices for use in public and private health services." Currently, between 34 and 42 percent of Americans (60 to 83 million people) use alternative and complementary healing practices, as do 20 to 70 percent of people in Western Europe, 33 percent in Finland, and 49 percent in Australia.[1]

The trend toward alternative practices has continued to grow in the United States since the 1990s. Studies show that 40 percent of people have developed an increasingly positive attitude toward alternative practices, whereas only 2 percent had more negative opinions. Both the general public—72 percent—and health maintenance organizations (HMOs)—73 percent—expect consumer demand for this area of health care to remain moderate to strong.

> "*The trend toward alternative practices has continued to grow in the United States since the 1990s.*"

Few people—4 to 11 percent—rely solely on alternative practices to treat illness, but the number relying on conventional health care only is declining.[2]

DEFINING ALTERNATIVE AND COMPLEMENTARY HEALING

Several definitions are used for alternative and complementary health-care practices. They are sometimes defined as practices outside of conventional, science-based Western medicine and not sanctioned by the official health-care system. A considerable range of practices and concepts is included in alternative and complementary healing. The glossary at the end of this chapter outlines many of these practices.

An Outdated Definition

There is no universally accepted definition. Many alternative health-care practices originated many years ago within cultural belief systems and healing traditions. A commonly used definition in the United States for alternative and complementary modalities comes from the National Center for Complementary and Alternative Medicine (NCCAM), an agency of the National Institutes of Health. The NCCAM definition is "those treatments and health-care practices not taught widely in medical schools, not generally used in hospitals, and not usually reimbursed by medical insurance companies."

This definition is quickly becoming outdated. Many medical and nursing schools now include courses on alternative and complementary health-care practices. Also, the practice of alternative medicine is gradually becoming part of conventional health care. Physicians, nurses, and other health-care professionals are responding to the growing public use of these practices by incorporating selected modalities into their own client care. Physicians have begun referring clients to a variety of alternative healers and using alternative therapies for their own health.

A Holistic Basis

In this chapter, alternative and complementary medicine is defined as the understanding and use of healing therapies not commonly considered part of Western biomedicine. The focus here is mainly on methods of self-care, wellness, self-healing, health promotion, and illness prevention. Therapies and practices are called *alternative* when used alone or with other alternative therapies, and *complementary* when used with conventional therapies.

The use of the term *healing* is preferred to *medicine.* Alternative and complementary modalities typically are based in holistic philosophies, which go beyond treatment or cure of the physiological and psychological dimensions of care commonly associated with modern, scientific biomedicine. Holism refers to treatment of the whole person (body–mind–spirit) in that person's environmental context (physical, biological, social, cultural, and spiritual).

What Do You Think?

Do you use any alternative health-care practices? What are they? Why do you use them?

_____

_____

_____

_____

_____

_____

_____

_____

_____

_____

_____

USE OF ALTERNATIVE AND COMPLEMENTARY THERAPIES

Who Uses Them

In most national studies of alternative therapy users, ethnic and racial minorities are underrepresented, particularly among persons who do not speak English. Such exclusions raise questions about whether the use rate of alternative therapies in the United States may exceed 42 percent, because the use of alternative therapies among immigrant populations and those with lower incomes tends to be high. Many such populations have grown up with these therapies as "folk" medicine, and their worldviews encompass different concepts of health, illness, and healing. Alternative health-care practices are most popular among women, people aged 35 to 49, people with higher educational levels (some graduate education), and those with annual incomes of more than $50,000.

Why Their Use Has Increased

Three general theories have been advanced to explain the growing use of alternative and complementary healing: (1) dissatisfaction with conventional health care, (2) a desire for greater control over one's health, and (3) a desire for cultural and philosophical congruence with personal beliefs about health and illness. Many other client-specific reasons have also been postulated, such as

> *Three general theories have been advanced to explain the growing use of alternative and complementary healing: (1) dissatisfaction with conventional health care, (2) a desire for greater control over one's health, and (3) a desire for cultural and philosophical congruence with personal beliefs about health and illness.*

belief in the effectiveness of alternative therapies and the individual's health status (Box 25.1). The rising cost of conventional health care may play a role as well.

Dissatisfaction

The increasing use of alternative therapies is due in part to the feeling that conventional health care is unable to deal with major health problems or improve a person's general health. People who have a high degree of distrust in conventional health care often rely primarily on alternative therapies. This lack of trust has increased recently for several reasons, including:

- Conflicting information from health-care–related studies and clinical trials about risk prevention and health promotion. For example, clients no longer

Box 25.1

Reasons for Use of Alternative and Complementary Modalities

People use alternative therapies alone or together with conventional health care for a variety of reasons. There is no single predictor of use, and the reasons for use may vary from situation to situation. Persons who seem to benefit the most from the alternative approach are those who:
- Prefer a personal relationship with healers
- Refuse to give up hope and hopefulness, regardless of the illness or life-state
- Desire to focus on wellness, health promotion and maintenance, and illness prevention
- Are concerned with gentle alleviation and management of suffering and illness rather than aggressive management of the end-stage of life through technology, medications, surgery, and other invasive procedures
- Wish to participate actively in decision-making about their health care
- Believe in the holistic aspects of existence rather than in the primacy of biological and physiological aspects
- Are "culture creatives"—persons at the leading edge of innovation and culture change who have been exposed to alternative lifestyles and worldviews compatible with those from which alternative and complementary modalities and theories have arisen
- Share cultural and philosophical views similar to those from which alternative and complementary modalities have developed

Source: Austin, JA: Why patients use alternative medicine. Journal of the American Medical Association 279:1548, 1998. From Holistic Health Promotion & Complementary Therapies Manual 1st edition by ASPEN, 1998. Reprinted with permission from Delmar Learning.

know what to believe about salt intake, normal cholesterol levels, alcohol use, or hormone replacement therapy.

- Continuing emphasis of conventional health care on curative rather than preventive aspects of care. The lack of emphasis on illness prevention limits the ability of individuals to live long lives relatively free of disability from major chronic illnesses, such as arthritis, diabetes, cancer, and cardiovascular disease.
- Growing concern about costs, safety, and access to conventional health care. Many people are concerned about the increased incidence of hospital-acquired diseases, the many deadly medication errors committed over the past few years, the ever-increasing number of invasive procedures, antibiotic-resistant bacteria, and reliance on impersonal technology.

Desire for Control

Some people who use alternative therapies believe conventional care is too intolerant, authoritarian, and impersonal. They feel that some conventional health-care professionals lack sensitivity to the wishes of clients and their families when developing treatment plans. Clients believe they should be partners in decision-making about their care rather than just having decisions handed down to them.

In the United States, the majority of people report being reluctant to tell conventional health-care professionals that they use alternative therapies. Although almost all (89 percent) who use alternative therapies do so under the supervision of an alternative healer, about half of this same group do not consult a conventional health-care professional before they begin. Fourteen percent of persons see both conventional health-care professionals and alternative healers. Similar patterns of self-care and nondisclosure to conventional health-care professionals are found throughout the industrialized world.[3]

Holistic Philosophy

Conventional health care is often faulted for its limited focus on the physiological dimension of health and curing to the exclusion of the unity of mind–body–spirit healing. Another negative characteristic of conventional health care is its excessive dependence on medicine, surgery, and technology rather than on the more natural and noninvasive alternative approach that focuses on self-care and self-healing.

Belief in Effectiveness

Clients who use alternative therapies do so because they believe those therapies will work, either alone or when combined with conventional treatments. Persons who consider their health to be poor or who have chronic illnesses report greater benefits from alternative than conventional health care and are more likely to try both at the same time. Referral from conventional health-care professionals, friends, or other users of alternative therapies is also a prominent reason for the simultaneous use of both systems. For many clients, alternative therapies simply make them feel better than conventional health care does.

Cost of Alternative Care

Estimated costs of alternative medicines (herbs and nutritional supplements), diet products, equipment, and books and courses totaled $14 billion in 2000. Sixty-seven percent of HMOs cover one or more alternative and complementary healing (ACH) modalities, but coverage is uneven and varies regionally. Chiropractic is the most common covered service (65 percent), followed by acupuncture (31 percent), massage therapy (11 percent), and vitamin therapy (6 percent). HMOs expect to increase coverage for acupuncture to 36 percent, acupressure to 31 percent, massage therapy to 30 percent, and vitamin therapy to 27 percent. The most important reasons for adding coverage for these services are public demand, legislative mandate, and demonstrated clinical effectiveness.

CLASSIFYING ALTERNATIVE METHODS

The underlying goals of any type of health care include preventing illness, promoting and maintaining health, and caring for people while alleviating the suffering caused by illness. However, despite these common elements, health-care practices vary profoundly in their modalities (technologies), practitioner education and monitoring, underlying concepts (models) of health and illness, modes of care delivery, and social and legal mandates to provide care. Because of the large number of variables, a confusing array of health-care systems, practitioners, and healing modalities has developed. Two systems that can be used to help define and classify alternative and complementary therapies are the Healing Matrix[4] and the NCCAM classification.

The Healing Matrix

The Healing Matrix (Table 25.1) contrasts conventional and alternative modalities and practitioners. The alternative modalities shown are (1) representative of those most commonly known by the general public, (2) sought in the United States and industrialized world, and (3) practiced most often by conventional health-care professionals, including nurses.

A Cross-Section of Care

Modalities in column 1 are technologies that cut across various healing systems. The technologies are arranged vertically from the most concrete to the most abstract. The remaining columns include various healing modalities from conventional, marginal, and alternative healing systems.

Physical Manipulation Technologies. These are also known as "bodywork therapies." They are administered by a therapist or by the clients themselves as part of a self-care program. They include

Table 25.1   The Healing Matrix

Technologies	Orthodox	Marginal	Alternative	
Physical manipulation	Surgery	Chiropractic	Rolfing	Craniosacral alignments
Ingested or applied substances	Physical therapy	Homeopathy	Feldenkrais	Massage therapy
Uses of energy	Pharmacology	Vitamin therapy	Naturopathic remedies	Yoga, Akido, Tai Chi
Mental	Laser surgery	Acupuncture	Herbs	Reflexology
Spiritual	Psychiatry	Acupressure	Flower remedies	Aromatherapy
		Secular or spiritual counseling	Reiki	Diet alternatives
		Established support groups (e.g., 12-step programs)	Magnetic or polarity healing	
		Therapeutic touch	Chakra balancing
		Self-help groups	Radionics
		Visualizations	Use of color, gems, and crystals
		Affirmations	Psychic, spiritual, or intuitive healing

Sources: Adapted from Engebretson, J, and Wardell, D: A contemporary view of alternative healing modalities. Nurse Practitioner 18:51, 1993.

health rituals and breathing exercises to better bring about the union of body–mind–spirit.

Ingested or Applied Substances. A number of substances, including herbs, vitamins and other nutritional supplements, and dietary regimens have the goal of helping the body heal itself, rid itself of toxins, and promote general health and wellness.

Energy Therapies. These modes of treatment maintain or restore health through the balancing of energy flow in the body. The goal is to restore the natural movement of vital forces or life essences that may have been disturbed by diseases or psychological factors.

Mental (Psychic) and Spiritual Therapies. Included in these therapies are group or individual counseling techniques that help the client develop or attain spiritual and personal growth. Examples include intuiting, revelations, visualization, astrological and other readings, and invoking the spirit world.

Conventional Health Care

The modalities listed in column 2 (orthodox [conventional]) are part of the official health-care system in the United States. They are based on knowledge rooted in scientific and biomedical principles.

Licensed Alternative Care

The modalities in column 3 (marginal) are generally learned through the study of the standard curricula in institutions of higher education. Alternative healers practicing such modalities are usually licensed by the state, and most have credentialing and a professional body that sets standards for their practice. These modalities are not considered conventional therapies in the United States but may be part of conventional health-care systems in other nations.

For example, acupuncture is an essential mode of treatment in traditional Chinese medicine, which, along with biomedicine, forms the conventional health-care system in the People's Republic of China. In 1997, The National Institutes of Health Consensus Panel on Acupuncture reviewed research studies and other information on its safety, efficacy, and effectiveness. The studies showed that there is sufficient evidence to approve acupuncture as an intervention for adult general and dental postoperative pain and to treat nausea and vomiting associated with chemotherapy.

Intuitively Based Care

The modalities presented in column 4 (alternative) are less physiological. They are based on a more intuitive

type of knowledge. Most alternative healers practicing such modalities are self-taught, have learned through working with more experienced practitioners, have attended courses or workshops on particular modalities, or have learned by a combination of methods. The alternative modalities in the bottom cell on the far right have the most intuitive knowledge base; that is, insights about the spiritual or physical self are gained through direct revelations or interpreted by another. These include readers (e.g., astrologers or seers) and spiritual healers in touch with divine forces.

The NCCAM Classification

In 1992, Congress mandated the establishment of an Office of Alternative Medicine in the National Institutes of Health to enhance the study of ACH. In 1998, the Office became the National Center for Complementary and Alternative Medicine (NCCAM). Its mission is to conduct and support both basic and applied research and training and the dissemination of ACH information to conventional health-care professionals, alternative healers, and the public.

Complementary and alternative medicine (CAM) is defined by the NCCAM as those practices not commonly included in or used by conventional medicine. Seven major categories of CAM are defined and subdivided into practices that (1) fall under CAM, (2) are found in conventional health care but are classified as behavioral medicine, and (3) are overlapping—that is, they can fall in the domain of either CAM or behavioral medicine. Table 25.2 summarizes the NCCAM classification.

(text continues on page 512)

Table 25.2 Categories of Alternative Practice

Alternative Medical Systems	

Traditional Oriental Medicine
Acupuncture
Diet
External and internal qi gong

Herbal formulas
Massage and manipulation (Tui Na)
Tai Chi

Traditional Indigenous Systems
Ayurvedic medicine
Curanderismo
Central and South American
Kampo medicine
Native-American medicine

Traditional African medicine
Traditional Aboriginal medicine
Unani-tibbi
Siddhi

Alternative Western Systems
CAM
Homeopathy
Naturopathy
Orthomolecular medicine

Overlapping
Anthroposophically extended medicine

Mind–Body Interventions		

Mind–Body Methods
CAM
Yoga
Tai Chi
Internal qi gong

Behavioral Medicine
Hypnosis
Meditation
Biofeedback

Overlapping
Art, music, and dance therapies
Humor
Journaling

Religion and Spirituality
CAM
Confession
Nonlocality

Nontemporality
Soul retrieval

"Special" healers
Spiritual healing

Social and Contextual Areas
CAM
Caring-based approaches (e.g.,
    holistic nursing, pastoral care)
Intuitive diagnosis

Overlapping
Community-based approaches (e.g.,
    Native American "sweat" rituals)
Explanatory models
Placebo

Biologically Based Therapies			

Phytotherapy or Herbalism

Aloe vera	Echinacea	Ginseng	Mistletoe
Bee pollen	Evening primrose	Green tea	Peppermint oil
Biloba	Garlic	Hawthorne	Saw palmetto
Cat's claw	Ginger	Kava Kava	Witch hazel
Dong Quai	Ginkgo	Licorice root	Valerian

Special Diet Therapies

Atkins	McDougall	Fasting	Paleolithic
Diamond	Ornish	High fiber	Vegetarian
Kelly-Gonzalez	Pritikin	Macrobiotic	
Gerson	Wigmore	Mediterranean	
Livingston-Wheeler	Asian	Natural hygiene	

Biologically Based Therapies

Orthomolecular Therapies
Single Nutrients (partial listing)

Amino acids	Folic acid	Lysine	Niacinamide	Thiamine
Ascorbic acid	Glutamine	Manganese	Potassium	Tyrosine
Boron	Glucosamine sulfate	Magnesium	Selenium	Vanadium
Calcium	Iodine	Medium-chain triglycerides	Silicon	Vitamin A
Carotenes	Inositol	Melatonin	Glandular products	Vitamin D
Choline	Iron	Niacin	Riboflavin	Vitamin K
Fatty acids	Lipoic acid		Taurine	

Pharmacological, Biological, and Instrumental Interventions
Products

Antineoplastons	Cone therapy	Hyperbaric oxygen
Bee pollen	Enderlin products	Induced remission therapy
Cartilage	Enzyme therapies	Ozone
Cell therapy	Gallo immunotherapy	Revici system
Coley's toxins	H_2O_2	

Procedures/Devices

Apitherapy	Electrodiagnostics	Neural therapy
Bioresonance	Iridology	
Chirography	MORA device	

Manipulative and Body-Based Methods

Chiropractic Medicine
Massage and Bodywork

Acupressure	Feldenkrais technique	Reflexology
Alexander technique	Osteopathic manipulative therapy (OMT)	Rolfing
Applied kinesiology	Pilates method	Swedish massage
Chinese Tui Na massage	Polarity	Trager bodywork
Craniosacral OMT		

Unconventional Physical Therapies

Colonics	Heat and electrotherapies	Light and color therapies
Diathermy	Hydrotherapy	

Energy Therapies

Biofield Therapies

External qi gong	Healing touch	Reiki
Healing science	Huna	Therapeutic Touch

Bioelectromagnetically Based Therapies*

Alternating and direct current fields	Magnetic fields	Pulsed fields

*unconventional use of electromagnetic fields

Source: Adapted from National Center for Complementary and Alternative Medicine: Classification of Alternative Medicine Practices, April 26, 2000. Available at: www.ccam.nih.gov/tcp/classify/lndex.html.

Category I

Category I includes alternative systems of theory and practice developed outside Western biomedicine. For example, acupuncture and Oriental medicine are grounded in traditional Chinese medicine. Also included in this category are traditional indigenous systems, which include all medical systems other than acupuncture and Oriental medicine that developed outside of Western biomedicine. It also includes unconventional Western systems not classified elsewhere that were developed in the West but are not considered part of biomedicine, such as homeopathy.

Finally, this category includes naturopathy, an unconventional medical system that has gained prominence in the United States. This eclectic approach consists of various natural systems, such as herbalism, lifestyle therapies, and diet as therapy.

Category II

Category II includes mind–body practices, religion and spirituality, and social and contextual areas. Mind–body medicine involves a variety of approaches to health care and contains three subcategories. Mind–body systems are seldom practiced alone but are usually combined with lifestyle interventions.

Mind–body methods may be part of a traditional medical system. They are sometimes used in conventional health-care practices; however they are characterized as CAM when used for conditions for which they are not normally prescribed. Religion and spirituality include treatments directed toward biological functions or clinical conditions. Social and contextual areas include treatment methods that are not included in other categories, such as cultural and symbolic interventions.

Category III

Biologically based therapies include products, interventions, and practices that are natural in origin and biologically based. They may or may not overlap with conventional medicine and its use of dietary supplements.

Phytotherapy, or herbalism, is the use of plant-derived products for purposes of prevention and treatment. Diet therapies use special diets to reduce risk factors or treat chronic diseases. Orthomolecular medicine is the use of nutritional

products and food supplements that are not included in other categories for prevention and treatment of disease. Pharmacological, biological, and instrumental interventions are those not covered in other categories and administered in an unconventional manner.

Category IV

Manipulative and body-based methods include body manipulation, body movement, or both.

Category V

Energy therapies are based on manipulation of biofields with bioelectromagnetically based therapies. Biofields include energy systems and energy fields internal and external to the body that are used for medical purposes. Bioelectromagnetics is the use of electromagnetic fields in an unconventional manner for medical reasons.

COMPARING CONVENTIONAL AND ALTERNATIVE PRACTICES

Many similarities exist between alternative and conventional health care. As they attempt to achieve similar goals, they may overlap in method, even though the methods are derived from different concepts of reality and different theoretical models. Table 25.3 summarizes characteristics often cited as common to alternative healing and contrasts them with those usually associated with conventional health care.

A Reductionist Philosophy

In general, conventional medicine focuses on the physical or material part of the person, the body. It is concerned with the structure, function, and connections or communication between material elements that compose the body, such as bones, muscles, and nerves. Conventional medicine generally views all humans as being very similar biologically. Disease is seen as a deviation from what is generally considered to be a normal biological or somatic state.

Conventional medicine is sometimes considered reductionistic because it tends to reduce very complex entities (humans) to seemingly equal and more simple beings who are all anatomically and physiologically similar. From this perspective, it is believed that all individuals will respond in more or

Table 25.3 Contrasts Between Conventional and Alternative Health Care

Conventional	Alternative/Complementary
Chemotherapy	Plants and other natural products
Curing/treating	Healing/ministering care
Disease category	Unique individual
End-stage	Hope/hopefulness
Focus is on disease and illness	Focus is on health and wellness
Illness treatment	Health promotion and illness prevention
Individual is viewed as disease category	Individual is viewed as unique being
Nutrition is adjunct and supportive to treatment	Nutrition is the basis of health, wellness, and treatment
Objectivism: person is separate from disease	Subjectivism: person is integral to the illness
Patient/Client	Person
Practitioner as authority	Practitioner as facilitator
Practitioner paternalism/client dependency	Practitioner as partner/person empowerment
Positivism/materialism: data are physically measurable	Metaphysical: entity is energy system or vital force
Reductionistic	
Specialist care	Holistic
Symptom relief	Self-care
Somatic (body biologic and physiologic) model	Alleviation of causative factors
Science is only source of knowledge and truth	Behavioral-psycho-social-spiritual model
Technological/invasive	Multiple sources of knowledge and truth
	Natural/noninvasive

less the same ways to causative agents, such as bacteria and viruses, and respond similarly to common treatments, such as medicines and surgery. In other words, a person with measles, cirrhosis of the liver, or breast cancer will have a similar course of illness as other persons with those illnesses and will respond to treatments in basically the same manner.

Diagnosis by Category

Conventional medicine has developed extensive disease categories, and great emphasis is placed on diagnosis and cure based on the assessment of physical signs and symptoms. Most newly developed medications, when they are in the human testing phase, are tested on men between the ages of 25 and 35, with the presumption that they will work similarly in women, the elderly, and children. That presumption is not always accurate and there is a growing trend at pharmaceutical companies to test medications on

> *Most newly developed medications, when they are in the human-testing phase, are tested on men between the ages of 25 and 35, with the presumption that they will work similarly in women, the elderly, and children. That presumption is not always accurate.*

groups of persons for whom they are more likely to be used.

Integration of Nonmaterial Factors

The physical body is the primary focus of conventional medicine. Because of this almost exclusive focus on the physical body, conventional medicine often does not consider or include the nonmaterialistic aspects of health and illness in diagnosis and treatment decisions. Thus, spiritual, psychological, sociocultural, behavioral, and energy system aspects play little or no role in conventional medical treatment.

Conventional medicine does not generally view the client as an integrated person-body that is affected simultaneously by both material and nonmaterial factors during everyday life. The integration of these elements is not seen as important to the person's state of wellness or illness; therefore, therapies based on the concept of holism are not deemed to be important. Although the concept of a psychosocial body has gained some interest in Western practice, it has not been effectively incorporated into conventional care. The energetic and spiritual bodies are largely ignored.

The Holistic Approach

The Multiple-Body View

In contrast, the alternative approach views the person-body as consisting of multiple, integrated elements that incorporate both the materialistic and nonmaterialistic aspects of existence. These elements include the physical (material), spiritual, energetic, and social bodies. This view allows for various interpretations of how the different components of the person-body interact and function to affect health and illness, and respond to different therapeutic interventions.

The integration of multiple bodies into a unified but distinctly individual person-body results in the belief that the person-body responds as a whole to factors that affect its state of well-being. Although the signs and symptoms of illness for one person are similar to another person's, they may indicate different underlying causes on the basis of variable risk factors. From this viewpoint, diagnostic measures and interventions cannot be based on only one aspect of the person's being, but must be tailored to the person-body of each individual.

A Capacity for Self-Healing

A variety of alternative modalities are often needed to diagnose and treat each individual holistically. It often is not obvious when the health problems of the physical body correspond to the dynamics of the energetic body or when the energetic body merges with the spiritual body, and how they all are eventually integrated into the psychosocial body. The mediating role of the psychosocial body in the alternative approach emphasizes each person's capacity for self-healing. The importance of the mind–body interaction to elicit the placebo response, and the need for clients to participate actively in the monitoring and maintenance of their health and well-being, are positive factors in the diagnosis and treatment of their illness.

The multiple-body view found in some alternative health-care practices requires an eclectic approach to health promotion and maintenance. The diagnosis and treatment of illness from a multiple body view require more than dependence on a single

healing tradition centered on a one-body concept or on a fixed set of diagnostic criteria. The alternative approach requires active participation of both well and ill persons to better promote health or diagnose and treat disorders, rather than mere passive acceptance of a diagnosis and treatment plan from conventional health-care professionals.

Combining Modalities

The alternative philosophy includes both the material and nonmaterial aspects of the individual, stimulation of the self-healing forces, and the determination of a person's unique needs. It uses the concepts and treatment modalities of several healing traditions simultaneously. These modalities are based on different worldviews or concepts of reality and address the individual healing needs of each person.

For example, acupuncturists may also use massage and other types of bodywork and energy-system methods; chiropractors may incorporate diet, herbs, and other kinds of naturopathic methodologies into chiropractic spinal manipulations; and massage therapists may include mind–body techniques such as meditation, imagery, and visualization.

What Do You Think?

Name someone you know or know of who has gotten better after an illness although not expected to. Why do you think this happened?

_____

_____

_____

_____

_____

_____

_____

_____

_____

_____

The concept of a multiple-body individual is central to alternative and complementary healing. Healers function as facilitators in the promotion of health and healing (Box 25.2). In contrast,

Box 25.2

Defining Alternative Healers

Alternative healers practice one or more alternative or complementary modalities and are not also licensed as conventional health-care professionals. Conventional health-care professionals who incorporate hands-on alternative and complementary modalities into their conventional patient care are termed *integrative practitioners*. They should undergo the same educational, certification, and licensing processes of both conventional and alternative healers for the modalities they use.

Creating a universally applicable definition of alternative healers is extremely difficult because of the wide variety of healing traditions in use and the number of specialized healing techniques contained within them. The difficulty is compounded by the fact that many alternative healers incorporate various modalities from different healing traditions into their practices. For example, chiropractors commonly use therapeutic touch, acupuncture, acupressure, massage therapy, and naturopathic or homeopathic therapies. Massage therapists may combine multiple types of massage (e.g., Alexander, Swedish, Trager, and sports) with therapeutic touch, aromatherapy, reflexology, nutritional supplements, and electromagnetic therapies. The growing use of alternative practices by conventional health-care professionals further complicates the task of defining and classifying alternative healers and their practices.

conventional therapy relies primarily on the concept of the physical-body individual, and conventional health-care providers function as experts in determining the meaning of physical signs and symptoms of health or illness and prescribing interventions to promote health or cure illness. The concepts of wellness and holism, self-healing, energy systems, nutrition, and plant-based medicine can be used to compare and contrast alternative and conventional methods of healing.

> **"** *The concept of a multiple-body individual is central to alternative and complementary healing. Healers function as facilitators in the promotion of health and healing.* **"**

Wellness and Holism

Therapy from Outside

Wellness, from the perspective of conventional health care, tends to focus on individuals who are seen as being at risk for illness. Prevention often begins when signs or symptoms arise and is directed at alleviating them rather than treating or removing their underlying cause. At-risk individuals are permitted to engage in risky behaviors as long as conventional health care can find treatments or palliative measures for diseases it cannot prevent. From this perspective, health is often defined as the absence of disease and is considered synonymous with wellness.

The focus of conventional health care is reductionistic rather than holistic because treatment and diagnosis are frequently centered on the cellular, organ, or system levels of the body. It emphasizes the biological–physiological (body) dimension of the client and treats only the disease process for which signs and symptoms are already evident. The cause of illness is attributed to external forces or risk factors that "invade" the body from the surrounding physical, social, or biological environments.

From the biomedical view, treatment usually centers on identifying potentially dangerous or invading agents and then destroying, immobilizing, or extracting them from the person's body. Interventions consist mainly of chemotherapeutic agents (medications), surgery, or other externally imposed treatments to prevent a person considered at risk from becoming ill or to prevent signs and symptoms from becoming full-blown diseases.

Therapy from Within

In contrast to conventional health care, the alternative model views wellness as a state in which individuals are in harmony or balance with their internal and external worlds. This approach is a common thread in nursing models or theories of health (see Chapter 4). Alternative modalities hold that wellness can rarely be imposed on a person by an outside entity or agency. Rather, wellness is achieved mainly by individuals through the process of self-care. The individual assumes responsibility for maintaining his or her own state of health or wellness. The individual, when ill, works to return to a state of wellness by restoring both the internal and external (environmental) state of balance and harmony.

"The human spirit incorporates the values, perception of meaning, and purpose in life that can positively or negatively affect the ability to heal and achieve wellness. "

External disruptions—such as work stress, personal tragedy, a troublesome interpersonal relationship, or illness of a parent, spouse, or child—are seen as capable of affecting internal harmony and producing signs and symptoms of physical, emotional, or spiritual illness. This provides a holistic view of individuals in which they are one with their internal and external environments, thereby requiring holistic care. Treatment must address the whole individual (body–mind–spirit) in an environmental (physical, biological, social, cultural, and spiritual) context.

Spirituality is an essential part of holistic treatment (see Chapter 20). The human spirit incorporates the values, perception of meaning, and purpose in life that can positively or negatively affect the ability to heal and achieve wellness. From this perspective, health (balance or harmony), or the absence of illness, is but one aspect of wellness.

Self-Care

In the alternative system, first-level measures involve self-care aimed at wellness and can generally be performed independently. Some examples include exercising, eating a well-balanced diet, praying, getting enough sleep, cleaning the house, using defensive driving measures, doing breast or testicular self-examinations, applying sunscreen at the beach, and practicing good hygiene.

The next level of self-care requires seeking the assistance of others to achieve balance in self and the environment. This level includes getting help to find satisfying employment, seeking prenatal care or taking parenting classes when pregnant, going to

"Conventional health practitioners tend to dismiss the effects of healing after alternative modalities have been used by blaming it on the placebo response. They feel that healing takes place only because the individual believes the treatment is effective. "

community meetings to address environmental safety and citizen quality-of-life issues, undergoing routine health screening examinations (such as mammography and dental checkups), obtaining glasses to correct myopia, and getting vaccinations and keeping them up to date. Other alternative measures, such as acupuncture and energy therapies, require a high degree of specialist assistance.

The third level of self-care requires a high degree of specialist assistance from alternative healers and others to deal with major disruptions in internal or external well-being. Measures from this level focus on the spiritual dimension and include searching for personal awakening, enlightenment, and self-actualization. Effective modalities to achieve this goal are often rooted in other systems of health care such as traditional Chinese medicine, Ayurveda, and spiritualism. In some cases, individuals may require the use of alternative modalities to deal with illnesses when conventional health care is no longer effective.

Self-Healing

Both alternative and conventional health care believe the body has the capacity to heal itself. The alternative system places self-healing as the central principle of its model and sees it as the basis of all healing. Thus, alternative healers focus on helping people determine why the cells of their body are sick and search for imbalances from a holistic perspective.

Conventional health care views the ability of the body to self-heal primarily through the normal process of replacing cells; examples include the physiological and biological processes involved in wound healing. Conventional care approaches the concept of body self-healing by questioning why the cells are not replacing themselves and attempts to facilitate healing through external means, such as surgery, medications, or other invasive measures.

The Placebo Response

Conventional health practitioners tend to dismiss the effects of healing after alternative modalities have been used by attributing them to the placebo response. They feel that healing takes place only because the individual believes the treatment is effective. In conventional medicine, the term *placebo* has come to signify a type of sham treatment instituted to please difficult or anxious clients, or a sugar pill given when health-care professionals have nothing more to offer the client. In biomedical clinical research, a placebo is a nontreatment given to the control group under the assumption that it will not change any physiological responses and will therefore prove the effectiveness of the active treatments.

> *Healers who believe in the therapeutic effectiveness of interventions and are able to convey that belief to their clients achieve more positive responses than healers who remain skeptical about the interventions they are prescribing.*

What Do You Think?

What are the ethical issues involved in using placebos? If you were being given a placebo and you found out, how would you feel? What if you improved with the placebo? Would you still feel the same way?

_____

_____

_____

_____

_____

_____

_____

_____

_____

_____

_____

_____

The placebo response plays an important part in the testing of new drugs. The commonly used double-blind study requires that neither researchers nor study participants know which group is receiving the study drug and which group is receiving an inert substance (placebo). At the conclusion of the study, researchers compare results and decide whether a higher percentage of the experimental group experienced the hoped-for results from the active medication than the control group received from the placebo. However, clinical studies have shown that some participants respond positively to placebo medications between 30 and 70 percent of the time. The clients with the highest positive results from placebos include those with:

- Pain from chronic disease, such as cancer pain, arthritis, back pain, angina pectoris, and gastrointestinal tract discomfort
- Autonomic nervous system disorders, such as phobias, psychoneuroses, depression, and nausea
- Neurohormonal disorders, such as asthma, other bronchial airflow conditions, and hypertension

How Does It Work?

Researchers do not have a good understanding of the mechanism by which the placebo response produces positive results. Some believe that the placebo effect is at work in all therapeutic intervention regardless of whether the intervention is an alternative or a conventional treatment. Four possible factors have been examined:

- An endorphin-mediated response
- Belief of the client
- Belief of the healer
- The client–healer relationship

Endorphin-Mediated Response. Endorphins are the body's natural painkillers that, when released, reduce pain and bring about a degree of euphoria. Relaxation therapies and other types of stress-reducing and stress-controlling techniques are believed to promote the release of endorphins that produce pain relief. When experimental groups were given medications that block the release of endorphins, clients with postoperative dental pain reported an increase in pain because of blocking of the placebo effect. The placebo response changes the perception of the client but does not affect the underlying disease process.

Belief of the Client. A person's belief in the effectiveness of the therapy is an important factor to its success and may be just as important as the therapy itself. Studies of client compliance in taking prescribed beta-blocker heart medications, conducted in the first year after myocardial infarction, showed that mortality rates were almost equal for those failing to take either the beta-blocker or placebo. Mortality rates for both these groups were higher than the rates for those who faithfully took their prescribed medications or placebos.

Belief of the Healer. Healers who believe in the therapeutic effectiveness of interventions and are able to convey that belief to their clients achieve more positive responses than healers who remain skeptical about the interventions they are prescribing. An attitude of caring and being in control tends to alleviate clients' anxieties and fears while increasing their hope and positive expectations.

Client–Healer Relationship. A trusting and close relationship between the client and healer has a positive psychological effect on clients and can become the mental catalyst they need for recovery. The ability of healers to communicate in an empathic manner increases client satisfaction with care; increases compliance with mutually set goals; increases feelings of empowerment, self-confidence, and self-worth; and decreases depression and anxiety.

Although conventional health care considers many of these approaches as speculative, incomplete, or insufficient to explain the placebo response, alternative healers see the placebo response as measurable and reproducible evidence that the mind and body are intertwined. The placebo response is viewed as proof that feelings, thoughts, and beliefs can change the physiological and structural functioning of individuals.

Remembered Wellness. The term *remembered wellness* is used to describe the physiological response that occurs after positive therapeutic interventions. Remembered wellness includes the person's prior learning, experiences, environment, beliefs, and perceptions. It can also include biological and genetic factors.

Remembered wellness is triggered by memories of past events or times when good health and feelings of confidence, strength, hope, and peace were part of the person's life. Alternative therapies access these memories by stimulating relaxation, such as the quieting of the body and mind to promote healing. Clinical research has demonstrated relaxation to be

effective in treating anxiety, pain, high blood pressure, and tachycardia and in managing stress. Research studies have confirmed a close relationship between the central nervous and immune systems and have shown that interaction occurs between the two mind–body pathways: the autonomic and neuroendocrine systems.

Much more research is required for a full scientific explanation of the how the mind and body interact to produce the placebo response and why remembered wellness produces the positive responses it often does. The placebo response remains an enigma to conventional health care and implies an element of deceitfulness when used deliberately in client treatments. For alternative medicine, the placebo response and remembered wellness are forces that can be harnessed to bring about healing.

Energy Systems

It has long been known scientifically that the human body is regulated by its own internal electrical energy system. Human beings cannot survive without the low levels of electricity that sustain and regulate life at the cellular and molecular levels. Electrical–chemical reactions are produced in the nervous system and help regulate other body systems, electrical impulses trigger heartbeats, and minute electrical currents regulate the production of hormones. The blood is composed largely of iron; therefore, magnetic forces exist in all parts of the body.

Conventional Uses of Energy
Conventional health care has long used various types of energy systems (e.g., electrical, magnetic, microwave, and infrared) for screening, diagnosis, and some types of treatment. Commonly used

modalities include electrocardiograms, magnetic resonance imaging, electroencephalograms, electomyelograms, x-rays, radiation treatments for cancer, low-frequency electric current to stimulate growth of bone cells (osteoblasts) to accelerate healing of fractures, types of electric shock therapy for cardiac arrest, cardioversions for cardiac arrhythmia, and pacemakers.

> *Alternative therapies refer to energy systems as fields, vital essences, balance, and flow that can be used by clients to prevent illness, promote health, and heal themselves. The basic concept is that external forces are not able to cause harm if the person is in the well state.*

Conventional health care also uses bioenergy (body energy) to determine the degree of injury and estimate recovery times through the study of cells as they decompose, die, reproduce, and respond to pathogens and traumas. The majority of conventional treatments for many diseases are chemical (medications), surgical, or involve immobilizing or manipulating the affected body part. They are used primarily *after* the disease has been diagnosed.

Energy in Alternative Healing

Conventional medicine has been slow to recognize how the energy of the body can be used for health promotion and healing. Alternative therapies refer to energy systems as fields, vital essences, balance, and flow that can be used by clients to prevent illness, promote health, and heal themselves. The basic concept is that external forces are not able to cause harm if the person is in the well state. Alternative healers may be needed to assist individuals to manipulate the energy system primarily for self-protection or healing. Major alternative and complementary modalities using bioenergy and other energy fields are energy medicine, vital essences and balance, and external energy forces.

Energy Medicine

This therapy includes a number of techniques that use external energy sources to stimulate tissue regeneration or improve the immune system response. Relaxation of muscles through electrical stimulation is thought to promote general body relaxation, increase circulation, enhance waste removal, improve nutrition and oxygenation, and restore energy balance. Examples of energy medicine

include electroacupuncture, biofeedback, magnet therapy, and sound and light therapy.

Vital Essences and Balance

In many alternative models, illness reflects blockage, loss, or imbalance of body energy or vital essence. Disturbance of internal body energy can result from external or internal factors. Treatment may be directed at removing the blockage of energy flow through such measures as acupuncture, acupressure, chiropractic adjustment, craniosacral therapy, or reflexology. It may also be directed at increasing the amount of energy and vital essence to restore balance in the body.

Ways of inducing these changes include diet, herbs, exercises, and spiritual techniques, such as yoga, meditation, and internal qi gong. Therapies related to the creative arts, such as music, drawing, singing, chanting, and dancing are also used to restore balance and vital essences.

External Energy Forces

External energy forces, it is believed, have the capacity for healing. Some of these external forces are actual energy treatments. Other forces include mobilizing the healing energy of faith, spirituality, prayer, shamanism, crystals, and hand-mediated energetic healing techniques, such as therapeutic touch and healing touch (Box 25.3).

Nutrition

Nutrition and diet have long been recognized by both alternative and conventional healing systems as important in health promotion and illness treatment. They can also be risk factors for or even cause disease. In conventional health care, nutrition and diet are usually considered as adjuncts to biomedical treatment. In alternative systems, nutrition is commonly seen as a way of life and as a method of preventing illness.

Benefits of Natural Foods

Conventional health care commonly focuses on the need for food and a well-balanced diet without close regard to food production or processing. The safety of food sources in the contemporary diet has been labels to carry a panel of "supplemental facts" or a "nutrition facts box," which includes ingredients.

The U.S. Postal Service and the Federal Trade Commission (FTC) also regulate nutritional supplements and herbal products. The U.S. Postal Inspection Service monitors products purchased by mail and may intercept supplements shipped through the mail for false claims, such as the statement that they can cure AIDS or cancer. The Office of Criminal Investigation can be contacted at (202) 268–2000.

The FTC has issued guidelines to ensure that advertising claims are substantiated by reliable scientific evidence. No longer acceptable are claims of effectiveness and safety based on testimonials and other anecdotal evidence. Also outlawed are vague disclaimers, such as "results may vary." The term "traditional use" (e.g., folk remedy), which implies that the product is effective even without scientific evidence, has also been banned. The risks or qualifying information of any product must be prominently displayed and easily understood.

Plants as Medicine

Both alternative and conventional health care use plants as medicines. Herbalism, or "botanical medicine," also known as phytotherapy or phytomedicine in England and other parts of Europe, is the study and use of herbs or crude-based plant products for food, medicine, or prophylaxis. They can also be used to heal, treat, or prevent illness and improve the spiritual and physical quality of life.

Herbs may be angiosperms (flowering plants, trees, or shrubs), algae, moss, fungus, seaweed, lichen, or ferns. Herbs used as medicines come from some part of the plant (leaf, root, flower, fruit, stem, bark, or seed), its syrup-like exudates, or some combination of these. In some herbal traditions, nonplant products are used alone or in combination, with or without plants. They may include animal secretions and parts (e.g., bones, organs, or tissues), stones and gemstones, minerals and metals, shells, and insects and insect products.

Botanical healing in the form of herbal medicines was widely used in the United States until the early 19th century, when it was gradually displaced by the increasing prominence of the scientific method and labeled quackery. Phytomedicine continues to be a prominent branch of conventional health care in Europe. Botanicals are used by 40 percent of German and French physicians in their daily practices.

Scientists have yet to determine the pharmaceutical qualities of most plants, and little is known about what toxicities they can produce. The world supports an estimated 250,000 to 500,000 flowering plant species, but only 5000 have been researched for their pharmacological effects.

Herbal Traditions

The use of herbal therapies varies according to culture and tradition. The three major groups of herbal therapies recognized throughout the world are from Western medicine, traditional Chinese medicine, and Ayurvedic medicine.

Western Pharmacology

The Western herbal tradition relies primarily on the pharmacological action of herbs, most of which are derived from the plant kingdom. There are presently 119 plant-derived pharmaceutical medicines. Plant chemicals constitute about 25 percent of prescriptions by conventional health-care professionals.

Chinese Medicine

Herbology is used in traditional Chinese medicine to enhance the flow and amount of chi, restore the harmonious balance of the complementary forces of yin and yang, and balance the five elements (fire, earth, metal, water, and wood). In the Chinese system, plants are prescribed according to their effects on the five elements and their corresponding body processes including organs, tissues, emotions, and temperatures (climates).

The Chinese believe that the five elements give rise to the five tastes that produce particular medicinal actions. Bitter-tasting herbs (fire) dry and drain. Sweet-tasting herbs (earth) reduce pain and increase tone. Acrid herbs (metal) rid the body of toxins. Salty herbs (water) nourish the kidney. Sour herbs (wood) clean, helping preserve chi and nourish yin. Herbs are also symbolically classified according to temperature changes they are thought to produce in the body: cold, cool, neutral, warm, and hot. The temperatures correspond to the symbolic climate qualities of the organs and the five elements.

Ayurvedic Medicine

Ayurvedic medicine also considers the taste, or "essence," of the herb as an integral element in herbology. Ayurveda recognizes six essences (sweet, sour, salty, pungent, bitter, and astringent) and five elements (ether, water, fire, air, and earth). The elements are manifested as three doshas, or humors (vata, pitta, and kapha) that govern body functioning and that must be kept in balance to maintain or restore a healthy state.

Vata, the principle of air, wind, or movement, is decreased by herbs that are sweet, sour, and salty, which exert a symbolic heating effect on the body. Vata is increased by herbs that are pungent, bitter, astringent, and cooling. Pitta, the principle of fire, is decreased by herbs that are sweet, bitter, astringent, and cooling and increased by those that are pungent, sour, salty, and heating. Kapha, the principle of water, is decreased by herbs that are pungent, bitter, astringent, and heating and increased by those that are sweet, sour, salty, and cooling.

Concerns About Herbal Therapies

There is growing concern in the United States about the use of herbal preparations by the general public without consultation with either conventional health-care professionals or alternative healers. Sales of herbal preparations have been growing tremendously. Another concern is the lack of licensing and standards for herbalists. Except for naturopaths, most herbalists have no foundation in phytochemistry or botanical medicine.

Also, in other cultural traditions, herbs are not prescribed for the

biological effects of their chemical ingredients. They are commonly prescribed according to the "doctrine of signatures," or their physical and taste characteristics. For example, herbs with heart-shaped leaves may be used to treat heart problems; those with red flowers or leaves may be used to control bleeding or blood disorders; and those with a sour taste may be given to decrease swelling or counteract the effects of "sugar" (diabetes mellitus).

Additional problems may arise because the public views most herbal remedies as natural products and therefore considers them to be pure, safe, relatively harmless, and more healthy than manufactured medicines. Recent problems with some natural products indicate that there is no guarantee of safety.

THE PARADOX OF ALTERNATIVE HEALING PRACTICES

A Lack of Validation

Nurses often feel uncomfortable with the use of herbal products and alternative therapies because of unclear definitions of various alternative and complementary practices and the widespread, yet often unregulated, use of alternative products and healers. This paradox arises because most nursing knowledge comes from the biomedical sciences, but most alternative modalities (1) have not yet been scientifically validated or proven safe by the scientific method and (2) are based in concepts of holism, self-care, and theoretical constructs that emanate from worldviews different from that of biomedicine and the scientific perspective.

> *Nurses often feel uncomfortable with the use of herbal products and alternative therapies because of unclear definitions of various alternative and complementary practices and the widespread, yet often unregulated, use of alternative products and healers.*

In other words, for most alternative modalities, little is known about whether or how they work, their side effects, or their interactions with conventional or other alternative modalities. Claims regarding their effectiveness come largely from testimonials of users or alternative healers rather than from evidence in scientific studies. Equally limited is valid knowledge about which conditions the various alternative modalities are effective against and about their short- and long-term effects.

The nursing profession has worked for many years to build its decision-making skills on knowledge derived from the scientific method and on the use of critical thinking and culture competence. Nurses promote self-care in clients by teaching them to make informed choices about their health-care options. Many of the alternative health-care practices in use today fly in the face of the nursing profession's movement toward evidence-based practice.

> "The challenge presented to nurses by alternative healing modalities relates to professional accountability. Nurses must learn about alternative modalities, their general safety and efficacy, and their use in specific health and illness conditions."

Few Regulatory Standards

The technical competence and knowledge of alternative healers are of considerable importance to nurses caring for clients who pursue alternative and complementary practices. Nurses and the general public are accustomed to determining the qualifications, assumed competency, and scope of practice of conventional health-care practitioners through externally regulated mechanisms. These external regulations include graduation from an accredited school, state-regulated licenses, credentialing, and attainment of specialty certifications from professional organizations or institutions of higher education. No such external processes or criteria exist to validate the competence and knowledge of most alternative practitioners.

The relative lack of regulatory standards makes selection of competent alternative practitioners exceedingly difficult. It is a major concern of the public, conventional health-care practitioners, and insurers, because clients may be subject to financial exploitation, ineffective therapies, and psychological and physical abuse.

A Challenge to Nurses

The challenge presented to nurses by alternative healing modalities relates to professional accountability. Nurses must learn about alternative modalities, their general safety and efficacy, and their use in specific health and illness conditions.

Human caring and cultural competence require that nurses be able to develop therapeutic partnerships with culturally diverse clients and empower them to take charge of their lives and

health care. They need to preserve the client's right to self-determination and to practice alternative lifestyles, as well as to pursue a variety of conventional or alternative therapies, with or without consulting alternative healers or conventional health-care professionals. Nurses must keep an open mind while relying on sound evidence for recommendations about alternative practices and practitioners.

Ask Questions

Box 25.4 lists some questions nurses need to ask when determining the quality and validity of information about an alternative modality. It is important to teach clients to ask similar questions so they can decide about alternative therapy and sort out the often conflicting advice of family, friends, conventional health-care professionals, alternative healers, and the media.

Many clients use alternative healing modalities without ever talking to a conventional health professional about them. They may fear a negative reaction. Others are not aware of the potential harm that may occur, especially when combining alternative therapies or alternative and conventional therapies. Some may consider the scientific evidence and conclude that most noninvasive and nondrug alternative therapies are harmless. Others may mistakenly assume that alternative therapies are regulated by the government and would not be available if they were dangerous.

Find Information

Lack of scientific information about alternative healing modalities is of concern to alternative healers, conventional health-care professionals, and clients. For nurses and their clients, the need to know where and how to find up-to-date, reliable information on alternative therapies is a must.

Information Resources

• The NCCAM offers one of the best general governmental resources for information on alternative modalities at the NCCAM Web site: www.nccam.nih.gov.

Box 25.4

Questions to Ask About Alternative Modalities

1. What evidence exists that the therapy is effective or harmful?
   - Is there experimental evidence? How effective is the alternative modality when examined experimentally?
   - Is there clinical practice evidence? How effective is the alternative modality when applied clinically?
   - Is there comparative evidence? How effective is the modality when compared with other treatments?
   - Is there summary evidence? Has the modality been evaluated and a consensus reached regarding its use and effectiveness for various health conditions?
   - Is there evidence of demand? Is the modality wanted by clients, practitioners, or both?
   - Is there evidence of satisfaction? Does the alternative modality meet the expectations of clients and practitioners?
   - Is there cost evidence? Is the modality covered by health insurance? Is it cost effective?
   - Is the meaning evident? Is the modality the best and right one for the client?
2. How strong is the evidence? Is it based on testimonials, clinical observations, or scientific research?
3. Can the results be attributed to the placebo effect? Is the benefit from the placebo effect adequate to the client's needs?
4. Does evidence exist that the benefits of the therapy outweigh the risks?
   - Is the alternative modality potentially useful?
   - Is the modality essentially without value except for the potential placebo effect?
   - Is the modality potentially harmful?
5. Is there another way to obtain the same hoped-for results?
6. Who else has tried this alternative modality, and what was their experience?
7. Are there reputable (licensed and certified) alternative healers available? What has been their experience with this alternative modality?
8. What information do regulatory agencies have about the modality or the alternative healers?
9. What information is available in the popular media about the modality or alternative healers? Has it been or can it be verified by clinical observations or research studies?

Sources: Barrocas, A: Complementary and alternative medicine: Friend, foe or OWA (other weird arrangements). Journal of the American Diet Association 97:1373, 1997.

Kurtzweil, P: An FDA Guide to Dietary Supplements. January 1999. www.vm.cfsan.fda.gov/~dms/fdsupp.html.

Micozzi, MS (ed): Fundamentals of Complementary and Alternative Medicine. Churchill Livingstone, New York, 1996.

National Center for Complementary and Alternative Medicine: Considering CAM? March 1, 2000. www.nccam.nih.gov/nccam/fcp/faq/considercam.html.

National Center for Complementary and Alternative Medicine: NCCAM Clearinghouse. April 6, 2000. www.nccam.nih.gov/nccam/faq/clearinghouse/index.html.

Spencer, JC, and Jacobs, JJ: Complementary/Alternative Medicine: An Evidence-Based Approach. Mosby, St. Louis, 1999.

Several authoritative sources on herbal medicines are available for practitioners and clients.

- The FDA maintains a site for reporting and obtaining information about adverse effects and interactions of herbals through MedWatch (800-FDA-1088 or www.fda.gov/medwatch).
- F.A. Davis maintains a Web site on herbal medicines (www.DrugGuide.com), as does the United States Pharmacopeia (www.usp.org/information/ index.html).
- The American Botanical Society (512-926-4900) has a Web site (www.herbalgram.org) and publishes the *Herbalgram*, a newsletter on herbal medications.
- MICROMEDEX has an evidence-based series on herbal medicines and dietary supplements, toxicologies, clinical protocols, and client education

(800-643-8116 or www.micromedex.com). It also links to the electronic database of herbal medicines from the Royal Pharmaceutical Society of Great Britain.

- Tyler's *The Honest Herbal* is one of the most reputable guides for the use of herbs.[5]
- *The Physicians' Desk Reference for Herbal Medicine* contains scientific findings on the efficacy, potential interactions, clinical trials, and case reports of herbs, as well as indexes on Asian, Ayurvedic, and homeopathic herbs.[6]
- An English translation of *The Complete German Commission E Monographs: Therapeutic Guide to Herbal Medicine* is a compendium of monographs published by Commission E, a panel of experts responsible for regulating herbal products in Germany, much as is done by the FDA in the United States. It contains information about the therapeutics of individual herbs, dosages, adverse effects, and pharmacology. The lack of regulatory standards for herbal products in the United States poses problems in applying findings from Commission E to herbal products manufactured in this country.[7]

A growing number of clients and even professionals are turning to the Internet for information about alternative products and local practitioners of alternative therapies. Because information posted to the Internet is not regulated, this avenue of inquiry requires caution. Only one Web site is available with reputable information about ACH and specific modalities.

- Quackwatch (www.quackwatch.com/) offers fact sheets and reviews of specific alternative modalities, as well as those associated with certain illnesses. It also has sections on how to determine whether a Web site devoted to alternative modalities is trustworthy.

Ask the Client

It is important to ask clients about their use of alternative therapies. Not doing so may place them

> *It is important to ask clients about their use of alternative therapies. Not doing so may place them at risk for adverse health outcomes.*

at risk for adverse health outcomes. When and how to assess for the use of ACH during the client assessment process is a matter of judgment and should be guided by the nurse's knowledge of individual clients. An appropriate time is often after the chief complaint has been documented, because this is the time when questions are asked about the clients' reasons for seeking health care and what they have already done for their problem.

What Do You Think?

Does the facility where you do your clinical practice ask about alternative therapies during the admission assessment? Are you taught to assess for this information in your nursing program?

_____

_____

_____

_____

_____

_____

_____

_____

_____

_____

_____

Discuss the use of alternative therapies tactfully and supportively. Keep complete and accurate documentation of all interactions with clients about alternative therapies and healers. And as much as possible, help direct clients toward the safest therapies and the most qualified practitioners.

Yir
ph
pli
of
rep
nat
fen
Yar

R e

1. F
n
I
2. C
H
4
3. C
f
c
2
4. E
a
5. F
t
H
6. N
N
7. E
N
E

B i

Cas

Dos

Megavitamin therapy A type of orthomolecular medicine in which diseases are prevented and cured by large doses of vitamins and other supplements. Dosages exceed the normal or recommended amounts needed for general good health or prevention of deficiencies. The disease to be treated or prevented determines the type, dosage, and mode of administration of vitamins, minerals, and nutrient supplements.

Meridians From traditional Chinese medicine. Meridians are invisible channels by which chi flows through the body. Blockage along a meridian causes illness.

Mind–body medicine Healing based on the interconnectedness of the mind and body, individual responsibility for self-care, and the self-healing capabilities of the body. Uses a wide range of modalities, such as imaging, massage, hypnotherapy, meditation, yoga, concepts of balance, herbs, and diet.

Moxibustion From traditional Chinese medicine, burning of *moxa* (dried or powered herbs) on or close to acupuncture points on the meridians to restore or improve the flow of chi.

Music therapy Use of music to enhance well-being and promote healing. Helps improve physical and mental functioning, alleviate pain, ease the psychological discomfort of illness, and improve quality of life, especially for terminally ill persons. Aids ability of mentally handicapped, autistic, and elderly persons with dementia to interact with others, learn, and relate to their environments.

Naturopathy A Western healing system that uses safe, natural therapies. Promotes holism and use of natural substances, treats cause rather than effect (symptoms), empowers and motivates individuals to take responsibility for their own health, prevents disease through lifestyle and education, and does no harm.

Neurolinguistic programming A system that focuses on how individuals learn, communicate, and change. *Neuro-* refers to the way the brain works and the consistent and observable patterns that emanate from human thinking. *Linguistic* refers to the expression (verbal and nonverbal) of those patterns of thinking. *Programming* refers to the ways such patterns of thinking are interpreted and how they can be changed. Changing the patterns gives people the ability to make better choices for healthy behavior.

Orthodox medicine A synonym for conventional, Western, scientific, biomedicine, or official health-care system.

Orthomolecular medicine A system that treats physiological and psychological disorders by re-establishing, normalizing, or creating the optimal nutritional balance in the body. Vitamins, minerals, amino acids, and other types of nutritional substances are administered. (*Ortho-* means "normal" or "correct.")

Osteopathy A Western system of medicine that considers the structural integrity of the body the most important factor in maintaining and restoring the person to health. The structural integrity or balance of the musculoskeletal system is maintained through physical therapy, joint manipulation, and postural re-education.

Oxygen therapy Use of various forms of oxygen to destroy pathogens and promote body healing. Includes hyperbaric, ozone, and hydrogen peroxide therapies.

Pharmacognosy Scientific study of the chemical properties of plants and natural products. A goal is to standardize herbal products to make sure they are free of harmful components and contain the identical amount of active ingredients.

Phytomedicine/phytotherapy A branch of botanical medicine, especially prominent in Europe, that includes the pharmaceutical study and therapeutic use of herbs, herbal derivatives, and herbal synthetics. Merges ancient herbal traditions with contemporary scientific investigation to standardize the active ingredients of herbal products.

Polarity therapy A combination of bodywork and other hands-on techniques to restore the natural flow of energy through the body. Other therapies may include reflexology, hydrotherapy, and breathing techniques.

Prana Vital energy or life-force that runs through the body. From Ayurvedic medicine.

Qi Gong (Chi Kung, Chi Gong) Technique from traditional Chinese medicine that combines movement, meditation and deep relaxation, and regulation of breathing. Enhanced flow of chi throughout the body nourishes vital organs.

Reflexology Pressure applied to the hands or feet to unblock nerve impulses. In this belief system, every part of the body has a corresponding area on the

---

Critical Thinking Exercises

- Contact three of the Web sites on alternative practices listed in this chapter. Evaluate them according to their quality, content, and usefulness to your practice.
- Identify a nurse practitioner or physician or other health-care provider in your area who uses alternative practices. Interview that person and arrange for a presentation to the class about alternative health-care practices.
- Select a client from your clinical experiences who is having pain. How might alternative practices help this client? Develop a care plan using both traditional and alternative methods for pain control.
- Identify and discuss three advantages of and three problems with alternative health-care practices.
- Select three nursing theories from Chapter 4 that use a holistic approach to nursing. Identify how and what alternative practices would work well with each one of these theories.

active moving, and forms of directed attention designed to re-educate the nervous system, teach subjects how to learn from their own kinesic feedback, and avoid movements that strain joints and muscles.

Gerson therapy Metabolic therapy developed by Max Gerson, a German physician. It is based on the belief that cancer results from metabolic dysfunctions in cells that can be countered by detoxification, a vegetarian diet, coffee enemas to stimulate excretion of liver bile, and the exclusion of sodium and an abundance of potassium.

Guided imagery A facilitated flow of thoughts that helps a person see, feel, taste, smell, hear, or touch something in the imagination. The power of the mind or imagination is used to stimulate positive physical responses and provide insight into health and an understanding of emotions as a cause of ill health.

Healing touch Healing tradition based on the belief in a universal energy system. Humans are seen as interpenetrating layers of energy systems just above and outside the body that are integrated with energy fields in the environment. Manipulation of such energy fields through touch can help restore a person's energy balance and health.

Hellerwork A type of bodywork developed by Joseph Heller as an outgrowth of Rolfing. It combines dialogue, body movement education, and deep touch to achieve greater mind–body awareness and structural body alignment with gravitational forces. Therapy is individualized to different body types.

Herbal medicine Use of the chemical makeup of herbs in much the same way as conventional medicine uses pharmaceuticals. The most ancient known form of health care, herbal medicine is basic to traditional Chinese, Ayurvedic, and Native American medical systems. Also called *botanical medicine, phytotherapy,* and *phytomedicine.*

Homeopathy A Western medical system based on the principle that "like cures like." Natural substances are prescribed in minute dilutions to cause the symptoms of the disease they are intended to cure, helping the body cure itself.

Humor therapy Deliberate use of laughter to improve quality of life by encouraging relaxation and stress reduction, distracting individuals from awareness of constant pain, and providing symptom relief.

Hydrotherapy Use of hot, cold, or contrasting water temperatures to maintain or restore health. Water, steam, or ice may be used in combination with baths, compresses, hot and cold packs, showers, and enemas or colonic irrigations. Minerals, herbs, and oils may be added to enhance the therapeutic effects. Also known as *water cure.*

Hypnotherapy Use of hypnosis, power of suggestion, and trancelike states to access the deepest levels of the mind. Used to bring about changes in behavior, treat health conditions, and manage medical and psychological problems.

Integrative medicine The practice of conventional health-care professionals who prescribe a combination of therapies from both systems. *Integrative* is synonymous with *complementary.*

Iridiology Iris diagnosis. In this belief system, each area of the body has a corresponding point on the iris of the eye. Thus, the state of health (balance) or disease (imbalance) can be diagnosed from the color, texture, or location of pigments in the eye.

Jin Shin Jyutsu A Japanese form of massage in which combinations of healing points on the body are held for a minute or more with the fingertips. The purpose is to enhance or restore the flow of chi.

Light and color therapy A method by which light is converted into electrical impulses, travels along the optic nerve to the brain, and stimulates the hypothalamus to send neurotransmitters to regulate the autonomic nervous system. Various colors of light are believed to stimulate different parts of the body.

Magnet therapy A type of electromagnetic therapy or energy medicine in which magnets are used to stimulate circulation, increase oxygen to cells, and facilitate healing by correcting disturbed or malfunctioning electromagnetic frequencies that the body emits.

Mantra A type of sound therapy used in Ayurvedic medicine to reach a higher level of spiritual and mental functioning. It changes the "vibratory patterns of the mind" to release unconscious negative thoughts, psychological stress, and emotional distress. Often achieved by uttering a mystical word or phrase and associated with meditation.

Meditation Use of contemplation to exercise the mind. A form of mental cleansing that enhances self-awareness and awareness of one's environment. Also called "mind-cure," this is an unseen force of healing. Thoughts and deep feelings are considered the primary arbiters of health through relaxation.

abandonment Leaving a client without the client's permission; terminating the professional relationship without providing for appropriate continued or follow-up care by another equally qualified professional.

accountability Concept that each individual is responsible for his or her own actions and the consequence of those actions; professional accountability implies a responsibility to perform the activities and duties of the profession according to established standards.

accreditation Approval of a program or institution by a voluntary professional organization to provide specific education or service programs.

act Legislation that has become law.

active euthanasia Acts performed to help end a sick person's life.

acute-severe condition Health problem of sudden onset; a serious illness or condition.

adaptation Process of exchange between a person and the environment to maintain or regain personal integrity; the key principle in the Roy Model of Nursing.

administrative A governmental agency that implements legislation.

administrative rule or regulation An operating procedure that describes how a government agency implements the intent of a statute; state boards of nursing implement the nurse practice act.

advanced nursing education Master's- or doctoral-level education that provides knowledge and skills in areas such as research, education, administration, or clinical specialties.

advanced placement A process by which a student is given credit for a required course through transfer or examination rather than by enrolling in and completing the course.

advanced practice Extended role; increased responsibilities and actions undertaken by an individual because of additional education and experience; nurse practitioners are advanced practice nurses.

advocate One who pleads for a cause or proposal; one who acts on behalf of another.

affective domain objectives Goals established in conjunction with the client that are directed toward changing feelings, values, and attitudes necessary for a positive effect on the client's health.

affidavit Written, sworn statement.

affiliation agreement A formal agreement between an educational institution and another agency that agrees to provide clinical areas for student practice.

aggressiveness Harsh behavior that may result in physical or emotional harm to others.

ambulatory care center Type of primary care facility that provides treatment on an outpatient basis.

answer Document filed in the court by the defendant in response to the complaint.

anxiety Uneasiness or apprehension caused by an impending threat or fear of the unknown.

apathy Lack of interest.

appeal Request to a higher court to review a decision in the hopes of changing the ruling of a lower court.

appellant Person who seeks an appeal.

arbitrator Neutral third party who assesses facts independently of the judicial system.

articulation Type of education program that allows easy entry from one level to another; for example, many BSN programs have articulation for nurses with associate degrees.

artificial insemination Insertion of sperm into the uterus with a syringe.

assault Attempt or threat to touch.

assertiveness Ability to express thoughts, feelings, and ideas openly and directly without fear.

assessment Process of collecting information about a client to help plan care.

associate degree nursing program Type of nursing education program that leads to an associate degree with a major in nursing; usually located in a community or junior college, these programs nominally last 2 years.

audit Close review of records or documents to detect the presence or absence of specific information.

Megavitamin therapy A type of orthomolecular medicine in which diseases are prevented and cured by large doses of vitamins and other supplements. Dosages exceed the normal or recommended amounts needed for general good health or prevention of deficiencies. The disease to be treated or prevented determines the type, dosage, and mode of administration of vitamins, minerals, and nutrient supplements.

Meridians From traditional Chinese medicine. Meridians are invisible channels by which chi flows through the body. Blockage along a meridian causes illness.

Mind–body medicine Healing based on the interconnectedness of the mind and body, individual responsibility for self-care, and the self-healing capabilities of the body. Uses a wide range of modalities, such as imaging, massage, hypnotherapy, meditation, yoga, concepts of balance, herbs, and diet.

Moxibustion From traditional Chinese medicine, burning of *moxa* (dried or powered herbs) on or close to acupuncture points on the meridians to restore or improve the flow of chi.

Music therapy Use of music to enhance well-being and promote healing. Helps improve physical and mental functioning, alleviate pain, ease the psychological discomfort of illness, and improve quality of life, especially for terminally ill persons. Aids ability of mentally handicapped, autistic, and elderly persons with dementia to interact with others, learn, and relate to their environments.

Naturopathy A Western healing system that uses safe, natural therapies. Promotes holism and use of natural substances, treats cause rather than effect (symptoms), empowers and motivates individuals to take responsibility for their own health, prevents disease through lifestyle and education, and does no harm.

Neurolinguistic programming A system that focuses on how individuals learn, communicate, and change. *Neuro-* refers to the way the brain works and the consistent and observable patterns that emanate from human thinking. *Linguistic* refers to the expression (verbal and nonverbal) of those patterns of thinking. *Programming* refers to the ways such patterns of thinking are interpreted and how they can be changed. Changing the patterns gives people the ability to make better choices for healthy behavior.

Orthodox medicine A synonym for conventional, Western, scientific, biomedicine, or official health-care system.

Orthomolecular medicine A system that treats physiological and psychological disorders by re establishing, normalizing, or creating the optimal nutritional balance in the body. Vitamins, minerals, amino acids, and other types of nutritional substances are administered. (*Ortho-* means "normal" or "correct.")

Osteopathy A Western system of medicine that considers the structural integrity of the body the most important factor in maintaining and restoring the person to health. The structural integrity or balance of the musculoskeletal system is maintained through physical therapy, joint manipulation, and postural re-education.

Oxygen therapy Use of various forms of oxygen to destroy pathogens and promote body healing. Includes hyperbaric, ozone, and hydrogen peroxide therapies.

Pharmacognosy Scientific study of the chemical properties of plants and natural products. A goal is to standardize herbal products to make sure they are free of harmful components and contain the identical amount of active ingredients.

Phytomedicine/phytotherapy A branch of botanical medicine, especially prominent in Europe, that includes the pharmaceutical study and therapeutic use of herbs, herbal derivatives, and herbal synthetics. Merges ancient herbal traditions with contemporary scientific investigation to standardize the active ingredients of herbal products.

Polarity therapy A combination of bodywork and other hands-on techniques to restore the natural flow of energy through the body. Other therapies may include reflexology, hydrotherapy, and breathing techniques.

Prana Vital energy or life-force that runs through the body. From Ayurvedic medicine.

Qi Gong (Chi Kung, Chi Gong) Technique from traditional Chinese medicine that combines movement, meditation and deep relaxation, and regulation of breathing. Enhanced flow of chi throughout the body nourishes vital organs.

Reflexology Pressure applied to the hands or feet to unblock nerve impulses. In this belief system, every part of the body has a corresponding area on the hands and feet. Thus, body parts can be stimulated by pressure applied to the appropriate sites. Reflexology is used to relieve tension, improve circulation, promote relaxation, and restore energy balance.

Reiki An ancient Buddhist version of healing touch practiced in Tibet and Japan. The word also means universal life-force. Energy is transferred to the person through the hands of the healer to restore energy balance in the body.

Relaxation response Physiological mechanism described by Herbert Benson in which body stress is reduced through regulation of internal activity, such as reduced metabolism and slowing of other physiological reactions.

Relaxation therapy Use of the relaxation response to reduce stress through release of physical and emotional tension. Various therapies are commonly included in other types of therapeutic programs. Examples are mind–body therapies such as biofeedback, hydrotherapy, imaging and visualization, meditation, qi gong, Tai Chi, and yoga.

Rolfing Technique of deep massage developed by Ida Rolf. Use of the knuckles is meant to counteract the effects of gravity on body balance. Fascia, connective tissue, and muscle are loosened and lengthened to help them return to their correct positions.

Rosen technique A type of bodywork in which muscle tension is seen as repressed emotional conflicts. Deep and gentle pressure is applied as persons are questioned about what they are experiencing.

Shamanism Ancient healing approach found in most cultural systems. Shamans communicate with the spirit world through trances and other altered states of consciousness. They attempt to control spirits and effect change in the physical world. The belief is that the soul of the shaman separates from the body and explores the cosmos in search of cures for ill clients.

Sound therapy Use of sound to affect different parts of the brain, regulate corticosteroid hormone levels, and affect the body's own rhythmic patterns.

Shiatsu Japanese form of massage, literally, *finger pressure*. Consists of firm pressure in a sequential and rhythmic manner. Pressure is exerted for 3 to 10 seconds on points along the body that correspond to acupuncture meridians. It is designed to "awaken the meridian."

Spiritual healing Cosmic healing energy transferred or channeled from practitioner to client through laying on of the hands.

Swedish massage The most common form of massage, focusing on superficial muscle layers. Practitioner uses kneading, friction, and long, gliding strokes to relieve muscle tension and promote relaxation.

Tai Chi From traditional Chinese medicine. Derived from qi gong but practiced at a much slower pace. Also one of the body–mind therapies. Combines contemplation (meditation) with movement or "moving meditation" and coordinated breathing.

Therapeutic massage Manipulation of soft tissues through a variety of techniques to affect the circulatory, lymphatic, and nervous systems.

Therapeutic touch A healing touch modality that does not involve actual touching of the client's body. The therapist's hands are used to sense and interact with the client's energy field to redirect it, alleviate energy blockage, and restore balance.

Traditional Chinese medicine A complete system of healing based on the concept of the uninterrupted flow of chi, or vital essence, and the concept of balance (yin and yang), representing corresponding and interrelated elements in the internal world of the body and the external world. All illness is attributed ultimately to a disturbance of chi.

Trager therapy A method of bodywork, developed by Milton Trager, meant to develop the ability to move more effortlessly. Use of gentle, rhythmic touch and movement exercises to assist in the release of accumulated tensions. Uses sensory-motor feedback or mental gymnastics (mentastics) to learn how the body moves.

Vibration medicine Healing systems that treat the body on an energy level. Cure is effected by ingestion of substances that adjust energy or rate of energy field vibration. Homeopathy is an example.

Visualization Also called guided imagery, centering, focusing, meditation, or distraction. Use of the imagination or power of the mind to get in touch with one's inner self. Involves all, several, or one of the senses to bridge the mind, body, and spirit.

Yin/yang Complementary but opposing phenomena or correspondents in Taoist philosophical thought that form the underpinning of traditional Chinese medicine. Yin and yang represent the interdependence of all elements of nature and body and mind. Yin represents the female force and passive, still, reflective aspects. Yang represents the male force and active, warm, moving aspects. For health to be maintained and wellness achieved, yin and yang must be in balance.

Yoga Literally, *union*, or the integration of mental, physical, and spiritual energies. Part of Ayurvedic medicine. The integration is accomplished through exercise in the form of assuming different body postures, meditation, and breathing.

References

1. Rosenbaum, C: The history of complementary and alternative medicine in the U.S. Annals of Pharmacotherapy 41(7–8): 1256–1260, 2007.
2. Ortiz, BI: Complementary and alternative medicine use among Hispanics in the United States. Annals of Pharmacotherapy 41(6): 994–1004, 2007.
3. Cook, DA: A web-based course on complementary medicine for medical students and residents improves knowledge and changes attitudes. Teaching & Learning in Medicine 19(3): 230–238, 2007.
4. Engebretson, J, and Wardell, D: A contemporary view of alternative healing modalities. Nurse Practitioner 18: 51, 1993.
5. Foster, S and Tyler, V: Tyler's Hones Herbal: A Sensible Guide to the Use of Herbs and Related Remedies. Haworth Press, Inc. Haworth, England, 1999.
6. Medical Economics Staff: Physicians' Desk Reference for Herbal Medicines, 4 ed. Thomson Health Care, New York, 2004.
7. Blumenthal, M, et al.: The Complete German Commission E Monographs: Therapeutic Guide to Herbal Medicine, American Botanical Council, Austin TX, 1998.

Bibliography

Cassidy, C: What does it mean to practice an energy medicine? Journal of Alternative and Complementary Medicine 10(1): 79–81, 2004.
Dosset, B: Florence Nightingale and holistic nursing. Imprint 52(2): 58–60, 2005.
Honda, K: Use of complementary and alternative medicine among United States adults: The influences of personality, coping strategies, and social support. Preventative Medicine 40(1): 46–53, 2005.
Huebscher, R: Natural, Alternative, and Complementary Health Care Practices. Mosby, St. Louis, 2004.
Mariano, C: An overview of holistic nursing. Imprint 52(2): 48–52, 2005.
National Center for Complementary and Alternative Medicine: Frequently Asked Questions. 2005. www.nccam.nih.gov/nccam/fcp/faq/index.html.
Savory-Posselius, M: Herbology. Home Health Care Management Practice 16(6): 456–463, 2004.
Stretch, K: A survey of CAM approaches to obesity. Massage Today 5(1): 1, 22, 2005.
Uzun, O: Nursing students' opinions and knowledge about complementary and alternative medicine therapies. Complementary Therapeutic Nurse Midwifery 10(4): 239–244, 2004.
Walach, H: Homeopathic proving symptoms: Result of a local, non-local, or placebo process? A blinded, placebo-controlled pilot study. Homeopathy 93(4): 179–185, 2004.
Weatherley-Jones, E: The placebo-controlled trial as a test of complementary and alternative medicine: Observations from research experience of individualized homeopathic treatment. Homeopathy 93(4): 186–189, 2004.
World Health Organization: WHO's Policy and Activities on the Traditional Medicine, 2005. www.who.int/dap/trm0.html.
Yoon, S: Herbal product use by African American older women. Clinical Nursing Research 13(4): 271–288, 2004.

abandonment Leaving a client without the client's permission; terminating the professional relationship without providing for appropriate continued or follow-up care by another equally qualified professional.

accountability Concept that each individual is responsible for his or her own actions and the consequence of those actions; professional accountability implies a responsibility to perform the activities and duties of the profession according to established standards.

accreditation Approval of a program or institution by a voluntary professional organization to provide specific education or service programs.

act Legislation that has become law.

active euthanasia Acts performed to help end a sick person's life.

acute-severe condition Health problem of sudden onset; a serious illness or condition.

adaptation Process of exchange between a person and the environment to maintain or regain personal integrity; the key principle in the Roy Model of Nursing.

administrative A governmental agency that implements legislation.

administrative rule or regulation An operating procedure that describes how a government agency implements the intent of a statute; state boards of nursing implement the nurse practice act.

advanced nursing education Master's- or doctoral-level education that provides knowledge and skills in areas such as research, education, administration, or clinical specialties.

advanced placement A process by which a student is given credit for a required course through transfer or examination rather than by enrolling in and completing the course.

advanced practice Extended role; increased responsibilities and actions undertaken by an individual because of additional education and experience; nurse practitioners are advanced practice nurses.

advocate One who pleads for a cause or proposal; one who acts on behalf of another.

affective domain objectivies Goals established in conjunction with the client that are directed toward changing feelings, values, and attitudes necessary for a positive effect on the client's health.

affidavit Written, sworn statement.

affiliation agreement A formal agreement between an educational institution and another agency that agrees to provide clinical areas for student practice.

aggressiveness Harsh behavior that may result in physical or emotional harm to others.

ambulatory care center Type of primary care facility that provides treatment on an outpatient basis.

answer Document filed in the court by the defendant in response to the complaint.

anxiety Uneasiness or apprehension caused by an impending threat or fear of the unknown.

apathy Lack of interest.

appeal Request to a higher court to review a decision in the hopes of changing the ruling of a lower court.

appellant Person who seeks an appeal.

arbitrator Neutral third party who assesses facts independently of the judicial system.

articulation Type of education program that allows easy entry from one level to another; for example, many BSN programs have articulation for nurses with associate degrees.

artificial insemination Insertion of sperm into the uterus with a syringe.

assault Attempt or threat to touch.

assertiveness Ability to express thoughts, feelings, and ideas openly and directly without fear.

assessment Process of collecting information about a client to help plan care.

associate degree nursing program Type of nursing education program that leads to an associate degree with a major in nursing; usually located in a community or junior college, these programs nominally last 2 years.

audit Close review of records or documents to detect the presence or absence of specific information.

active moving, and forms of directed attention designed to re-educate the nervous system, teach subjects how to learn from their own kinesic feedback, and avoid movements that strain joints and muscles.

Gerson therapy Metabolic therapy developed by Max Gerson, a German physician. It is based on the belief that cancer results from metabolic dysfunctions in cells that can be countered by detoxification, a vegetarian diet, coffee enemas to stimulate excretion of liver bile, and the exclusion of sodium and an abundance of potassium.

Guided imagery A facilitated flow of thoughts that helps a person see, feel, taste, smell, hear, or touch something in the imagination. The power of the mind or imagination is used to stimulate positive physical responses and provide insight into health and an understanding of emotions as a cause of ill health.

Healing touch Healing tradition based on the belief in a universal energy system. Humans are seen as interpenetrating layers of energy systems just above and outside the body that are integrated with energy fields in the environment. Manipulation of such energy fields through touch can help restore a person's energy balance and health.

Hellerwork A type of bodywork developed by Joseph Heller as an outgrowth of Rolfing. It combines dialogue, body movement education, and deep touch to achieve greater mind–body awareness and structural body alignment with gravitational forces. Therapy is individualized to different body types.

Herbal medicine Use of the chemical makeup of herbs in much the same way as conventional medicine uses pharmaceuticals. The most ancient known form of health care, herbal medicine is basic to traditional Chinese, Ayurvedic, and Native American medical systems. Also called *botanical medicine, phytotherapy,* and *phytomedicine.*

Homeopathy A Western medical system based on the principle that "like cures like." Natural substances are prescribed in minute dilutions to cause the symptoms of the disease they are intended to cure, helping the body cure itself.

Humor therapy Deliberate use of laughter to improve quality of life by encouraging relaxation and stress reduction, distracting individuals from awareness of constant pain, and providing symptom relief.

Hydrotherapy Use of hot, cold, or contrasting water temperatures to maintain or restore health. Water, steam, or ice may be used in combination with baths, compresses, hot and cold packs, showers, and enemas or colonic irrigations. Minerals, herbs, and oils may be added to enhance the therapeutic effects. Also known as *water cure.*

Hypnotherapy Use of hypnosis, power of suggestion, and trancelike states to access the deepest levels of the mind. Used to bring about changes in behavior, treat health conditions, and manage medical and psychological problems.

Integrative medicine The practice of conventional health-care professionals who prescribe a combination of therapies from both systems. *Integrative* is synonymous with *complementary.*

Iridiology Iris diagnosis. In this belief system, each area of the body has a corresponding point on the iris of the eye. Thus, the state of health (balance) or disease (imbalance) can be diagnosed from the color, texture, or location of pigments in the eye.

Jin Shin Jyutsu A Japanese form of massage in which combinations of healing points on the body are held for a minute or more with the fingertips. The purpose is to enhance or restore the flow of chi.

Light and color therapy A method by which light is converted into electrical impulses, travels along the optic nerve to the brain, and stimulates the hypothalamus to send neurotransmitters to regulate the autonomic nervous system. Various colors of light are believed to stimulate different parts of the body.

Magnet therapy A type of electromagnetic therapy or energy medicine in which magnets are used to stimulate circulation, increase oxygen to cells, and facilitate healing by correcting disturbed or malfunctioning electromagnetic frequencies that the body emits.

Mantra A type of sound therapy used in Ayurvedic medicine to reach a higher level of spiritual and mental functioning. It changes the "vibratory patterns of the mind" to release unconscious negative thoughts, psychological stress, and emotional distress. Often achieved by uttering a mystical word or phrase and associated with meditation.

Meditation Use of contemplation to exercise the mind. A form of mental cleansing that enhances self-awareness and awareness of one's environment. Also called "mind-cure," this is an unseen force of healing. Thoughts and deep feelings are considered the primary arbiters of health through relaxation.

infrared treatment. These points are believed to have neurological connections to other body areas. Also called *ear acupuncture*.

Ayurvedic medicine A personalistic, holistic, and naturalistic approach to health maintenance and treatment of illness, originating in India. Maintains balance of the three doshas (bioenergies) of the body through diet and herbs, meditation, breathing exercises (pranayama), massage with medicated oils, yoga and other forms of vigorous exercise, and exposure to the sun for higher consciousness.

Bach flower essences Administration of homeopathic preparations of oil concentrates extracted from flowers. Originated by Edward Bach, an English physician, this method is aimed at emotional states rather than the signs and symptoms of physical illness. Specific concentrates or combinations of concentrates are associated with various emotional states. Each client is diagnosed individually because there is no corresponding psychological equivalent for every physical state.

Biofeedback Form of training that helps a person to consciously control or change normally unconscious body functions to improve overall health. Also refers to the method of immediately reporting back information to the client about a biological process being measured so the person can consciously alter or influence the process.

Bodywork General term used to describe various forms of massage therapy, energy balancing, deep-tissue manipulation, and movement awareness.

Botanical medicine Use of an entire plant or herb for treating illness or maintaining health.

Chakras Circles found along the midline of the body, in alignment with the spinal cord, that distribute energy throughout the body. If they are blocked, energy flow is inhibited.

Chelation therapy Use of minerals combined with amino acids, given intravenously or orally, to help cleanse the body of unnecessary or toxic minerals that block blood circulation. From the Greek word *chele* (to bind or to claw).

Chi (Qi, Shi) From traditional Chinese medicine. Chi is the invisible life-force that circulates through the body along meridians, or channels. Maintaining or restoring the flow of chi restores and promotes health.

Chiropractic A Western medical system postulating that partial joint dislocations (subluxations) cause the body to be misaligned. Removal or adjustment of subluxations balances the spinal–nervous system and restores and maintains health.

Craniosacral therapy Manipulation of the bones of the skull to treat craniosacral dysfunctions caused by restriction in the flow of cerebrospinal fluid and misalignment of bones. *Cranio* refers to the cranium and *sacral* to the sacrum.

Crystal therapy Use of quartz and other gemstones, believed to emit electromagnetic energy. Frequently used with light and color therapy. Also called *gem therapy*.

Cupping From traditional Chinese and Ayurvedic medicines. Method using a heated cup placed over the skin to draw out impurities, decrease blood pressure, increase circulation, and relieve muscle pain.

Curanderismo Healing tradition, found in Mexican-American communities, based in concepts of supernaturalism, balance, and holism. From the Spanish verb *to heal*.

Dance therapy Use of dance movement to enhance wellness and aid healing. Sharpens levels of awareness, enhances self-confidence, helps with motor coordination and physical skills, and assists with communication, especially with severely disturbed psychiatric clients.

Doshas Three (*vata, pitta,* and *kapha*) basic metabolic types, life-forces, or bioenergies in Ayurvedic medicine. Each has certain characteristics and tendencies that combine to determine a person's constitution. When they are in balance, mind and body are coordinated, resulting in vibrant health and energy. When they are out of balance, the body is susceptible to outside stressors, such as microorganisms, poor nutrition, and work overload.

Energy medicine Measurement of electromagnetic frequencies emitted by the body. The object is to diagnose energy imbalances that may cause or contribute to present or future illnesses, and to use electromagnetic forces to counteract imbalances and restore the body's energy balance.

Environmental medicine Method that explores the role of environmental and dietary allergens in health and illness.

Feldenkrais method A type of bodywork or physical movement developed by Moshe Feldenkrais that stresses awareness through movement and helps the body work with gravity. Incorporates imaging,

Conclusion

Alternative and nontraditional health-care practices are a growing part of health care in the United States. It is essential that nurses become aware of what these practices entail and how they may affect or interact with conventional therapies that the client is already receiving. Admission assessments for these practices, when clients enter the health-care system for whatever reason, should become a routine part of client evaluation. Nurses traditionally have approached health care from a holistic viewpoint that addresses all of the client's needs— mind, body, and spirit. As health care moves more toward alternative practices, nurses are the logical choice to coordinate a comprehensive approach to health care that includes both traditional and alternative practices. Without this coordination, an already fragmented health-care system will become even more so.

GLOSSARY OF ALTERNATIVE AND COMPLEMENTARY HEALING TERMS

Inclusion of particular ideas or practices in this glossary does not imply endorsement of them. Health-care practitioners and their clients must carefully evaluate the claims and qualifications of alternative and complementary healing practices and practitioners before coming to conclusions about them.

Acupressure Use of fingers or hands to apply pressure over acupuncture points on meridians to restore or enhance the flow of chi. Believed to maintain or restore energy balance. From traditional Chinese medicine.

Acupressure massage Use of massage techniques such as rubbing, kneading, percussion, and vibration over acupuncture points to improve circulation of chi.

Acupuncture Insertion of needles along meridian channels to alleviate blockage of chi and reestablish the balance of energy in the body. The insertion points are believed to be linked to specific internal organs. Originating in traditional Chinese medicine, acupuncture is now commonly considered a complete treatment system on its own.

Alexander technique A technique developed by Frederick Matthias Alexander that realigns body posture through imaging and relaxation. Decreases muscle tension and fatigue, stress, and back and neck pain. Based on the belief that poor posture during daily activities contributes to physical and emotional problems.

Allopathic medicine A synonym for conventional medicine. Practitioner uses medicines to counteract symptoms or heal by producing different effects or a second condition different from the one being treated. From the Greek words *allos* (other) and *pathos* (suffering).

Applied kinesiology Study of muscle activity, strength, and health effects through the muscle-gland-organ link. Muscle dysfunction may be counteracted by nutrition, manual procedures (e.g., massage), pressure over muscle attachment points, and realignment.

Aromatherapy A type of herbal therapy that uses the odors of essential oils extracted from plants to treat various conditions, such as headaches, tension, and anxiety. Chemical composition of the oils produces pharmacological effects that include antibacterial, antiviral, antispasmodic, diuretic, vasodilative, and mood-harmonizing actions. The oils may be applied by massage, inhaled, placed in baths and other forms of hydrotherapy, or taken internally.

Art therapy Use of artistic self-expression through drawing, sculpture, and painting to diagnose and treat behavioral or emotional problems.

Aura Magnetic field thought to surround every person, plant, and animal. Adjustment of the field is believed to affect health, emotions, spirit, and mind.

Auriculotherapy A method developed in France in which points on the external ear are stimulated with acupuncture needles, massage, electronics, or

Critical Thinking Exercises

- Contact three of the Web sites on alternative practices listed in this chapter. Evaluate them according to their quality, content, and usefulness to your practice.
- Identify a nurse practitioner or physician or other health-care provider in your area who uses alternative practices. Interview that person and arrange for a presentation to the class about alternative health-care practices.
- Select a client from your clinical experiences who is having pain. How might alternative practices help this client? Develop a care plan using both traditional and alternative methods for pain control.
- Identify and discuss three advantages of and three problems with alternative health-care practices.
- Select three nursing theories from Chapter 4 that use a holistic approach to nursing. Identify how and what alternative practices would work well with each one of these theories.

auscultation Assessment technique that requires listening with a stethoscope to various parts of the body to detect sounds produced by organs.

authoritarian Type of leadership style in which the leader gives orders, makes decisions for the group as a whole, and bears most of the responsibility for the outcomes. Also called autocratic, directive, or controlling.

autonomy State of being self-directed or independent; the ability to make decisions about one's future.

autopsy Examination of a body after death to determine the cause of death.

baccalaureate degree nursing program Type of nursing education program that leads to the bachelor's degree with a major in nursing; usually located in a college or university, the length of the program is 4 years.

bargaining agent Organization certified by a governmental agency to represent a group of employees for the purpose of collective bargaining.

baseline data Initial information obtained about a client that establishes the norms for comparison as the client's condition changes.

basic human rights Those considerations society deems reasonably expected for all people; right to self-determination, protection from discomfort and harm, dignity, fair treatment, and privacy.

battery Nonconsensual touching of another person that does not necessarily cause harm or injury.

behaviorism Psychological theory based on the belief that all behavior is learned over time through conditioning.

behavior modification Method to change behavior through rewards for positive behavior.

belief Expectations or judgments based on attitude verified by experiences.

beneficence Ethical principle based on the beliefs that the health-care provider should do no harm, prevent harm, remove existing harm, and promote the good and well-being of the client.

bereavement State of sadness brought on by the loss or death of a significant other.

bill Proposed law that is moving through the legislative process.

bill of rights List of statements that outline the claims and privileges of a particular group, such as the Client's Bill of Rights.

bioethical issues Issues that deal with the health, safety, life, and death of human beings, often arising from advances in medical science and technology.

biofeedback Ability to control autonomic responses in the body through conscious effort.

body substance isolation (BSI) Universal precautions; guidelines established by the Centers for Disease Control and Prevention (CDC) and the Occupational Safety and Health Administration (OSHA) to protect health-care professionals and the client from diseases carried in the blood and body fluids, such as HIV and hepatitis B; involves the use of gloves whenever one is in contact with blood or body fluids and the use of masks, gowns, and eye covers if a chance of aerosol contact with fluids exists.

brain death Irreversible destruction of the cerebral cortex and brain stem manifested by absence of all reflexes; absence of brain waves on an electroencephalogram.

breach of contract Failure by one of the parties in a contract to fulfill all the terms of the agreement.

burden of proof Requirement that the plaintiff submit sufficient evidence to prove a defendant's guilt.

burnout syndrome A state of emotional exhaustion that results from the accumulative stress of an individual's life, including work, personal, and family responsibilities.

cadaver donor Clinically or brain-dead individual who previously agreed to allow organs to be taken for transplantation.

capitated payment system System of reimbursement in which a flat fee is paid for health-care services for a prescribed period of time. Expenses incurred in excess of this fee are provider losses.

capricious Unpredictable; arbitrary.

career ladder Articulation of educational programs that permit advancement from a lower level to a higher level without loss of credit or repetition of coursework.

career mobility Opportunity for individuals in one occupational area to move to another without restrictions.

case management Health-care delivery in which a client advocate or health-care coordinator helps the client through the hospitalization to obtain the most appropriate care.

case manager Health-care provider who coordinates cost-effective quality care for individuals who are generally at high risk and require long-term complex services.

certification Official recognition of a degree of education and skills in a profession by a national specialty organization; recognition that an institution has met standards that allow it to deliver certain services.

challenge examination Examination that assesses levels of knowledge or skill to grant credit for previous learning and experience; passing a challenge examination gives the individual credit for a course not actually taken.

chart Legal document that contains all the pertinent information about a client who is in a hospital or clinic; usually includes medical and nursing history, medical and nursing diagnosis, laboratory test results, notes about the client's progress, physician's orders, and personal data.

charting Process of recording (written or computer-generated) specific information about the client in the chart or medical record.

civil law Law concerned with the violation of the rights of one individual by another; it includes contract law, treaty law, tax law, and tort law.

claims-made policy Type of malpractice insurance that protects only against claims made during the time the policy is in effect.

client More modern term for patient; an individual seeking or receiving health-related services.

client goal Statement about a desired change, outcome, or activity that a client should achieve by a specific time.

clinical education Hands-on part of a nursing program that allows the student to practice skills on actual clients under the supervision of a nursing instructor.

clinical forensic nurse Professional nurse who specializes in management of crime victims from trauma to trial through collection of evidence, assessment of victims, or making judgments related to client treatment associated with court-related issues.

clinical ladder Type of performance evaluation and career advancement in which nursing positions for direct client care have two or more progressive levels of required skill leading to advancement in salary and responsibility; it allows nurses to remain in direct client care while making career advancements rather than having to move into administration.

clinical pathways Case-management protocols used to enhance quality of care, encourage cost-effectiveness, and promote efficiency.

closed system System that does not exchange energy, matter, or information with the environment or with other systems.

code of ethics Written values of a profession that act as guidelines for professional behavior.

cognitive domain objectives Most basic type of objectives for client learning that merely outline the knowledge that will be taught to the client.

collective bargaining Negotiations for wages, hours, benefits, and working conditions for a group of employees.

collective bargaining unit Group of employees recognized as representatives of the majority, with the right to bargain collectively with their employer and to reach an agreement on the terms of a contract.

committee Group of legislators, in the House or Senate, assigned to analyze bills on a particular subject.

common law Law based on past judicial judgments made in similar cases.

comparable worth Method for determining employees' salaries within an organization so that the same salary is paid for all jobs that have equivalent educational requirements, responsibilities, and complexity regardless of external market factors.

competencies Behaviors, skills, attitudes, and knowledge that an individual or professional has or is expected to have.

competency-based education Courses or programs based on anticipated student outcomes.

complaint Legal document filed by a plaintiff to initiate a lawsuit, claiming that the plaintiff's legal rights have been violated.

compliance Voluntary following of a prescribed plan of care or treatment regimen.

computer technology Use of highly advanced technological equipment to store, process, and access a vast amount of information.

concept Abstract idea or image.

conceptual framework Concept, theory, or basic idea around which an educational program is organized and developed.

conceptual model Group of concepts, ideas, or theories that are interrelated but in which the relationship is not clearly defined.

confidentiality Right of the client to expect the communication with a professional to remain unshared with any other person unless a medical reason exists or unless the safety of the public is threatened.

consensus General agreement between two or more individuals or groups regarding beliefs or positions on an issue or finding.

consent Voluntary permission given by a competent person.

consortium Two or more agencies that share sponsorship of a program or an institution.

constitutional law Law contained within a federal or state constitution.

continuing care Nursing care generally provided in geriatric day-care centers or in the homes of elderly clients.

continuing education Formal education programs and informal learning experiences that maintain and increase the nurse's knowledge and skills in specific areas.

continuing education unit (CEU) Specific unit of credit earned by participating in an approved continuing education program.

continuous quality improvement (CQI) Type of total quality management whose primary goal is the improvement of the quality of health care.

contract Legally binding agreement between two or more parties.

contractual obligation Duty to perform a service identified by a contract.

copayment Percentage of the cost of a medical expense that is not covered by insurance and must be paid by the client.

core curriculum Curriculum design that enables a student to leave a career program at various levels, with a career attained and with the option to continue at another higher level or career; it is organized around a central or core body of knowledge common to the profession.

coroner Elected public official, usually a physician, who investigates deaths from unnatural causes, including homicide, violence, suicide, and other suspicious circumstances.

correctional/institutional nurse Registered nurse who specializes in the health care of those in custody in secure settings such as jails or prisons.

credentialing Process whereby individuals, programs, or institutions are designated as having met minimal standards for the safety and welfare of the public.

crime Violation of criminal law.

criminal action Process by which a person charged with a crime is accused, tried, and punished.

criminal law Law concerned with violation of criminal statutes or laws.

criterion-referenced examination Test that compares an individual's knowledge with a predetermined standard rather than to the performance of others who take the same test.

critical thinking The intellectual process of rationally examining ideas, inferences, assumptions, principles, arguments, conclusions, issues, statements, beliefs, and actions for which all the relevant information may not be available. This process involves the ability to use the five types of reasoning (scientific, deductive, inductive, informal, practical) in application of the nursing process, decision-making, and resolution of ambiguous issues.

curriculum Group of courses that prepare an individual for a specific degree or profession.

customary, prevailing, and reasonable charges The typical rate in a specific locale that payers traditionally reimburse physicians.

damages Money awarded to a plaintiff by a court in a lawsuit that covers the actual costs incurred by the plaintiff.

database Information collected by a computer program on a specific topic in a specified format.

defamation of character Communication of information that is false or detrimental to a person's reputation.

defendant Person accused of criminal or civil wrongdoing. A party to a lawsuit against whom the complaint is served.

delegation Assignment of specific duties by one individual to another individual.

democratic Type of leadership style in which the leader shares the planning, decision-making, and responsibilities for outcomes with the other members of the group. Also called participative leadership.

deontology Ethical system based on the principle that the right action is guided by a set of unchanging rules.

dependent practitioner Provider of care who delivers health care under the supervision of another health-care practitioner; for example, a physician's assistant is supervised by a physician, or a LPN is supervised by a RN.

deposition Sworn statement by a witness that is made outside the courtroom; sworn depositions may be admitted as evidence in court when the individual is unable to be present.

diagnosis Statement that describes or identifies a client problem and is based on a thorough assessment.

diagnosis-related groups (DRGs) Prospective payment method used by the U.S. government and many insurance companies that pay a flat fee for treatment of a person with a particular diagnosis.

differentiated practice Organizational process of defining nursing roles based on education, experience, and training.

dilemma Predicament in which a choice must be made between two or more equally balanced alternatives; it often occurs when attempting to make ethical decisions.

directed services Health-care activities that require contact between a health-care professional and a client.

discharge planning Assessment of anticipated client needs after discharge from the hospital and development of a plan to meet those needs before the client is discharged.

disease Illness; a functional disturbance resulting from an individual organism's inability to adapt to certain stressors; an abnormal physiologic state caused by microorganisms, cancer, or other conditions.

distributive justice Ethical principle based on the belief that the right action is determined by that which will provide an outcome equal for all persons and will also benefit the least fortunate.

due process Right to have specific procedures or processes followed before the deprivation of life, liberty, or property; the guarantee of privileges under the 5th and 14th Amendments to the U.S. Constitution.

duty Obligation to act created by a statute, contract, or voluntary agreement.

emerging health occupations Health-care occupations that are not yet officially recognized by government or professional organizations.

employee Individual hired for pay by another.

Employee Retirement Income Security Act (ERISA) Federal law that grants incentives to employers to offer self-funded health insurance plans to their employees.

employer Individual or organization that hires other individuals for pay to carry out specific duties during certain hours of employment.

empowerment Process in which the individual assumes more autonomy and responsibility for his or her actions.

endorsement Reciprocity; a state's acceptance of a license issued by another state.

end product Output of a system not reusable as input.

energy Capacity to do work.

entry into practice Minimal educational requirements to obtain a license for a profession.

environment Internal and external physical and social boundaries of humans; all those things that are outside a system.

essentials for accreditation Minimal standards that a program must meet to be accredited.

ethical dilemma Ethical situation that requires an individual to make a choice between two equally unfavorable alternatives.

ethical rights (moral rights) Rights that are based on moral or ethical principles but have no legal mechanism of enforcement.

ethical system System of moral judgments based on the beliefs and values of a profession.

ethics Principles or standards of conduct that govern an individual or group.

ethnic group Individuals who share similar physical characteristics, religion, language, or customs.

euthanasia Mercy killing; the act or practice of killing, for reasons of mercy, individuals who have little or no chance of recovery by withholding or discontinuing life support or by administering a lethal agent.

evaluation Fifth step in the nursing process; used to determine whether goals set for a client have been attained.

evaluation criteria Outcome criteria; desired behaviors or standards.

expanded role Extended role; increased responsibilities and actions undertaken by an individual because of additional education and experience.

expert witness Individual with knowledge beyond the ordinary person, resulting from special education or training, who testifies during a trial.

external degree Academic degree granted when all the requirements have been met by the student; a type of outcomes-based education in which credit is given when the individual demonstrates a certain level of knowledge and skill, regardless of how or when these skills are attained; challenge examinations are often used.

false imprisonment Intentional tort committed by illegally confining or restricting a client against his or her will.

family Two or more related individuals living together.

Federal Tort Claims Act Statute that allows the government to be sued for negligence of its employees in the performance of their duties; many states have similar laws.

feedback Reentry of output into a system as input that helps maintain the internal balance of the system.

fee for service Payment is expected each time a service is rendered. Includes physicians' office visits, diagnostic procedures (laboratory tests, x-rays), and minor surgical procedures.

fellowship Scholarship or grant that provides money to individuals who are highly qualified or highly intelligent.

felony Serious crime that may be punished by a fine of more than $1000, more than 1 year in jail or prison, death, or a combination thereof.

fidelity The obligation of an individual to be faithful to commitments made to self and others.

for-profit Health-care agencies in which profits can be used to raise capital to pay stockholders dividends on their investments. Also called proprietary agencies.

foreign graduate nurse Individual graduated from a school of nursing outside the United States. This individual is required to pass the U.S. NCLEX-RN CAT to become a registered nurse in the United States.

forensic nurse Registered nurse who specializes in the integration of forensic science and nursing science to apply the nursing process to individual clients, their families, and the community, bridging the gap between the health care system and the criminal justice system.

forensic psychiatric nurse Registered nurse who specializes in application of psychosocial nursing knowledge linking offending behavior to client characteristics; nurse specializing in forensic psychological evaluation and care of offender populations with mental disorders.

forensic science Body of empirical knowledge used for legal investigation and evidence-based judgment in police or criminal cases.

fraud Deliberate deception in provision of goods or services; lying.

functional nursing Nursing care in which each nurse provides a different aspect of care; nurses are assigned a set of specific tasks to perform for all clients, such as passing medications.

general systems theory Set of interrelated concepts, definitions, and propositions that describe a system.

genetics Scientific study of heredity and related variations.

gerontology Study of the process of aging and of the effects of aging on individuals.

goal Desired outcome.

Good Samaritan Act Law that protects health-care providers from being charged with contributory negligence when they provide emergency care to persons in need of immediate treatment.

grievance Complaint or dispute about the terms or conditions of employment.

group practice Three or more physicians or nurse practitioners in business together to provide health care.

health Complete physical, mental, and social well-being; a relative state along a continuum ranging from severe illness to ideal state of being; the ability to adapt to illness and to reach the highest level of functioning.

health-care consumer Client or patient; an individual who uses health-care services or products.

health-care team Group of individuals of different levels of education who work together to provide help to clients.

health insurance purchasing cooperative (HIPC) Large groups of people or employers who band together to buy insurance at reduced costs. HIPCs may be organized by private groups or the government.

health literacy A client's ability to read, comprehend, and act on health-care instructions provided by a nurse or other health care worker.

health maintenance organization (HMO) Prototype of the managed health-care system; method of payment for a full range of primary, secondary, and tertiary health-care services; members pay a fixed annual fee for services and a small deductible when care is given.

health policy Goals and directions that guide activities to safeguard and promote the health of citizens.

health practitioner Individual, usually licensed, who provides health-care services to individuals with health-care needs.

health promotion Interventions and behaviors that increase and maintain the level of well-being of persons, families, groups, communities, and society.

health systems agency (HSA) Local voluntary organization of providers and consumers that plans for the health-care services of its geographic region.

hearsay Evidence not based on personal knowledge of the witness and usually not allowed in courts.

holistic Treatment of the total individual, including physical, psychological, sociologic, and spiritual elements, with emphasis on the interrelatedness of parts and wholes.

home health care Health-care services provided in the client's home.

hospice care Alternative way of providing care to terminally ill clients in which palliative care is used; the major goals of hospice care are control of pain, provision of emotional support, promotion of social interaction, and preparation for death; family support measures and anticipatory grief counseling are also used if appropriate.

hospital privileges Authority granted by a hospital, usually through its medical board, for a health-care practitioner to admit and supervise the treatment of clients within that hospital.

hypothesis Prediction or proposition related to a problem, usually found in research.

ideal role image Projection of society's expectations for nurses that clearly delineates the obligations and responsibilities, as well as the rights and privileges those in the role can lay claim to. Is often unrealistic.

illness Disease; a functional disturbance resulting from an individual organism's inability to adapt to certain stressors; an abnormal physiologic state caused by microorganisms, cancer, or other conditions.

implementation Fourth step in the nursing process, in which the plan of care is carried out.

incidence Number of occurrences of a specific condition or event.

incident report Document that describes an accident or error involving a client or family member that may or may not have resulted in injury; the purpose of the incident report is to track incidents and to make changes in the situations that caused them; the incident report is not part of the chart.

incompetency Inability of an individual to manage personal affairs because of mental or physical conditions; the inability of a professional to carry out professional activities at the expected level of functioning because of lack of knowledge or skill or because of drug or alcohol abuse.

indemnity insurance Health insurance in which the contractual agreement is between the consumer and the insurance company. Providers are not involved in these arrangements, and rates are not pre-established.

independent nurse practitioner Nurse who has a private practice in one of the expanded roles of nursing.

independent practice association (IPA) Type of HMO usually organized by physicians that requires fee-for-service payment.

independent practice organization (IPO) Type of IPA in which a group of providers deals with more than one insurer at a time.

independent practitioner Health-care provider who delivers health care independently with or without supervision by another health-care practitioner.

indirect services Health-care actions that do not require direct client contact but that still facilitate care, such as the supply and distribution department of a hospital.

informed consent Permission granted by a person based on full knowledge of the risks and benefits of participation in a procedure or surgery for which the consent has been given.

injunction Court order specifying actions that must or must not be taken.

input Matter, energy, or information entering a system from the environment.

inquest Formal inquiry about the course or manner of death.

institutional licensure Authority for an individual health-care provider to practice that is granted by the individual's employing institution; the institution determines the educational preparation, training, and functions of each category of provider it employs; no longer legally permitted, unlicensed assistive personnel (UAPs) act under a form of de facto institutional licensure.

intentional tort A willful act that violates another person's rights or property and may or may not cause physical injury.

interrogatories Written questions directed to a party in a lawsuit by the opposing side as part of the discovery process.

intervention Nursing action taken to meet specific client goals.

invasion of privacy Type of quasi-intentional tort that involves (1) an act that intrudes into the seclusion of the client, (2) intrusion that is objectionable to a reasonable person, (3) an act that intrudes into private facts or published as facts or pictures of a private nature, and (4) public disclosure of private information.

Joint Commission on Accreditation of Healthcare Organizations (JCAHO) Organization that performs accreditation reviews for health-care agencies.

judgment Decision of the court regarding a case.

jurisdiction Authority of a court to hear and decide lawsuits.

justice Fairness; giving people their due.

Kardex Portable card file that contains important client information and a care plan.

laissez-faire Type of leadership style in which the leader does little planning, sets few goals, avoids decision-making, and fails to encourage group members to participate. Also called permissive or nondirective leadership.

law Formal statement of a society's beliefs about interactions among and between its citizens; a formal rule enforced by society.

legal complaint Document filed by a plaintiff against a defendant claiming infringement of the plaintiff's legal rights.

legal obligations Obligations that have become formal statements of law and are enforceable under the law.

legal rights (welfare rights) Rights that are based on a legal entitlement to some good or benefits and are enforceable under the legal system with punishment for violations.

legislator Elected member of either the House of Representatives or the Senate.

legislature Body of elected individuals invested with constitutional power to make, alter, or repeal laws.

liable Obligated or held accountable by law.

libel Written defamation of character.

license Permission to practice granted to an individual by the state after he or she has met the requirements for that particular position; licensing protects the safety of the public.

licensed practical nurse (LPN) Licensed vocational nurse; technical nurse licensed by any state, after completing a practical nursing program, to provide technical bedside care to clients.

licensing board Government agency that implements the statutes of a particular profession in accordance with the Professions Practice Act.

licensure Process by which an agency or government grants an individual permission to practice; it establishes a minimal level of competency for practice.

licensure by endorsement Method of obtaining a license to practice by having a state acknowledge the individual's existing comparable license in another state.

licensure by examination Method of obtaining a license to practice by successfully passing a state-board examination.

living will Signed legal document in which individuals make known their wishes about the care they are to receive if they should become incompetent at a future date; it usually specifies what types of treatments are permitted and what types are to be withheld.

lobbyist Person who attempts to influence political decisions as an official representative of an organization, group, or institution.

locality rule standard of care Legal process that holds an individual nurse accountable both to what is an acceptable standard within his or her local community and to national standards as developed by nurses throughout the nation through the American Nurses Association (ANA), national practice groups, and health-care agencies.

malfeasance Performance of an illegal act.

malpractice Negligent acts by a licensed professional based on either omission of an expected action or commission of an inappropriate action resulting in damages to another party; not doing what a reasonable and prudent professional of the same rank would have done in the same situation.

managed care System of organized health-care delivery systems linked by provider networks; health maintenance organizations are the primary example of managed care.

mandatory licensure Law that requires all who practice a particular profession to have and to maintain a license in that profession.

manslaughter Killing of an individual without premeditated intent; different degrees of manslaughter exist, and most are felonies.

mediation Legal process that allows each party to present their case to a mediator, who is an independent third party trained in dispute resolution.

medical examiner Coroner; a physician who investigates deaths that appear to be from other than natural causes.

Medicaid State health-care insurance program, supported in part by federal funds, for health-care services for certain groups unable to pay for their own health care; amount and type of coverage vary from state to state.

medically indigent Individuals who cannot personally pay for health-care services without incurring financial hardship.

Medicare Federally run program that is financed primarily through employee payroll taxes and covers any individual who is 65 years of age or older as well as blind and disabled individuals of any age.

Medicare Utilization and Quality Peer Review Organization (PRO) Organization that reviews the quality and cost of Medicare services.

Medigap policies Health insurance policies that are purchased to cover expenses not paid by Medicare.

midwife Individual experienced in assisting women during labor and delivery; they may be lay midwives, who have no official education, or certified nurse midwives, who are RNs in an expanded role, having received additional education and passed a national certification examination.

misdemeanor Less serious crime than a felony; punishable by a fine of less than $1000 or a jail term of less than 1 year.

model Hypothetical representation of something that exists in reality. The purpose of a model is to attempt to explain a complex reality in a systematic and organized manner.

morality Concept of right and wrong.

moral obligations Obligations based on moral or ethical principles but *not* enforceable under the law.

morals Fundamental standards of right and wrong that an individual learns and internalizes during the early stages of childhood development, based primarily on religious beliefs and societal norms.

mores Values and customs of a society.

mortality Property or capacity to die; death.

motivation Internal drive that causes individuals to seek achievement of higher goals; desire.

multicompetency technician Allied health-care provider who has skills in two or more areas of practice through the process of cross-training.

multiskilled practitioner Health-care professional who has skills in more than one area of health care, such as a RN who has training in physical therapy.

national health insurance Proposed system of payment for health-care services whereby the government pays for the costs of the health care.

negative entropy Tendency toward increased order in a system.

negligence Failure to perform at an expected level of functioning or the performance of an inappropriate function resulting in damages to another party; not doing what a reasonable and prudent person would do in a similar situation.

no-code order Do not resuscitate (DNR) order; an order by a physician to withhold cardiopulmonary resuscitation and other resuscitative efforts from a client.

nonfeasance Failure to perform a legally required duty.

nonmaleficence Ethical principle that requires the professional to do no harm to the client.

nontraditional education Methods of education that do not follow the traditional lecture and clinical practice methods of learning; may include computer-simulated learning, self-education techniques, or other creative methods.

nonverbal A type of communication that uses any methods except written and spoken messages and constitutes 93 percent of the communication between individuals. It includes body language, gestures, facial expression, tone, pace, personal space, etc.

normative ethics Questions and dilemmas requiring a choice of actions where there is a conflict of rights or obligations between the nurse and the client, the nurse and the client's family, or the nurse and the physician.

norm-referenced examination Examination scored by comparison with standards established on the performance of all others who took the same examination during a specific time; the NLN achievement examinations are norm referenced.

not-for-profit (nonprofit) agencies Agencies in which all profits must be used in the operation of the organization.

nurse clinician Registered nurse with advanced skills in a particular area of nursing practice; if certified by a professional organization, a nurse clinician may also be a nurse practitioner, but more often this designation refers to nurses in advanced practice roles such as nurse specialists.

nurse practice act Part of state law that establishes the scope of practice for professional nurses, as well as educational levels and standards, professional conduct, and reasons for revocation of licensure.

nurse practitioner Nurse specialist with advanced education in a primary care specialty, such as community health, pediatrics, or mental health, who is prepared independently to manage health promotion and maintenance and illness prevention of a specific group of clients.

nurse specialist (clinical nurse specialist) Nurse who is an expert in providing care focused on a specialized field drawn from the range of general practice, such as cardiac nurse specialist.

nurse theorist Nurse who analyzes and attempts to describe what the profession of nursing is and what nurses do through nursing models or nursing theories.

nursing assessment Systematic collection and recording of client data, both objective and subjective, from primary and secondary sources using the nursing history, physical examination, and laboratory data, for example.

nursing diagnosis Statements of a client's actual or potential health-care problems or deficits.

nursing order Statement of a nursing action selected by a nurse to achieve a client's goal; may be stated as either the nurse's or the client's expected behavior.

nursing process Systematic, comprehensive decision-making process used by nurses to identify and treat actual and potential health problems.

nursing research Formal study of problems of nursing practice, the role of the nurse in health care, and the value of nursing.

nursing standards Desired nursing behaviors established by the profession and used to evaluate nurses' performances.

obligations Demands made on individuals, professions, society, or government to fulfill and honor the rights of others. Obligations are often divided into two categories–moral and legal (welfare).

occurrence policy A type of malpractice insurance that protects against all claims that occurred during the policy period regardless of when the claim is made.

omission Failure to fulfill a duty or carry out a procedure recognized as a standard of care; often forms the basis for claims of malpractice.

oncology Area of health care that deals with the treatment of cancer.

open curriculum Educational system that allows a student to enter and leave the system freely; often uses past education and experiences.

open system System that can exchange energy, matter, and information with the environment and with other systems.

ordinance Local or municipal law.

outcome criteria Standards that measure changes or improvements in clients' conditions

out-of-pocket expenses Amount the client is responsible for paying for a health-care service.

output Matter, energy, or information released from a system into the environment or transmitted to another system.

palliative Type of treatment directed toward minimizing the severity of a disease or illness rather than curing it; for example, for a client with terminal cancer, relief of pain is the main goal (palliative), rather than cure.

panel of approved providers A list of physicians, nurse practitioners, pharmacies, and other health-care providers that are approved by an insurance plan and to whom reimbursement will be made by the insurer.

passive learning A type of client education in which the material is merely presented to the client without his or her involvement. Least effective type of learning because it usually does not change attitudes or behaviors.

patient Client; an individual seeking or receiving health-care services.

patient day Client day; the 24-hour period during which hospital services are provided that forms the basis for charging the patient, usually from midnight to midnight.

pediatrics Study and care of problems and diseases of children younger than the age of 18.

peer review Evaluation against professional standards of the performance of individuals with the same basic education and qualifications; formal process of review or evaluation by coworkers of an equal rank.

perceived role image The individual's own definition of the role, which is usually more realistic than the ideal role, involving rejection or modification of some of the norms and expectations of society.

percussion Physical examination involving the tapping of various parts of the body to determine density by eliciting different sounds.

performed role image The duties performed by the practitioner of a role. Often produces reality shock in new graduate nurses.

perjury Crime committed by giving false testimony while under oath.

permissive licensure Law that allows individuals to practice a profession as long as they do not use the

Entries followed by *b*, *f*, or *t* denote boxes, figures and tables, respectively.